CHEMICAL PRINCIPLES

P. W. SELWOOD

UNIVERSITY OF CALIFORNIA, SANTA BARBARA

NEW YORK • CHICAGO • SAN FRANCISCO • TORONTO • LONDON

CHEMICAL PRINCIPLES

HOLT, RINEHART AND WINSTON

Preface

This book was written for the first-year college chemistry student whose preparation has included at least two years of preparatory mathematics and one of chemistry. A year of physics, though not essential, is certainly to be desired.

The plan of the book is to present the basic principles of chemistry in the first half, and descriptive inorganic chemistry in the second. The first half follows the general pattern that has proved to be successful in several recent texts, and the approach to general chemistry has been this: A student of science should not be asked to accept anything on faith. Now it is true that no matter how able a student may be, and no matter how long his educational career, he cannot possibly test for himself every statement in science. Nevertheless, I believe that he should be able to see how, in principle, he could make such tests, time and patience permitting. Failing this, we give up the very essence of science; we make of it a discipline where proof is abandoned and substituted by faith in the statements of higher authority.

There has, of recent years, been an increasing tendency to introduce modern valence bond theory to students of elementary chemistry. This has consisted in part of presenting the Schröedinger equation, and explaining how solution of the equation leads to quantum numbers and interaction energies. This has not been attempted in the present text. I believe that no student can understand the covalent bond until he has had a course in quantum mechanics; and to understand quantum mechanics he must first understand differential equations. Few first-year college students have mastered differential equations, and most of them never do. For this reason, I have treated the covalent bond descriptively, so far as this is possible, but I have not asked the student to accept, on faith, much that he cannot verify for himself—if not by actual test, then at least in principle.

Treatment of the inorganic half of the text deviates sharply from the current practice of many authors. Some thirty years of lecturing on general and inorganic chemistry at various levels has convinced me that the Periodic Table is not the most satisfactory plan of organization for presentation of the chemical elements and their properties. Too often the course has a tendency to bog down in a dreary recital of groups, trends, and exceptions. And this is likely to occur at the very moment in the spring when the lecturer must redouble his efforts to maintain the interest of his class.

The idea that an alternative approach to inorganic chemistry is preferable is certainly not new. An alternative was tried by Ephraim some fifty years ago. But, although his textbooks were widely used, his method was abandoned because the unifying principles especially applicable to inorganic chemistry had not at that time been fully developed.

The situation is quite different now. Inorganic chemistry has not only moved to an important position in science, but the wealth of experience, which a study of *all* the chemical elements can provide, makes it virtually imperative to place a generous part of descriptive inorganic chemistry in the first year. The method of presentation I have chosen is to consider first the chemical elements, then the binary compounds and, finally, more complex compounds. Full use, in so far as possible in an elementary presentation, has been made of modern structural chemistry, and emphasis has been placed on the separation, the synthesis, and the purification of the elements and their compounds.

All this material having been covered, it then becomes quite easy to present in a final chapter some examples of molecular structure and properties of organic compounds, without which no treatment of general chemistry can be considered complete.

No author of a book such as this can fail to be awed by the swift march of science. More than once I have found it best to illustrate a point by reference to a compound, or even to an element, that was unknown when I started writing the text. Even as the final chapters were being written I had to go back and change the words "inert gas" to read "group zero gas." Some of the "inert" gases are no longer inert. Other corrections will doubtless prove to have been required after the book goes to press. But if no author had the courage to write a text, no student would gain the knowledge to prove the text wrong.

SANTA BARBARA, CALIFORNIA   P. W. S.
FEBRUARY, 1964

Contents

1

Gases

1.1 States of Matter

Chemistry is the science of matter and its transformations, and matter is anything that has mass and occupies space. Matter may exist in one or more of three states: gas, liquid, and solid.

A gas has the unique property that it may completely and uniformly fill any vessel in which it may be contained. The volume and shape of the container become the volume and shape of the gas. The gas will not only penetrate to all parts of the vessel, but equal weights of the gas will be found in equal portions of the volume.

A sample of matter in the liquid state may have a volume that is independent of the container. In this the liquid state is in contrast to the gaseous, but a sample of liquid will assume the shape of any vessel in which it may be placed so far as the vessel may be filled. A liquid is like a gas in adapting itself, at least in part, to the shape of the container; but it is unlike a gas in that any given sample of liquid has a definite volume which is not necessarily the volume of the container.

A sample of matter in the solid state always possesses both a volume and a shape that are characteristic of the particular sample but which are independent of the container, if any. It is true that a powdered solid may tend, in part, to assume the shape of the container, but this is true only because the powdered particles possess to some degree the properties of a liquid in that the particles are free to move with respect to each other.

Matter in the gaseous state is somewhat less complex than is the case when it becomes a liquid or a solid. The natural laws describing the behavior of gases are comparatively simple, and they yield a wealth of information concerning the molecules and atoms of which matter is composed. It is, therefore, to this state that our attention will be first directed.

Gases have three properties of special importance for our present purposes. These properties are compressibility, thermal expansion, and diffusibility. By *compressibility* is meant the property of a gas to change its volume when the pressure exerted on, and by, the sample is changed. The gas may be thought of as having a sort of elastic quality, its volume responding rapidly to changes in pressure; as the pressure increases, the volume decreases. This property of gases is described by Boyle's law.

The *thermal expansion* of gases is a matter of common experience. If a gas sample is heated, it tends to expand; if cooled, it tends to contract. Ultimately, all gases may be converted to liquids or to solids, although some gases do so only at astonishingly low temperatures. The thermal expansion of gases is described by Charles' law.

By *diffusibility* is meant the ability of a gas to permeate any space in which it may be put. If a gas sample is placed in an otherwise empty container, the gas almost instantly diffuses throughout the container, filling it completely. Or, if the container is already filled with air or some other gas, diffusion of an added gas, although much slower nevertheless reaches the same final stage of filling the container completely and uniformly. The gas is said to diffuse through the space, or through another gas. The diffusibility of gases is described by Graham's law.

1.2   Boyle's Law

If the pressure P_1 exerted by, and on, a gas sample is changed to P_2, it will be found that the new volume V_2 is related to the old volume V_1 by the expression

$$P_1 V_1 = P_2 V_2 \qquad (1.1)$$

This is the mathematical expression for **Boyle's law** which may, in words, be stated as follows:

The volume of a fixed mass of gas varies inversely as the pressure, provided the temperature does not change.

Boyle's law is based on the experimental observation that for a given mass of gas at a fixed temperature, the product of volume and pressure is approximately constant over a considerable range of pressure.

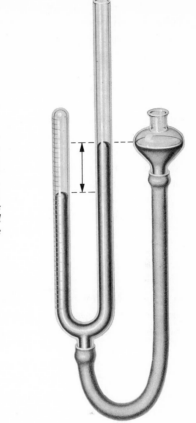

Fig. 1.1 *Apparatus for demonstrating Boyle's law.
A quantity of gas is trapped in the tube at left.
This is subjected to greater or less pressure by
raising or lowering the mercury reservoir which
is attached to the rest of the apparatus by a flexible rubber tube. The volume of the gas is read
directly. The pressure in millimeters of mercury is
the difference in level of mercury in closed and
open sides plus the barometric pressure of the
atmosphere.*

TABLE **1.1** TYPICAL EFFECT OF PRESSURE ON
GAS VOLUME

(Data obtained on a sample of hydrogen
at 25° C)

Pressure, P, mm mercury	Volume, V, ml	$P \times V$, mm × ml
50.0	884	44,200
170	260	44,200
310	143	44,200
498	88.8	44,200
760	58.1	44,100
1000	44.1	44,100

An experimental arrangement for investigating this relationship between volume and pressure is shown in Fig. 1.1, and some typical data so obtained are given in Table 1.1. It will be observed that over the range of pressure given, the product of pressure times volume is constant within the limits of probable experimental error, with due regard for an appropriate number of significant figures.

Boyle's law may be used to find the effect of changing pressure on the volume of a gas sample, as shown in the following problem.

PROBLEM: A given mass of nitrogen has a volume of 280 ml at a pressure of 845 mm of mercury. What volume will this sample occupy if the pressure is changed to 330 mm and the temperature remains unchanged?

SOLUTION: Boyle's law, as stated in Eq. 1.1, may be written as

$$V_2 = V_1 \times \frac{P_1}{P_2}$$

in which the new volume V_2 is equal to the old volume V_1 corrected for the change of pressure from P_1 to P_2. Substituting in the preceding equation,[1]

$$V_2 = 280 \text{ ml} \times \frac{845 \text{ mm}}{330 \text{ mm}}$$
$$= 718 \text{ ml}$$

1.3 Pressure Measurement

The fundamental unit of pressure in the cgs system is the dyne per square centimeter. By definition, 1.013250×10^6 dyne cm^{-2} is said to be 1 atmosphere. One atmosphere (1 atm) so defined is very close to the pressure necessary to support a column of mercury 760 mm high, and is often referred to as standard pressure. It is convenient to use the height of a mercury column as a measure of pressure, and it will be so used throughout this book. A pressure designated as being h millimeters is thus actually $h/760$ atm.

Gas pressures are often measured with the aid of a U-shaped tube partially filled with mercury as shown in Fig. 1.2. One end of the tube is connected to the gas sample under investigation; the other, to the air. If the mercury in the open side of the tube stands higher than that in the

---

[1] Hereafter, when we encounter a fraction involving (as above) the same units in both numerator and denominator, we shall omit the units. The fraction 845 mm/330 mm will be written 845/330.

closed end, then the pressure exerted by, and on, the gas sample is given by the difference in heights of the mercury in open and closed sides plus the pressure exerted by the air on the open side. Such a device is called a *manometer*. The pressure of the air is not necessarily equal to one defined atmosphere, but may vary somewhat with the elevation above sea level and with atmospheric conditions.

It is possible to construct a manometer that is open to the air on one side, but completely sealed off under vacuum on the other. Two forms of this device are shown in Fig. 1.3. Under these conditions, it is the pressure exerted by the air itself that is being measured. Such a device is called a *barometer*. The pressure exerted by the air is given by the difference in heights of mercury in open and closed sides of the barometer. Corrections of various kinds must generally be applied for very precise measurements.

The use of a manometer may be illustrated by the following simple example: Suppose that on the side of the manometer open to the atmosphere, the mercury stands 43 mm lower than that on the closed side. The

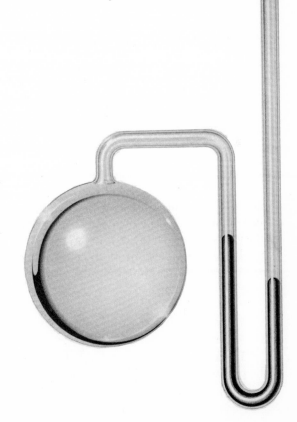

Fig. 1.2 Simple mercury manometer attached to a flask containing a gas sample.

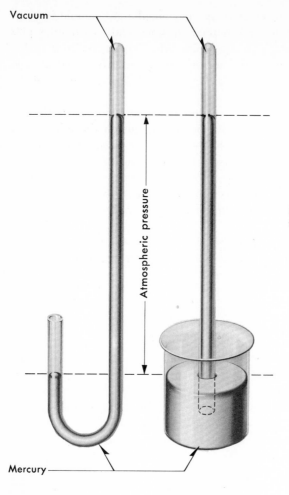

Vacuum

Atmospheric pressure

Mercury

Fig. 1.3 Simple mercury barometers. Two forms are shown.

atmospheric pressure is found to be 738 mm. The pressure on the gas sample is obviously less than that exerted by the air. The actual pressure on the gas is 738 mm — 43 mm = 695 mm.

It is convenient in dealing with gases to designate a standard pressure. *Standard pressure* is 1 atm, or very nearly 760 mm of mercury.

1.4 Partial Pressure

If two or more gases are mixed, their total pressure is the sum of the pressures that each gas would exert if it were alone.

The pressure exerted by each gas in a mixture of gases is said to be the partial pressure of that gas, and the statement above is **Dalton's law of partial pressures.** Expressed mathematically,

$$P_{\text{total}} = P_A + P_B + P_C + \cdots \qquad (1.2)$$

where P_{total} is the total pressure, and P_A, P_B, etc., are the partial pressures of the several gases A, B, etc., in the mixture. It will scarcely be necessary to give experimental data illustrative of this law.

PROBLEM: If the total pressure exerted by a mixture of oxygen and nitrogen is 760 mm of mercury, and the partial pressure of the nitrogen is 610 mm, what is the partial pressure of the oxygen?

SOLUTION:

$$P_{\text{total}} = P_{\text{oxygen}} + P_{\text{nitrogen}}$$

whence

$$\begin{aligned}
P_{\text{oxygen}} &= P_{\text{total}} - P_{\text{nitrogen}} \\
&= 760 \text{ mm} - 610 \text{ mm} \\
&= 150 \text{ mm}
\end{aligned}$$

Dalton's law of partial pressures is of special value in finding the pressure of a gas that has been collected by displacement of water. Under these conditions, the gas contains some water vapor for which correction must be made. The method for doing this will be described in Chapter 3. This law may not be applied to gas mixtures that react chemically with each other. It could not, for instance, be applied to a mixture of ammonia and hydrogen chloride, which react on contact to form solid ammonium chloride.

1.5 Charles' Law

If the absolute temperature T_1 of a gas sample is changed to T_2, it will be found that the new volume V_2 is related to the old volume V_1 by the expression

$$\frac{V_1}{T_1} = \frac{V_2}{T_2} \qquad (1.3)$$

This is the mathematical expression for **Charles' law,** which may be stated as follows:

The volume of a fixed mass of gas varies directly as the absolute temperature, provided the pressure does not change.

Charles' law is based on the experimental observation that for a given sample of gas at constant pressure, the volume divided by the absolute temperature is approximately a constant over a considerable range of temperature. An experimental arrangement for investigating this relationship is shown in Fig. 1.4, and some typical data are shown in Table 1.2. It will be observed that over the range of temperature given, the volume divided by the absolute temperature is a constant within probable limits of experimental error.

Charles' law may be used to find the effect of changing temperature on the volume of a gas sample, as shown in the following problem.

PROBLEM: If the volume of a gas is 150 ml at 298° K, what would the volume be at 653° K, assuming that the pressure does not change?

SOLUTION: Charles' law, Eq. 1.3, may be written as

$$V_2 = V_1 \times \frac{T_2}{T_1}$$

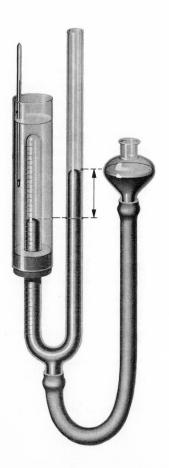

Fig. 1.4 Apparatus for demonstrating Charles' law. The gas sample is surrounded by a tube which holds a liquid, the temperature of which may be changed. In this experiment the mercury reservoir is used to hold the pressure constant. It is difficult to attain much accuracy in this experiment, but the relation of pressure to temperature, as shown in Fig. 1.5, is much more easily and accurately measured.

TABLE 1.2 TYPICAL EFFECT OF TEMPERA-
TURE ON GAS VOLUME
(Data obtained on a sample of hydrogen at
1 atm)

Temperature, T, °K	Volume, V, ml	V/T, ml/°K
218	420	1.93
300	578	1.93
385	739	1.92
450	868	1.93
610	1180	1.94

in which the new volume V_2 is equal to the old volume V_1 corrected for the temperature change from the old temperature T_1 to the new temperature T_2. Substituting in the preceding equation,

$$V_2 = 150 \text{ ml} \times \frac{653}{298}$$

$$= 329 \text{ ml}$$

1.6 Temperature Measurement

The *absolute temperature scale* is based on thermodynamic reasoning that lies beyond the scope of this book. On this scale, the triple point of water (Sec. 4.3) is designated as 273.16° Kelvin (°K).

Temperature may be measured over a very wide range with the gas thermometer, in which the volume of a gas is measured at constant pressure or the pressure is measured at constant volume. A simplified thermometer of the latter type is shown in Fig. 1.5. This thermometer gives results in agreement with the absolute scale, provided certain corrections are made. The most important of these corrections is that at each temperature a series of measurements must be made at various pressures until it is possible to estimate, by extrapolation, what the pressure and volume would be under conditions where both Boyle's law and Charles' law would accurately describe the behavior of any real gas. The gas thermometer may be employed from about 1.5° K to 1000° K, but below about 1.5° K, the gas thermometer has no meaning because no known substance is a gas at or below that temperature.

The familiar mercury thermometers are often calibrated in the *Celsius, or centigrade* (°C), scale for scientific use, or in the Fahrenheit (°F)

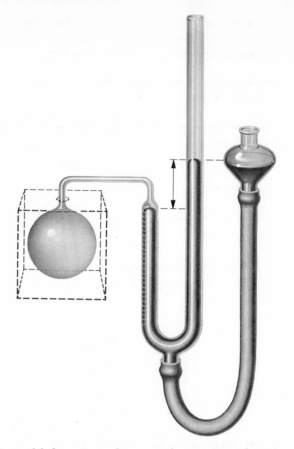

Fig. 1.5 A simplified constant-volume gas thermometer. The volume is kept constant by raising, or lowering the mercury until it just touches the indicial point shown. The pressure necessary to maintain this volume is then measured for each change of temperature of the gas sample in the round bulb.

scale for everyday use in English-speaking countries. These thermometers are based on the very nearly linear (straight line) expansion of mercury with rising temperature. For use in cold regions, the mercury may be replaced by colored alcohol.

The degrees on the Celsius scale are the same size as those on the absolute scale, but the zero point is quite different. The temperature of melting ice at 1 atm (or of freezing water) is designated as 0° C, and the temperature of boiling water under 1 atm pressure, as 100° C. The temperature 0° C is the same as 273.15° K. The Celsius temperature may be converted to absolute temperature by adding 273.15 degrees. For most purposes of this book, it will suffice to add 273 degrees.

On the Fahrenheit scale, the melting point of ice is 32° F and the boiling point of water at 1 atm pressure is 212° F. Fahrenheit may be converted to Celsius, and vice versa, as follows:

$$°C = \tfrac{5}{9}(°F - 32°)$$
$$°F = \tfrac{9}{5}°C + 32°$$

The relationship of the three scales is shown in Fig. 1.6.

Various other methods of temperature measurement are available. One of these is the platinum resistance thermometer. The electrical resistance of platinum, as does that of most metals, becomes less as the temperature is lowered. Another device is the thermocouple. The thermocouple operates on the principle that two unlike metals such as copper and iron, when placed in contact with each other, will develop a small electric potential. The size of this potential depends on the temperature; it may be measured by a sensitive voltmeter or, better, by a potentiometer. For very high temperatures, optical pyrometers are used. These depend on the color and brightness of an object heated red or white hot. Magnetic methods are used for temperatures near the absolute zero.

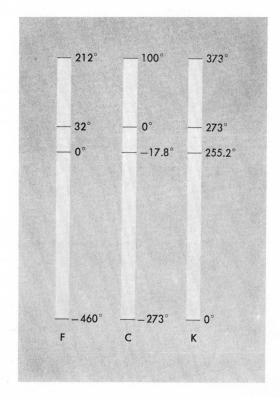

Fig. 1.6 Temperature scales.

In much work on gases it is convenient to designate a standard temperature in the same way that a standard pressure is designated. *Standard temperature* is 0° C. Standard temperature and pressure are designated STP.

1.7   Simultaneous Change of Pressure and Temperature

Boyle's law and Charles' law may be combined into one, more general, law; but the change in going from an initial state characterized by P_1, V_1, T_1 to a final state characterized by P_2, V_2, T_2 will be considered in two steps, as follows:

Keeping the temperature constant, let the pressure change from P_1 to P_2. This will cause a change of volume from V_1 to V_{12}, where V_{12} is the volume at T_1 and P_2. Then, from Boyle's law,

$$P_1V_1 = P_2V_{12}$$

Now, keeping the pressure constant, let the temperature change from T_1 to T_2. This will cause a change of volume from V_{12} to V_2, where V_2 is the volume at T_2 and P_2. Then, from Charles' law,

$$\frac{V_{12}}{T_1} = \frac{V_2}{T_2}$$

Multiplying one equation by the other, we obtain

$$\frac{P_1V_1V_{12}}{T_1} = \frac{P_2V_{12}V_2}{T_2}$$

and eliminating V_{12},

$$\frac{P_1V_1}{T_1} = \frac{P_2V_2}{T_2} \tag{1.4}$$

This equation states, in words, that the volume of a gas varies inversely as the pressure and directly as the absolute temperature. The equation may be used to solve any problem in which five of the six quantities (P_1, V_1, T_1, P_2, V_2, T_2) are known.

PROBLEM: The volume of a gas sample at 720 mm and 24° C is 412 ml. What is the volume at standard temperature and pressure (STP)?

SOLUTION: Rearranging Eq. 1.4 so that the unknown quantity V_2 is at the left, and substituting,

$$V_2 = V_1 \times \frac{P_1}{P_2} \times \frac{T_2}{T_1}$$

$$= 412 \text{ ml} \times \frac{720}{760} \times \frac{273}{273 + 24}$$

$$= 359 \text{ ml}$$

PROBLEM: A sample of gas occupies 3.85 liters at $-20°$ C and 760 mm pressure. At what pressure will it occupy 3.00 liters if the temperature is raised to 250° C?

SOLUTION: Rearranging Eq. 1.4 so that the unknown quantity P_2 is at the left, and substituting,

$$P_2 = P_1 \times \frac{V_1}{V_2} \times \frac{T_2}{T_1}$$

$$= 760 \text{ mm} \times \frac{3.85}{3.00} \times \frac{273 + 250}{273 - 20}$$

$$= 2020 \text{ mm}$$

1.8 Graham's Law

If the diffusion rates of two gases (A and B) are compared, it will be found that:

$$\frac{r_A}{r_B} = \frac{\sqrt{d_B}}{\sqrt{d_A}} \tag{1.5}$$

where r_A and r_B are the rates of diffusion and d_A and d_B are the densities of the two gases, respectively. This is the mathematical expression of **Graham's law,** which may be stated as follows:

The rate of diffusion of a gas is inversely proportional to the square root of the density of the gas.

Graham's law may be demonstrated as shown in Fig. 1.7. Ammonia gas is less dense than is hydrogen chloride gas. If 1 ml of ammonia is put in one end of a long glass tube and 1 ml of hydrogen chloride in the other end, the two gases will diffuse along the tube toward each other. The ammonia has the lower density, and hence the meeting place, indicated by the formation of white ammonium chloride, is nearer one end of the tube than the other.

Graham's law may be used to compare the rates of diffusion of two gases, or if the rates are known, it may be used to compare the

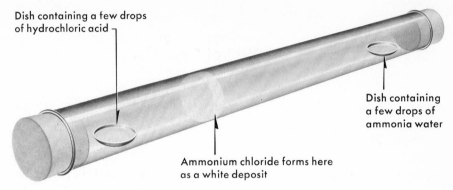

Dish containing a few drops
of hydrochloric acid

Dish containing
a few drops of
ammonia water

Ammonium chloride forms here
as a white deposit

Fig. 1.7 Demonstration of Graham's law of diffusion.

densities. Density is the mass per unit volume and may be expressed in any units of mass and volume. It is convenient to express gas densities in grams per liter.

PROBLEM: Compare the rate of diffusion of ammonia ($d = 0.758$ gram/liter) with that of hydrogen chloride $d = 1.630$ grams/liter).

SOLUTION: Substituting directly in Eq. 1.5,

$$\frac{r_{NH_3}}{r_{HCl}} = \frac{\sqrt{1.630}}{\sqrt{0.758}}$$
$$= 1.47$$

The ammonia will diffuse 1.47 times faster than the hydrogen chloride. In a calculation of this kind it must be assumed that the two gases are at the same temperature and pressure. Both diffusion rates and densities vary as the conditions are changed. The densities given in the problem refer to standard conditions.

PROBLEM: The density of gas A is 4.95 grams/liter and it diffuses 3.20 times faster than gas B. What is the density of gas B?

SOLUTION: Rearranging Eq. 1.5 and substituting,

$$d_B = d_A \times \frac{r_A^2}{r_B^2}$$
$$= 4.95 \text{ grams/liter} \times 3.20^2$$
$$= 50.7 \text{ grams/liter}$$

EXERCISES

1. The volume of a gas sample at 720 mm is 550 ml. What is the volume at standard pressure? The mass and the temperature of the sample are assumed to remain constant.
2. The volume of a gas at 25° C is 380 ml. What is the volume at standard temperature? Mass and pressure are constant.
3. The volume of a gas at 45° C and 600 mm pressure is 125 ml. What is the volume at −10° C and 1120 mm pressure?
4. A sample of nitrogen, collected at 23° C and 765 mm pressure, occupies 495 ml. What is its volume at STP?
5. At 300° C and 1500 mm pressure, a gas occupies 825 ml. At what temperature would it occupy 500 ml if the pressure were lowered to 900 mm?
6. At 180° C and 1.75 atm pressure, a gas sample occupies 235 ml. At what pressure would it occupy 1350 ml if the temperature were raised to 250° C?
7. The density of a gas under standard conditions is 1.429 grams/liter. What will the density be at 30° C and 735 mm?
8. A liter of air under standard conditions weighs 1.293 grams. What is the weight of air in a room 5.0 meters long, 5.0 meters wide, and 3.0 meters high, at 23° C and 750 mm pressure?
9. A given mass of gas has a volume of 18.3 cu ft at 150° F and a pressure of 1550 psi. What will the volume be (in cubic feet) at 0° C and 15 psi? (psi means pounds per square inch.)
10. The density of neon is 0.90 gram/liter and that of bromine 7.1 grams/liter. What is the ratio of their rates of diffusion?
11. Gas X is found to diffuse 2.7 times faster than gas Y. The latter has a density of 4.15 grams/liter. What is the density of gas X?
12. Compare the rates of diffusion of ammonia and hydrogen chloride at 100° C and 580 mm pressure.
13. At one time, the absolute zero was defined as the temperature at which the volume of an imaginary gas would become zero. Determine if this is approximately true, by plotting the volumes given in Table 1.2 against the temperatures.

2

Molecules

2.1   Kinetic Molecular Theory

The properties of gases, described in the preceding chapter, may
be explained by the theory that gases consist of minute particles, that
the particles are, on the average, widely separated from each other, and
that they are in constant motion. These minute particles are called
molecules. This theory accounts in a satisfactory manner for many properties of gases. Two of these properties are their compressibility, as
described by Boyle's law, and their diffusibility, as described by Graham's
law.

Gases are highly compressible—under pressure the volume of a gas
may be diminished manyfold. This must surely mean that the spaces
between the molecules must be very large when compared with the
molecules themselves. Nevertheless there must be vast numbers of molecules in any quantity of gas because, in spite of the smallness and lightness
of molecules and in spite of the empty spaces between them, we still
find that samples of gases have appreciable weights; the air in a room
weighs many pounds. The number of molecules necessary to give this
weight must be almost inconceivably large.

Molecules must themselves be almost incompressible because under
very high pressure, and especially at lower temperatures, a limit is reached
beyond which a gas cannot be further compressed. At these extremes of
pressure the molecules of the gas must be effectively in mutual contact.

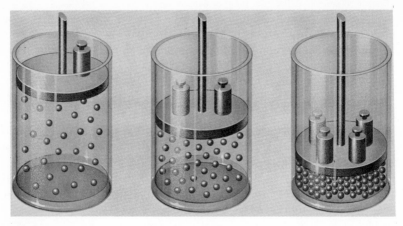

Fig. 2.1 *If a gas is compressed, the number of molecules in a given volume is increased. The pressure exerted by these molecules striking the walls is thus also increased. At very high pressure the molecules are effectively in contact with each other, and little further compression is possible.*

The very small degree of compressibility shown by liquids and solids, in comparison with gases, must mean that the molecules of substances in these states are also effectively in mutual contact. Perhaps in the interiors of distant stars, forces may be available to compress molecules still further, but we have not yet mastered this problem on earth.

The impacts of rapidly moving molecules on the walls of a container produce the effect of a steady pressure. There are so many molecules that no perceptible irregularity is found in the pressure exerted by them. If the volume in which the gas is contained is diminished, then the pressure will be increased in proportion because the number of molecules striking the walls will be increased. Thus Boyle's law is accounted for by the theory.

Similarly, we know that a gas admitted into a vacuum diffuses almost instantaneously to fill the whole space. The molecules must not only be moving at random, but also moving at high velocity. The molecules in denser gases (and therefore containing, presumably, heavier molecules) must move more slowly than lighter molecules. But when one gas diffuses through another, the rate of diffusion is much less than when the gas diffuses in a vacuum. This can only mean that gas molecules make frequent collisions. In a vacuum they are free to move rapidly, but in the presence of another gas, the molecules, although continuing to move rapidly, make slow and irregular progress because of the many collisions they suffer. Thus Graham's law is understandable—at least this is true in a qualitative sense. And if two gases are mixed, then as long as they do not suffer any chemical changes, the molecules of each gas will strike the walls of the container independently. The total number of impacts per unit time will be the sum of the impacts made by each gas alone and this, of course, is Dalton's law of partial pressures.

2.2   *Molecular Motion and Heat*

The kinetic molecular theory also has an explanation for Charles' law. But before presenting this explanation, we must say something about heat and show how it differs from temperature.

If a beakerful of water is placed over a gas flame, the temperature of the water will rise. The rate at which the temperature rises depends not only on the height of the gas flame and on external conditions, but also it depends very definitely on the quantity of water present. If the water is to reach a certain temperature, it is necessary to supply more heat when the quantity of water is larger.

Heat is conveniently measured in calories. The calorie (cal) is very nearly the quantity of heat necessary to raise the temperature of 1 gram of water from 14° C to 15° C. The kilocalorie (kcal) is 1000 cal.

For most substances other than water, it requires less than 1 cal to raise the temperature of 1 gram of the substance one Celsius degree. The number of calories necessary to raise the temperature of 1 gram of a substance one Celsius degree is called the *specific* heat of the substance.

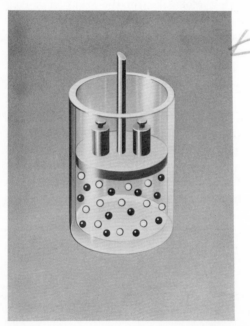

Fig. 2.2 *In a mixture of gases the molecules of each gas move independently. The total pressure is thus equal to the sum of the individual pressures.*

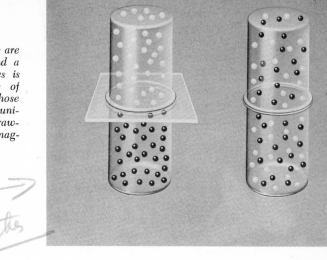

Fig. 2.3 Cylinders of different gases are placed mouth to mouth (left) and a glass partition separating the gases is removed (right). The molecules of each gas begin to diffuse through those of the other, and ultimately form a uniform mixture. The circles in the drawing, representing molecules, are magnified several million times.

(Specific heat is often called "heat capacity.") Water has, therefore by definition, a specific heat of very nearly 1 cal gram⁻¹ deg⁻¹ at 14° C, but this changes slightly as the temperature is changed. The specific heat of benzene is about 0.33 cal gram⁻¹ deg⁻¹ and that of gold is only 0.031 cal gram⁻¹ deg⁻¹.

If molecules actually exist and move with high speeds, then their motions must be completely random. To be sure, in a wind or inside an air hose the molecules must have a certain directed motion in addition to their random motions. But in a closed space protected from temperature changes, there must be just as many molecules moving in one direction as in any other.

Furthermore, if molecules have mass and motion, they must each be possessed of some kinetic energy. Kinetic energy is equal to the product of the mass times the square of the velocity. An assumption of the kinetic molecular theory is that the average kinetic energy of the molecules is directly proportional to the absolute temperature. The average velocity of the molecules must accordingly be directly proportional to the square root of the absolute temperature.[1] The force exerted by a molecule striking a surface is directly proportional to its velocity, and the pressure so produced by many molecules is proportional to the number of collisions in unit time. But the number of collisions is also proportional to the velocity, so that the pressure exerted by the molecules must be proportional

---

[1] This would be strictly true if all molecules were moving with the same velocity. Actually, we should use the root-mean-square velocity (that is, the square root of the average of the velocities each squared); thus

$$\bar{v} = \frac{1}{N} (v_1^2 + v_2^2 + v_3^2 + \cdots + v_N^2)^{1/2}$$

where N is the total number of molecules.

to the square of the velocity and hence proportional to the absolute temperature.

To express this relationship of pressure to absolute temperature, the following example is given: According to the kinetic molecular theory, if the absolute temperature is doubled, the force of each collision is increased by a factor of $\sqrt{2}$. The number of collisions per unit time is also increased by a factor of $\sqrt{2}$. The pressure is the product of the force of the collision times the number of collisions in unit time; that is to say, the pressure increases by $\sqrt{2} \times \sqrt{2} = 2$. In other words, as the absolute temperature is doubled, the pressure is doubled, provided, of course, the volume remains the same.

If, as the absolute temperature is raised, the pressure is deliberately maintained constant, then the volume must expand until (although the average molecular collision with the wall is harder) there will be fewer molecules striking the wall in unit time. When the temperature of a gas is raised, the product of pressure times volume must increase in direct proportion. If the pressure is held constant, we have the situation described by Charles' law. The absolute temperature of a gas is thus seen to be a measure of its kinetic energy, and the heat necessary to raise the temperature of a gas at constant volume is used merely to increase the kinetic energy of the molecules.

2.3   *Deviations from the Gas Laws*

A theory of science differs from a natural law in that the latter is an attempt at description of related phenomena, one that rests on such a wealth of supporting evidence that little serious doubt exists concerning its truth or its approximation to the truth. But a theory may not be true. A theory is an attempt at rationalization of many phenomena, some of which may appear quite diverse; the theory is supported by experimental observation and logical deduction. Whether or not the theory is actually true is of rather less importance than whether the theory, by its very formulation, suggests new ideas and new experiments leading to new discoveries. A useful theory is a tool of science, but it is a tool of the mind rather than a piece of apparatus consisting of wires and gages.

The kinetic molecular theory has been extraordinarily rich as a source of new ideas. We shall describe only two logical deductions from the theory and will show how these have led to greater insight concerning molecules. If molecules exist, it is scarcely conceivable that they are simply points in space. However small they are, and however vast in comparison are the distances between them, molecules must nevertheless occupy a finite fraction of the total volume. If, then, a gas is compressed under high pressure, it might be thought that the volume occupied by the individual molecules would sooner or later become an appreciable fraction of the whole gas volume. This being the case, it might be thought that the gas sample would increasingly resist further compression as the pressure continued to rise and that this resistance would be over and above the normal change described by Boyle's law. To express this another way, the volume available to the molecules for moving about becomes less than the observed volume V and should be considered $V - b$, where b is the volume of all the individual molecules in the sample. At low pressures, when the volume is high, b is so small compared with V that it may generally be neglected. But at high pressures, the volume V should diminish less rapidly than predicted by Boyle's law. If the product PV is plotted against P, it might be expected that PV would not remain constant, as required by Boyle's law, but rather would tend to increase. The rate of increase would be a measure of b, the actual size of the molecules.

As shown in Fig. 2.4, the effect described above actually occurs. The product PV is plotted against increasing P for hydrogen and for an imaginary ideal gas (that is, one whose behavior is accurately described by Boyle's law and Charles' law). Figure 2.4 also includes a plot for methane, which shows the effect of molecular volume and also another effect to be described below.

It is possible to estimate the dimensions of molecules from the constant b described above. There are several methods for estimating the sizes of molecules; the method based on deviations from the gas laws is called the *van der Waals volume*. Thus, in a liter of nitrogen at room temperature, a little under 2 ml (0.2 percent) may be considered as actually occupied by molecules. How this may be related to the sizes of individual molecules will be considered later.

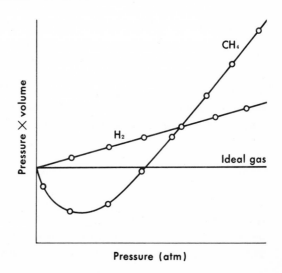

Fig. 2.4 If the product PV for a gas is measured at various pressures it will be found that for some gases, such as hydrogen, PV increases with increasing pressure instead of remaining constant as predicted by Boyle's law. For other gases, such as methane PV first diminishes then increases. The product PV may at 1000 atm be twice its value at 1 atm.

Another, related possible deduction may be made from the kinetic molecular theory. We know that all gases become liquid or solid as the temperature is lowered. This implies that some kind of cohesive forces must act between molecules, which otherwise would remain as gases even near absolute zero.

If there are such cohesive forces, then they should have the effect of drawing the molecules somewhat closer together than they would be if the molecules simply acted according to Boyle's law. This would be similar to a small pressure added to the normal applied pressure. Thus a plot of PV against P should show a deviation such that PV becomes *smaller* than expected because V is diminishing more rapidly, owing to this internal pressure.

Such an effect actually occurs, as shown for methane in Fig. 2.4. As the pressure continues to rise, the effect is overwhelmed by the opposite effect due to the volume b, as described above. These forces between molecules are small for gases such as helium and hydrogen except at low temperatures. But the forces are fairly large for gases such as methane and gaseous chloroform. They are known as *van der Waals forces,* and we shall have reference to them again.

2.4 Brownian Movement

The weight of experimental evidence is all heavily in favor of the kinetic molecular theory. But the idea of rapidly moving molecules received its earliest and strongest support from the phenomenon known as the *Brownian movement.*

In his celebrated experiment, Brown took fine pollen grains, dropped them in water, and then examined them under the microscope. He observed that the pollen grains were in irregular movement, sometimes going one way, sometimes another. Brown soon found that all very finely powdered matter shows this effect. The motions are due to the impacts of molecules. The observed motions are small and sluggish compared with the movements of the molecules, but the grains of pollen are jostled back and forth under the impact of molecular bombardment. No more convincing evidence of molecular motion could be desired.

2.5 Electron Microscope

An ordinary optical microscope is limited in its resolving power; that is to say, its ability to make visible very small particles, by the wavelength of light. The wavelength of visible light is at least a thousand times greater than the supposed diameter of the molecules to which we have

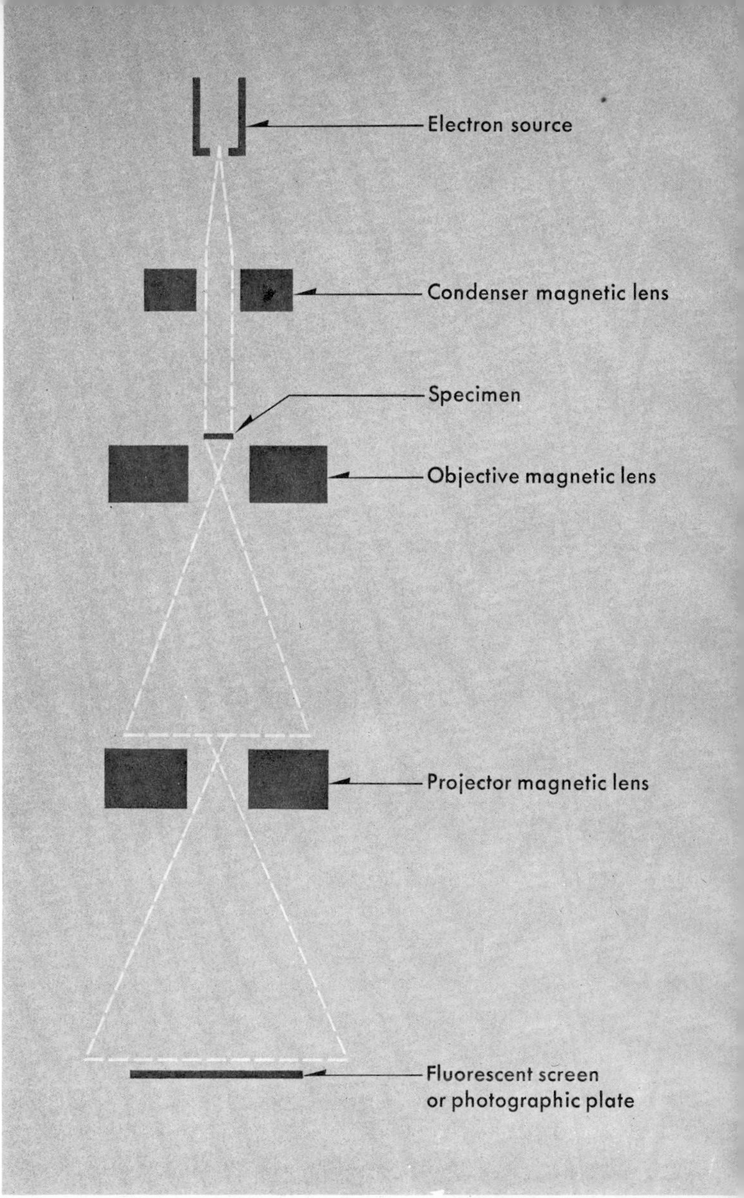

Fig. 2.5 Principle of the electron microscope. This is much like an optical microscope except that the lenses are magnetic fields and a beam of electrons is used instead of visible light.

been addressing our attention. The chances of improving an optical microscope until individual molecules can be seen is quite remote.

In a later chapter it will be shown that electricity consists of electrons and that these electrons are much smaller than the smallest molecule. Although electrons are particles and have a definite mass, they also have properties usually associated with electromagnetic waves such as radio waves or ordinary light. It was postulated by De Broglie that the wavelength λ related to a particle in motion may be calculated from the formula $\lambda = h/mv$, where h is Planck's constant, m is the mass of the particle, and v is the velocity of the particle. From the De Broglie

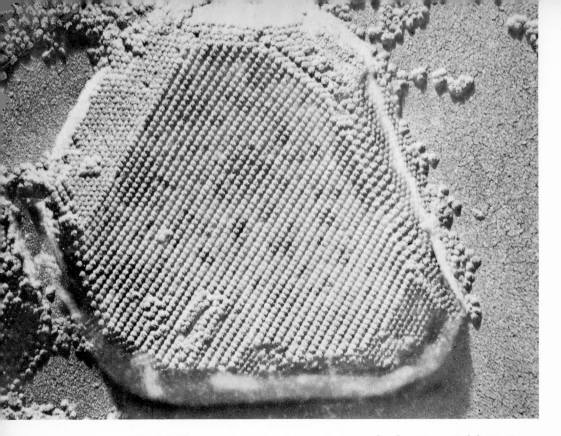

Fig. 2.6 Electron microscope picture of virus molecules. (From Ralph W. G. Wyckoff, World of the Electron Microscope, Yale University Press, 1958. Courtesy of Dr. Ralph W. G. Wyckoff.)

relationship, the wavelength associated with an electron moving at one-fifth the velocity of light is found to be about 1×10^{-9} cm and this is about 50 times smaller than the diameter of a typical molecule.

It is possible to construct a microscope that exploits this De Broglie wavelength of electrons. The electron microscope is shown diagrammatically in Fig. 2.5. In Fig. 2.6 there is shown an electron microscope picture of individual molecules arranged in orderly rows, as in a crystal. To be sure, these molecules do not form a gas, and they are the extremely large molecules of a disease-producing virus. Nevertheless, they are molecules, and the ability to make them visible is one of the triumphs of science.

2.6 Mass Spectrometer

The density of a typical gas may be low, but it is not negligible. A liter of dry air at STP has a mass of 1.293 grams. This must represent the total mass of the molecules of which the gas is composed. Our next problem is, then, to find the mass of the individual molecules of a gas. This may be done with an instrument called a *mass spectrometer*.

In the mass spectrometer the gas molecules are placed in a chamber and are heated by a filament. An electric field gives the molecules an electric charge and then accelerates them into an evacuated space. As charged molecules, called *ions,* move into the evacuated space, they are subjected to a magnetic field. The lines of force of the field are perpendicular to the page in the diagram shown in Fig. 2.7.

An electrically charged particle moving across a magnetic field is forced to travel in a circular path. The ions thus deflected may strike and mark, a photographic plate, or they may be detected electrically. It is possible to obtain the masses of individual molecules with this device because there is a relationship among the mass, the electric charge, the magnetic field, and the radius of curvature of the circular path into which the molecules are forced. The relationship is as follows:

The kinetic energy E of a moving molecule is, as previously described, given by

$$E = \tfrac{1}{2}mv^2$$

where m is the mass of the molecule and v its velocity. This energy E is also equal to the voltage ϕ (phi), through which the molecule moves in the electric field, multipled by the charge e on the molecule, so that

$$\tfrac{1}{2}mv^2 = \phi e$$

In a magnetic field of intensity H a moving electrically charged particle follows a circular path having a radius r, given by

$$r = \frac{mv}{He}$$

and from this,

$$m = \frac{eH^2r^2}{2\phi}$$

Fig. 2.7 One form of the mass spectrograph.

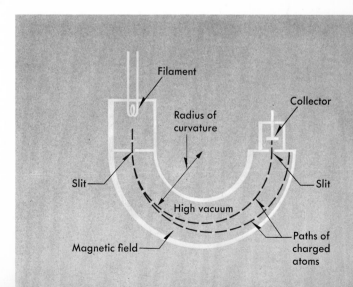

Filament

Collector

Radius of curvature

Slit

Slit

High vacuum

Magnetic field

Paths of charged atoms

It follows that the mass of a molecule may be found if we know e, H, r, and ϕ. All these values may be measured without too much difficulty. In practice, some molecules acquire a double (or higher) charge. This complicates matters, but not to an impossible degree.

The mass of the helium molecule found with the mass spectrometer is 6.66×10^{-24} gram, a mass so fantastically small as almost to defy the imagination. Though the actual masses of many other molecules may be found in this manner, the accuracy is not very high. The mass spectrometer is most useful for the astonishing precision with which it may be used to compare the masses of two different molecules. Further reference to this procedure will be made in Chapter 5.

2.7   *Some Properties of Molecules*

This chapter will be concluded with some remarks concerning the velocities with which molecules move under normal conditions in the gas state. Theoretical calculations suggest that in any gas sample, some molecules move slowly at any given instant; some move rapidly. It is possible to consider an average velocity, but this situation is conveniently described by a *Maxwell distribution curve*, as shown in Fig. 2.8. The vertical coordinate gives the fraction of molecules (for example, 2 percent, 5 percent) moving with a velocity within a few percent of the velocities given by the horizontal coordinate. Thus, in a given sample, one might say that 2 percent of the molecules are moving at 100 ± 10 mph, and 1 percent are moving at 1000 ± 100 mph, and so on. At $0°$ C in helium the average

Fig. 2.8 Maxwell distribution curve showing the distribution of gas molecule velocities.

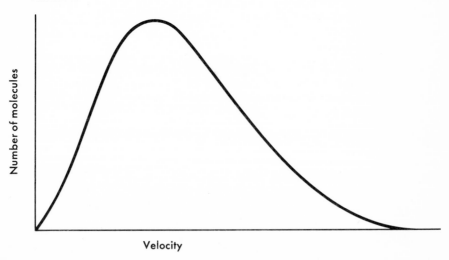

Number of molecules

Velocity

speed of the molecules is about 2580 mph. If the temperature is raised, the average speed increases.

Another quantity of interest is the distance a molecule must travel before it strikes another. The *mean free path* (that is, the distance that the average helium molecule must travel under normal conditions before it collides with another molecule) is about 3×10^{-6} cm. This is many times the diameter of the molecule; a gas sample is certainly mostly empty space. The molecules "occupy" the space only by virtue of their rapid, random motions.

EXERCISES

1. What, in brief, is the kinetic molecular theory?
2. What explanation has the kinetic molecular theory to offer for the behavior of gases as described by (a) Boyle's law, (b) Charles' law, (c) Graham's law, (d) Dalton's law of partial pressures?
3. What kinds of deviations from Boyle's law are commonly observed and what explanation for them has the kinetic molecular theory?
4. What explanation has the kinetic molecular theory for the Brownian movement?
5. What is the scientific principle that makes possible the electron microscope?
6. How does the mass spectrometer work?
7. Approximately what is the mass of a helium molecule?
8. If the absolute temperature of a gas is doubled, the average kinetic energy of the molecules is doubled. What happens to the average velocity of the molecules?
9. Why is it that 2 grams of a gas in a given volume will exert twice the pressure exerted by 1 gram of the same gas at the same temperature?
10. There is 1 gram of hydrogen in a container and 2 grams of hydrogen in another container at the same temperature. If 100 cal of heat is added to each, which sample will have the higher final temperature?
11. In a typical mass spectrometer the transport of matter is very small. For instance, the weight of nitrogen actually carried through the instrument during a molecular mass determination is about 3×10^{-21} gram/sec. How many years would it take to collect a gram of nitrogen at this rate?
12. A part of the kinetic molecular theory not considered in this chapter states that the average kinetic energy of the molecules of a gas is equal to the average kinetic energy of the molecules

of any other gas at the same temperature. Assuming that this is true, prove that Graham's law must be correct. [*Hint:* Put the kinetic energy of one gas equal to that of another. Then assume that the density of a gas is directly proportional to the mass of the molecules (this is proved in a later chapter) and that the rate of diffusion is directly proportional to the speed of the molecules.]

13. If Planck's constant $h = 6.62 \times 10^{-27}$ gram cm^2/sec, find the De Broglie wavelength associated with (a) an electron of mass 9.1×10^{-28} gram moving at 5.9×10^8 cm/sec, and (b) a rifle bullet of mass 2.0 grams moving at 3.5×10^4 cm/sec.

14. On Fig. 2.8 show the approximate effect on the distribution of molecular velocities of doubling the absolute temperature.

3

Liquids

3.1 *Liquefaction*

If the temperature of a gas sample is sufficiently lowered, the gas may become a liquid; at still lower temperature it will become a solid. For some gases, such as argon and carbon dioxide, the only serious change in the molecules as they go from gas to liquid to solid is that their freedom of motion is increasingly restricted until they become virtually immobilized. For other gases, such as nitrogen dioxide and ferric chloride, some major changes occur in the composition and structure of the molecules as they go from one state to another. In this and the following chapter there will be presented some general properties of matter in the liquid and solid states, and some of the relationships among all three states. The more serious complications involving molecular rearrangement, which often occur, will be deferred until later.

The obvious change that takes place during liquefaction is that the liquid has a free surface. This is in sharp contrast to a gas, which invariably fills a container and which has no perceptible surface excepting that in contact with the walls of the container. The mere existence of the free liquid surface imparts some special properties to a liquid. The surface of a liquid behaves like a skin that tends to resist penetration. It may frequently be observed that certain small insects are able to walk on water, even though the density of the insect may be greater than that of water. Similarly, most liquids will rise in a capillary tube because of this effect,

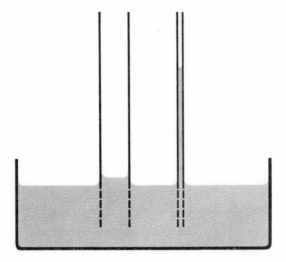

Fig. 3.1 Liquid rising in capillary tubes owing to surface tension.

which is called *surface tension*. Furthermore, liquids almost invariably have a markedly greater viscosity than do gases; that is to say, liquids have a greater resistance to stirring or to flow.

Liquids do not have the compressibility that is characteristic of gases; the volume of a liquid may be diminished only slightly, even though extremes of pressure may be applied. Similarly, the volume of a liquid does not depend on temperature to a degree anything like that shown by a gas. To be sure, all liquids show changes of volume, generally expansion, on warming—yet the changes are small compared with the changes shown by the volumes of gases at constant pressure.

The density of a liquid is also generally quite different from that of a gas. For example, the density of carbon dioxide gas at STP is about 1.976 grams/liter, but liquid carbon dioxide at the *same* temperature has a density of 914 grams/liter, or over 465 times greater. This can only mean that the molecules of the liquid are very much closer together than those of the gas. The fact that the liquid cannot be appreciably compressed, even at very great pressure, suggests that the molecules in the liquid state are near to being in actual physical contact and are held toward each other, at least in part by the van der Waals forces to which reference was made in the preceding chapter. But although the molecules of a liquid must be close together, it is also clear that they must be relatively free to move with respect to each other. Otherwise, it would be difficult to understand how a liquid could flow.

3.2   *Critical Temperature*

If a gas is cooled, it may become a liquid, but the temperature at which this change occurs depends upon the pressure. Carbon dioxide is, for instance, a gas at 0° C and 1 atm, but it is a liquid at 0° C and 50 atm.

If the temperature of a gas is raised, it will be found that a temperature is reached *above* which the gas cannot be liquefied, no matter what pressure is applied. This is known as the *critical temperature*, which may be defined as the highest temperature at which a substance may exist as a liquid. The pressure just sufficient to cause liquefaction at the critical temperature is called the *critical pressure.*

At the critical temperature and critical pressure the densities of gas and liquid are the same. The critical temperature for carbon dioxide is 31.1° C and the critical pressure is 73.0 atm. Under these conditions, the density of the carbon dioxide is 460 grams/liter, which is an extremely high density for a gas.

As matter passes through the critical temperature, the meniscus (or surface) associated with the liquid state appears or disappears, depending on whether the temperature is falling or rising. Above this temperature, the

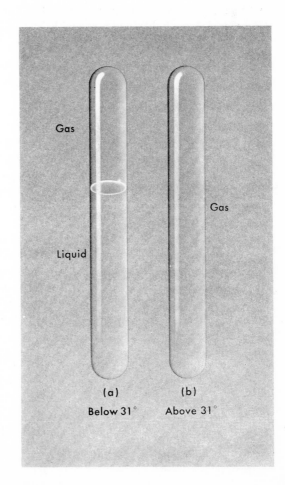

Fig. 3.2 (a). Below 31° C carbon dioxide is easily liquefied by application of pressure. (b) Above 31° C carbon dioxide cannot be liquefied.

Gas

Liquid

Gas

(a)
Below 31°

(b)
Above 31°

TABLE 3.1   REPRESENTATIVE CRITICAL TEMPERATURES AND
PRESSURES

Substance	Critical temperature, °C	Critical pressure, atm
Helium	−267.9	2.26
Hydrogen	−239.9	12.8
Oxygen	−118.8	49.7
Water	374.0	217.7
Mercury	>1500	>200

vapor fills the container completely; below it, the liquid fills only part of the container. The critical temperatures and pressures for a few substances are shown in Table 3.1.

In terms of molecular interactions, the critical temperature must be the highest temperature at which the van der Waals forces between the molecules can hold them reasonably close together.

3.3   Heat of Vaporization

It will be recalled that the quantity of heat, measured in calories, necessary to raise the temperature of 1 gram of a substance 1 deg (centigrade) is called the *specific heat* of the substance, and that the specific heat of water at 14° C is very nearly equal to 1 cal gram^{-1} deg^{-1}.

If a liquid is to be converted to a gas, it is invariably true that a relatively large quantity of heat is required even though no change of temperature occurs. To convert 1 gram of water at its normal boiling point of 100° C to steam (water vapor) at 100° C requires 539.6 cal. The heat necessary to convert 1 gram of a substance from liquid to gas, with no temperature change, is called the *heat of vaporization*. (Other terms sometimes used are latent heat of vaporization and specific heat of vaporization.)[1]

The heat of vaporization changes somewhat with changing temperature. We shall be concerned with that at the normal boiling point only. Table 3.2 gives the boiling point under 1 atm pressure, and also gives the heat of vaporization for a few substances.

---

[1] We shall use the terms *vapor* and *gas* interchangeably. Vapor is more frequently used for a substance that, though present as a gas, generally exists as a liquid at room temperature. The word "gas" is more frequently used for a substance like oxygen, which becomes a liquid at very low temperature only. Some writers restrict the word "vapor" to the gaseous fraction of a sample in which gas and liquid are in contact with each other.

TABLE 3.2   HEATS OF VAPORIZATION AT THE NORMAL
BOILING POINT

Substance	Boiling point, °C	Heat of vaporization, cal gram⁻¹
Helium	-268.94	5.97
Hydrogen	-252.8	106.7
Oxygen	-218.4	51
Water	100.0	539.6
Mercury	356.6	70.6

If one knows the heat of vaporization and the specific heat, one may calculate the heat necessary to convert a given mass of liquid at any temperature to the gaseous state at the normal boiling point.

PROBLEM: How many calories of heat will be required to convert 65.1 grams of water from 23° C to steam at 100° C.

SOLUTION: The specific heat of water is approximately 1 cal gram⁻¹ deg⁻¹ over the whole temperature range. To warm 65.1 grams of water from 23° C to 100° C will require

$$65.1 \text{ grams} \times 1 \text{ cal gram}^{-1} \text{ deg}^{-1} \times (100 - 23)\text{deg} = 5010 \text{ cal}$$

Then, to convert 65.1 grams of water at 100° C to steam at 100° C will require

$$65.1 \text{ gram} \times 539.6 \text{ cal gram}^{-1} = 35,128 \text{ cal}$$

This makes a total heat requirement of

$$5010 \text{ cal} + 35,128 \text{ cal} = 40,140 \text{ cal}, \quad \text{or } 40.1 \text{ kcal}$$

Notice that the final answer is rounded off to leave a number of significant figures that is justifiable in terms of the number given in the problem.

It may be seen from the preceding problem that the heat effect associated with the change of state from liquid to gas is much greater than that involved in warming the liquid to the boiling point. It will be understood also that if the sequence of changes had been reversed (namely, from gas at 100° C to liquid at 23° C), the heat effects would have been exactly the same but of opposite sign. Heat would have been given up by the system instead of being taken in.

A change of any kind in which heat is evolved, as in the liquefaction or condensation of steam, or as in the burning of a piece of coal, is called an *exothermic* change. One in which heat is taken in, as in the conversion of a liquid to a gas, is called an *endothermic* change. We shall have extensive reference to these terms in later chapters.

3.4   *Equilibrium Vapor Pressure*

All liquids have a tendency to evaporate. Some, such as gasoline, do so very rapidly; others, such as mercury, evaporate so slowly as to be scarcely perceptible. A liquid evaporates because there is always some of the substance present above it as a vapor or gas, and this vapor, in contact with the liquid, has a pressure, as do all gases. The maximum pressure exerted by a vapor *in contact with the liquid* is called the *equilibrium vapor pressure* (or sometimes simply the vapor pressure). The equilibrium

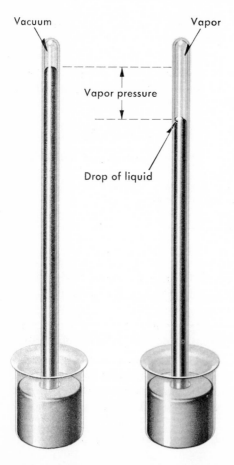

Vacuum

Vapor

Vapor pressure

Drop of liquid

Fig. 3.3 *Method for measuring equilibrium vapor pressure. A few drops of the liquid to be studied are introduced, with a medicine dropper, into the mercury column. The liquid drops float up through the mercury, and the vapor partially fills the space at the top of the tube. The pressure exerted by the vapor forces the mercury down a moderate distance.*

TABLE 3.3 EQUILIBRIUM VAPOR PRESSURES FOR SOME
LIQUIDS AT 20° C

Substance	Vapor pressure, mm Hg
Mercury	1.2×10^{-3}
Water	17.5
Carbon dioxide	4.3×10^4

vapor pressure for any given substance has a definite value at any given temperature. The vapor pressure rises with increasing temperature. A method for measuring vapor pressures is shown in Fig. 3.3, some typical equilibrium vapor pressures are shown in Table 3.3, and the equilibrium vapor pressure of water as the temperature is raised is shown in Fig. 3.4. More complete data for water will be found in the Appendix.

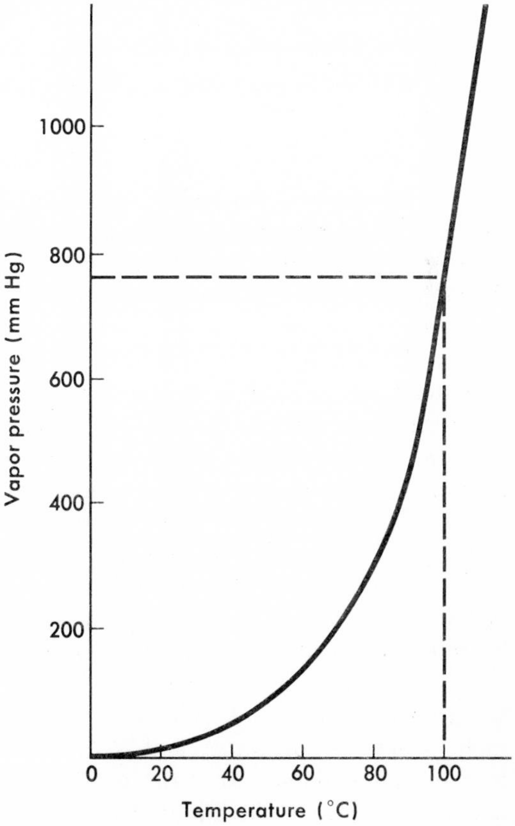

Fig. 3.4 Equilibrium vapor pressure of water over a range of temperatures. The normal boiling point (100°C) at 760 mm pressure is indicated.

Gas being generated

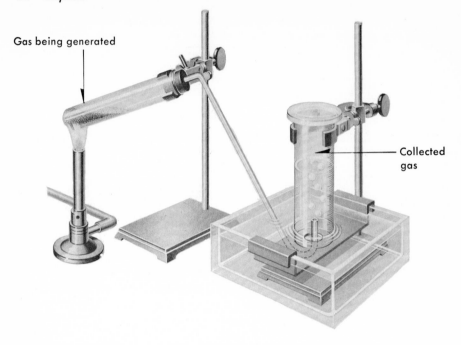

Collected gas

Fig. 3.5 Certain gases may be collected by displacement of water. The gas thus need not come in contact with the atmosphere.

The reason why liquids evaporate should now be clear: Some of the substance is present as a vapor. If this vapor diffuses, or is blown away, then more liquid will turn to vapor. This process may continue until all the liquid is gone.

If the temperature of a liquid is raised until the vapor pressure equals the atmospheric pressure (see Fig. 3.4), then the liquid starts to bubble and is said to be boiling. The *boiling point* is defined as the temperature at which the vapor pressure is equal to the atmospheric pressure. This definition of boiling point implies that if the atmospheric pressure, as determined by a barometer, changes from day to day, then the boiling point of any liquid must also change. Water boils at 100° C only if the barometric pressure is 1 atm. On a day when the barometer stands at 738.5 mm, the boiling point of water is only 99.2° C. The boiling point of water at various atmospheric pressures is easily found by reference to the table of equilibrium vapor pressures in the Appendix.

Frequently a gas may be collected by displacement of, or in contact with, a liquid. A cylinder, shown in Fig. 3.5, is filled with a liquid such as mercury or water, and is then inverted still full over a dish also containing the liquid. Now the gas to be collected is led through a tube under the surface of the liquid in the dish and up into the inverted cylinder.

In this way the gas may be collected without having it escape into, or come in contact with, the air.

The volume of a gas sample so collected depends, of course, on the pressure and temperature. If the liquid displaced is one (such as mercury) with a low vapor pressure at the temperature of collection, no further problem arises. But for water at room temperature, the vapor pressure is appreciable, and the gas sample will be contaminated with water vapor; then an appropriate correction must be made. This may be done by an application of Dalton's law of partial pressures (Sec. 1.4). The measured pressure on the gas sample is actually equal to the partial pressure of the gas plus the partial pressure of the water vapor, and the latter varies with the temperature. The method for finding the volume of the dry gas sample, corrected for the partial pressure of the water vapor, is shown in the following problem.

PROBLEM: Under 700 mm pressure, 275 ml of oxygen is collected over water at 23° C. What is the volume of the dry oxygen at STP?

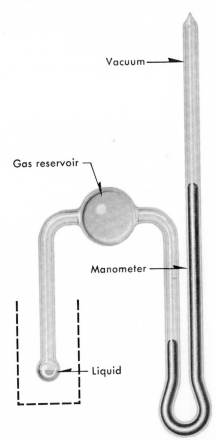

Fig. 3.6 Vapor pressure thermometer. A sample of gas in a vessel of appropriate design is connected to a manometer. The thermometer operates only when a portion of the gas is liquefied. Under these circumstances the manometer indicates the equilibrium vapor pressure. The temperature of the liquid may then be obtained by reference to standard tables.

Vacuum

Gas reservoir

Manometer

Liquid

SOLUTION: The vapor pressure of water at 23° C is about 21 mm. The pressure on the oxygen sample, as collected, is then 700 mm — 21 mm. The corrected volume is

$$V = 275 \text{ ml} \times \frac{700 - 21}{760} \times \frac{273}{296}$$

$$= 226 \text{ ml}$$

The fact that liquids have definite equilibrium vapor pressures that are dependent on the temperature makes it possible to use the vapor pressure in measuring temperature. Such devices are called *vapor pressure thermometers;* a diagram is shown in Fig. 3.6. In principle the thermometer is simply a vessel containing a sample of the liquid, which is chosen for its suitability for the temperature range to be measured. The sample holder is connected to a manometer and the vapor pressure, as measured by the manometer, may be related directly to the temperature of the sample by the use of standard tables of data in reference books. The vapor pressure thermometer is especially convenient and accurate in the region below room temperature. Thus a few drops of liquid nitrogen will suffice for measuring the temperature in the neighborhood of its normal boiling point, which is —195.8° C. Some idea of the accuracy with which temperatures may be measured in this way may be gained from the knowledge that at —200.9° C the vapor pressure of nitrogen is 400 mm, whereas at —195.8° C it is 760 mm. A temperature change of 5.1° C produces a pressure change of 360 mm, and it is no problem to read the pressure with a precision of ±0.1 mm.

3.5   *Relative Humidity*

Air normally contains more or less water vapor. If a measured volume of air is passed over a drying agent such as anhydrous calcium chloride or concentrated sulfuric acid, the increase in weight of the drying agent, owing to absorption of the water, will give the weight of water originally present in the air.

The water vapor content of the atmosphere is generally reported as relative humidity. *Relative humidity* may be defined as the ratio of the actual pressure of water vapor in the air to the equilibrium vapor pressure of water at the same temperature. The equilibrium vapor pressure of water at various temperatures may be obtained from tables. This represents the maximum pressure of vapor that may be maintained in air. Any excess pressure of water vapor would result in the formation of fog droplets or dew. Air normally contains less than this maximum pressure of water vapor except when it is raining. At 25° C the equilibrium vapor pressure of water is 23.5 mm. Suppose the actual partial pressure of the water vapor to be 14.0 mm on a certain day when the temperature is 25° C. Then the relative humidity is 14.0/23.5 = 59.6 percent.

Relative humidity is conveniently measured by determining the dew point. The *dew point* is the temperature at which moisture will condense as liquid from the air. It may be found by cooling a surface, such as the outside of a beaker, until a mist forms on the surface. Suppose that the dew point is thus found to be 10° C, and the room or atmosphere temperature is 23° C. The vapor pressures of water at these two temperatures are found from tables to be 9.1 mm and 20.9 mm, respectively. The relative humidity is then 9.1/20.9 = 43.5 percent. For meteorological purposes, more complicated instruments are used.

3.6   Physical Equilibrium

Normally, in the gaseous state, the van der Waals forces between the molecules are of minor importance, but when the kinetic energy of the molecules is lowered by lowering the temperature, the van der Waals attractive forces may become dominant. The molecules still move, but their movements are greatly restricted as compared with those in the gaseous state. The mean free path, instead of being very much greater than the diameter of a molecule, becomes equal to, or less than, a diameter.

Although the molecules in liquids move more slowly than those in gases, they retain the characteristic that some molecules are, at any instant, moving much more rapidly than others. If a very rapidly moving molecule happens to be near the surface of the liquid, it may fly away to become a gas molecule. The liquid is said to evaporate. Heat is necessary to give molecules sufficient energy to leave the surface of the liquid, and this heat is the heat of vaporization.

If a liquid is evaporating by loss of the most rapidly moving molecules, then the average velocity of the remaining molecules must diminish. If the average velocity of the remaining molecules is diminishing, then the liquid will get colder. This is the kinetic molecular explanation of the cooling effect always observed during evaporation of a liquid, and is the mechanism by which the evaporation of perspiration helps to keep the skin cool on hot days. If the relative humidity is high, then the atmosphere is nearly saturated with water and the mechanism is less efficient.

If a liquid, instead of being allowed to evaporate into the air, is placed in a closed container, then evaporation will at first proceed as usual. But the molecules in the vapor state are no longer able to escape completely and may in time find their way back into the liquid. After a while a steady state will be reached in which the number of molecules returning to the liquid is exactly equal to the number escaping. It may then be said that *equilibrium* has been reached. Not only is the number of molecules returning equal to the number escaping but also, at any given temperature, the number of molecules and their average velocity in the vapor state is constant. In other words, the pressure exerted by the molecules in the vapor state is constant. This pressure is the equilibrium vapor pressure described above. If now the temperature is raised, the average molecular velocity will be raised; more molecules will have enough energy to escape from the liquid. This effect will contribute to raising the vapor pressure, which rises very rapidly with increasing temperature, as shown in Fig. 3.4.

This idea of an equilibrium being set up between molecules escaping from and returning to a liquid is of great importance in chemistry. Notice that there is no thought of all motion stopping when equilibrium is reached; on the contrary, great numbers of molecules are moving. The essential point is that the number of molecules escaping from the liquid is exactly equal to the number returning. Such an equilibrium, in which motion is inherent, is often called a *dynamic* equilibrium. When, as in this case, no chemical change is involved, it is referred to as a *dynamic physical equilibrium*.

EXERCISES

1. In measuring liquids, it is generally enough to specify the volume; for gases the volume, temperature, and pressure must be given. Why is this true?
2. A substance may exist either in the liquid state or as a gas. Compare (a) compressibility, (b) rate of diffusion, and (c) kinetic energy of molecules in each of the two states.
3. The critical temperature for helium is $-267.9°$ C, but that for sulfur is about $1040°$ C. Suggest a reason for this difference.
4. How does the kinetic molecular theory explain the cooling effect observed during evaporation of a liquid?
5. Why does a liquid that partly fills a closed container show a constant vapor pressure, provided the temperature does not change?
6. Draw a graph showing the dependence of equilibrium vapor pressure on temperature for a typical liquid, and indicate the boiling point of the liquid.
7. The volume of a gas sample collected over water at $21°$ C and 738 mm is 477 ml. What is the volume of the dry gas at STP?
8. A sample of nitrogen, collected over water at $23°$ C and 765 mm pressure, occupies 495 ml. What is its volume, dry, at STP?
9. A sample of dry oxygen at STP occupies 425 ml. At what total

pressure will it occupy 475 ml over water if the temperature is changed to 20° C?

10. How many calories of heat will be required to convert 100 grams of water at 20° C to steam at 100° C?

11. The heat of vaporization of mercury at the normal boiling point (356.6° C.) is 70.6 cal gram^{-1}, and the specific heat averages about 0.0325 cal gram^{-1} deg^{-1} over the region from room temperature to the normal boiling point. Find the number of calories necessary to convert 150 grams of mercury from liquid at 25° C to vapor at 356.6° C.

12. What is the boiling point of water:
    (a) when the barometer stands at 750 mm?
    (b) in Mexico City when the barometer is 582 mm?
    (c) on a space flight when the pressure is 10.4 mm? (This problem should be done by interpolation from the data in a table of vapor pressures. It cannot easily be done arithmetically.)

13. Try plotting the logarithm of the vapor pressure against $1/T$ to see if more accurate answers to Exercise 12 are possible. (Use °K.)

4

Solids

4.1 *Crystallization*

Liquids, if cooled sufficiently, become solids. Some substances, such as carbon, solidify at such high temperatures that comparatively little is known about these substances in the liquid state. Other substances, such as helium, solidify only under elevated pressure near the absolute zero. Solids are characterized by a certain rigidity, that is to say, a tendency to maintain a definite shape and, in further contrast to liquids, even the softest solid is far harder than any liquid. But solids resemble liquids in resisting compression. Pressures many thousands of times greater than normal atmospheric pressure have an almost negligible effect on the volumes of both solids and liquids. Almost all solids have the remarkable property of forming in regular geometric patterns or crystals. The transition of a liquid to a solid is, therefore, quite frequently referred to as *crystallization.*

The temperature at which crystallization occurs is the same, for any given substance, as the temperature at which the reverse, or melting, process occurs. The precise temperature at which solid and liquid may exist in equilibrium is called the *melting* (or *freezing*) *point*. The melting point is a specific property of a substance and, as such, is often used to aid in the identification of chemical substances. This is particularly true of organic compounds. The melting point of most solids is changed only slightly by changing the pressure. The melting point of ice is, for instance, changed only a small fraction of a degree by changing the pressure from

760 mm down to 10 mm, while the boiling point may in this way be changed from 100° C to near 0° C.

In certain circumstances a liquid may be cooled below the freezing point without solidification taking place. If water is cooled, without shaking, it may be taken down 5 or even 10 degrees below 0° C, the normal freezing point of water. This effect is know as *supercooling;* it is shown by many liquids. If now the water is vigorously stirred, or if a small piece of ice is added to it, some of the water sample will crystallize almost instantly. Supercooled liquids are not in equilibrium. They are said to be in a *metastable state*. It may be wondered if solids can be heated *above* the melting point without melting taking place. This effect, the reverse of supercooling, does *not* appear to take place.

Solids may appear in a great variety of crystalline forms. The science of crystallography differentiates among six fundamentally different crystal systems, but in this book we shall be concerned more with the individual molecules in a crystal and how these molecules may be arranged with respect to each other. For that reason, no attempt will be made to present the various crystal classes except to point out that the outward appearance of a crystal is often deceptive and may not obviously coincide with the symmetry class to which it belongs. The particular form of a crystal within a class of crystals depends on the crystal habit, and this can lead to almost endless variations in the apparent geometric form of the crystal. Furthermore, most of the solids with which we shall deal are made up of very small crystals, sometimes imperfectly or irregularly formed. These crystallites may be so small as to be scarcely visible under a microscope, and they may be aggregated and interlocked in such a manner as almost to defy any attempt at identification of the crystallites themselves. Such an aggregate is said to be *polycrystalline*, and most solids are polycrystalline. It occasionally occurs that a solid has no crystalline form. The solid is then said to be *amorphous*, but truly amorphous solids are rare.

The molecular basis for the existence of crystals is that the molecules of which they are formed are lined up in astonishingly regular geometric patterns—countless millions of molecules being arranged in symmetrical rows and planes. The molecules in a solid may vibrate, but they rarely wander far from definite, fixed positions. The arrangement of the molecules is then reflected in the outward appearance of the crystal, even though a crystal large enough to see may easily contain 10^{20} molecules. How this geometric pattern is known will be presented in Sec. 4.4.

4.2 *Heat of Fusion*

If a liquid is permitted to become colder until it passes through the change from liquid to solid, it will be found that the temperature of the

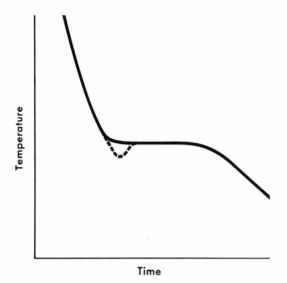

Fig. 4.1 A cooling curve (a plot of temperature versus time) for a substance going from the liquid phase to the solid. Some supercooling is indicated by the dotted line.

system will remain almost constant during the period when both liquid and solid are present. A plot of temperature against time, as of a molten metal cooling through the freezing point, is shown in Fig. 4.1. Such a plot is called a *cooling* curve, and it often reveals information concerning the identity and purity of the substance under investigation.

It will be noted that as heat is lost from the liquid, the temperature falls regularly until the freezing point is reached; after crystallization is complete, the temperature begins to fall once more. It will be recalled that energy in the form of heat is required to convert a liquid to a gas and that heat is evolved as the heat of vaporization when a gas is converted to a liquid. Similarly, heat is required to melt a solid or, conversely, heat is evolved during crystallization. This is called the *heat of fusion*. The melting of a solid is an endothermic change; crystallization from the

TABLE 4.1 SOME HEATS OF FUSION

Substance	Heat of fusion, cal gram⁻¹	Melting point, °C
Hydrogen	14.0	− 259.14
Oxygen	3.30	− 219
Water	79.7	0.0
Sulfur	13.2	119
Sodium chloride	124	804.3
Gold	15.8	1064

liquid to the solid state is an exothermic change. The reason, in a cooling curve, that little or no temperature change occurs at the freezing point is that the heat of fusion is being liberated and thus warms the system at a rate just sufficient to counteract the normal cooling rate. Some heats of fusion are given in Table 4.1.

It will be noted that it takes much more heat to melt a piece of ice than it does to warm the same weight of water up to room temperature.

PROBLEM: What quantity of heat is required to convert 45.0 grams of ice at 0° C to liquid water at 25° C.

SOLUTION: The heat of fusion of ice is 79.7 cal gram^{-1}. It will therefore require

$$45.0 \text{ grams} \times 79.7 \text{ cal gram}^{-1} = 3587 \text{ cal}$$

to melt the ice. To this must be added a quantity of heat sufficient to raise the temperature of the sample to 25° C. Recalling that the specific heat of water over this temperature range is about 1 cal gram^{-1} deg^{-1}, the number of calories required is

$$45.0 \text{ grams} \times 1 \text{ cal gram}^{-1} \text{ deg}^{-1} \times 25 \text{ deg} = 1125 \text{ cal}$$

The total quantity of heat required is then

$$3587 \text{ cal} + 1125 \text{ cal} = 4.71 \text{ kcal}$$

Frequently a solid may suffer a change of crystalline form as the temperature is lowered or raised. When this occurs, it is almost invariably associated with either a heating or a cooling effect. The heating or cooling, as the case may be, is thus a convenient method for detecting the occurrence of such changes, which are often referred to as *changes of phase*. The heat effects associated with such crystalline transitions are very similar to the heats associated with changes of state, namely, the heat of fusion and the heat of vaporization. The study of such transitions is conveniently carried out by placing two containers adjacent to each other in a chamber that may be heated or cooled at will. One container holds the sample under investigation; the other, a standard sample known to undergo no changes of phase in the temperature range to be investigated. Two thermometers are required; one to measure the temperature of the standard sample and the other to measure the difference in temperature between the standard and the unknown. The most convenient method for measuring these temperatures is to use two thermocouples arranged as shown in Fig. 4.2. An example of the information obtainable is shown in Fig. 4.3. The whole procedure is known as *differential thermal analysis*.

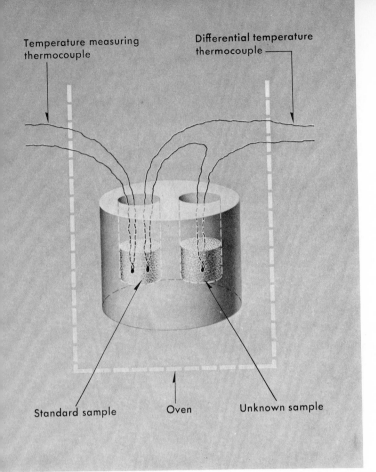

Temperature measuring
thermocouple

Differential temperature
thermocouple

Standard sample   Oven   Unknown sample

Fig. 4.2 Procedure for differential thermal analysis.
The electric potential from
the thermocouples is a measure of the temperature or of
the difference in temperature of standard and un-
known samples.

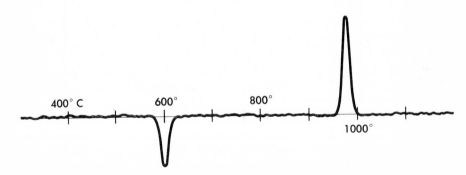

400° C   600°   800°
                                        1000°

Fig. 4.3 Typical results obtained by differential thermal analysis. Two phase
transitions are indicated—one an endothermic change as the temperature is
raised through 600° C and the other a large exothermic change at about
950° C.

4.3   Phase Diagrams

From what has been said in previous sections, it should be clear that not only is the volume of a gas dependent on temperature and pressure, but also that the transitions from the gas state to liquid and to solid are dependent on temperature and pressure, although the freezing point is not dependent on pressure to the degree shown by the boiling point. These various relationships are conveniently shown in plots called phase diagrams. A *phase diagram* is a plot showing the temperatures and pressures at which the various phases of a substance or substances are in equilibrium.

Figure 4.4 is a phase diagram for water, slightly distorted so as to show clearly the several kinds of information that may be presented in this way. In this diagram, pressure is plotted vertically and temperature (in any convenient scale) is plotted horizontally. Only three phases are represented in this diagram; namely, ice, water, and steam (that is, solid, liquid, and gas). But if the solid should exist in two or more crystalline forms, as mentioned in the preceding section, then these forms are considered to be different phases and are represented in the diagram. Such a situation actually occurs for sulfur.

The line labeled "liquid-gas" represents the range of temperatures and corresponding pressures at which the liquid phase and the gas phase

Fig. 4.4 Phase diagram for water.

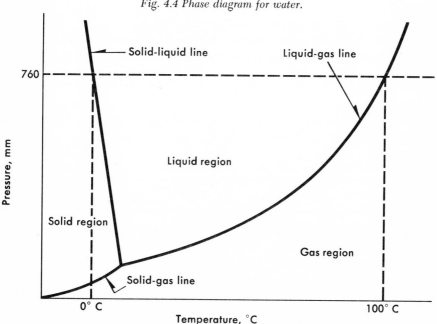

are in equilibrium. In other words, this represents the equilibrium vapor pressure previously discussed. The line labeled "solid-liquid" represents the temperatures and corresponding pressures at which the solid and liquid phases are in equilibrium, and it will be noted that (for water) as the pressure is raised, the freezing point diminishes a little. Finally, the line labeled "solid-gas" represents the temperatures and corresponding pressures at which the solid and gas phases are in equilibrium. It may come as a surprise to see that ice has a measurable vapor pressure just below the normal freezing point.

In the whole region labeled "gas," the only phase that may be present is the gas phase. In the "liquid" region some gas may, of course, be present, but if the temperature and pressure lie anywhere inside the "liquid" region, then such gas as may be present will condense until the pressure and temperature lie on the "liquid-gas" line. Similarly, only solid may be present within the "solid" region at equilibrium. Note that a supercooled liquid is not in equilibrium and is not represented on the diagram.

At one, and only one, point do the three equilibrium lines meet. This is known as the *triple point*, and is the only temperature and pressure at which all three phases may be present in equilibrium. The triple point for water has been selected (Sec. 1.6) as the standard calibration point on the absolute (Kelvin) temperature scale. It is arbitrarily said to be 273.16° K. The pressure at the triple point of water is 4.58 mm. Under 1 atm pressure (760 mm), the liquid and solid phases of water are in equilibrium at 273.15° K. This is the normal freezing or melting point of water, and on the Celsius (centigrade) scale it is 0° C.

Phase diagrams are especially useful in the study of metals, and we shall refer to them from time to time. It will be observed that, provided the temperature is kept below 0° C, it is quite possible for solid ice to go directly to the gas phase without ever melting and thus going through the liquid phase. The reverse process is, of course, also possible. This kind of transition from solid to gas, and vice versa, is called *sublimation*. A familiar example is the evaporation of dry ice.

4.4   X-Ray Diffraction

Radiant energy, of which visible light is one example, is conveniently described as a wave motion not unlike the waves that occur on the surface of a body of water. As may all wave motion, radiant energy may be characterized in terms of a wavelength, λ, which is the distance between successive peaks (or wave crests) and a frequency, ν, which is the number of waves passing a given point in unit time. Wave motion is described by the following relationship:

$$c = \nu\lambda \tag{4.1}$$

where c is the velocity of the wave front.

Radiant energy has a velocity of 2.998×10^{10} cm sec^{-1}, which is roughly equivalent to 186,000 miles per second. Ordinary red light has a frequency of about 3.75×10^{14} sec^{-1}; hence the wavelength of visible red light is given approximately as follows:

$$\lambda = \frac{c}{\nu}$$
$$= \frac{2.998 \times 10^{10} \text{ cm sec}^{-1}}{3.75 \times 10^{14} \text{ sec}^{-1}}$$
$$= 8.00 \times 10^{-5} \text{ cm}$$

Radiant energy has no mass or electric charge in the ordinary sense.[1] Forms of radiant energy other than visible light include radio waves, infrared (heat) waves, ultraviolet, x-rays, gamma rays, and possibly cosmic rays. These differ from visible light only in the wavelength and hence the frequency; all have the same velocity. Radio waves may be several kilometers long; x-rays about 10^{-8} cm. Waves of radiant energy of these several kinds constitute what is known as the *electromagnetic spectrum*.

Our chief concern in this section is with x-rays. If an evacuated tube is arranged so that a heated metal wire at one end carries a strong charge of negative electricity running up to 20,000 or 30,000 volts, and a piece of metal arranged (as shown in Fig. 4.5) at the other end of the tube carries a positive charge, then it will be found that x-rays are emitted from the positive electrode. These x-rays, discovered by W. C. Roentgen in 1895, have the remarkable property of being able to pass through glass, thin metal sheets, and, most spectacularly, through human tissue so that the bones and other physiological structures are made visible with the aid of a fluorescent screen or photographic plate. The use of x-rays in medical diagnosis and treatment is well known; their use in scientific research is no less important.

If visible light is passed through a prism, a rainbow of colors (a *spectrum*) is produced. The same effect is obtained if the light is passed through, or reflected from, a sheet of glass or metal on which a very large number of parallel equally spaced scratches have been made. Such a sheet of glass or metal is called a *diffraction grating*. But x-rays have such

---

[1] According to Einstein's mass-energy relationship, there is an equivalence between mass and energy. Reference to this will be made in Chapter 7.

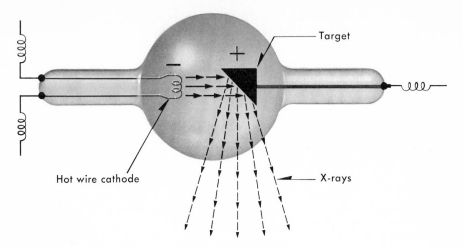

Fig. 4.5 X-ray tube. Cathode rays (electrons) from the hot wire strike
the target from which x-rays are then emitted.

a short wavelength that it is not easy to rule a diffraction grating suitable
for producing an x-ray spectrum. However, it so happens that the molecules in a crystal are lined up in orderly rows and planes, and these
planes serve somewhat the same purpose as do the scratches on a conventional diffraction grating. A crystal interposed in a beam of x-rays
serves to break the beam into its component wavelengths; that is to say,
into a spectrum. But, with x-rays we are not dealing with visible light
and hence no rainbow of colors is produced. What amounts to the same
thing, however, is that the different wavelengths of the x-rays present in
the beam are separated by the crystal and may be recorded on a photographic plate. An experimental arrangement for studying *x-ray diffraction*
is shown in Fig. 4.6.

Let us assume that two identical waves start from the same point
at the same time. Then, from Fig. 4.7(a), it may be seen that these waves
reinforce each other, giving a resultant wave that is stronger (has a
greater amplitude) than either of the original waves but which is, of
course, of the same wavelength and frequency. The two wave fronts are
said to be "in phase."[2] By contrast, let it be assumed, as shown in Fig.
4.7(b), that two identical waves start from the same point, but that one
wave is half a wavelength (half the distance between crests) later than
the other. The two wave fronts are said to be "out of phase," and the net
resultant wave will have a negligible intensity because the crest of one wave
will just counteract the trough of the other.

[2] Do not confuse this use of the word "phase" with the quite different meaning it had
in Sec. 4.3.

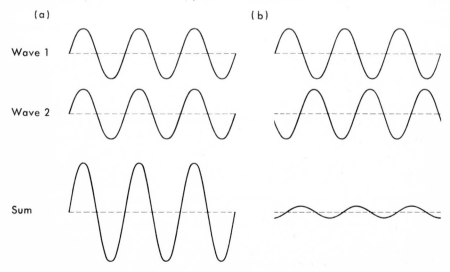

Fig. 4.6 Diffraction of x-rays. The rays from the tube are narrowed by a slit in a metal screen, then allowed to strike a crystal. The crystal diffracts the x-rays, and the exact angle through which the x-rays are diffracted may be found by having the rays strike, and thus mark a photographic plate.

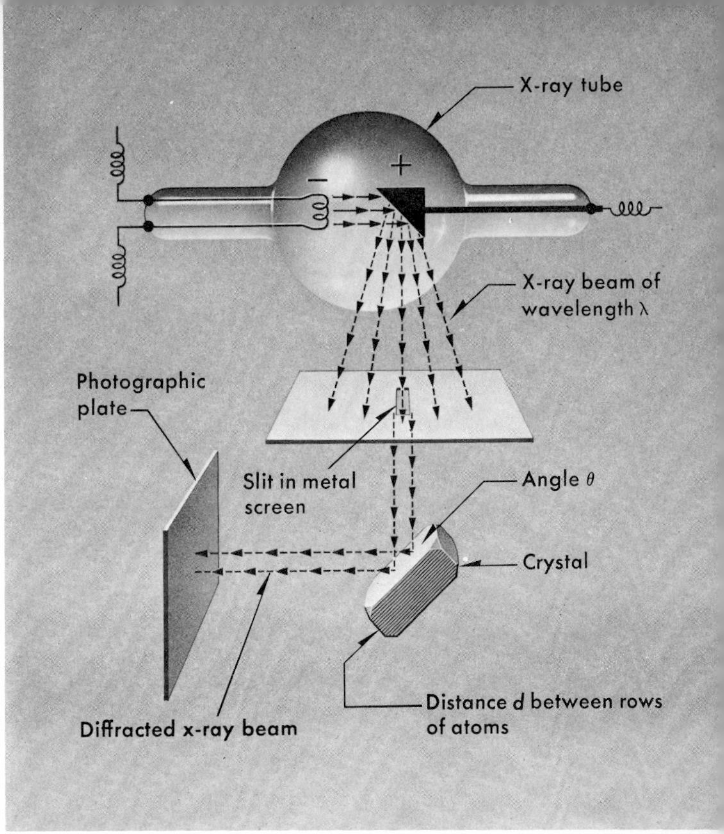

X-ray tube

X-ray beam of wavelength λ

Photographic plate

Slit in metal screen

Angle θ

Crystal

Distance d between rows of atoms

Diffracted x-ray beam

Fig. 4.7 (a) Two wave fronts start in phase. The resultant wave is larger. But (b) if the waves are out of phase the resultant wave is smaller.

(a)

(b)

Wave 1

Wave 2

Sum

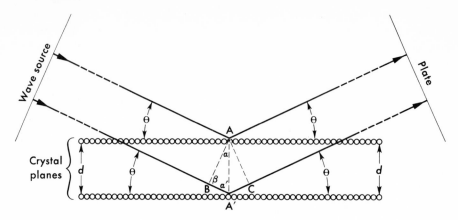

Fig. 4.8 Principle of x-ray diffraction that yields the distance between layers of atoms in accordance with the Bragg equation.

Now let an experiment be arranged so that two trains of identical waves start from the same point at the same time and that they strike a crystal as shown in Fig. 4.8. The crystal consists of planes of molecules arranged as shown. If one of the wave trains is reflected from the upper plane of molecules and the other from the lower plane, then the latter will reach the photographic plate somewhat later than the former because the path to the lower plane is somewhat longer. If, however, the increase in path length to and from the lower plane is just equal to the distance between wave crests (that is, just equal to the wavelength of the x-rays), then the two wave trains will reinforce each other and cause a strong blackening of the photographic plate.

Such a reinforcement of wave crests will occur under the following circumstances: Consider two wave crests that reach the line *AB* together, as shown in Fig. 4.8. To reach the photographic plate in phase, these wave crests must *leave* the line *AC* together. This will occur if the distance $BA' + A'C$ is a whole number times the wavelength of the x-rays. This is to say: $(BA' + A'C) = n\lambda$, where n is any whole number and λ, as before, is the wavelength.

The distance BA' is equal to $d \sin \theta$, where d is the distance between the planes of molecules and θ is the angle at which the x-ray wave train strikes the crystal planes,[3] and $(BA' + A'C) = 2d \sin \theta$. Reinforcement of the x-ray wave crests will occur whenever

$$n\lambda = 2d \sin \theta \qquad (4.2)$$

[3] In a right-angled triangle such as *ABA'*, the sine of the angle α is equal to BA'/AA'. Hence $BA' = (\sin \alpha)/AA'$. But $AA' = d$, the distance between the planes. Hence, $BA' = d \sin \alpha$ and $(BA' + A'C) = 2d \sin \alpha$. In any triangle, the sum of all interior angles is 180 degrees, and as the angle $\beta = 90$ degrees and $\alpha' = 90$ degrees $- \alpha$, it follows that the angle $\alpha = \theta$. Therefore $(BA' + A'C) = 2d \sin \theta$.

This is the *Bragg equation* relating x-ray wavelength and reflection angle to the distance between successive planes of molecules in a crystal. It has proved to be one of the most useful relationships ever devised for revealing the structure of the solid state.

PROBLEM: It is found that a beam of x-rays of wavelength 1.12×10^{-8} cm, as diffracted from a crystal, produces blackening of the photographic plate at angles θ equal to 11.6, 23.6, and 36.6 degrees. Find the distance d between successive planes of molecules in the crystal.

SOLUTION: The sines of the angles are found from tables or slide rule to be as follows: 11.6 degrees, 0.200; 23.6 degrees, 0.400; 36.6 degrees, 0.597. These sines are in the proportion 1:2:3, which must obviously correspond to the values of n in the Bragg equation. Then, solving for the case of $n = 1$,

$$
\begin{aligned}
d &= \frac{n\lambda}{2 \sin \theta} \\
&= \frac{1 \times 1.12 \times 10^{-8} \text{ cm}}{2 \times 0.200} \\
&= 2.8 \times 10^{-8} \text{ cm}
\end{aligned}
$$

4.5 *Space Lattice*

It will be clear that the arrangement of molecules in crystals may be such that more than one set of planes may be identified. The distance between planes of various sets may be obtained by turning the crystal in the x-ray beam so that one set of planes and then another causes diffraction of the beam. In this way, it is possible to accumulate information sufficient to make a scale model of almost any given crystal, which will show the arrangement of molecules and their relative distances apart. Such crystal-structure determinations can be quite tedious, but they can often be completed with great precision, going in favorable cases as far as seven significant figures. The distances between molecules in typical crystals tends to be about 10^{-8} cm, as in the problem given in the preceding section. For this reason, a measure called the *angstrom* unit is frequently used in reporting the results of x-ray crystal-structure determinations. One angstrom unit (1 Å) is equal to 1.0×10^{-8} cm.

The general arrangement of molecules in a crystal gives rise to a repeating unit known as a *space lattice*. Some space lattices are very simple; others, more complex. The simplest space lattice is one made up of molecules arranged at the corners of a cube, as shown in Fig. 4.9. This arrangement is known as *simple cubic*. A larger number of molecules, all

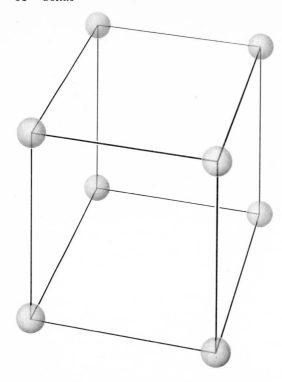

Fig. 4.9 A simple cubic unit cell. The atoms are reduced in size for convenience in showing the arrangement.

Fig. 4.10 A larger group of atoms in a more realistic simple cubic arrangement.

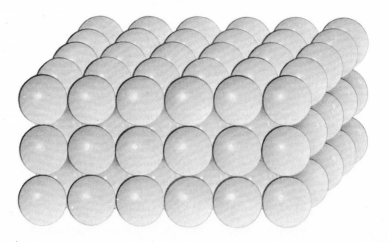

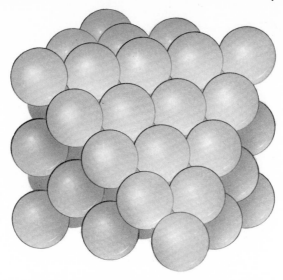

Fig. 4.11 A group of atoms in close-packed array.

arranged in a simple cubic lattice, is shown in Fig. 4.10, but few substances adopt the simple cubic.

It will be noted that the simple cubic is not the most economical
possible arrangement for getting the largest number of molecules into the
smallest volume. A more efficient arrangement is that shown in Fig. 4.11,
in which the maximum possible use is made of the space available for
packing spheres of equal diameter. This arrangement is called *close packed.*
There are several alternative close-packed arrangements. One form is
shown in Fig. 4.12, in which eight molecules are arranged at the corners
of a cube, as in simple cubic, but six more molecules are at the centers of
each of the six cube faces. This arrangement is a very common one among
metals. It is called *face-centered cubic* (fcc).

Figures 4.9 and 4.12, showing the grouping of molecules that is
repeated over and over again in the space lattice, illustrate unit cells.
Thus the simple cubic unit cell appears to have eight molecules, but
as these have to be shared with eight other neighboring unit cells, the
number of molecules per unit cell in this arrangement is actually only one.
The face-centered cubic has four. Still another very common space lattice
is the *body-centered cubic* (bcc). The unit cell for this, containing two
molecules, is shown in Fig. 4.13. Of the three unit cells shown, only the
face-centered cubic is a close-packed lattice. It will be noticed also that
in each of these lattices, any given molecule has a definite number of
nearest neighbors. The number of nearest neighbors possessed by each
molecule in a space lattice is called its coordination number. In the simple

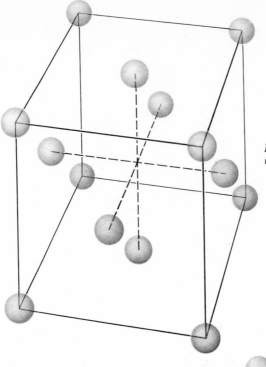

Fig. 4.12 A face-centered cubic unit cell.

Fig. 4.13 A body-centered cubic unit cell.

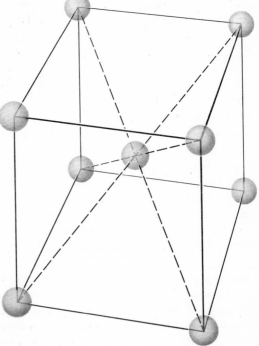

cubic, the coordination number is 6; in the face-centered cubic, it is 12 (and this is true of all close-packed lattices); and in body-centered cubic, it is 8.

The length of a unit cell is useful in many kinds of studies. This information, which is derived from x-ray diffraction as described in the preceding section, is available in standard tables. For instance, for solid argon (fcc), the unit cell dimension (often called the lattice constant) is 5.43 Å; for iron (bcc), it is 2.86 Å; and for one form (simple cubic) of solid oxygen, it is 6.83 Å.

EXERCISES

1. Explain the terms crystalline, polycrystalline, amorphous, sublimation, phase, x-rays, spectrum, space lattice, and coordination number.
2. What quantity of heat is necessary to convert 100 grams of ice at 0° C to liquid water at 100° C?
3. Benzene melts at 5.5° C, and its normal boiling point is 80.1° C. Its heat of fusion is 30.3 cal gram^{-1}, its heat of vaporization at 80° C is 94.3 cal gram^{-1}, and its specific heat between 5° C and 80° C averages about 0.41 cal gram^{-1} deg^{-1}. How many calories will be required to convert 100 grams of solid benzene at 5.5° C to vapor at 80.1° C?
4. A sample of pure water is at −10° C and 0.5 atm pressure. At constant pressure the sample is slowly warmed to 100° C. What phases are present at each temperature?
5. A sample of water is at 0° C and 10 mm pressure. At constant temperature the pressure is raised to 2 atm. What phases are present at each pressure?
6. Draw the phase diagram for water and add to it a dotted line showing the probable pressure-temperature relationship for super-cooled water.
7. Draw a phase diagram for water to include the region of the critical temperature.
8. Gamma rays, as from a nuclear bomb, have a wavelength of about 0.1 Å. What must be the frequency of gamma rays?
9. The distance between planes in a crystal is 3.52 Å. At what angles may x-rays of wavelength 1.54 Å be reflected, according to the Bragg equation?
10. Consider Figs. 4.10 and 4.11, showing simple cubic and close-packed structures. Find rows of atoms that have the same d in the Bragg equation for both structures.

11. Compute the packing efficiency (the fraction of the volume actually occupied) for equivalent spheres in simple cubic packing. (A similar calculation for close-packed structures is more difficult.)

12. Compare the three states of matter in terms of density, effect of changing pressure and temperature, hardness, viscosity, molecular arrangement, and molecular motions.

5

Atoms

In Chapter 2 it was shown that the mass of a molecule may be obtained with a fair degree of accuracy by use of the mass spectrometer, that all (or nearly all) the molecules of helium have the same mass, and that the mass of each molecule of helium is approximately 6.66×10^{-24} gram.

The masses of molecules are more conveniently given in terms of the atomic mass unit (amu). A molecule having a mass of 1 amu weighs 1.6603×10^{-24} gram. On this basis the mass of the helium molecule expressed in atomic mass units is

$$\frac{6.66 \times 10^{-24} \text{ gram}}{1.6603 \times 10^{-24} \text{ gram per amu}} = 4.00 \text{ amu}$$

This is commonly called the *molecular weight* of helium. This chapter will be devoted to the number of molecules present in 1 gram of matter containing molecules of mass 1 amu, to the relation of molecular weights to gas densities, and to the reasons underlying the choice of the atomic mass unit.

Imagine a hypothetical gas in which all the molecules have the same mass and that the mass is exactly 1 amu. This gas has then a molecular weight of exactly 1. Our first question is: How many such molecules would be present in 1.000 gram of this gas? The answer is readily found, for if each molecule has a mass of exactly 1 amu, it must weigh 1.6603×10^{-24} gram. Then the number of molecules per gram must be

$$\frac{1.000 \text{ gram}}{1.6603 \times 10^{-24} \text{ gram}} = 6.023 \times 10^{23}$$

It is also true that if we had taken 2 grams of a gas with a molecular weight of 2, or X grams of a gas with molecular weight X, the number of molecules would have been exactly the same because

$$\frac{X \text{ grams}}{X \times 1.6603 \times 10^{-24} \text{ gram}} = 6.023 \times 10^{23}$$

and this will be true of any gas, provided the mass taken in grams is numerically equal to the molecular weight expressed in atomic mass units.

The number 6.023×10^{23} assumes therefore considerable significance. It is known as **Avogadro's number.** This number of molecules of any substance is called a *mole* of that substance, and *the weight of a mole is the molecular weight expressed as grams.*

The word "mole" is a collective noun like flock (of birds) or galaxy (of stars). But mole has the added meaning of a very definite number of particles, namely, Avogadro's number. It will also be noted that while we have followed the usual custom of using gram-moles, it would have been possible to use any other unit of mass such as the pound, in which case Avogadro's number might have been different.

5.2 Gram-molecular Volume

It has been shown above that a mole of helium weighs 4.00 grams. The density of helium gas may be found by direct measurement. This may be done by taking a glass bulb of known volume, as shown in Fig. 5.1, and weighing it empty and then filled with helium to a known pressure and at a known temperature. The difference in weights, after appropriate corrections for the buoyancy of air, gives the mass of the helium. The density is the mass divided by the volume. The density of helium at STP is 0.1785 gram liter^{-1}.

This information makes it possible to calculate the volume occupied at STP by 1 mole of helium. If 0.1785 gram of helium occupies 1.000 liter, then 1 mole of helium (4.00 grams) must occupy

$$\frac{4.00 \text{ grams mole}^{-1}}{0.1785 \text{ gram}} \times 1.000 \text{ liter} = 22.4 \text{ liters mole}^{-1}$$

If this volume, 22.4 liters, were characteristic of helium alone, then it would not be very important, but it is actually found to be approximately

Fig. 5.1 *Gas density bulb.*

true of *any* gas that 1 mole at STP has a volume of 22.4 liters. This is therefore known as the *gram-molecular* (or molar) *volume*.

Table 5.1 gives several examples of gases. In each case the weight of a mole was obtained by taking the mass of the molecule on the mass spectrometer, converting to atomic mass units, and expressing the molecular weight thus obtained as grams. The gas densities were found by direct measurement, as described above (with corrections to STP as necessary),

TABLE 5.1 GAS DENSITIES AND GRAM-MOLECULAR VOLUMES

Gas	Weight of 1 mole, grams mole⁻¹	Gas density, grams liter⁻¹	Gram-molecular volume, liters mole⁻¹
Hydrogen	2.00	0.08988	22.3
Methane	16.0	0.7168	22.3
Nitric oxide	30.0	1.7837	22.4
Argon	40.0	1.3402	22.4

and the final column in Table 5.1 gives the volume of a mole at STP as found by dividing the weight of a mole by the density.

It may be seen that a mole of any gas (and this is generally true) occupies about the same volume and that at STP this volume is very near 22.4 liters. If correction is made for the deviations from the gas laws shown by all real gases, then the gram-molecular volume is found to be almost exactly 22.4 liters.

It has already been shown above that a mole of any gas contains by definition the same number of molecules. We are therefore forced to the conclusion that:

Equal volumes of all gases, at the same temperature and pressure, contain the same number of molecules.

This is **Avogadro's principle,** first formulated by Amadeo Avogadro, about 1811, on the basis of reasoning quite different from that given above.

5.3   *Gas Densities and Molecular Weights*

If the mass of a mole is numerically equal to the molecular weight, and if a mole of any gas at STP occupies 22.4 liters, then it follows that the molecular weight of any gas, expressed as grams, occupies 22.4 liters. This makes it possible to find the molecular weight of any gas, provided the density is known.

PROBLEM: The density of ozone at STP is 2.144 grams liter^{-1}. Find the molecular weight of ozone.

SOLUTION: The mass of 1 mole of any gas is the mass of 22.4 liters of the gas at STP. If the density is 2.144 grams liters^{-1}, then 1.000 liter weighs 2.144 grams and 22.4 liters weigh

$$22.4 \text{ liters mole}^{-1} \times \frac{2.144 \text{ grams}}{1.000 \text{ liter}} = 48.1 \text{ grams mole}^{-1}$$

The mass of a mole of ozone is 48.1 grams and the molecular weight is 48.1.

PROBLEM: What number of moles of a gas is contained in 3.75 liters at STP?

SOLUTION: 22.4 liters of any gas at STP contains almost exactly 1 mole. Therefore, 3.75 liters would contain

$$\frac{3.75 \text{ liters}}{22.4 \text{ liters mole}^{-1}} = 0.167 \text{ mole}$$

A more generally useful method for relating gas densities to molecular weights is to use the gas laws described in Chapter 1. Equation 1.4 showed that

$$\frac{P_1 V_1}{T_1} = \frac{P_2 V_2}{T_2}$$

from which it may be inferred that for any given sample of gas, the product of pressure times volume is equal to a constant multiplied by the absolute temperature.

But the volume of a gas must also depend on the total number of molecules present, provided pressure and temperature remain constant. If the total mass of gas is doubled (that is, if the total number of molecules is doubled), then the volume must double if the other conditions remain the same. Furthermore, the total number of molecules in a gas sample must be proportional to the total number of moles of gas present. This must be true because, by definition, 1 mole of any gas contains 6.023×10^{23} molecules. Equation 1.4 may then be rewritten to include the number of moles of gas present, as follows:

$$PV = nRT \tag{5.1}$$

where P, V, and T are the pressure, volume, and absolute temperature, respectively; n is the number of moles of gas in the sample; and R is a constant.

Equation 5.1 is an *equation of state*. This particular equation of state is called the *perfect gas law* because it accurately describes the behavior of a gas sample that shows none of the deviations discussed in Sec. 2.3. Equation 5.1 represents the behavior of real gases with reasonably satisfactory accuracy, provided the pressure is *low* and the temperature is *well above* the normal boiling point.

Before we use the perfect gas law in any numerical calculation, it will be necessary to evaluate the constant R, which is called the *gas constant*. The actual value of R will depend on the particular units used for P, V, n, and T. Following the custom most frequently employed in chemistry, we shall express pressure in atmospheres, volume in liters, n in gram-moles, and temperature in degrees Kelvin. Then, for 1 mole of any gas at STP: $P = 1$ atm, $V = 22.4$ liters, $n = 1$ mole, and $T = 273°$ K. Hence,

$$
\begin{aligned}
R &= \frac{PV}{nT} \\
&= \frac{1 \text{ atm} \times 22.4 \text{ liters}}{1 \text{ mole} \times 273 \text{ deg}} \\
&= 8.21 \times 10^{-2} \text{ liter atm mole}^{-1} \text{ deg}^{-1}
\end{aligned}
$$

The most accurate determination, based on a molar volume of 22.414 liters and the temperature 273.15° K, yields $R = 8.206 \times 10^{-2}$ liter atm mole^{-1} deg^{-1}.

With the use of the perfect gas law and the gas constant given, it is possible to obtain a reasonably accurate molecular weight for any gas for which the volume and mass of a sample, under specified conditions, is known:

PROBLEM: A sample of mercury vapor at 520° C and 322 mm pressure occupies 779 ml and weighs 1.014 grams. What is the molecular weight of mercury?

SOLUTION: The temperature is $520° + 273° = 793°$ K, and the pressure is $322/760 = 0.424$ atm. The volume is 799×10^{-3} liters. Then

$$n = \frac{PV}{RT}$$

$$= \frac{0.424 \text{ atm} \times 779 \times 10^{-3} \text{ liter}}{8.21 \times 10^{-2} \text{ liter atm mole}^{-1} \text{ deg}^{-1} \times 793 \text{ deg}}$$

$$= 0.507 \times 10^{-2} \text{ mole}$$

If 0.507×10^{-2} mole of mercury weighs 1.014 grams, then 1 mole must weigh

$$\frac{1 \text{ mole}}{0.507 \times 10^{-2} \text{ mole}} \times 1.014 \text{ grams} = 200 \text{ grams}$$

and the molecular weight of mercury is 200.

PROBLEM: A substance is known from other measurements to have a molecular weight of 121. Assuming that the substance is a gas and that it does not decompose at high temperature, at what temperature will the gas exert a pressure of 740 atm if the sample weighs 1200 grams and is confined in a volume of 1.88 liters?

SOLUTION: If the molecular weight is 121, then 1 mole must weigh 121 grams and 1200 grams must be 1200/121 moles. Then, from the perfect gas law,

$$T = \frac{PV}{nR}$$

$$= \frac{7.40 \times 10^2 \text{ atm} \times 1.88 \text{ liters}}{\frac{1200}{121} \text{ mole} \times 8.21 \times 10^{-2} \text{ liter atm mole}^{-1} \text{ deg}^{-1}}$$

$$= 1708° \text{ K, or } 1435° \text{ C}$$

5.4 Atomic Weights

In the preceding section, it was shown that the molecular weight of any gas may be obtained from the gas density. Ammonia is a gas at room temperature and 1 atm, and its molecular weight, so determined, is 17. But if ammonia is very strongly heated and then cooled again, it will be found that the gas is no longer ammonia but a mixture of nitrogen and hydrogen. This is easily proved because nitrogen freezes at $-209.9°$ C, but hydrogen does not freeze until the temperature is lowered to $-259.1°$ C. The gases may be separated by holding the temperature just below the freezing point of nitrogen and then pumping off the hydrogen. In this way, the relative proportions of nitrogen and hydrogen may be found and expressed as percentages by volume or by weight, as desired. When this is done, the percentage by weight of nitrogen present is found to be 82.3. If 1 mole of ammonia weighs 17 grams, then it is clear that the weight of nitrogen in a mole of ammonia must be 0.823×17 grams $= 14$ grams.

Table 5.2 lists a series of substances, including nitrogen itself. All these are gases, and all except the nitrogen itself may be decomposed by heat into nitrogen plus either hydrogen or oxygen. It is relatively simple to find the molecular weight of each gas and also to find the percentage by weight of nitrogen present. With this information it is possible to calculate, as above, the weight of nitrogen present in 1 mole of each substance.

It is obvious from Table 5.2 that a molecule of nitrogen contains twice as much nitrogen as a molecule of ammonia; a hydrogen azide molecule contains three times as much. The fact that no substance has ever been found with less than 14 grams of nitrogen per mole suggests that there is a particle of nitrogen weighing just *half* as much as a molecule of nitrogen gas. This smallest particle of nitrogen is called an *atom* of nitrogen. The ammonia molecule must contain only one of these nitrogen atoms, as must the nitric oxide molecule, but the nitrous oxide and hydrogen azide molecules must contain two and three atoms of nitrogen, respectively.

TABLE **5.2** WEIGHT OF NITROGEN IN 1 MOLE OF SEVERAL GASES

Substance	Weight of 1 mole grams	Nitrogen weight percent	Nitrogen weight per mole
Nitrogen	28	100.0	28
Ammonia	17	82.3	14
Nitrous oxide	44	63.7	28
Nitric oxide	30	46.7	14
Hydrogen azide	43	97.8	42

Some molecules are found to consist of one atom only. This is true of helium and of mercury (at high temperature). Other molecules may contain many atoms; the molecule of phosphorus contains four atoms, and the molecule of sulfur may contain eight.

It is possible to construct, in the manner indicated above, a table showing the relative weights of many different kinds of atoms. The method is not particularly accurate, but it is the classical method by which the existence of atoms was proved, and one that played a great part in the development of the atomic theory. The relative weights of atoms determined in this way are called *atomic weights.*

5.5   Isotopes

Krypton is a gas in which the molecules consist of one atom only. The molecular weight of krypton is the same as the atomic weight. This gas provides, therefore, a good opportunity to compare the weight of an atom as found by the gas-density method with that found by the mass spectrometer.

The density of krypton at STP is 3.708 grams liter^{-1}, from which the molecular weight must be approximately 83.1, without any corrections for deviations from the perfect gas law. But the mass spectrometer yields results that at first glance are very different. Signals are obtained corresponding to atomic masses of 78, 80, 82, 83, 84, and 86 amu, but nothing at all corresponds to 83.1. This shows clearly that the atoms of krypton are not all of the same weight and that the number 83.1 obtained from the gas density is some kind of average.

The mass spectrometer may be made to yield not only the masses of the molecules but also their relative abundances. This is possible because the more abundant molecules give a darker impression on the photographic

TABLE **5.3**   ATOMIC MASSES AND
RELATIVE ABUNDANCES FOR
ISOTOPES OF KRYPTON

Mass, amu	Relative abundance, percent
78	0.354
80	2.27
82	11.56
83	11.55
84	56.90
86	17.37

plate, or a more intense signal if the recording is done electrically. The range of masses and the percentage abundance of each mass is shown for krypton in Table 5.3.

With this information it is possible to compute the average mass and to compare the result with that obtained from the gas density. The average is found by multiplying each mass by the corresponding percentage and then adding the results, as follows:

$$78 \times \frac{0.354}{100} = 0.276$$

$$80 \times \frac{2.27}{100} = 1.816$$

$$82 \times \frac{11.56}{100} = 9.479$$

$$83 \times \frac{11.55}{100} = 9.587$$

$$84 \times \frac{56.90}{100} = 47.796$$

$$86 \times \frac{17.37}{100} = 14.938$$

$$Total = \overline{83.89}$$

From this it follows that the true molecular weight and atomic weight of krypton is close to 83.9 (the most accurate determination gives 83.80). But this atomic weight is indeed merely an average. All atoms of krypton do *not* have the same mass. The krypton atoms of the several different masses are said to be *isotopes* of krypton. As we shall see later, the existence of isotopes is by no means limited to krypton.

5.6   Field Emission Microscopy

The smallest object that can be discerned with the unaided eye is about 0.01 mm in diameter. Atoms are approximately 100,000 times smaller. A microscope capable of this magnification was invented by E. W. Müller, and with it atoms are made visible. The device is called a *field emission microscope*.

The field emission microscope is shown diagrammatically in Fig. 5.2. It consists of a very sharp, needle-pointed tip of the metal under investigation; tungsten and platinum are convenient. The tip is enclosed in an evacuated chamber to which a low pressure of helium is admitted. The tip is then connected to a high, positive electric potential. This potential has the effect of charging the helium atoms (as in the mass spectrometer) as they strike or approach the tip. The positively charged helium atoms are then repelled by the charge on the tip, and they travel in straight lines

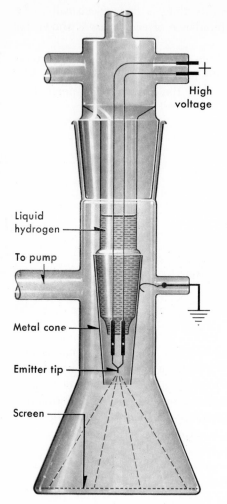

High
voltage

Liquid
hydrogen

To pump

Metal cone

Emitter tip

Screen

Fig. 5.2 *Field emission microscope.*

at high speed until they strike a viewing screen similar to that in a tele-vision set.

As the charged helium atoms strike the screen, they create an image of the surface of the tip. The tip may be about 10^{-5} cm in diameter; the screen, about 10 cm across. The magnification is then about one million fold. By cooling the tip with liquid hydrogen, the sharpness of the image is much improved.

Figure 5.3 shows a typical field emission microscope picture of platinum atoms. The various crystal faces exposed at the tip are responsible for the geometric patterns observed. The individual platinum atoms appear as the smallest light spots making up the overall pattern. The resolution is about 2.7 Å; that is, it is possible to see particles only 2.7 Å apart.

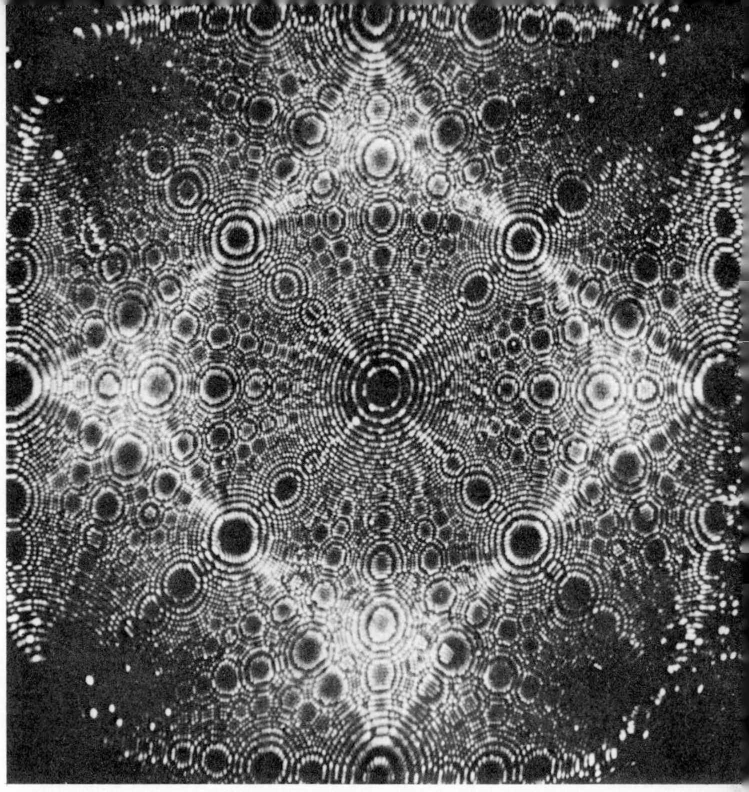

Fig. 5.3 Atoms of platinum on the tip of a field emission microscope. (Photograph by E. W. Muller, Pennsylvania State University.)

5.7   Atomic Mass Unit

The highest absolute accuracy obtainable with the mass spectrometer involves an uncertainty of about 1 part in 1000. The accuracy attainable in finding atomic weights by the gas density method is somewhat poorer. The mass spectrometer is theoretically capable of much greater accuracy, and it may be used to *compare* the masses of atoms and molecules with a very high precision. The demands of modern science and engineering are such that atomic masses must often be known to many decimal places.

Full use may be made of the capabilities of the mass spectrometer by selecting a standard atom and arbitrarily designating it to have a certain number of atomic mass units. Then all other atoms may be compared with the standard. This procedure meets most of the needs mentioned above.

For many years the standard of atomic mass was the oxygen atom, which was arbitrarily said to have a mass of 16 atomic mass units (amu). But difficulties accumulated, and finally the oxygen standard had to be abandoned. A new standard was selected in 1961. This new standard is the isotope of carbon called carbon-12. Carbon-12 is assumed to have a mass corresponding to exactly 12 amu. The *atomic mass unit is then defined as 1/12 the mass of a carbon-12 atom.*

The differences between atomic weights based on the old oxygen standard and the new carbon-12 standard are very small, and will not concern us in this book. But the differences must be considered in calculations involving nuclear explosions.

EXERCISES

1. The weight of a certain atom is 10.6 times that of carbon-12. What atomic weight may be expected for such atoms?
2. In a group of atoms, 15.0 percent has a mass of 21 amu; and 85.0 percent, a mass of 23.0 amu. What is the atomic weight?
3. Chlorine has two natural isotopes of mass about 35 and 37 amu, respectively. What percentage of each must be present in chlorine if the atomic weight is 35.5?
4. The radius of a neon molecule is 1.12 Å. The density of neon gas at STP is 0.90 grams liter^{-1}. What fraction of a liter of neon gas is actually empty space?
5. How many moles are present in the following volumes of any gas at STP? (a) 2.48 liters; (b) 125 ml; (c) 0.385 liter.
6. How many moles are present in: (a) 3.85 liters of any gas; (b) in 450 ml? (STP)
7. By use of the perfect gas law, find the pressure exerted by 1 mole of acetylene vapor at 65° C and in a volume of 100 ml.
8. At what temperature would 3.00 moles of sulfur dioxide exert a pressure of 100 atm in a volume of 8.25 liters?
9. Find the molecular weight of a vapor, 119 ml of which at 80° C and 720 mm pressure weighs 1.05 grams.
10. The molecular weight of a gas is 154. Find the weight of 1000 ml of this gas at 150° C and 760 mm pressure.
11. What is the density of a gas at STP if the molecular weight is 44?
12. The best vacuum achieved in the laboratory corresponds to a pressure of about 10^{-11} mm of mercury. How many molecules per liter remain in this vacuum?
13. Two gases have molecular weights of 32 and 64, respectively. Compare their rates of diffusion under identical conditions. (Recall that the rate of diffusion varies inversely as the square root of the density and that densities of gases are directly proportional to molecular weights.)
14. The diffusion rate of an unknown gas X is found to be 2.2 times slower than that of nitrogen, the molecular weight of which is 28. Find the molecular weight of X.
15. The following table gives the densities (STP) and the weight percents for several substances containing oxygen.

Substance	Gas density STP, gram liter^{-1}	Oxygen weight percent
Oxygen gas	1.429	100
Water	0.803	88.9
Carbon dioxide	1.966	72.7
Sulfur dioxide	2.860	50.0
Sulfur trioxide	3.570	60.0
Nitrous oxide	1.965	36.4

From the above information find a probable value for the atomic weight of oxygen.

6

Atomic Structure

6.1   The Nuclear Atom

A glass tube may be arranged, as shown in Fig. 4.5, with a heated wire filament at one end and a metal plate at the other. The filament is connected to the negative end of a source of electric potential; the plate, to the positive end. The potential applied should be several thousand volts. If nearly all air is now pumped from the tube, it will be found that electricity is carried between the heated filament and the plate. The invisible ray carrying the electricity is called a *cathode ray*. The cathode ray will cause a glow on the plate if the plate is coated with fluorescent material, as is a television screen.

It will now be found that the cathode ray may be deflected by the presence of a magnetic field in much the same manner as that already described for the charged molecules in the mass spectrometer. From a knowledge of the magnetic field intensity and the deflection produced, it is possible to obtain an estimate of the ratio e/m where e is the charge carried by the cathode ray particles and m is their mass. The ratio so found is approximately -1.76×10^8 coulombs/gram; the negative sign shows that the charge carried by the cathode rays is negative. The ratio found also shows that the cathode rays have an astonishingly high charge per gram.

The electric charge, e carried by the cathode rays is known from various kinds of measurements, one of which, performed by R. Millikan, is to measure the rate of movement of charged oil droplets in an electric field. The charge so found per cathode ray particle is -1.60×10^{-19} coulomb. From this it follows that the mass associated with cathode ray particles is

$$\frac{-1.60 \times 10^{-19} \text{ coulomb}}{-1.76 \times 10^{8} \text{ coulomb gram}^{-1}} = 9.11 \times 10^{-28} \text{ gram}$$

These little particles, discovered by J. J. Thomson in the year 1897, are called *electrons*. An electron is about 1837 times lighter than a hydrogen atom.

In 1896 it was discovered by H. Becquerel that some atoms have the property of emitting rays, of which electrons are one kind. This phenomenon is known as *radioactivity*, and it suggests that atoms, or at least some atoms, must contain electrons. But atoms normally carry no electric charge; furthermore, even hydrogen, which is the lightest atom known, weighs nearly 2000 times as much as an electron. The implication of this is clear: Atoms must contain some positive electricity, and the mass associated with the positive electricity must be many times greater than that of an electron.

A current view concerning the structure of an atom is based on that of E. Rutherford and N. Bohr who, about the year 1911, advanced the hypothesis that atoms consist of a positive nucleus and that this nucleus is surrounded by one or more negative electrons. In the neutral atom the number of electrons is numerically equal to the positive charge

Fig. 6.1 Rutherford's scattering experiment. It might be expected that alpha particles passing through a thin sheet of gold foil would be scattered in every direction. Actually only a few alphas are deflected, thus showing that gold atoms, and presumably other atoms, are mostly empty space.

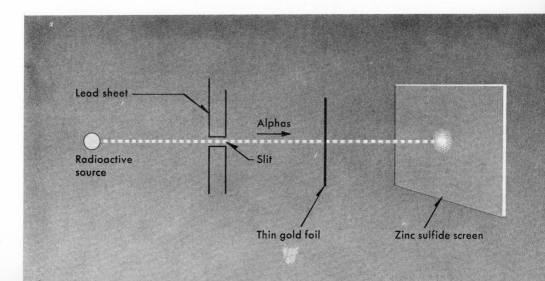

Fig. 6.2 The wave-mechanical concept of an atom is represented by these figures for hydrogen (top) and for argon (bottom). The electron, or electrons, are represented as a cloud of varying density around the nucleus.

of the nucleus. Most of the mass of the atom is concentrated in the nucleus. At relatively tremendous distances from the nucleus are situated the electrons. The electrons contribute little to the mass of the atom, but they balance, or neutralize, the positive charge of the nucleus. The nucleus and all the electrons take up only a very little space; the atoms are as nearly empty space as is the solar system.

Support for the Rutherford-Bohr theory of the atom comes from many sources, one of which is the Rutherford scattering experiment. In this experiment, charged helium atoms, called alpha rays, from radium are directed through a thin gold foil onto a zinc sulfide screen, as shown in Fig. 6.1. The gold foil is about 4×10^{-5} cm thick, and as an atom of gold is roughly 4×10^{-8} cm in diameter, the charged helium atoms must have had to pass through about 1000 layers of gold atoms to reach the zinc sulfide screen and cause it to glow. It might have been thought that under these circumstances nearly all the charged helium atoms would bounce off the gold atoms and be scattered in every direction. But actually nearly all the helium, as shown by the scintillations made on the zinc sulfide, goes through the gold as though no gold foil were present.

Occasionally a helium atom is observed to bounce back as if it had encountered a very heavy object, but this occurs only once in about 100,000 times. It is clear that the positive nucleus, carrying most of the mass of the gold atom, must be concentrated in an almost incredibly small volume. Rutherford estimated the diameter of the nucleus to be about 10^{-12} cm. If this is correct, then the density of the nucleus of an atom must be about 10^{14} grams cm^{-3}. An atomic nucleus the size of a grain of sand would weigh 100,000 tons.

Electrons are strange, shadowy conceptions. According to a principle developed by W. Heisenberg (the **Heisenberg uncertainty principle**), it is impossible to say at one and the same time that an electron is at a certain point in space and that it is moving with a certain velocity. Electrons do have mass and electric charge, but their properties are in part those of a cloud of negative electricity, perhaps concentrated more in one spot and less in another. As pointed out in Sec. 2.5, electrons act in some respects more like waves than like matter. A current view of atomic structure is that the electrons surround the nucleus in the form of a diffuse cloud, or shell, of negative electricity. Sometimes this shell is spherical, sometimes egg-shaped. An attempt at representing this is shown in Fig. 6.2.

6.2 The Nucleus

The atom of hydrogen is the lightest atom known, and from each atom of hydrogen, one and only one electron has ever been removed. It is therefore not unreasonable to assume that the hydrogen atom contains one and only one electron. When one electron is removed from a hydrogen atom, the particle that remains is, presumably, the nucleus of the hydrogen atom. This nucleus has a mass of about 1 amu, and its electric charge is the same as that of an electron but opposite in sign. That is to say, the charge on the hydrogen nucleus is $+1.60 \times 10^{-19}$ coulomb. It is more convenient to use the charge of an electron as a standard of electric charge for these subatomic particles. On this basis the charge of a hydrogen nucleus is $+1$. This particle, the nucleus of an ordinary hydrogen atom, is called a *proton*.

Hydrogen has three isotopes, of which hydrogen-1 is the common kind. Hydrogen-2, often called deuterium, occurs in nature mixed with hydrogen-1 to the extent of about 1 part in 6500; and hydrogen-3, called tritium, may be made artificially. Now, there is no reason to believe that the atoms of hydrogen-2 and hydrogen-3 contain more than one electron each—the charge on the nucleus of each is $+1$, but the atomic masses are very nearly 2 and 3 amu, respectively. This strongly suggests that at least some atomic nuclei must contain particles of mass approximately 1 amu but with no electric charge. Further evidence concerning this matter is that some radioactive atoms actually emit particles of 1 amu but zero charge. These particles are called *neutrons*.

The structure of the atomic nucleus is still far from being understood. Fortunately, the nucleus may be described as a system of protons and neutrons with certain forces between them. What these forces are need not concern us for the present.

The electron, the proton, and the neutron are sometimes referred to as fundamental particles. But each particle has been produced from, or converted into, something else. If there are any truly fundamental particles, they may not yet have been discovered. Altogether over a score of subatomic particles have been found. Some of these, such as mesons, neutrinos, and antiprotons have such strange properties that they are sometimes called the "nuclear zoo." For our purpose, atomic nuclei may be considered to be formed from protons and neutrons. A summary of their properties, together with those of the electron, is given in Table 6.1.

TABLE 6.1   SUBATOMIC PARTICLES

Name	Charge	Approx mass, amu
Proton	$+1$	1
Neutron	0	1
Electron	-1 (arbitrary)	5.48×10^{-4}

6.3   *Chemical Elements and Atomic Numbers*

The charge on the nucleus of an atom, expressed in terms of the charge of the proton, is called the *atomic number*. Thus hydrogen, with a nuclear charge of 1, is said to have an atomic number of 1. Chlorine, with a nuclear charge of 17, has an atomic number of 17.

A chemical element is defined as matter in which all the atoms have the same atomic number.

Hydrogen is a chemical element because all its atoms have the same nuclear charge and hence the same atomic number. This is true even though the different isotopes of hydrogen have different masses and even though ordinary hydrogen has a molecular weight of 2 because the molecules of hydrogen each consist of 2 atoms in combination.

The nuclear charge of an atom is fixed by the number of protons in the nucleus; a chemical element might therefore be defined as matter in which all the atoms have the same number of protons. If an atom is electrically neutral, then the atomic number is equal to the number of electrons in the atom. Many atoms gain or lose electrons when they enter into chemical combination; only the neutral atom has the same number of electrons and protons.

Our definition of a chemical element says nothing about the masses of the atoms. The different isotopes of an element have different masses and they may undergo radioactive disintegration by entirely different mechanisms, but if the charges of the nuclei of two atoms are the same, then they are considered to be atoms of the same chemical element.

The nuclear charge of an element, and hence its atomic number, was first determined experimentally in Rutherford's laboratory. This was done by an elaboration of Rutherford's alpha-ray scattering experiment, described above. A convenient and more accurate method for finding atomic numbers was based by H. G. J. Moseley on the diffraction of x-rays.

Moseley's method for finding atomic numbers is as follows: It will be recalled (Sec. 4.4) that x-rays are emitted from the target of an x-ray tube, under appropriate bombardment. Moseley discovered that different chemical elements used as the target in the tube produce different wavelengths of x-rays. Furthermore, there is a simple relationship between the frequency of the x-rays emitted and the atomic number of the element used as target. Moseley's relationship is that the square root of the frequency of the x-rays produced is related to the atomic number as follows:

$$\sqrt{\nu} = a(Z - b) \tag{6.1}$$

where ν is the frequency, a and b are constants, and Z is the atomic number. The apparatus used for this experiment is similar to that shown in Fig. 4.6. Some of the results are shown in Fig. 6.3. By this means, the atomic numbers of nearly all elements have been found, new elements have been identified, and order has been brought out of confusion among the over 100 chemical elements known.

Next to its atomic number the most important property of an atom is its atomic mass. The chemical element chlorine has an isotope of mass approximately 35 amu. This atom, with the atomic number 17, must have 17 protons in its nucleus. The 17 electrons surrounding the nucleus contribute very little to the atomic mass. The chlorine atom must therefore have 18 neutrons in its nucleus, in addition to the 17 protons. Another isotope of chlorine of about 37 amu must have 17 protons and 20 neutrons in the nucleus. The sum of the number of protons and neutrons in the nucleus of an atom is called its *mass number*.

The relation between mass numbers and atomic weights is as follows: If all the atoms of an element are of the same weight, then the atomic weight is approximately equal to the mass number. But if an element has isotopes, then the atomic weight is approximately the average of the several mass numbers found in nature, each being weighted in

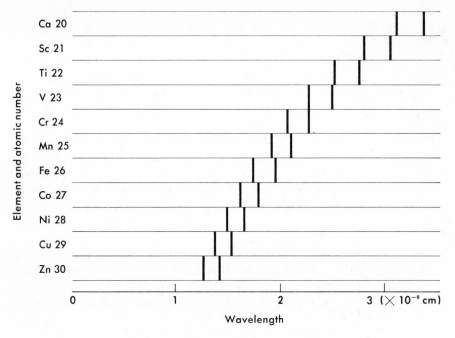

Fig. 6.3 *The Moseley relationship. This figure is diagrammatic only. It shows how if different elements are made the target in an x-ray tube, the wavelength (and hence the frequency) of the rays depends on the atomic number of the element. The vertical lines are meant to represent the relative positions where the photographic plate would be blackened if the several elements indicated were placed, one at a time, as the target in the x-ray tube of Fig. 4.5. It will be noted that each element gives more than one line.*

accordance with the proportion present. For instance, boron has natural isotopes of mass numbers 10 and 11, and these are normally present in boron in the proportions of 18.8 percent and 81.2 percent, respectively. The atomic weight is then approximately

$$(10 \times 0.188) + (11 \times 0.812) = 10.81$$

Both isotopes have 5 protons in the nucleus, but boron-10 has 5 neutrons and boron-12 has 7 neutrons. Mass numbers are a convenience in the identification of isotopes. The more explosive isotope of uranium with mass number 235, is often referred to as uranium-235. Its nucleus contains 92 protons and 143 neutrons.

The chemical elements are conveniently designated by *symbols* such as Al for aluminum, O for oxygen, and H for hydrogen. Symbols for all known chemical elements are given on the inside front cover of this book. The atomic number is indicated, whenever necessary, at the lower left corner of the symbol for the element. An international committee has recommended that the mass number be placed at the upper left of

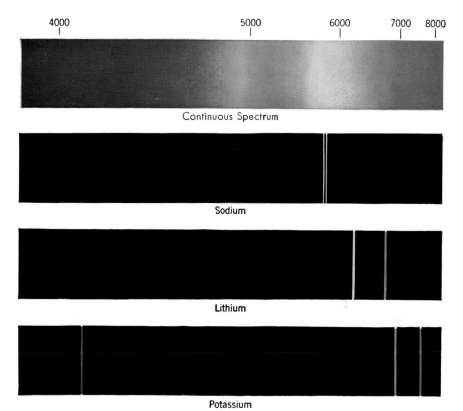

4000   5000   6000   7000   8000

Continuous Spectrum

Sodium

Lithium

Potassium

Continuous spectrum as from a body heated white hot (at top), and three bright-line spectra emitted by atoms, as indicated, in hot gases. The numbers at the top are wavelengths expressed in Ångstrom units.

the symbol, although many authors place it at the upper right. Thus, $^{35}_{17}\text{Cl}$ (sometimes written $_{17}\text{Cl}^{35}$) signifies chlorine, the atomic number of which is 17. The particular isotope designated has a mass number 35. Uranium-235 is properly designated $^{235}_{92}\text{U}$.

The precision attainable in comparing atomic masses by the mass spectrometer shows that atoms do not necessarily have atomic masses exactly equal to the mass number. Of course the most familiar isotope of hydrogen, ^1_1H, has a mass number of 1, but its actual mass is 1.007825 amu. Most of the elements of lower atomic numbers have true masses somewhat greater than the mass number. Elements of atomic numbers from about calcium to barium (20 to 56) have true masses slightly less than the mass numbers; and the elements of highest atomic numbers have true masses slightly greater than their mass numbers. These slight deviations are of little importance for most chemical reactions, but they are of the highest importance in the release of atomic energy. The only isotope of the only element for which the true mass is exactly equal to the mass number is that established by definition as the standard of atomic mass, namely, $^{12}_6\text{C}$.

6.4   Energy Levels

The energy necessary to remove an electron from a neutral gaseous atom is called the *ionization potential*. Ionization potentials are known with considerable accuracy, and when more than one electron is present in an atom, different energies may be required to remove the different electrons. Even when only one electron is present it may, under varying conditions, require different energies. The various energy states that an electron may possess, considered in relation to the atom as a whole, are known as *energy levels*. The term *electron shell* is often used, especially in chemistry, to mean the same thing as energy level. The total number of electrons in any neutral atom is numerically equal to the atomic number of the atom. How these electrons are arranged in the various energy levels will now be described.

If white light, as from the sun, is passed through a glass prism, the result is that the light is broken up into a rainbow of colors called the *spectrum*. The spectrum may be examined most conveniently on an instrument called a spectroscope (Fig. 6.4). If now there is substituted for the sunlight a colored flame, such as might be observed from a fireworks display, the spectrum takes on an entirely different appearance. Instead of a continuous rainbow we see only a few sharp, colored lines. The lines are different for each chemical element that may be present in the colored flame. Some elements produce only a few lines; others, many thousands. The various elements may readily be identified by the wavelengths of their characteristic lines in the spectrum, and this is the basis of spectrochemical analysis. But our present concern is what the spectrum

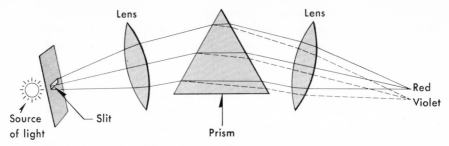

Fig. 6.4 *The optical spectroscope. Light from a source is passed through a slit and a lens, then through a glass prism which breaks the light up into the component colors of its spectrum. The second lens merely brings the light to a focus.*

may be able to tell us concerning the arrangement of the electrons in the atoms.

The spectrum of hydrogen may be excited by passing an electric discharge through a tube in which hydrogen is contained at low pressure. The spectrum so obtained is simple and consists mainly of groups of lines in several series in the infrared, the visible, and the ultraviolet. A rather crude representation of the hydrogen spectrum is shown in Fig. 6.5, together with the names (after the discoverers) assigned to the several series of lines.

Careful study of these spectrum lines of hydrogen leads to the conclusion that the wavelengths of the lines in the several series may be predicted by a mathematical equation. The equation is

$$\frac{1}{\lambda} = R\left(\frac{1}{n_2^2} - \frac{1}{n_1^2}\right) \tag{6.2}$$

where λ is the wavelength of any line, R is the Rydberg constant (not to be confused with the gas constant, p. 63), and n_2 and n_1 are described below. This equation states, in words, that the reciprocal of the wavelength of any spectral line of hydrogen is proportional to the difference between two numbers. The two numbers are $1/n_2^2$ and $1/n_1^2$. Furthermore, for any given series (for instance, the Lyman series) n_2 is always the same, as indicated in Fig. 6.5, while n_1 may be any whole number greater than n_2.

Consideration of the facts presented above led N. Bohr to the conclusion that the single electron in a hydrogen atom has normally a minimum of energy; it is said to be in the *ground state*. But, if hydrogen is strongly heated, or if an electric current is passed through the gas, the electrons acquire more energy and are said to be in *excited* states. The several levels of energy (that is, energy levels) available are shown in Fig. 6.6. It is believed that the various spectral lines are caused by electrons falling from a higher energy level to a lower level. As shown in

Fig. 6.6, all the lines in the Lyman series are caused by electrons falling into the lowest level of the atoms. For this state, $n_2 = 1$. For the Balmer series, $n_2 = 2$, and so forth. The individual lines in each series depend on the particular excited level ($n_1 = 2$, 3, 4, etc.) from which each electron falls.

The Rydberg constant may be found by experiment or it may be derived theoretically. The agreement is excellent, but the method of derivation need not concern us here. What does concern us is that calculations based on Eq. 6.2 yield values for the spectral lines of hydrogen that are in astonishingly good agreement with the wavelengths actually found by experiment. For instance, for the Balmer series, for which $n_2 = 2$, it is possible to calculate the wavelengths of several lines simply by substituting the numbers $n_2 = 2$ and $n_1 = 3$, 4, 5, etc. Some results obtained are as given in the accompanying table

n_1	λ_{calc}, Å	λ_{obs}, Å
3	6564.7	6564.6
4	4862.7	4862.8
5	4341.7	4341.7

The values assigned above to n_1 and n_2 are called *quantum numbers*. There are actually four quantum numbers necessary to describe fully the energy state of an electron, but we shall have reference to two only. The numbers assigned to n_1 and n_2 are called principal quantum numbers.

Fig. 6.5 A diagrammatic representation of the spectrum of hydrogen showing a few of the lines observed in three of the spectral series. The reciprocal wavelength, or the frequency, of each line may be represented by the Rydberg equation. For each series of lines n_2 is the same, as shown. For each line in a series n_1 is one or more greater than n_2.

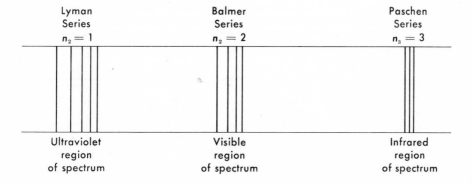

Lyman Series $n_2 = 1$	Balmer Series $n_2 = 2$	Paschen Series $n_3 = 3$
Ultraviolet region of spectrum	Visible region of spectrum	Infrared region of spectrum

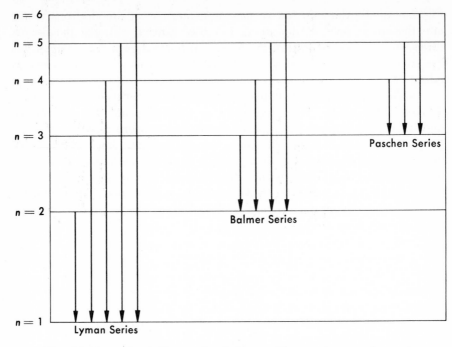

Fig. 6.6 Energy-level diagram for hydrogen. The quantum number n_2 in the Rydberg equation represents the level to which electrons fall to produce a given series of lines. The quantum number n_1 is the level from which electrons fall to produce the individual lines in each series.

If an electron is in an energy level for which the principal quantum number $n = 1$, then the electron is said to be in the K energy level. If an electron is in an energy level for which the principal quantum number $n = 2$, then the electron is said to be in the L level.

The energy-level diagram shown in Fig. 6.6 is oversimplified because each level except the first is actually divided into sublevels that are described by subordinate quantum numbers. These sublevels become

TABLE **6.2**   ELECTRON ENERGY LEVELS AND SUBLEVELS

Name of level	K	L	M	N
Principal quantum number (n). :	1	2	3	4
Subordinate quantum numbers possible..	s	$s\ p$	$s\ p\ d$	$s\ p\ d\ f$
Maximum number of electrons possible..	2	2 6	2 6 10	2 6 10 14
Maximum total electrons in each level $(2n^2)$................................	2	8	18	32

increasingly significant as we go to elements of higher atomic number and which therefore have more and more electrons. The energy states related to subordinate quantum numbers are designated by the letters *s*, *p*, *d*, and *f*. Table 6.2 shows the notation used for the principal and subordinate levels. It also shows the maximum possible number of electrons that may be accommodated in each level and sublevel.

The designation of an electron in the *M* level (or shell) with subordinate quantum number *d* is 3*d*; that of an *f* electron in the *N* shell is 4*f*. The number of electrons in a given level and sublevel is shown by superscript; for example, $3d^2$ means that two electrons are present with a principal quantum number of 3 and a subordinate quantum number of *d*.* In Table 6.3 will be found the electron distribution so far as known, for all the chemical elements. This table has been prepared from spectroscopic data on, for the most part, free neutral atoms in the vapor state. While the information so obtained is invaluable in the understanding of chemical phenomena it must be warned that most chemical substances consist of atoms in combination with each other and that this is true even of metals such as iron and copper, and of gases such as hydrogen and oxygen. The electron distributions shown in Table 6.3 cannot generally be applied to chemical systems without some consideration of the state and the state of combination of the atoms under study.

---

* Some authorities use the term *orbital* to mean the level and sublevel as distinguished from the electrons which may be in those levels. Thus one says: as of $3d^2$, that there are two electrons in the 3*d* orbital.

TABLE **6.3** ARRANGEMENT OF ELECTRONS IN THE ATOMS

		K (1)	*L* (2)	*M* (3)	*N* (4)	*O* (5)	*P* (6)	*Q* (7)
		s	*s p*	*s p d*	*s p d f*	*s p d f*	*s p d f*	*s*
1	H	1						
2	He	2						
3	Li	2	1					
4	Be	2	2					
5	B	2	2 1					
6	C	2	2 2					
7	N	2	2 3					
8	O	2	2 4					
9	F	2	2 5					
10	Ne	2	2 6					
11	Na	2	2 6	1				

TABLE **6.3**   (*Continued*)

		K (1)	L (2)	M (3)	N (4)	O (5)	P (6)	Q (7)
		s	*s p*	*s p d*	*s p d f*	*s p d f*	*s p d f*	*s*
12	Mg	2	2 6	2				
13	Al	2	2 6	2 1				
14	Si	2	2 6	2 2				
15	P	2	2 6	2 3				
16	S	2	2 6	2 4				
17	Cl	2	2 6	2 5				
18	Ar	2	2 6	2 6				
19	K	2	2 6	2 6	1			
20	Ca	2	2 6	2 6	2			
21	Sc	2	2 6	2 6 1	2			
22	Ti	2	2 6	2 6 2	2			
23	V	2	2 6	2 6 3	2			
24	Cr	2	2 6	2 6 5	1			
25	Mn	2	2 6	2 6 5	2			
26	Fe	2	2 6	2 6 6	2			
27	Co	2	2 6	2 6 7	2			
28	Ni	2	2 6	2 6 8	2			
29	Cu	2	2 6	2 6 10	1			
30	Zn	2	2 6	2 6 10	2			
31	Ga	2	2 6	2 6 10	2 1			
32	Ge	2	2 6	2 6 10	2 2			
33	As	2	2 6	2 6 10	2 3			
34	Se	2	2 6	2 6 10	2 4			
35	Br	2	2 6	2 6 10	2 5			
36	Kr	2	2 6	2 6 10	2 6			
37	Rb	2	2 6	2 6 10	2 6	1		
38	Sr	2	2 6	2 6 10	2 6	2		
39	Y	2	2 6	2 6 10	2 6 1	2		
40	Zr	2	2 6	2 6 10	2 6 2	2		
41	Nb	2	2 6	2 6 10	2 6 4	1		
42	Mo	2	2 6	2 6 10	2 6 5	1		
43	Tc	2	2 6	2 6 10	2 6 6	1		
44	Ru	2	2 6	2 6 10	2 6 7	1		
45	Rh	2	2 6	2 6 10	2 6 8	1		
46	Pd	2	2 6	2 6 10	2 6 10			
47	Ag	2	2 6	2 6 10	2 6 10	1		
48	Cd	2	2 6	2 6 10	2 6 10	2		
49	In	2	2 6	2 6 10	2 6 10	2 1		
50	Sn	2	2 6	2 6 10	2 6 10	2 2		
51	Sb	2	2 6	2 6 10	2 6 10	2 3		
52	Te	2	2 6	2 6 10	2 6 10	2 4		

TABLE 6.3   (*Continued*)

		K (1)	L (2)	M (3)	N (4)	O (5)	P (6)	Q (7)
		s	s p	s p d	s p d f	s p d f	s p d f	s
53	I	2	2 6	2 6 10	2 6 10	2 5		
54	Xe	2	2 6	2 6 10	2 6 10	2 6		
55	Cs	2	2 6	2 6 10	2 6 10	2 6	1	
56	Ba	2	2 6	2 6 10	2 6 10	2 6	2	
57	La	2	2 6	2 6 10	2 6 10	2 6 1	2	
58	Ce	2	2 6	2 6 10	2 6 10 2	2 6	2	
59	Pr	2	2 6	2 6 10	2 6 10 3	2 6	2	
60	Nd	2	2 6	2 6 10	2 6 10 4	2 6	2	
61	Pm	2	2 6	2 6 10	2 6 10 5	2 6	2	
62	Sm	2	2 6	2 6 10	2 6 10 6	2 6	2	
63	Eu	2	2 6	2 6 10	2 6 10 7	2 6	2	
64	Gd	2	2 6	2 6 10	2 6 10 7	2 6 1	2	
65	Tb	2	2 6	2 6 10	2 6 10 9	2 6	2	
66	Dy	2	2 6	2 6 10	2 6 10 10	2 6	2	
67	Ho	2	2 6	2 6 10	2 6 10 11	2 6	2	
68	Er	2	2 6	2 6 10	2 6 10 12	2 6	2	
69	Tm	2	2 6	2 6 10	2 6 10 13	2 6	2	
70	Yb	2	2 6	2 6 10	2 6 10 14	2 6	2	
71	Lu	2	2 6	2 6 10	2 6 10 14	2 6 1	2	
72	Hf	2	2 6	2 6 10	2 6 10 14	2 6 2	2	
73	Ta	2	2 6	2 6 10	2 6 10 14	2 6 3	2	
74	W	2	2 6	2 6 10	2 6 10 14	2 6 4	2	
75	Re	2	2 6	2 6 10	2 6 10 14	2 6 5	2	
76	Os	2	2 6	2 6 10	2 6 10 14	2 6 6	2	
77	Ir	2	2 6	2 6 10	2 6 10 14	2 6 7	2	
78	Pt	2	2 6	2 6 10	2 6 10 14	2 6 9	1	
79	Au	2	2 6	2 6 10	2 6 10 14	2 6 10	1	
80	Hg	2	2 6	2 6 10	2 6 10 14	2 6 10	2	
81	Tl	2	2 6	2 6 10	2 6 10 14	2 6 10	2 1	
82	Pb	2	2 6	2 6 10	2 6 10 14	2 6 10	2 2	
83	Bi	2	2 6	2 6 10	2 6 10 14	2 6 10	2 3	
84	Po	2	2 6	2 6 10	2 6 10 14	2 6 10	2 4	
85	At	2	2 6	2 6 10	2 6 10 14	2 6 10	2 5	
86	Rn	2	2 6	2 6 10	2 6 10 14	2 6 10	2 6	
87	Fr	2	2 6	2 6 10	2 6 10 14	2 6 10	2 6	1
88	Ra	2	2 6	2 6 10	2 6 10 14	2 6 10	2 6	2
89	Ac	2	2 6	2 6 10	2 6 10 14	2 6 10	2 6 1	2
90	Th	2	2 6	2 6 10	2 6 10 14	2 6 10	2 6 2	2
91	Pa	2	2 6	2 6 10	2 6 10 14	2 6 10 2	2 6 1	2
92	U	2	2 6	2 6 10	2 6 10 14	2 6 10 3	2 6 1	2
93	Np	2	2 6	2 6 10	2 6 10 14	2 6 10 5	2 6	2

TABLE **6.3**   (*Continued*)

		K (1)	L (2)	M (3)	N (4)	O (5)	P (6)	M (7)
		s	*s p*	*s p d*	*s p d f*	*s p d f*	*s p d f*	*s*
94	Pu	2	2 6	2 6 10	2 6 10 14	2 6 10 6	2 6	2
95	Am	2	2 6	2 6 10	2 6 10 14	2 6 10 7	2 6	2
96	Cm	2	2 6	2 6 10	2 6 10 14	2 6 10 7	2 6 1	2
97	Bk	2	2 6	2 6 10	2 6 10 14	2 6 10 8	2 6 1	2 ?
98	Cf	2	2 6	2 6 10	2 6 10 14	2 6 10 10	2 6 1	2 ?
99	Es	2	2 6	2 6 10	2 6 10 14	2 6 10 10	2 6 1	2 ?
100	Fm	2	2 6	2 6 10	2 6 10 14	2 6 10 11	2 6 1	2 ?
101	Md	2	2 6	2 6 10	2 6 10 14	2 6 10 12	2 6 1	2 ?
102		2	2 6	2 6 10	2 6 10 14	2 6 10 13	2 6 1	2 ?
103	Lw	2	2 6	2 6 10	2 6 10 14	2 6 10 14	2 6 1	2 ?

6.5 *Atomic and Molecular Dimensions*

The size of an atom or a molecule is not easy to define. The electrons and protons in atoms carry electric charges, and the electrons in particular have some properties that are more closely associated with electromagnetic radiation than with particles of matter. Calculations based on quantum mechanics have been made to find the probability of an electron being found at any given distance from the center of an atom. The result of such a calculation for the hydrogen atom in its ground state is shown in Fig. 6.7. It will be noted that, in one sense, there is no limit to the size of the atom because there is a definite, though increasingly small, probability that the electron will be found at a great distance from the nucleus. A further complication arises, as indicated in the preceding section, because most substances consist of atoms in chemical combinations, and what the diameter of an atom may be under such circumstances is not easy to say.

A crude approach to atomic and molecular dimensions is to consider that, in the liquid state, the molecules are thought to be touching each other. Argon will serve as a convenient example, especially so because nearly all its atoms consist of one isotope only—namely, argon–40, —and the molecules of argon consist of single atoms.

One mole of argon weighs 39.9 grams and the density of liquid argon at $-186°$ C is 1.40 grams cm^{-3}. The volume occupied by a mole of liquid argon at this temperature must be

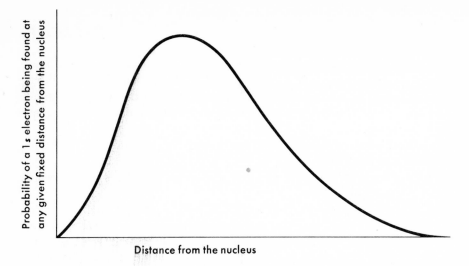

Fig. 6.7 *The probability that a 1s electron may be found at any given radial distance from the nucleus is given by this diagram. It will be understood that the probability is spherically symmetrical about the nucleus.*

$$V = 39.9 \text{ grams}/(1.40 \text{ gram cm}^{-3})$$
$$= 28.5 \text{ cm}^3$$

One mole of any substance contains, by definition, 6.023×10^{23} molecules; hence we may tentatively say that the volume of each argon atom is

$$V = 28.5 \text{ cm}^3/(6.023 \times 10^{23})$$
$$= 4.73 \times 10^{-23} \text{ cm}^3$$

This is obviously only a rough approximation because, although the atoms are doubtless touching each other in the liquid, it does not mean that they completely occupy all the space. Furthermore, the density of argon, as does that of most liquids, changes somewhat with temperature. There is the further problem of what is meant by molecules "touching" each other. In the case of liquid argon we might say that "touching" means the average distance of nearest approach.

In Sec. 2.3 it was shown that all real gases show deviations from the perfect gas law and that one of these deviations is related to the molecular volume. An estimate of the radius of an argon molecule obtained in this way is about 1.5×10^{-8} cm. It is also possible to obtain a value for the radius by making x-ray diffraction studies of crystalline argon. The radius so obtained is also about 1.5×10^{-8} cm. Atomic and molecular radii obtained in these ways are often called van der Waals radii. What values may be assigned to atoms in chemical combination with each other will be discussed in later chapters.

EXERCISES

1. The charge of an electron is -1.60×10^{-19} coulomb. An ordinary electric light bulb uses a current of about 0.5 amp (0.5 coulomb/sec). About how many electrons go through the bulb per minute?

2. What is the experimental evidence that an atom is mostly empty space?

3. What is a current view concerning the structure of the atomic nucleus?

4. Compare the mass and the charge of the electron, the proton, and the neutron.

5. What is a chemical element?

6. Some atoms, identified in the accompanying table merely by letters, have the atomic number and the mass number shown. Select those that are (a) isotopes of the same element, and (b) isobars (atoms of the same mass but of different atomic number).

Atom	Atomic number	Mass number
(a)	4	8
(b)	55	127
(c)	55	145
(d)	88	228
(e)	89	228
(f)	94	239

7. Write symbols (for example, $^{35}_{17}\text{Cl}$) showing atomic numbers, mass numbers, and also names (for example, chlorine) for each of the atoms shown in the above exercise.

8. If, in an x-ray tube, a molybdenum target is substituted for a copper target, what change will occur in the wavelength of the x-rays emitted?

9. Explain Moseley's method for finding the atomic number of an element.

10. Explain the emission of light of definite wavelengths by an atom of hydrogen excited by an electric discharge.

11. What is the maximum number of electrons permitted in each of the first three (K, L, M) energy levels?

12. From memory, show the distribution of electrons in the various energy levels for elements of atomic numbers 1 to 20.

13. What is the maximum number of electrons permitted in each of the s, p, d, f sublevels?

14. What element might be expected to have the electron distribution

    $$1s^2 \quad 2s^2 \quad 2p^6 \quad 3s^2 \quad 3p^6 \quad 3d^{10} \quad 4s^2 \quad 4p^6 \quad 5s^2$$

15. Write out the electron distribution for uranium.
16. Most atoms are about 10^{-8} cm in diameter. The diameter of a nucleus is about 10^{-12} cm. Suppose an atom could be expanded until it was as large as a basketball; would the nucleus be visible without a microscope?
17. Why is the van der Waals radius only a crude approximation to the actual size of a molecule?

7

Radioactivity

7.1 Types of Nuclear Decay

Some naturally occurring chemical elements have the property of spontaneous disintegration, and many other such elements may be made artificially. H. Becquerel discovered in 1896 that uranium has the ability to blacken a photographic plate, and he correctly surmised that uranium emits a radiation capable of penetrating paper and thin sheets of metal. Other radioactive chemical elements, including radium, were discovered by Marie and Pierre Curie. These discoveries opened a new world of subatomic phenomena to scientific research. This chapter will be devoted to a general description of the effects that may be observed, of the several kinds of radioactivity, and of certain implications concerning the nucleus of an atom and its stability.

The rays emanating from radioactive matter cause a variety of effects in addition to that of darkening a photographic plate. One effect is the ability to discharge an electroscope. An electroscope consists essentially of an insulated metal rod to which is attached a delicate strip of gold leaf. The electroscope may be charged by holding near it a piece of hard rubber that has just previously been rubbed with cat's fur. The gold leaf will then stand away from the rod for several hours until the electric charge leaks away (Fig. 7.1). But if a piece of uranium is brought near the charged electroscope, the gold leaf will fall within a few seconds.

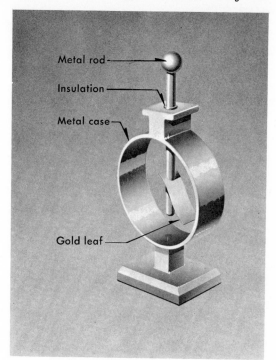

Metal rod
Insulation
Metal case
Gold leaf

Fig. 7.1 Electroscope.

The rays from radioactive matter, or the paths followed by the rays, may be made visible by a variety of methods. If a piece of paper is coated with zinc sulfide and then held near a minute speck of radium or other radioactive substance, the zinc sulfide screen seems to glow. Examination of this glow under a magnifying glass shows myriads of tiny scintillations. These scintillations are caused by the particles discharged by the disintegrating atoms. The particles strike the zinc sulfide, which in turn emits a flash of light wherever it is struck. The paths taken by rays from radioactive matter are normally invisible, but they may be observed in a Wilson cloud chamber. If moist air is compressed and then suddenly decompressed, there is created a tendency for a fog or mist to form in the air. The particles that shoot out from radioactive atoms undergoing decay create disturbances in the air through which they pass. These disturbances serve as centers for the formation of water droplets. The paths of the rays are then made visible as thin little streamers of fog. These fog tracks reveal the direction and distance traversed by the invisible rays.

The electric charge and the mass associated with rays from radioactive matter may be investigated by methods not unlike that used with the mass spectrometer. The first three kinds of rays to be discovered are called

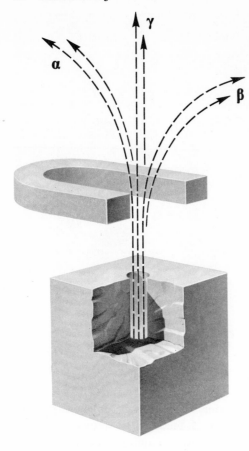

Fig. 7.2 Deflection of alpha (α), beta (β), and gamma (γ) rays in a magnetic field. This shows that alpha and beta rays are electrically charged but of opposite sign. Gamma rays carry no charge.

alpha (α), beta (β), and gamma (γ) rays. Alpha rays, if permitted to pass through a magnetic field, are deflected in such a manner as to indicate that they have a mass of about 4 amu and carry a charge twice that of an electron and opposite in sign; that is to say, they carry a double positive charge. Alpha rays are actually atoms (or rather ions) of helium that, having lost two electrons, carry a double positive charge. They are ejected from radioactive atoms with velocities up to 10 percent of that of light. Beta rays are electrons that carry, of course, a negative charge, and weigh about 1/1837 amu. They move with velocities up to 90 percent of that of light. Gamma rays are a form of electromagnetic radiation with a wavelength of the order of 0.1 Å. They have no mass in the ordinary sense, and they are not deflected in a magnetic field. They carry no electric charge and their velocity is that of light, namely, 3×10^{10} cm sec^{-1}.

Alpha, beta, and gamma rays are by no means the only kinds of rays emitted by radioactive matter, although historically they are the most important. Other kinds of rays include neutrons, of mass 1 amu and zero charge; protons, of mass 1 amu and a single positive charge; deuterons (ions of $_1^2\text{H}$), of mass 2 amu and single positive charge; and positrons (positive electrons), of mass 1/1837 amu and single positive charge. The various names, symbols, and properties of the commoner rays emitted by radioactive atoms are summarized in Table 7.1. There is also a kind of radioactivity in which the nucleus "swallows," so to speak, one of the electrons that normally surround the nucleus. As this electron generally comes from the K level (Sec. 6.4), the process is called K capture, but L capture also occurs. Another kind of radioactivity involves some sort of internal transition with the emission of nothing by gamma rays. Finally, there is nuclear fission, which results in fragmentation of the whole nucleus. We shall have more to say about this later.

A device of major importance in the study of radioactivity is the Geiger-Müller counter, shown diagrammatically in Fig. 7.3. A small metal cylinder is arranged inside a glass tube, and a thin metal wire passes through the center of the cylinder. The wire is insulated from the cylinder and a high voltage is applied across the cylinder and wire. The glass tube contains a small amount of a vapor such as a mixture of alcohol and argon. If now any ionizing radiation, as from a radioactive substance, enters the counter tube, it sets up a slight electric discharge from cylinder to wire. This discharge may be amplified and recorded in a number of ways, and it becomes possible to measure the intensity of the radiation from any radioactive source by placing it near the geiger tube. The intensity of radiation may be recorded as a dial reading or as a number of clicks, or may be recorded graphically on a sheet of paper. Such instruments of many varieties are available commercially and find applications in all types of nuclear research.

Radioactivity is a specific property of certain isotopes. For any given chemical element, one or more isotopes may exhibit radioactivity; others may not. It is convenient to have a name for all the isotopes of

TABLE 7.1 PROPERTIES OF RAYS FROM RADIOACTIVE ATOMS

Name	Other names	Symbol	Other symbols	Charge, $\times e^-$	Mass, amu
Alpha	helium ion	α	He^{2+}, $_2^4He^{2+}$	2+	4
Beta	electron, negatron	β	e^-, β^-	1−	1/1837
Gamma		γ		0	0
Neutron		n	$_0^1n$	0	1
Proton	hydrogen ion	p	H^+, $_1^1H^+$	1+	1
Deuteron	deuterium ion	d	D^+, $_1^2H^+$	1+	2
Positron	positive electron	e^+	β^+	1+	1/1837

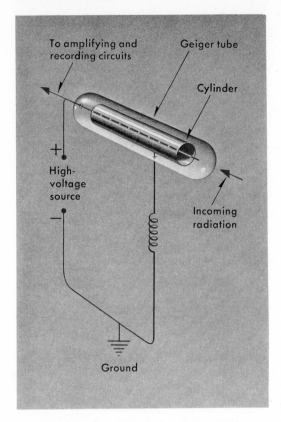

Fig. 7.3 Geiger-Müller tube and part of the electric circuit for counting ionizing radiations, as from radioactive sources.

all the chemical elements. Such a name is *nuclide*. A chart listing most of the known nuclides is provided with this book. The chart shows the atomic number, symbol, mass number, and actual mass in atomic mass units for the nuclides. It also gives information concerning the decay processes suffered by radioactive nuclides.

7.2 The Half-life

The nuclei of some atoms have a certain inherent instability. Out of every large group of atoms, say of radium, some will disintegrate soon; others, later. For a single atom of radium it would be impossible to predict the moment of disintegration; but for the very large numbers of atoms present in weighable amounts of radium, the number of atoms that will have disintegrated in any given time interval is predictable.

The mass of a radioactive element that will disintegrate in a given time depends solely on the inherent instability of the nuclei and on the number of atoms taken at the start of the measurements. The time necessary for half the mass of any sample to decay is called the *half-life* of the nuclide under consideration. If one were to start with 1 gram of radium, then at the end of one half-life, there would be 0.5 gram of radium left. At the end of the second half-life, there would be 0.25 gram left, and so on.

Let n_0 be the number of atoms present at the beginning of any investigation, and let n be the number remaining after the lapse of time t. Then it is found by experiment that

$$\log \frac{n_0}{n} = \frac{kt}{2.3} \tag{7.1}$$

where k is called the decay constant. The factor 2.3 relates natural logarithms to common logarithms (to the base 10). The *decay constant* is the fraction of the number of atoms initially present that disintegrates in unit time, provided that this is very short compared to the half-life.

When half of the atoms present have undergone disintegration (that is to say, at the end of one half-life, $t_{1/2}$), it will be clear that $n = n_0/2$, and hence

$$
\begin{aligned}
k &= \frac{2.3 \log (n_0/n)}{t_{1/2}} \\
&= \frac{2.3 \log 2}{t_{1/2}} \\
&= \frac{0.693}{t_{1/2}}
\end{aligned}
\tag{7.2}
$$

With the above relationship of half-life to decay constant, it is possible to calculate what fraction of a radioactive sample will remain after any given interval of time.

PROBLEM: The half-life of polonium-210, $^{210}_{84}\text{Po}$, is 138 days. If one starts with 0.2000 gram of $^{210}_{84}\text{Po}$, what weight will remain after 21 days?

SOLUTION: The decay constant

$$
\begin{aligned}
k &= \frac{0.693}{t_{1/2}} \\
&= \frac{0.693}{138d} \\
&= 5.02 \times 10^{-3} \text{ day}^{-1}
\end{aligned}
$$

The number of atoms present in a sample is proportional to the mass, so that the masses m_0 and m may be substituted for the numbers of atoms n_0 and n; hence

$$\log \frac{m_0}{m} = \log \frac{0.2000 \text{ gram}}{m}$$

and as

$$\log \frac{m_0}{m} = \frac{kt}{2.3}$$

we have

$$\log \frac{0.2000 \text{ gram}}{m} = \frac{kt}{2.3}$$

$$= \frac{5.02 \times 10^{-3} \text{ day}^{-1} \times 21 \text{ days}}{2.3}$$

$$= 0.0459$$

Now, taking the antilog of both sides of the equation,

$$\frac{0.2000 \text{ gram}}{m} = 1.11$$

and

$$m = 0.180 \text{ gram}$$

It will be noted that in working the above problem, it is necessary to express the half-life and the elapsed time in the same units of time.

PROBLEM: How long will it take for 25 percent by weight of any sample of actinium-227 to disintegrate? The half-life is 22 years.

SOLUTION:

$$k = \frac{0.693}{t_{1/2}}$$

$$= \frac{0.693}{22y}$$

$$= 3.15 \times 10^{-2} \text{ year}^{-1}$$

and

$$t = \frac{2.3}{k} \log \frac{m_0}{m}$$

$$= \frac{2.3}{3.15 \times 10^{-2} \text{ y}^{-1}} \times \log \frac{1}{0.75}$$

$$= \frac{2.3 \times 0.126}{3.15 \times 10^{-2} \text{ y}^{-1}}$$

$$= 9.2 \text{ years}$$

PROBLEM: The half-life of promethium-146 is 710 days. How many disintegrations occur per gram of ^{146}Pm per second?

SOLUTION: This problem may be solved readily if it is recalled that the decay constant, k, is the fraction of the total number of atoms present that decay in a time t, provided t is very short compared with $t_{1/2}$. It is necessary that t and $t_{1/2}$ be expressed in the same units.

Converting days to seconds, we have

$$k = \frac{0.693}{6.1 \times 10^7 \text{ sec}} = 1.13 \times 10^{-8} \text{ sec}^{-1}$$

The original 1.000 gram sample of ^{146}Pm must have contained

$$\frac{1.000}{146} \times 6.02 \times 10^{23} = 4.13 \times 10^{21} \text{ atoms}$$

The fraction disintegrating per second is 1.13×10^{-8} hence the number of atoms disintegrating per second is

$$4.13 \times 10^{21} \times 1.13 \times 10^{-8} = 4.7 \times 10^{13}$$

The rate of decay of a nuclide, and hence its half-life, is virtually independent of temperature, pressure, or any other ascertainable condition. A very slight dependence on mode of chemical combination has been demonstrated for certain kinds of decay. For instance, beryllium-7 decays by K capture; when the beryllium is chemically combined with fluorine, it has a half-life about one part in a thousand longer than when it is uncombined.

The radioactivity of a given nuclide is often expressed in terms of the curie. The curie represents 3.7×10^{10} disintegrations per second. This is approximately the number of disintegration which occur per gram of natural radium in each second. The half life of radium-226 (the most abundant isotope) is 1620 years.

7.3 Nuclear Stability

The reasons why some atomic nuclei undergo spontaneous disintegration while others do not is still far from being completely understood. Some clues to nuclear stability may be found in the chart of the nuclides. For instance, of the 265 stable nuclides shown in the chart, 156 have an even number of protons plus an even number of neutrons, but only 5 have an odd number of each. Some of the information contained in that chart is summarized in Fig. 7.4 where the number of protons present in the nuclei of the atoms is plotted against the number of neutrons also present. The points shown represent only those atomic nuclei which are stable. It will

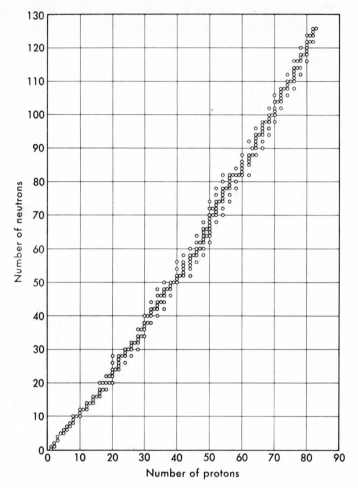

Fig. 7.4 *Stable nuclei lie in a "zone of stability" in which the ratio of neutrons to protons present rises with increasing atomic number.*

be noted that for the elements of lower atomic number the stable isotopes are, for the most part, those in which the number of protons is approximately equal to the number of neutrons. But as the atomic number becomes larger the proportion of neutrons to protons begins to rise until in, for instance, the element lead there are about three neutrons for every two protons in all the stable nuclei. Figure 7.4 represents what may be called the *zone of stability*, or the ratio of neutrons to protons which tends to yield stable nuclei; and this ratio rises with rising atomic number. It is also to be noted that there are no stable isotopes of elements with more than 83 protons, that is, with atomic number 84 or higher.

The several kinds of radioactive emission described in the preceding section may be thought of as changes that have as their purpose the shift of the nucleus in question into the zone of stability. The kind of ray emitted will then depend on whether the nucleus has too high or too low a neutron to proton ratio, or whether it lies in the region where all nuclei are radioactive.

If the neutron to proton ratio is too high for stability, then the obvious solution is for the nucleus to emit a neutron, but such simple processes are fairly rare. Lowering of the neutron to proton ratio occurs more frequently by emission of a beta ray. Krypton-87 decays by this mechanism, which may be represented as

$$\ce{^{87}_{36}Kr} \xrightarrow{t_{1/2} = 78 \text{ min}} \ce{^{87}_{37}Rb} + e^-$$

in which the electron (or negatron) has of course, a charge of 1— and an almost negligible mass. (It will be noted that in any equation such as that above, the total number of mass units and the total number of charge units must remain constant.) It may be wondered how an electron can come from a nucleus that is supposed to contain only neutrons and protons. The probability is that a neutron in the nucleus is converted to a proton plus an electron. The net increase of nuclear charge by one unit changes the krypton into the element of next higher atomic number, namely, rubidium.

If, on the other hand, the nucleus of an atom has too low a neutron to proton ratio for stability, it may conveniently lower the number of protons by the process of K capture. An example of K capture is found in argon-37, as follows:

$$\ce{^{37}_{18}Ar} \xrightarrow{t_{1/2} = 34 \text{ days}} \ce{^{37}_{17}Cl}$$

argon being transmuted to chlorine. Another way in which the neutron to proton ratio may be raised to bring the nucleus nearer the zone of stability is by emission of a positive electron, or positron. This occurs for nitrogen-13, which decays as follows:

$$\ce{^{13}_{7}N} \xrightarrow{t_{1/2} = 10 \text{ min}} \ce{^{13}_{6}C} + e^+$$

becoming carbon-13.[1]

Alpha ray emission occurs frequently for elements of atomic number higher than 83. It represents a more complicated mechanism for diminishing the number of protons, even though the alpha particle itself contains two neutrons in addition to two protons. An example of alpha emission is found in polonium-212, which decays as follows:

$$\ce{^{212}_{84}Po} \xrightarrow{t_{1/2} = 3 \times 10^{-7} \text{ sec}} \ce{^{208}_{82}Pb} + \ce{^{4}_{2}He}$$

[1] Nitrogen-13 does not occur in nature, but it may be made artificially. The reaction shown is a famous one because it was the first demonstration, by I. Curie and F. Joliot in 1933, of artificial radioactivity.

The product, a stable nuclide that also occurs naturally, is lead-208. Alpha emission is generally followed by several additional steps, some of which will be described in the next section.

The emission of gamma rays is different from those processes described above, since no change occurs in mass number or atomic number. A gamma ray is a form of energy, and its emission represents the discharge of excess energy from the nucleus. Just as the electron system surrounding the nucleus can have excited states from which electrons fall to normal states with emission of electromagnetic energy, so the nuclei may have excited states. But the energy released during the change from the excited to the normal state of a nucleus is considerably greater than that involving electronic states. This accounts for the very high frequency, short wavelength, and dangerously high penetrating power of gamma rays.

This section will be concluded with a review of the changes in a nucleus that occur during the emission of several kinds of rays, although examples of the more familiar kinds have been given above. Each process refers to the change produced by one particle coming from one nucleus.

Neutron emission lowers the mass number by one unit, but does not change the atomic number. The nucleus remains, therefore, as an isotope of the same element.

Beta-ray emission raises the atomic number by one unit, but does not appreciably change the mass.

K capture lowers the atomic number by one unit, but does not change the mass number.

TABLE 7.2   TRANSMUTATIONS CAUSED BY NUCLEAR DECAY

Positron emission lowers the atomic number by one unit, but does not change the mass number.

Alpha ray emission lowers the atomic number by two units and the mass number by four units.

Gamma rays carry off excess energy, but cause no change in atomic number or mass number.

Table 7.2 may serve to summarize the several changes described above. The diagram shows the effect of each particle on both atomic number and the neutron number (that is, the number of neutrons present) as it leaves the nucleus.

7.4   Disintegration Series

Let us suppose that there is a large quantity of a nuclide that, because of its long half-life, decays at a rate which remains almost constant over many years. Let this nuclide A decay into B, which has a short half-life and which in turn decays to a stable nuclide C, thus

$$A \xrightarrow{t_{1/2} \text{ long}} B \xrightarrow{t_{1/2} \text{ short}} C(\text{stable})$$

Because A is present in large amount and has a long half-life, the number of atoms of B being formed per unit time is practically constant. But B, with its short half-life, is decaying at a rate that depends on the number of atoms of B present. It is clear that a steady state will be reached in which the number of atoms of B disintegrating per unit time is just equal to the number being generated from A. Whether the number of atoms of B present at the steady state is large or small depends on the quantity and half-life of A and on the half-life of B.

This phenomenon of the steady state is frequently encountered. It makes possible the natural occurrence of many radioactive elements, which, if deprived of the parent element (A as above), would quickly disappear entirely. The steady state is sometimes referred to as a *radioactive equilibrium,* but the equilibrium that occurs is quite different from the reversible equilibrium described in Sec. 3.4 in connection with the equilibrium vapor pressure. Radioactive equilibrium is set up as a result of processes that operate in one direction only, namely, that of decay. The situation is not unlike the steady state of a mountain lake where water flows in at one end and out at the other.

Sequences of radioactive changes, some of which give rise to many steady states, can be very complicated. One of these will be described. This is the uranium-radium disintegration series, starting with uranium-238.

Uranium-238 emits alpha particles to become thorium-234. The process has a half-life of 4.5 billion years. Thorium-234 in turn emits beta rays, thus yielding protactinium-234, which also emits beta rays, thus yield-

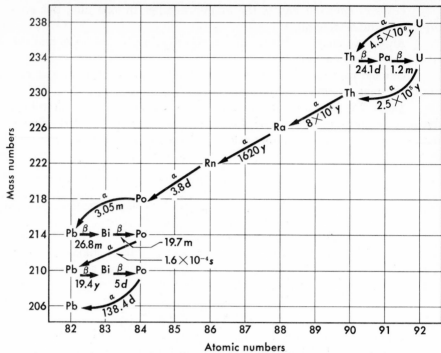

TABLE 7.3 RADIOACTIVE DISINTEGRATION OF URANIUM

ing uranium-234. This sequence of changes continues on until, at long last, the final product is a stable nuclide, lead-206. These various changes are shown in Table 7.3, which gives not only the nuclides formed, but also the kind of radiation accompanying each change and the half-life of each nuclide (in seconds, minutes, days, or years). The chart does not show a few minor complications caused by some nuclides disintegrating in more than one way. There are two other such series known among the naturally occurring elements and many such series among the synthetic radio-elements.

7.5 *Fission*

In each of the several kinds of radioactive disintegration described in the preceding section, the fragment ejected by the nucleus is light in mass as compared with the nucleus itself. Some of the isotopes of elements of the highest atomic numbers undergo disintegration by a process involving splitting of the nucleus into two (or more) fragments, one of which may be only moderately heavier than the other. This is the reaction of nuclear fission that was discovered by O. Hahn and F. Strassmann in 1939.

They showed that, under certain circumstances, an atom of uranium of atomic number 92 could undergo fission to yield an atom of barium of atomic number 56.

This reaction of nuclear fission appears to occur spontaneously in certain nuclides. More frequently it may be caused to occur by bombardment of uranium-235 or plutonium-239 by neutrons. No single representation will suffice to show all the changes that occur during nuclear fission, but one example may, and does, occur as follows:

$$^{235}_{92}U + {^1_0}n \rightarrow {^{140}_{56}}Ba + {^{93}_{36}}Kr + 3{^1_0}n$$

That is to say that in this example, absorption of neutrons by uranium-235 leads to fission in which the products are barium-140 and krypton-93, plus excess neutrons over and above those used in the bombardment. Uranium-235 also decays in a more prosaic fashion by alpha emission, with a half-life of 7.1×10^8 years.

The excess neutrons in fission arise from the circumstance previously described, namely, that the zone of stability shows that elements of lower atomic number, such as barium and krypton, require for stability a lower neutron to proton ratio than does an element of higher atomic number, such as uranium. This fact is of vital importance in causing nuclear chain reactions leading to the liberation of atomic energy.

The barium and krypton formed, as above, are called *fission products*. Examination of the chart of the nuclides with this book will show that the isotopes formed, barium-140 and krypton-93, still have too high a neutron to proton ratio for stability and that they are both beta ray (and gamma ray) emitters with half-lives of 12.8 days and 33 sec, respectively.

Fission products are, in general, extremely radioactive and therefore dangerous; but they also serve as sources of many useful isotopes. The details of these and related preparations of synthetic nuclides will be deferred until Chapter 20.

The reader does not need to be reminded that nuclear fission is a violently exothermic process. In Sec. 3.3 it was shown that the condensation of 1 gram of steam to liquid water is an exothermic process yielding about 540 cal. The fission of 1 gram of uranium-235 yields over ten million times more energy. This energy emerges in the form of gamma rays, heat, and in the kinetic energy with which the fission products, excess neutrons, and other particles are ejected.

In the year 1905, A. Einstein derived an equation relating energy to mass.

$$E = mc^2 \tag{7.3}$$

where E is the energy, m is the mass, and c is the velocity of light. This, probably the most famous equation in history, makes it possible to calculate the energy equivalent of any mass of matter. The units used for the Einstein mass-energy equation are: energy in ergs, mass in grams, and the velocity of light in centimeters per second. One erg is equal to 2.39×10^{-8} cal. The velocity of light is 3.00×10^{10} cm sec^{-1}. The energy equivalent per gram of matter is, therefore

$$E = 1.00 \text{ gram} \times (3.00 \times 10^{10} \text{ cm sec}^{-1})^2$$
$$= 9.00 \times 10^{20} \text{ erg}$$
$$= 2.15 \times 10^{13} \text{ cal}$$
$$= 5.62 \times 10^{26} \text{ mev (million electron volts)}$$

A large energy equivalent is thus seen to be obtainable from a relatively small mass of matter. The source of this mass is to be found in the mass defect, or the deviations of the actual atomic masses from the mass numbers, as mentioned in Sec. 6.3. The actual atomic mass of uranium-235 is slightly greater than 235 amu; those of barium-140 and krypton-93, slightly less than 140 and 93 amu, respectively. (The actual atomic masses of all known nuclides will be found in the nuclide chart.) When uranium-235 undergoes nuclear fission, the collective mass of the products, including any excess neutrons, is a little less than the mass of the uranium. This mass loss, as its energy equivalent, is the source of the great destruction caused by the atomic bomb. The fission of uranium-235 results in the release of about 8.7×10^{-4} gram of matter per gram of uranium as its energy equivalent.

7.6   Fusion

In Sec. 6.3 it was stated that the actual masses of the lightest atoms are somewhat greater than their mass numbers. It might be thought, therefore, that energy could be released by the union of two light nuclei as well as by the fission of a heavy nucleus. This is indeed the case; the process is called *nuclear fusion* and its occurs in the sun and in thermonuclear bombs. We shall first examine in more detail what happens when nucleons (protons or neutrons or both) come together to form an atomic nucleus.

The actual mass of a hydrogen-1 atom is 1.007825 amu; that of a neutron is 1.008665. An atom of hydrogen-2 (deuterium) having a nucleus containing 1 proton and 1 neutron might be expected, therefore, to have a mass of 2.016490 amu, but the actual mass is 2.01410 amu. This small difference of 0.00239 amu is the loss of mass, accompanied by a release of energy, in accordance with Eq. 7.3.

The energy involved in nuclear fission or fusion is often expressed in electron volts (ev) or million electron volts (mev). One ev $= 160 \times 10^{-12}$ erg $= 3.83 \times 10^{-20}$ cal. But Einstein's mass-energy equation shows that energy may also be expressed in grams (Sec. 7.5), from which it follows that 1 amu (1.66 × 10⁻²⁴ gram) is equivalent to 933 mev, and the energy released when an atom of hydrogen-1 unites with a neutron to form hydrogen-2 is 0.00239 × 933 = 2.23 mev. This is called the *binding energy* of the nuclide, $^2_1$H.

PROBLEM: Find the binding energy of helium $^4_2$He, which has an actual mass of 4.00260 amu.

SOLUTION: This nucleus contains two protons and two neutrons. Hence,

$$
\begin{aligned}
\text{Two H atoms} &= 2.01565 \\
\text{Two neutrons} &= \underline{2.01733} \\
\text{Total} &= \overline{4.03298} \\
\text{Actual mass} &= 4.00260 \\
\text{Difference} &= \overline{0.03038}
\end{aligned}
$$

and the binding energy is 0.03038 × 933 Mev = 28.3 Mev.

Binding energies are often given in million electron volts per *nucleon* present. In the case of $^4_2$He, given above, there are four nucleons (two protons and two neutrons) in the nucleus. The binding energy per nucleon is then 28.3 mev/4 = 7.08 mev. Figure 7.5 shows binding energies per nucleon for all the chemical elements, and from this it should be clear that energy may be released by the fusion of the lightest atoms or by fission of the heaviest atoms, provided in each case that an *increase* of binding energy occurs.

It is obvious that nuclear fusion reactions do not take place whenever one hydrogen atom meets another. Fusion reactions are, of course,

Fig. 7.5 Binding energy per nucleon (proton or neutron) present in the nucleus of each atom plotted against mass number.

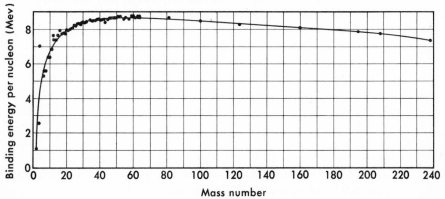

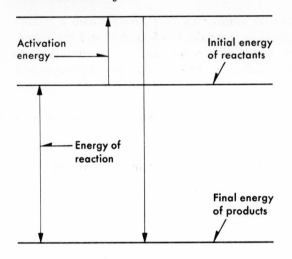

Fig. 7.6 This diagram illustrates the difference between activation energy and energy of reaction. Reactants in nuclear fusion (and this is also true of many chemical reactants) behave as if they lie in a trough of energy from which they must be lifted before reaction may start.

exothermic to an extraordinary degree. But before fusion can occur, it is necessary that energy be absorbed by the system. The situation is like a barrier that can be surmounted only by the application of energy, after which this energy and vastly more is returned. Figure 7.6 shows diagrammatically this relation between the net quantity of energy released during fusion and the energy necessary to initiate the reaction. The latter is called the *activation energy*, and this requirement explains why it is necessary to use a fission bomb in order to explode a thermonuclear (fusion) bomb.

EXERCISES

1. Uranium-235, $^{235}_{92}U$, loses successively an α particle, a β particle, an α particle, and a β particle. What is the name, atomic number, and mass number of the nuclide formed?
2. Starting with a nucleus of atomic number Z and mass number A, show the effect of each change indicated.

Change	Effect on Z	Effect on A
β out.................	?	?
Neutron out...........	?	?
α out.................	?	?
Positron out...........	?	?

3. It is found that a sample of radioactive matter is half disintegrated in 18.0 hr. How much will remain after 42.5 hr?

4. A sample of radioactive matter weighing 0.535 gram was found to have lost 18.8 percent of its radioactivity in 40 days and 4 hr. Find the half-life of this sample.

5. As radium emits α rays, it is possible to count the disintegrations with a Geiger counter. The α particles soon pick up electrons and become helium molecules. In a certain experiment, 6.10×10^{16} counts yielded 2.44×10^{-3} ml of helium at STP. From these data calculate Avogadro's number.

6. Atomic nuclei that consist simultaneously of a "magic number" of protons plus a magic number of neutrons are very stable against radioactive transmutation. Three of these "magic numbers" are 2, 8, and 20. The helium isotope ^4_2He is one of these stable nuclei; select two more.

7. Bromine-80 has been obtained in the form of a radioactive nuclide that emits only gamma rays with a half-life of 4.5 hr. Explain this phenomenon and write a nuclear equation for the change.

8. Whenever K capture occurs, it is found that x-rays are emitted. What is the source of these x-rays?

9. Predict possible radioactivity of the following nuclides and write a nuclear equation for each process (predictions may be verified by reference to the nuclide chart with this book: ^3_1H, $^{10}_6\text{C}$, $^{12}_6\text{C}$, $^{37}_{16}\text{S}$, $^{55}_{26}\text{Fe}$, $^{79}_{35}\text{Br}$, $^{127}_{53}\text{I}$, $^{201}_{82}\text{Pb}$, $^{208}_{82}\text{Pb}$, $^{214}_{82}\text{Pb}$, $^{210}_{85}\text{At}$, $^{250}_{98}\text{Cf}$.

10. Write a balanced, possible equation for the fission of uranium-233.

11. Why is the energy released in nuclear fission so much greater than that released in ordinary radioactivity, such as the α emission of uranium-238?

12. The interior of the earth is thought by some authorities to be largely metallic iron. Discuss the possibility that all this iron could blow up in one vast nuclear fission explosion.

13. The sun's energy is thought to come from the reaction

$$4^1_1\text{H} \rightarrow {}^4_2\text{He} + 2e^+$$

The sun radiates 4.0×10^{33} ergs/sec. Find the number of tons of hydrogen consumed by the sun every second.

14. May one say that the source of the energy released is the same in fission as in fusion?

15. What is the binding energy per nucleon (proton or neutron, or both) in nickel-60, the atomic mass of which is 59.9303 amu?

16. Plutonium-244 undergoes spontaneous fission with a half-life for this reaction that is said to be 2.5×10^{10} years. How many of these fissions must occur per gram of $^{244}_{94}\text{Pu}$ every second?

17. Discuss possible reasons why fission can occur spontaneously, whereas fusion requires a very large activation energy.

8

Chemical Reactivity

8.1 The Union of Atoms

With a few possible exceptions, all atoms have the ability to combine with other atoms. This kind of transformation is called *chemical combination,* and it does not directly involve the nucleus, as is the case for nuclear fusion described in the preceding chapter.

Sometimes the bond between atoms is so weak and transient that no effective combination can be said to have taken place. In other cases, the bond is so strong that very powerful forces are necessary to tear the atoms apart again. Sometimes the combinations formed are comparatively simple, as in the union of two atoms of hydrogen. Sometimes the combinations are of extraordinary complexity, as is the case for the proteins of animal tissue, concerning which we are still far from a complete understanding.

If the union of two or more atoms is between atoms of different chemical elements, as of hydrogen uniting with oxygen to form water, then the substance so formed is said to be a *chemical compound.* There are only about 100 chemical elements, but the combinations of these elements yield compounds numbering in the hundreds of thousands.

Most matter familiar in everyday life consists of *mixtures.* Water as found in lakes and oceans may, for instance, contain more or less salt, air may contain more or less moisture. Mixtures may be composed of chemical elements or of compounds, or of both. Mixtures, in contrast to pure chemical compounds, are characterized by variable composition, and many (though not all) also show a lack of homogeneity. When examined under a microscope, many mixtures exhibit several different kinds of substances that may be separated mechanically, as is true of a mixture of sugar and sand. But pure chemical compounds are always homogeneous; they appear to be, and they are, the same throughout. A pure chemical compound cannot be separated into its components without disrupting the atomic combinations and so destroying the compound.

There is still another way in which a chemical compound differs from a mixture. Iron is commonly distinguished from copper by being harder, by being a different color, by being attracted to a magnet, and in other ways. These characteristics by which one substance may be distinguished from another are known as *properties*. The freezing point of water, its lack of color, the fact that its normal boiling point is 100° C, the fact that it may be decomposed into hydrogen and oxygen—all these are properties of water. Another property is density. The metal lead is often said to be "heavier" than, say, water. What is meant is that lead has a higher density than water. As are freezing point and boiling point (under specified conditions), density is a characteristic property of a pure substance, whether it be element or compound. But mixtures have no unique characteristic set of properties. One may dissolve more or less sugar in water so that the mixture has the property of being very sweet or of being only slightly sweet.

Not all properties are characteristic of pure substances. A sample of water may weigh 100 grams. This is a property of that particular sample of water, but not necessarily of any other sample of water. However, the property of freezing below 0° C is characteristic of all samples of pure water. Properties such as freezing point and density, which are characteristic of all pure samples of a substance, are called *specific properties*. Other properties, such as volume, mass, and temperature, may be called accidental properties.

If atoms combine to form groups of atoms, or if such groups are changed or disrupted, a *chemical change* is said to have occurred. Whenever a chemical change takes place, there is an abrupt change of specific properties. Water differs in its specific properties in every respect from the two elements of which it is formed. If a sample of water is warmed slightly a change of accidental properties may take place, but there is no major change of specific properties. Changes of temperature, shape, degree of magnetization, and the like, which do not involve the making or breaking of bonds between atoms, are called *physical changes*. In most cases, it is easy to distinguish between chemical and physical change, but as we shall see later, there are cases in which it is difficult.

8.2   *Laws of Chemical Combination*

The modern concept of matter as being composed of atoms was established by J. Dalton in a series of publications which began in the year 1808. Dalton's atomic theory was based on inductive reasoning from the law of definite proportions, and it was supported by deductive reasoning that led to the law of multiple proportions. We shall, for historical reasons, present these two laws briefly as being natural consequences of the concepts of atoms and molecules previously described.

The chemical element carbon combines with oxygen to form a poisonous gas, carbon monoxide, the molecular weight of which is 28. The carbon monoxide molecule must therefore consist of one atom of carbon of 12 amu and one atom of oxygen of 16 amu. The proportion by weight of carbon to oxygen in carbon monoxide is then 12:16 or 3:4. It is obvious that the only way this ratio could be changed would be to have one atom of carbon unite with two or more atoms of oxygen or, conversely, one atom of oxygen unite with two or more atoms of carbon. But in neither of these cases would the product be carbon monoxide. Hence, we may state the **law of definite proportions** as follows:

In any chemical compound the elements are always present in a definite proportion by weight.

The definite proportion may be quite different for different substances: In methane, it is one part of hydrogen to three of carbon; in water, it is one part of hydrogen to eight of oxygen.

A notable exception to the law of definite proportions occurs when different isotopes take part in chemical combination. Carbon monoxide may be formed from carbon-12 and oxygen-18, in which case the ratio by weight of carbon to oxygen is 2:3 rather than 3:4. If the law of definite proportions is found applicable to most chemical substances, it is because the various isotopes are nearly always mixed in the same proportions in any sample of a naturally occurring element.

The law of multiple proportions may be illustrated by reference to the two substances carbon monoxide and carbon dioxide. The first consists of molecules containing one carbon atom for each oxygen atom, and the second consists of molecules containing one carbon atom for each two oxygen atoms. The ratio by weight of carbon to oxygen in carbon dioxide is obviously 12:32 or 3:8, whereas that in ordinary carbon monoxide is 3:4. The weight of oxygen in proportion to carbon is twice as great in the one case as in the other.

The **law of multiple proportions** may be stated as follows:

If an element unites with another element in more than one proportion by weight, the weights of one element that unite with a fixed weight of the other bear a simple ratio to each other.

The simple ratio in the case illustrated is $2:1$. Here, again, the law is applicable only to systems of fixed isotopic composition.

8.3 Formulas

Just as there are symbols for the chemical elements, so it is convenient to have formulas for the chemical compounds. The formula NaCl may be used to represent the ultimate pair of atoms, or ions, that may be thought of as comprising the substance sodium chloride. This formula shows not only that sodium chloride consists of sodium and chlorine but also that the sodium and chlorine atoms have combined in equal numbers. Similarly, the formula H_2O for water implies (by use of the subscript 2 after the symbol for hydrogen) that in this substance there are two atoms of hydrogen for each atom of oxygen.

Formulas for a few other substances are: hydrogen,[1] H_2; methane, CH_4; carbon tetrachloride, CCl_4; magnesium chloride, $MgCl_2$; sodium hydroxide, NaOH; calcium hydroxide, $Ca(OH)_2$; sodium sulfate, Na_2SO_4; calcium sulfate, $CaSO_4$; and ammonium chloride, NH_4Cl. It will be noted that calcium hydroxide is written $Ca(OH)_2$ rather than CaO_2H_2. The first (correct) way carries the implication that two OH^- (hydroxide) ions[2] are present for each calcium. The second (incorrect) way suggests that one calcium is somehow combined with two oxygens and two hydrogens. The subscript 2 outside the parentheses means that the whole group of atoms inside the parentheses is taken twice. The formula for aluminum sulfate, $Al_2(SO_4)_3$, shows that there are three SO_4^{2-} (sulfate) ions for every two aluminum ions in this compound.

Chemical formulas are, unfortunately, used in rather different senses. The formula NaCl generally means nothing more than that in this compound there is one sodium atom for each chlorine atom, but the formula HCl is assumed to mean not only that this compound contains one hydrogen atom for each chlorine atom, but also that there is a molecule of this formula and that its molecular weight is 36.5. Generally, this situation need not give rise to serious confusion, but where confusion is possible, it has been resolved in this book by writing brackets of the form $\langle NaCl \rangle_\infty$ around the formulas of compounds and elements where no particulate molecule and no measurable molecular weight is implied.

Just as there are atomic weights for the chemical elements, there are formula weights for the compounds. *Formula weights* are the sum

---

[1] The union of two or more atoms of the same element to form a single molecule does not imply that the element becomes a chemical compound; many atoms of the elements combine in this way. Other examples are: O_2, N_2, O_3, and S_8.

[2] An *ion* is an atom, or group of atoms, that has acquired an electric charge through the loss or gain of one or more electrons.

of the atomic weights of all atoms represented in the formula. The formula weight for sodium chloride, NaCl, is $22.990 + 35.453 = 58.443$. The formula weight for water, H_2O, is $(2 \times 1.0080) + 15.9994 = 18.0154$. The formula weight for magnesium phosphate, $Mg_3(PO_4)_2$ is $(2 \times 24.32) + (2 \times 30.98) + (8 \times 15.9994) = 262.92$. In such cases where the formula actually represents a particulate molecule, as for H_2O, the formula weight is the molecular weight.

The word "mole" was defined in Sec. 5.1 as 6.023×10^{23} molecules of any substance. But the word is often used for substances, such as sodium chloride, which do not ordinarily form molecules. It is the custom to say that a mole of sodium chloride weighs 58.443 grams, just as a mole of water weighs 18.0154 grams. In this sense: The weight of a mole of any substance, be it element or compound, is the formula weight expressed as grams.

Some authors avoid the possible ambiguity involved in this use of the word "mole" by restricting its use to substances that actually form molecules, and by using the term *gram-formula weight* for those such as sodium chloride, which do not as a rule occur as molecules. In reference to elements, it is customary to use the term *gram-atom,* which means simply the atomic weight expressed as grams and which is therefore the weight in grams of 6.023×10^{23} atoms of the element. Thus a gram-atom of H weighs 1.0080 grams; a mole of H_2 weighs 2.0160 grams.

When, as sometimes occurs, it is necessary to designate specific isotopes in the formula, this may be done as follows: $H_2{}^{18}O$, which means water formed from (presumably) ordinary hydrogen and oxygen-18. A mole of *this* water weighs 20.0154 grams.

This section will be concluded with some brief remarks on nomenclature. Many chemical compounds consist of two different elements only. Examples are hydrogen chloride, HCl; water; and ammonia, NH_3. These are all referred to as *binary compounds*. All binary compounds may be named by stating the name of the more electropositive element first, followed by the name of the more electronegative element with its ending changed to "-ide." Thus HCl is hydrogen chloride, H_2O is hydrogen oxide, and NH_3 is hydrogen nitride (or, according to some authorities, nitrogen hydride). Some of these substances are, of course, so well known that, like water and ammonia, they have special names of their own. Sometimes when two elements unite in more than one proportion, it may be necessary to specify the proportions, as in the following cases: N_2O, dinitrogen oxide (or nitrous oxide); NO, nitrogen oxide (or nitric oxide); NO_2, nitrogen dioxide; and N_2O_5, dinitrogen pentoxide. The reader may wonder how he is to know which element is the more electropositive and which the more electronegative. These terms will be discussed in Sec. 8.6. Rules for naming more complicated compounds will be given as they are encountered.

8.4 *Equations*

The relationships between reactants and products in chemical change may conveniently be shown by chemical equations. This procedure will be illustrated by several examples.

Zinc unites with sulfur to form the compound zinc sulfide, the formula for which is ZnS. The atomic weights of zinc and sulfur being 65.38 and 32.07, respectively, it follows that when an atom of zinc unites with an atom of sulfur, 65.38 amu of zinc combine with 32.07 amu of sulfur. The product is found by actual test to weigh 97.45 amu, within limits of experimental error.

The facts stated above may be summarized as follows:

$$Zn + S \rightarrow ZnS$$

Notice that all atoms are accounted for, there being the same number of each kind of atom in the reactants to the left of the arrow as there are in the products to the right of the arrow. The equation is therefore said to be *balanced,* as it is written.

A chemical equation has both qualitative and quantitative significance. It tells what substances undergo chemical reaction to form what products, and it tells the relative weights of each substance involved. The equation above may most conveniently be read as follows:

"1 gram-atom (or mole) of zinc weighing 65.38 grams unites with 1 gram-atom (or mole) of sulfur[3] weighing 32.07 grams to yield 1 mole of zinc sulfide weighing 97.45 grams."

Another example is the combustion of methane in oxygen to yield carbon dioxide and water. A skeleton equation may first be written as follows:

$$CH_4 + O_2 \rightarrow CO_2 + H_2O$$

but this is obviously incomplete because some of the atoms shown at the left are missing on the right, and vice versa. Simple equations such as this may be balanced by inspection; thus,

$$CH_4 + 2O_2 \rightarrow CO_2 + 2H_2O$$

The equation may now be read as:

"One molecule of methane unites with two molecules (each containing two atoms) of oxygen to yield one molecule of carbon dioxide and two molecules of water."

A more useful statement of the equation is:

"One mole of methane weighing 16.0 grams unites with 2 moles of

---

[3] It is true that sulfur generally forms molecules of formula S_2 or S_8, but we may safely ignore this complication, at least for the moment.

oxygen weighing 64.0 grams to yield 1 mole of carbon dioxide weighing 44.0 grams and 2 moles of water weighing 36.0 grams."

It will be recalled that all gases have the same molar volume, which at STP is 22.4 liters. Methane, oxygen, and carbon dioxide are all gases at STP and the volume of water as steam may be corrected to STP. It is possible, therefore, to give the equation above still another useful interpretation:

"One mole of methane occupying 22.4 liters unites with 2 moles of oxygen occupying 44.8 liters to yield 1 mole of carbon dioxide occupying 22.4 liters and 2 moles of water vapor occupying 44.8 liters, all volumes being measured or (as is obviously required for water) corrected to STP."

This last interpretation applies only to reactants and products that are molecular in nature and form gases. It will be noted that the ratio of volumes given above is 1:2:1:2. This is an illustration of **Gay-Lussac's law of combining volumes** which played a part in the historical development of chemistry. The law may be stated as follows:

Whenever gases interact chemically, or when gaseous products are formed, the ratios of the volumes of these gaseous substances may be expressed as the ratios of small whole numbers.

8.5   Valence

The combining power of atoms is called valence. At one time the word "valence" had a more restricted meaning, but now it is used to mean any more or less stable attraction between one atom, or group of atoms, and another. To some degree, the word has been replaced by the term *chemical bonding*.

There are four principal ways in which atoms may be held together. These are electrovalence (or electron transfer), covalence (or electron sharing), metallic valence, and the van der Waals forces which were mentioned in Chapter 2. Atoms held to each other by van der Waals forces, which are weak relative to the other kinds of valence, are not generally considered to be chemically bonded to each other, and chemical compounds are not formed in this way. Metallic valence is that which holds together the atoms of a metal such as iron, silver, or tungsten. These forces are strong, but poorly understood. Consideration of metallic valence will be deferred until later; our chief concern will be with electrovalence and covalence.

Valence is closely related to the number of electrons of highest principal quantum number normally present in an atom. Reference to Table 6.2 will show that for hydrogen this number is 1, for carbon, 4; for oxygen, 6; for sodium, 1; for magnesium, 2; and for chlorine, 7. These electrons are commonly said to be in the *valence shell* and are often designated by electron dot symbols, as follows:

$$\text{H}\cdot \quad \cdot\overset{\displaystyle\cdot}{\underset{\displaystyle\cdot}{\text{C}}}\cdot \quad :\overset{\displaystyle\cdot\cdot}{\underset{\displaystyle\cdot\cdot}{\text{O}}}\cdot \quad \text{Na}\cdot \quad \cdot\text{Mg}\cdot \quad :\overset{\displaystyle\cdot\cdot}{\text{Cl}}\cdot$$

It will be understood that these are merely convenient symbols and that they are not meant to be reproductions of what an atom may be expected to look like.

Electrovalence will be illustrated by reference to sodium chloride. The sodium atom has one electron in its valence shell. The energy necessary to remove this electron is not large, and the electron is easily lost. But when this occurs, the sodium atom must be left with a positive charge because the nucleus still contains its 11 protons. The change may be represented as follows:

$$\text{Na}\cdot \quad \longrightarrow \quad \text{Na}^+ \quad + \quad e^-$$

neutral	becomes	positive	plus	electron
sodium		sodium ion		
atom				

Chlorine, on the other hand, readily gains an electron; but in so doing, the chlorine thereby acquires a negative charge and becomes a chloride ion:

$$:\overset{\displaystyle\cdot\cdot}{\underset{\displaystyle\cdot\cdot}{\text{Cl}}}\cdot \quad + \quad e^- \quad \longrightarrow \quad [:\overset{\displaystyle\cdot\cdot}{\underset{\displaystyle\cdot\cdot}{\text{Cl}}}:]^-$$

neutral	plus	electron	becomes	negative
chlorine				chloride
atom				ion

Opposite electric charges attract each other. The sodium ions are attracted to the chloride ions, and the change that occurs may be regarded as simply a transfer of one electron from each sodium atom to each chlorine atom. If the reaction is between chlorine and an atom such as magnesium, which has two electrons in its valence shell, then two chlorine atoms will be required for each magnesium atom:

$$\cdot\text{Mg}\cdot \quad + \quad 2:\overset{\displaystyle\cdot\cdot}{\underset{\displaystyle\cdot\cdot}{\text{Cl}}}\cdot \quad \longrightarrow \quad \text{Mg}^{2+} \quad + \quad 2[:\overset{\displaystyle\cdot\cdot}{\underset{\displaystyle\cdot\cdot}{\text{Cl}}}:]^-$$

neutral	plus	2 neutral	becomes	double	plus	2 negative
magnesium		chlorine		positive		chloride
atom		atoms		magnesium		ions
				ion		

As a consequence of this, the formula for magnesium chloride is $MgCl_2$.

The union of two hydrogen atoms to form a molecule of hydrogen is a rather different process from that described above. This reaction may be represented as a sharing of electrons:

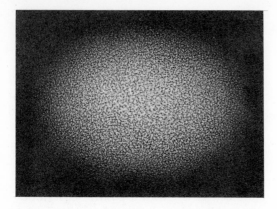

Fig. 8.1 This drawing shows the probable distribution of electrons, averaged over a period of time, in a particle formed by the union of two hydrogen atoms. Such representations are doubtless much nearer the truth than the formal diagrams given below, but the more accurate drawing is obviously much less convenient to use.

$$H\cdot \quad + \quad H\cdot \quad \longrightarrow \quad H\!:\!H$$

hydrogen   plus   hydrogen   becomes   hydrogen
atom   atom   molecule

This process is called *covalence*. If a hydrogen molecule could be seen, it would probably be an elongated blur as shown in Fig. 8.1. A conventional representation is to join the atoms with a line, H—H, in which the line stands for a pair of electrons shared in holding the atoms together. Other examples of covalence are found in methane, CH_4; molecular chlorine, Cl_2; and in carbon tetrachloride, CCl_4.

$$\dot{\underset{\cdot}{C}}\cdot + 4H\cdot \rightarrow \begin{matrix} H \\ H\!:\!\ddot{C}\!:\!H \\ \ddot{H} \end{matrix} \quad or \quad \begin{matrix} H \\ | \\ H\!-\!C\!-\!H \\ | \\ H \end{matrix}$$

$$:\!\ddot{C}\!l\cdot + :\!\ddot{C}\!l\cdot \rightarrow :\!\ddot{C}\!l\!:\!\ddot{C}\!l\!: \quad or \quad :\!\ddot{C}\!l\!-\!\ddot{C}\!l\!:$$

$$\dot{\underset{\cdot}{C}}\cdot + 4\!:\!\ddot{C}\!l\cdot \rightarrow \begin{matrix} :\!\ddot{C}\!l\!: \\ :\!\ddot{C}\!l\!:\!C\!:\!\ddot{C}\!l\!: \\ :\!\ddot{C}\!l\!: \end{matrix} \quad or \quad \begin{matrix} :\!\ddot{C}\!l\!: \\ | \\ :\!\ddot{C}\!l\!-\!C\!-\!\ddot{C}\!l\!: \\ | \\ :\!\ddot{C}\!l\!: \end{matrix}$$

Many cases are also known in which both electrovalence and covalence occur simultaneously in the same compound. An example is ammonium chloride, NH_4Cl, in which the hydrogen atoms are united to the nitrogen by covalence to form the positive ammonium ion, NH_4^+ which is then held to negative chloride ions by electrovalence.

It should be noted that electrovalence and covalence have this in common that both involve the formation of an electron pair. In the one case this pair is held almost entirely to the negative ion, while in covalence the pair may be shared more or less equally between the two atoms involved in the bond.

8.6   *Electrovalence and Electronegativity*

For those atoms that form ions by the loss or gain of electrons, the number of electrons that may be lost or gained is generally predictable. Atoms such as sodium, magnesium, or aluminum, which contain respectively one, two, and three electrons in the valence shell, commonly lose all of these electrons, thereby acquiring positive charges as follows: Na^+, Mg^{2+}, and Al^{3+}. But there appear to be no positive ions of charge greater than 4+, and this occurs only rarely. Atoms having a valence shell containing six or seven electrons, such as oxygen or chlorine, tend to add two or one electrons, respectively, to complete an octet of electrons, thus acquiring negative charges as follows: O^{2-}, Cl^-. Neon or argon, which already have eight electrons in the valence shell, neither lose nor gain electrons and appear to be chemically inert. This tendency to completion of the octet of electrons in the valence shell occurs so frequently that it is known as the octet rule. But, as we shall see later, there are many exceptions to this rule.

A more difficult problem is to predict whether two atoms will enter into an electrovalent bond or a covalent bond. Figure 8.2 shows *ionization potentials* for a few atoms. This is the energy necessary to remove one electron from each atom, the atoms being considered to be in the form of gas molecules, containing only one atom each:

$$X \rightarrow X^+ + e^-$$

This is helpful because those atoms that have low ionization potentials form positive ions, and those with high ionization potentials do so less readily. However, the ionization potential alone does not give an answer to our problem.[4]

The energy released by an atom in becoming a negative ion by gain of one or more electrons is called the *electron affinity*.

$$Y + e^- \rightarrow Y^-$$

Table 8.1 shows some electron affinities. Those with the highest electron affinities are those that most readily form negative ions.

What is needed is the relative ability of an atom to hold one or more extra electrons when that atom is part of a chemical compound. This

---

[4] Another measure of tendency to lose electrons is the *work function*. This is the energy required to remove an electron from a solid metal, such as a piece of iron. But the work function has only an indirect bearing on our problem.

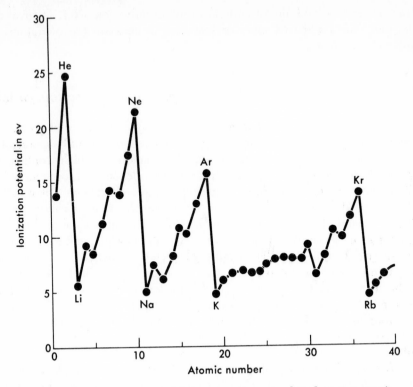

Fig. 8.2 The ionization potential for some elements plotted against atomic number.

property is called *electronegativity*, but unfortunately there is no completely satisfactory measure of this property. The best measure of electronegativity, from a theoretical standpoint, is probably the average of the ionization potential and the electron affinity, but the latter is difficult to measure and few electron affinities are known.

Numerous attempts have been made to find other quantitative measures of electronegativity. These are based mostly on the strengths of the valence bonds between various atoms and also on the distances between atoms in a compound. Inasmuch as there is no complete agreement concerning these matters, no attempt will be made to present the details of the calculations, but a few electronegativity values obtained by various means are given in Table 8.1. This table will be sufficient for our purposes in this book.

The method of using Table 8.1 to predict the kinds of bonds formed between the elements is as follows: Atoms of low electronegativity form metallic bonds between each other. These may be between atoms of the

TABLE **8.1** IONIZATION POTENTIALS,* ELECTRON AFFINITIES, AND RELATIVE ELECTRONEGATIVITIES OF SOME ELEMENTS

Element	Ionization potential, ev	Electron affinity, ev	Electronegativity
Cesium, Cs	3.89	....	0.86
Barium, Ba	5.21	....	0.97
Sodium, Na	5.14	....	1.01
Calcium, Ca	6.11	....	1.04
Magnesium, Mg	7.64	....	1.23
Silver, Ag	7.57	....	1.42
Mercury, Hg	10.43	....	1.44
Aluminum, Al	5.96	....	1.47
Lead, Pb	7.41	....	1.55
Zinc, Zn	9.36	....	1.66
Bismuth, Bi	8.0	....	1.67
Tin, Sn	7.33	....	1.72
Silicon, Si	8.15	1.90	1.74
Antimony, Sb	8.5	....	1.82
Boron, B	8.28	0.3	2.01
Tellurium, Te	8.96	....	2.01
Phosphorus, P	11.0	0.8	2.06
Hydrogen, H	13.60	0.7	2.1
Arsenic, As	10.5	....	2.20
Iodine, I	10.44	....	2.21
Sulfur, S	10.36	2.07	2.44
Selenium, Se	9.75	....	2.48
Carbon, C	11.25	1.13	2.50
Chlorine, Cl	13.01	3.82	2.83
Nitrogen, N	14.54	0.2	3.07
Oxygen, O	13.61	1.48	3.50
Fluorine, F	17.42	3.62	4.10

* The term *ionization potential*, as almost always used, refers to an energy and not to a potential.

same element, as in cesium metal or gold metal, or between different elements, as in alloys and intermetallic compounds that may or may not have definite compositions.[5]

Atoms of high electronegativity form covalent bonds between each other. Examples are found in Cl_2, HI, and ICl.

Atoms of high electronegativity unite with atoms of low electro-

---

[5] It is also true that at elevated temperatures, some elements of low electronegativity (such as sodium) form diatomic molecules of which Na_2 is an example. This bond must be, at least in part, covalent.

negativity with the formation of electrovalent bonds. Examples are CsF, CaH₂, MgO.

Virtually all possible gradations between electrovalent and covalent are possible. A bond that includes both electrovalent and covalent character is called a *polar bond*.

The nature of the bonds between atoms is generally of controlling importance in establishing the physical and chemical properties of the substances formed. This section will therefore be concluded with some remarks concerning how electrovalent bonds between atoms play a part in determining the space lattice and other properties. Substances containing highly polar bonds, approaching pure electrovalent character, are often referred to as *salts*.

In purely electrovalent substances the valence bond is merely an electrostatic attraction between one ion and all oppositely charged ions in the immediate neighborhood. In the case of sodium chloride this effect may be illustrated as follows:

$$
\begin{array}{ccc}
Cl^- & & Na^+ \\
| & Cl^- & | & Na^+ \\
| & / & | & / \\
Cl^- - - -Na^+ - - -Cl^- & \qquad & Na^+ - - -Cl^- - - -Na^+ \\
/ & | & / & | \\
Cl^- & | & Na^+ & | \\
Cl^- & & Na^+
\end{array}
$$

Each sodium ion is surrounded by, and attracted to, six equidistant chloride ions; and each chloride ion is in turn surrounded by, and attracted to, six sodium ions. The net result is that for each sodium ion there must be one chloride ion. The arrangement of the ions in the space lattice, as revealed by x-ray diffraction studies, is that shown in Fig. 8.3. Such substances do not conduct electricity as solids, but when they are melted and the ions are free to move, they become good conductors. This is an important experimental method for distinguishing electrovalence from covalence.

8.7   *Covalence*

The forces operating to hold atoms together in covalent bonding were not understood until the development of a new branch of mathematical physics, called *quantum mechanics*, in 1926. The complicated mathematics of quantum mechanics cannot be presented here. It is generally true in science that even the most complicated idea can be presented

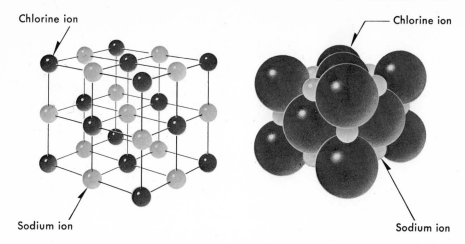

Fig. 8.3 *The arrangement of ions in sodium chloride, as revealed by x-ray diffraction studies, is shown above. The relative positions of the ions are more easily seen in the diagram at the left, but the actual relation of the ions is probably more accurately shown at the right. It will be understood that the diagrams show only a small fragment of the actual crystal.*

in some kind of classical description or analogy, but this is not true of the covalent bond, which depends on quantum-mechanical effects that have no classical counterpart. We shall have to content ourselves, for the present, with a brief description of the properties associated with the covalent bond.

Covalent bonds are often just as strong, or stronger, than electro-valent bonds. But covalent bonds have the unique property that they are formed along definite directions in space. A good example is found in the molecule of water, in which the two bonds between hydrogen and oxygen, although partially electrovalent, are directed at somewhat over 90 degrees from each other; thus,

$$\ddot{\text{O}}$$
$$\text{H} \qquad \text{H}$$

rather than in a straight line as might have been expected. This directional property, and the failure to conduct electricity appreciably even though the substance is a liquid, are two of the most useful criteria in the recognition of covalence. If a substance readily forms gas molecules, it is conclusive evidence of at least partially covalent character of the bonds that hold the atoms in the molecule, but many covalent substances (of which diamond is a notable example) do not readily vaporize. In Fig. 8.4 there are shown some models of typical molecules of water, ammonia, and carbon

Water   Ammonia   Carbon tetrachloride

Fig. 8.4 Models of the molecules of three substances. These models are made up on the basis of information gained from electron diffraction, and other, studies. The relative sizes of the atoms and their geometrical arrangement are probably accurate.

tetrachloride. All contain bonds that are at least in part covalent between hydrogen and oxygen, hydrogen and nitrogen, and chlorine and carbon, respectively. It is necessary to remember that while covalence may be operative intramolecularly in such substances, yet the forces holding one molecule to another may be weak van der Waals forces. A consequence of this is that carbon tetrachloride is difficult to decompose, but solid carbon tetrachloride is a soft substance that has a low melting point. This is simply a reflection of the fact that the intermolecular forces are weak and different in kind from the forces within the molecule.

Compelling evidence concerning the pairing of electrons that takes place during covalent bond formation was found by G. N. Lewis. Electrons normally spin somewhat in the sense that the earth rotates on its axis. Electron spin gives rise to a small magnetic dipole, like the effect of a compass needle. Covalence can occur only when the spins of the two electrons involved are in the opposite sense, and when electron pairing occurs, the normal attraction or turning in a magnetic field disappears. There are, however, a few substances that happen to possess an odd number of electrons. This must mean that one electron remains unpaired, and when this occurs, the substance is invariably attracted to a magnet. An example is nitric oxide, NO. The nitrogen atom possesses a total of 7 electrons and the oxygen 8, giving a total of 15.

One further point to be mentioned is the effect of substituting one isotope for another in a chemical compound. The effect is generally very small indeed; except, of course, for the possible occurrence of radioactivity in one isotope and not in another. But the small differences in physical and chemical properties caused by substituting one isotope for another are often of importance, and this is especially true in the development of atomic energy. We shall have more to say about this matter later.

EXERCISES

1. A sample of sand was found to contain 2.81 grams of silicon and 3.20 grams of oxygen. Another sample of sand contained 4.68 grams of silicon and 5.32 grams of oxygen. Is the law of definite proportions illustrated by these data?

2. Water contains 11.1 percent of hydrogen, hydrogen peroxide contains 5.89 percent of hydrogen, the balance being oxygen in both cases. Do these substances illustrate the law of multiple proportions?

3. In the Appendix there will be found a list of ions and their names. Write formulas for each of the following:

ammonium bromide	manganous hydroxide
calcium bicarbonate	lithium hydride
cupric nitrate	ferric perchlorate
silver sulfate	lead (plumbous) sulfide
potassium permanganate	magnesium (ortho) silicate
sodium hypochlorite	mercuric chloride
sodium hypochlorite	zinc (ortho) phosphate

4. Find formula weights for each of the following: H_2SO_4, $(NH_4)_2CO_3$, $Al_2(SO_4)_3$.

5. How many atoms are present in 1.00 gram of lead?

6. What is the weight in grams of 1 mole of heptane, C_7H_{16}? In 1 mole of potassium ferrocyanide, $K_4Fe(CN)_6$?

7. How many moles are present in 35.0 grams of sulfuric acid, H_2SO_4? In 500 grams of potassium nitrate, KNO_3?

8. How many moles are present in 2.48 liters of any gas (STP)?

9. What volume (STP) would be occupied by 0.35 mole of nitric oxide gas, NO?

10. Name the following: Sb_2O_3, $Co(NO_3)_2$, $PbCrO_4$, $Mn(ClO_3)_2$, $Na_2S_2O_3$, SrO.

11. $Zn + H_2SO_4 \rightarrow H_2 + ZnSO_4$. State the meaning of this equation in terms of substances, moles, weights, and where appropriate, the gas volumes involved.

12. Balance the following skeleton equations:
    (a) $Na_2SO_3 + HCl \rightarrow NaCl + SO_2 + H_2O$
    (b) $Mg_3N_2 + H_2O \rightarrow Mg(OH)_2 + NH_3$
    (c) $Pb + PbO_2 + H_2SO_4 \rightarrow PbSO_4 + H_2O$
    (d) Sodium plus water to form hydrogen plus sodium hydroxide
    (e) Calcium hydroxide plus carbon dioxide to form calcium carbonate plus water
    (f) Aluminum nitrate plus ammonium hydroxide to form aluminum hydroxide plus ammonium nitrate

13. Write electron dot symbols for the elements of atomic numbers 1 to 20.

14. Give appropriate electron dot diagrams for the following:

H^+	$Ca(OH)_2$
CH_4	Na^+
NH_3	$CaCl_2$
H_2S	$Mg(OH)_2$
$SiCl_4$	$(NH_4)_2SO_4$

15. From the standpoint of molecular structure, valence forces, and properties, predict what kind of a substance each of the following might be expected to be:

$BaCl_2$	Sb
AsH_3	Mg
F_2	CS_2
OF_2	Mg_3N_2
BF_3	PH_3

16. Which of the following might be expected to be attracted to a magnet: N_2O, NO_2, N_2O_4, N_2O_5?

17. The structure of sodium chloride in Fig. 8.3 shows that this consists of two interpenetrating space lattices, one of Na^+ ions, the other Cl^- ions. Identify these lattices as simple cubic, face-centered cubic, or body-centered cubic.

Stoichiometry

The word "stoichiometry" means the measurement of weight relationships that occur in chemical compounds and in chemical transformations.

9.1 Quantitative Analysis

The relative weights of the elements present in a chemical compound may be found by quantitative analysis. Two examples will be described. These are chosen because of the good accuracy that may be obtained with reasonable care and because of the historical importance of the reactions involved.

The first example is to find the proportions by weight of mercury and oxygen in the compound mercuric oxide. This is the reaction that led J. Priestley in the year 1774 to the discovery of oxygen, and A. Lavoisier in 1777 to proof of the composition of air and the part played by oxygen in combustion. A sample of mercuric oxide may be weighed as accurately as possible and then strongly heated. This causes decomposition of the mercuric oxide to mercury and oxygen. In properly designed equipment, all the mercury may be collected and weighed, and the oxygen gas allowed to escape. Typical data are as follows:

	Grams
Original weight of mercuric oxide	5.903
Final weight of mercury	5.467
Loss = weight of oxygen	0.436

The relative weights of mercury and oxygen in mercuric oxide are therefore 5.467 to 0.436. If it is so desired, the proportions of the elements in the mercuric oxide may be expressed as percentages, as follows:

$$\text{Proportion of mercury} = \frac{5.467}{5.903} = 92.61 \text{ percent}$$

$$\text{Proportion of oxygen} = \frac{0.436}{5.903} = 7.39 \text{ percent}$$

A slightly more complicated example is the indirect analysis of water as first performed by J. J. Berzelius in the year 1819. If hydrogen is passed over heated copper oxide, the copper oxide is reduced to copper metal and water is formed. If the copper oxide is weighed at the start of the analysis, and the copper metal at the conclusion, the difference in weight will be the weight of oxygen originally present in the copper oxide. If now the weight of water formed is also determined, then the weight of oxygen obtained from the copper oxide, subtracted from the weight of water formed, gives the weight of hydrogen used in formation of the water.

This analysis may be performed by placing the copper oxide in a porcelain boat and then weighing the boat plus copper oxide. Hydrogen

Fig. 9.1 The composition of water may be found by passing hydrogen (dried over calcium chloride) over a weighed quantity of hot copper oxide: $H_2 + CuO \rightarrow Cu + H_2O$. The water generated in the reaction is collected in a tube full of calcium chloride (right), which makes it convenient to weigh the water. The composition of water is then computed from the weight of water formed and from the loss in weight of the copper oxide.

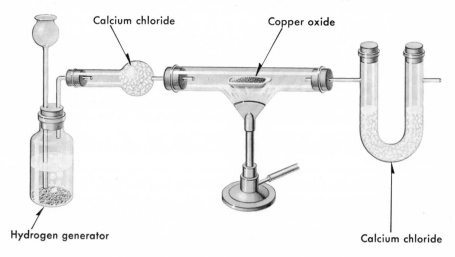

Calcium chloride   Copper oxide

Hydrogen generator   Calcium chloride

is then passed over the copper oxide, which is heated until no further change takes place. The water formed is collected in a weighed tube containing calcium chloride, or some other agent that strongly absorbs water. The calcium chloride tube is weighed again at the conclusion of the analysis. The apparatus used for this experiment is shown in Fig. 9.1. Typical data are as follows:

	Grams
Copper oxide plus boat before heating................	16.452
Copper metal plus boat after heating.................	12.030
Weight of oxygen (16.452 − 12.030)...................	4.422
Weight of calcium chloride tube before experiment......	15.907
Weight of calcium chloride tube after experiment.......	20.883
Weight of water (20.883 − 15.907)...................	4.976
Weight of hydrogen (4.976 − 4.422)...................	0.554

Hence the composition of water by weight is 0.554 gram of hydrogen to 4.422 grams of oxygen, or approximately 1 part by weight of hydrogen to 8 parts by weight of oxygen. (The most precise determinations give 1.008 parts by weight of hydrogen to 8 parts by weight of oxygen.) Expressed in percentages, the composition of water is

$$\text{Proportion of hydrogen} = \frac{0.554}{4.976} = 11.1 \text{ percent}$$

$$\text{Proportion of oxygen} = \frac{4.422}{4.976} = 88.9 \text{ percent}$$

9.2   Formula from Composition

From a knowledge of chemical composition by weight and the atomic weights of the elements involved, it is possible to find the formula of a chemical compound. This important class of problems will be illustrated by several examples.

In 25.0 grams of calcium sulfide there are 13.9 grams of calcium and 11.1 grams of sulfur. With the above information and the atomic weights of calcium and sulfur, we shall proceed to find the formula of calcium sulfide. To do this, it is necessary to find the ratio of gram-atoms of calcium to gram-atoms of sulfur.

The atomic weight of calcium is 40.1 (rounded off to the first decimal for ease in making the calculations). From this it follows that

40.1 grams of Ca would be 1 gram-atom of Ca. Hence, 13.9 grams of Ca would be

$$\frac{13.9 \text{ grams}}{40.1 \text{ grams gram-atom}^{-1}} = 0.347 \text{ gram-atom of Ca}$$

Similarly, as the atomic weight of sulfur is 32.1, 11.1 grams of sulfur would be

$$\frac{11.1 \text{ grams}}{32.1 \text{ grams gram-atom}^{-1}} = 0.347 \text{ gram-atom of S}$$

It appears, therefore, that in this particular sample of calcium sulfide, 0.347 gram-atom of Ca is combined with 0.347 gram-atom of S. In other words, the ratio of gram-atoms, and hence of atoms, is 1:1, and the formula for calcium sulfide must be written as CaS.

The arithematical operations shown above may conveniently be summarized as follows:

Symbol	Parts by weight	Atomic weight	Gram-atoms
Ca	13.9	40.1	13.9/40.1 = 0.347
S	11.1	32.1	11.1/32.1 = 0.347

The ratio 0.347:0.347 is equal to the ratio 1:1; hence the formula is CaS. The formula could, of course, be Ca_2S_2, etc., but the simplest formula consistent with the proper ratio of gram-atoms is to be preferred unless (as shown in the next section) there are some definite reasons for using a more complicated formula.

Now we shall find the formula for a slightly more complicated compound, sodium carbonate (washing soda). A 10-gram sample of sodium carbonate contains 4.34 grams of sodium, 1.13 grams of carbon, and 4.52 grams of oxygen. Proceeding as before:

Symbol	Parts by weight	Atomic weight	Gram-atoms
Na	4.34	23.0	4.34/23.0 = 0.189
C	1.13	12.0	1.13/12.0 = 0.094
O	4.52	16.0	4.52/16.0 = 0.283

The ratio of numbers is 0.189Na : 0.094C : 0.283O. It is not clear from these numbers what the ratios would be in whole numbers, but these whole numbers are readily found by dividing each of the numbers by the smallest one of the three; that is, by 0.094. Then

$$\frac{0.189}{0.094} = 2 \text{ gram-atoms of Na}$$

$$\frac{0.094}{0.094} = 1 \text{ gram-atom of C}$$

$$\frac{0.283}{0.094} = 3 \text{ gram-atoms of O}$$

The formula of sodium carbonate is therefore Na_2CO_3. Notice that 0.283 divided by 0.094 is not exactly 3, but is nearer 3.01. But 3.01 is so near to 3 that we conclude the small discrepancy is due to experimental error. No experiment, no matter how carefully performed, can yield perfect numerical results. In such problems as these, small deviations from whole numbers are often encountered.

One more example of formula finding will be given. This is for the compound ferric (iron) oxide. This substance contains 70.1 percent of iron, and 30.0 percent of oxygen. Expression of the composition in percentage means simply that 100 parts by weight of ferric oxide contain 70.1 parts of iron and 30.0 parts of oxygen. The very slight deviation of the total from 100 percent is not unusual in experimentally measured compositions.

Symbol	Parts by weight	Atomic weight	Gram-atoms
Fe	70.1	55.8	70.1/55.8 = 1.26
O	30.0	16.0	30.0/16.0 = 1.88

Dividing, as usual, by the smaller one of the two quantities, we have $1.26/1.26 = 1$ gram-atom of Fe, and $1.88/1.26 = 1.49$ gram-atoms of O. It is still not clear what the formula should be in whole-number subscripts until we multiply both quantities by 2; then 2 gram-atoms of Fe are combined with 3 gram-atoms of O. The formula is Fe_2O_3. Notice that the ratio of gram-atoms of iron to oxygen is not changed in these final operations which lead to whole numbers. The ratio 1.26 : 1.88 is the same as 1 : 1.49, and these are the same (within experimental error) as 2 : 3.

9.3 Molecular Formulas

The method described in the preceding section correctly gives the ratio of atoms present in any chemical compound, but it does not necessarily give any information concerning the number of atoms that may be present in a molecule. If, therefore, it is desired to know the true molecular formula of a compound, it becomes necessary to determine the molecular weight by the gas density (or other) method and to use this information in conjunction with the method described above for obtaining the simplest formula. The procedure will be illustrated by two examples.

PROBLEM: Hydrogen peroxide contains 94.1 percent by weight of oxygen and 5.9 percent of hydrogen. The molecular weight of hydrogen peroxide, as found from the density of its vapor, is 34. What is the correct formula for hydrogen peroxide?

SOLUTION:

Element	Parts by weight	Atomic weight	Gram-atoms
O	94.1	16.0	94.1/16.0 = 5.9
H	5.9	1.0	5.9/1.0 = 5.9

The simplest formula, as found by the above method, is obviously 1 atom of oxygen for 1 atom of hydrogen, or HO. But the formula weight of HO is only $1 + 16 = 17$, whereas the molecular weight is stated to be 34. The correct molecular formula is clearly $(HO)_2$, or as commonly written, H_2O_2. The formula HO gives the correct ratio of atoms in the molecule, but it does not give the total number of atoms in the molecule. Formulas such as HO are commonly called *empirical*, or simplest, formulas, as opposed to correct, or molecular, formulas, such as H_2O_2. Molecular formulas should always be used whenever the substance has a known molecular weight.

A slightly more complicated example is found in the compound benzene.

PROBLEM: Benzene consists of 92.3 percent of carbon and 7.7 percent of hydrogen. It is found that 403 ml of benzene vapor at 100° C and 740 mm pressure weighs 1.0 grams. What is the correct formula for benzene?

SOLUTION:

Element	Parts by weight	Atomic weight	Gram-atoms
C	92.3	12.0	92.3/12.0 = 7.7
H	7.7	1.0	7.7/1.0 = 7.7

The ratio of atoms in this compound is clearly 1:1, and the empirical formula is CH.

The next step is to find the molecular weight. Correcting the volume of the vapor to STP,

$$V_2 = V_1 \times \frac{T_2}{T_1} \times \frac{P_1}{P_2}$$

$$= 403 \text{ ml} \times \frac{273}{373} \times \frac{740}{760}$$

$$= 287 \text{ ml}, \quad \text{or } 0.287 \text{ liters}$$

This volume, 0.287 liters, weighs 1.0 gram; 1 mole (22.4 liters at STP) would therefore weigh

$$\frac{22.4 \text{ liters}}{0.287 \text{ liter}} \times 1.0 \text{ gram} = 78 \text{ grams}$$

The molecular weight of this compound is 78, and inasmuch as the formula weight of CH is $12 + 1 = 13$, and 78 divided by 13 is 6, the true molecular formula for benzene must be C_6H_6.

9.4   Composition from Formula

If the simplest formula of a chemical compound is known, then the parts by weight of each element present are easily found. This will be illustrated by two examples, namely, by carbon dioxide and calcium phosphate.

PROBLEM: The formula for carbon dioxide is CO_2. Find the percentage by weight of each element present.

SOLUTION: The formula weight of carbon dioxide is $(1 \times 12.0) + (2 \times 16.0) = 44.0$, of which 12.0 parts are carbon and 32.0 parts are oxygen. The fraction of the total that is carbon is $12.0/44.0 = 0.273$, or 27.3 percent. The fraction that is oxygen is $32.0/44.0 = 0.727$, or 72.7 percent.

PROBLEM: The formula for calcium phosphate is $Ca_3(PO_4)_2$. Find the percentage by weight of each element present.

SOLUTION: The formula weight of calcium phosphate is found as follows:

$$3Ca = 3 \times 40.1 = 120.3$$
$$2P = 2 \times 31.0 = 62.0$$
$$8O = 8 \times 16.0 = \underline{128.0}$$
$$310.3$$

Then,

Parts by weight	Ca = 120.3/310.3 = 0.387,	or	38.7
Parts by weight	P = 62.0/310.3 = 0.200,	or	20.0
Parts by weight	O = 128.0/310.3 = 0.413,	or	41.3

100.0 percent

9.5 Calculations from Equations

One of the most useful types of calculations is that which finds the relative weights of substances taking part in a chemical change. This will be shown by several examples. In all such calculations it is essential to have reactants and products expressed in a chemical equation and to make certain that the equation is correctly balanced.

PROBLEM: Carbon heated together with iron oxide yields metallic iron and carbon dioxide according to the following equation:

$$2Fe_2O_3 + 3C \rightarrow 4Fe + 3CO_2$$

Find the weight of carbon necessary to react with 100 grams of ferric oxide, Fe_2O_3.

SOLUTION: The equation may be interpreted as follows: 2 moles of ferric oxide plus 3 gram-atoms of carbon yield 4 gram-atoms of iron plus 3 moles of carbon dioxide.

The formula weight of ferric oxide is $(2 \times 55.8) + (3 \times 16.0) = 159.6$. If 159.6 grams of ferric oxide are 1 mole, then 100 grams of ferric oxide are 100/159.6 mole.

The equation states that 2 moles of ferric oxide require 3 gram-atoms of carbon. Therefore, 1 mole of ferric oxide must require 3/2 gram-atoms of carbon, and 100/159.6 mole of ferric oxide must require $100/159.6 \times 3/2$ gram-atom of carbon.

If 1 gram-atom of carbon weighs 12.0 grams, then $100/159.6 \times 3/2$ gram-atom of carbon must weigh $100/159.6 \times 3/2 \times 12.0$ grams = 11.3 grams.

It requires 11.3 grams of carbon to react with 100 grams of iron oxide according to the equation given.

PROBLEM: What weight of potassium chlorate, $KClO_3$, must be heated to obtain 250 grams of oxygen according to the following equation?

$$2KClO_3 \rightarrow 2KCl + 3O_2$$

SOLUTION: The 250 grams of oxygen must be 250/32.0 moles of oxygen.

According to the equation, 2 moles of $KClO_3$ are required to produce 3 moles of O_2. Then 250/32.0 moles of O_2 may be produced from 250/32.0 × 2/3 moles of $KClO_3$. If 1 mole of $KClO_3$ weighs 122.6 grams, then 250/32.0 × 2/3 moles of $KClO_3$ must weigh 250/32.0 × 2/3 × 122.6 grams = 640 grams.

It will require 640 grams of $KClO_3$ to produce 250 grams of O_2.

After experience has been gained, it will be possible to state the whole solution in one line, as shown in the next problem.

PROBLEM: What weight of hydrogen chloride gas, HCl, is required for the production of 100 grams of chlorine, Cl_2, according to the following equation?

$$4HCl + MnO_2 \rightarrow MnCl_2 + Cl_2 + 2H_2O$$

SOLUTION: The weight of hydrogen chloride needed is

$$\frac{100}{71.0} \text{ moles } Cl_2 \times \frac{4 \text{ moles HCl}}{1 \text{ mole } Cl_2} \times \frac{36.5 \text{ grams HCl}}{1 \text{ mole HCl}} = 205 \text{ grams HCl}$$

It will be recalled that the volume occupied by 1 mole of any gas at STP is 22.4 liters. With this information it is possible to solve stoichiometric problems involving volumes, provided the substances under consideration are gases. This will be illustrated by two problems, the first of which is similar to the one given immediately above.

PROBLEM: What volume of hydrogen chloride is required for the production of 100 grams of chlorine by reaction with maganese dioxide?

SOLUTION: The number of moles of hydrogen chloride required is 100/71.0 × 4, and if 1 mole of any gas occupies 22.4 liters, then 100/71.0 × 4 moles of any gas will occupy

$$\frac{100}{71.0} \text{ moles } Cl_2 \times \frac{4 \text{ moles HCl}}{1 \text{ mole } Cl_2} \times \frac{22.4 \text{ liters HCl}}{1 \text{ mole HCl}} = 126 \text{ liters HCl}$$

If the gas volumes involved are not at STP, it is not difficult to make the appropriate corrections, as shown in the next problem.

PROBLEM: What volume of oxygen, as collected over water at 18° C and 752 mm pressure, may be obtained by the complete decomposition of 250 grams of potassium chlorate? (The vapor pressure of water at 18° C is 15 mm.)

SOLUTION: The volume of oxygen obtainable under the conditions stated is

$$\frac{250}{122.6} \text{ moles KClO}_3 \times \frac{3 \text{ moles O}_2}{2 \text{ moles KClO}_3} \times \frac{22.4 \text{ liters O}_2}{1 \text{ mole O}_2} \times \frac{291}{273} \times \frac{760}{737}$$

$$= 75.3 \text{ liters O}_2$$

9.6   Calorimetry

Virtually all chemical reactions involve either the liberation or the absorption of energy. In most instances, part of this energy is in the form of heat. The heat of a reaction must be considered as much a product of the reaction as any of the other more tangible products. This section will be devoted to a description of an experimental method for obtaining the quantity of heat liberated, or taken in, during a typical chemical reaction. This procedure is known as *calorimetry*.

The quantity of heat involved in a chemical reaction may be found by placing a weighed amount of the reactants in a calorimeter, two forms of which are shown in Fig. 9.2. A calorimeter is an insulated chamber supplied with a sensitive thermometer for accurate observation of the temperature changes that take place. The heat given off in, say, the burning of carbon to carbon dioxide could be found by placing a weighed amount of carbon in the calorimeter, together with a substance that will readily give up oxygen, or with an arrangement for the introduction of oxygen gas. The carbon is then ignited by a spark or other means. The heat given off is generally permitted to raise the temperature of a weighed amount of water. The specific heat of water is, of course, known. From the weight of water and the rise in temperature of the water, it is possible to calculate the quantity of heat liberated by the burning carbon. With a few corrections, the heat of the reaction, or the heat of combustion, of the carbon may then be calculated.

PROBLEM: A sample of sugar weighing 2.91 grams was burned in a calorimeter, which contained 3245 grams of water. The temperature of the water rose 3.17 deg (Celsius). It was also found that it required 379 cal deg^{-1} to raise the temperature of the glass and metal calorimeter. Find the heat of combustion per gram of sugar.

SOLUTION: The specific heat of water is, by definition, about 1 cal gram^{-1} deg^{-1}. To raise the temperature of 3245 grams of water 3.17 degrees would require

$$3245 \text{ grams} \times 3.17 \text{ deg} \times 1 \text{ cal gram}^{-1} \text{ deg}^{-1} = 10,280 \text{ cal}$$

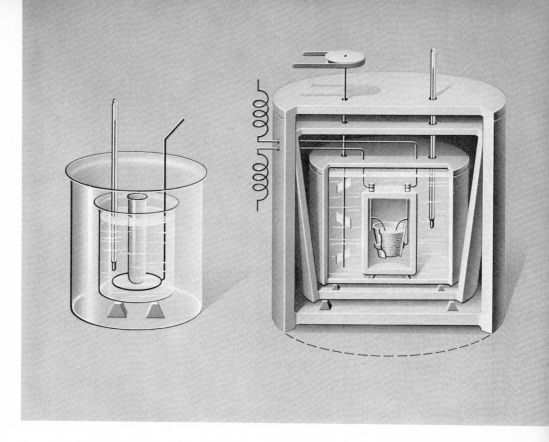

To this must be added the heat required to raise the temperature of the calorimeter itself. This is

$$3.17 \text{ deg} \times 379 \text{ cal deg}^{-1} = 1200 \text{ cal}$$

The total heat liberated during burning of 2.91 grams of sugar is then

$$10{,}280 \text{ cal} + 1200 \text{ cal} = 11{,}480 \text{ cal}$$

and the quantity of heat liberated per gram of sugar is

$$\frac{11{,}480 \text{ cal}}{2.91 \text{ grams}} = 3950 \text{ cal gram}^{-1}$$

$$= 3.95 \text{ kcal gram}^{-1}$$

9.7   *Thermochemical Equations*

A chemical equation shows the relationships between the masses of reactants and products. It may also show the number of calories of energy liberated or taken in. In such a case, the equation is called a *thermochemical* equation. The procedure for obtaining a thermochemical equation is illustrated in the following problem, which involves a typical exothermic reaction.

PROBLEM: The combustion of carbon in oxygen to yield carbon dioxide liberates 7.92 kcal gm^{-1}, as found in a calorimeter experiment. Write the thermochemical equation. (Heats of reaction depend on the temperature of measurement, but this complication need not, for the moment, concern us.)

SOLUTION: The equation

$$C + O_2 \rightarrow CO_2$$

states that 1 gram-atom (12.0 grams) of carbon unites with 1 mole of oxygen to yield 1 mole of carbon dioxide. If 1 gram of carbon burns to give 7.92 kcal, then 12.0 grams of carbon would give

$$12.0 \text{ grams} \times 7.92 \text{ kcal gram}^{-1} = 95.0 \text{ kcal}$$

The thermochemical equation is then

$$C + O_2 \rightarrow CO_2 + 95.0 \text{ kcal}$$

A typical example of an endothermic reaction is the formation of carbon disulfide, which is written

$$C + 2S \rightarrow CS_2 - 19.6 \text{ kcal}$$

This may also be written

$$C + 2S + 19.6 \text{ kcal} \rightarrow CS_2$$

which may be read as follows: The union of carbon and sulfur to form carbon disulfide is an endothermic reaction in which 1 gram-atom (12.0 grams) of carbon unites with 2 gram-atoms (64.0 grams) of sulfur to yield 1 mole (76.0 grams) of carbon disulfide with the simultaneous absorption of 19.6 kcal of heat.

One more example will be given of a thermochemical equation.

PROBLEM: The heat of combustion of aluminum is about 7.4 kcal $gram^{-1}$. Write the thermochemical equation for the formation of aluminum oxide, Al_2O_3, from aluminum and oxygen.

SOLUTION: The ordinary equation is

$$4Al + 3O_2 \rightarrow 2Al_2O_3$$

and the atomic weight of aluminum is 27.0. If 1 gram of Al burns to liberate 7.4 kcal, then 4 gram-atoms of Al would liberate

$$4 \times 27.0 \text{ grams} \times 7.4 \text{ kcal gram}^{-1} = 799 \text{ kcal}$$

The thermochemical equation is then

$$4Al + 3O_2 \rightarrow 2Al_2O_3 + 799 \text{ kcal}$$

The amount of heat change per gram in the formation of any given compound (such as the aluminum oxide above) from its elements is a definite quantity dependent in no way upon the method of preparation or upon the intermediate steps in the procedure. For instance, if a gram of iron slowly corrodes in air to ferric oxide, the number of calories liberated is the same as when a gram of iron burns brilliantly in pure oxygen, provided the final product is the same. In one case the heat is liberated slowly over many days, whereas in the other, it is all liberated in a few seconds. The same result would be achieved if the iron were first converted into another substance entirely, such as ferric nitrate, and then converted to ferric oxide.

The fact that the heat of formation of a substance from its elements does not depend on the method of preparation makes possible the indirect calculation of such heats without the necessity for a direct calorimetric determination. This will be illustrated by a calculation of the heat of formation of carbon monoxide from the elements carbon and oxygen:

$$2C + O_2 \rightarrow 2CO$$

It has been found experimentally that the combination of carbon with oxygen to form carbon dioxide is exothermic, as given above, and that the combustion of carbon monoxide is also exothermic in accordance with the equation

$$2CO + O_2 \rightarrow 2CO_2 + 135 \text{ kcal}$$

and, as

$$2C + 2O_2 \rightarrow 2CO_2 + 190 \text{ kcal}$$

one may subtract the first of these two equations from the second to obtain

$$2C + 2O_2 - 2CO - O_2 \rightarrow 2CO_2 + 190 \text{ kcal} - 2CO_2 - 135 \text{ kcal}$$

whence

$$2C + O_2 \rightarrow 2CO + 55 \text{ kcal}$$

The heat of formation of carbon monoxide is thus found to be $(55/2)$ kcal = 27.5 kcal/mole, or $(27.5 \text{ kcal}/28 \text{ grams}) = 980 \text{ cal/gram}$.

9.8   Conservation of Mass

Inasmuch as virtually all chemical changes involve some change of energy, it might be thought that, in accordance with Einstein's mass-energy relationship (Eq. 7.1), some change of mass would occur in a reaction such as the combustion of carbon. A simple calculation will show that such a change of mass must occur but that it is too small to be measured in any way except indirectly through the energy change.

PROBLEM: The heat of formation of carbon monoxide is 980 cal gram^{-1}. What loss of mass must occur during the formation of 1 gram of carbon monoxide from carbon and oxygen? (1 cal = 4.19×10^7 ergs.)

SOLUTION:

$$m = \frac{E}{c^2}$$

$$= \frac{9.80 \times 10^2 \text{ cal gram}^{-1} \times 4.19 \times 10^7 \text{ erg cal}^{-1}}{(3.0 \times 10^{10} \text{ cm sec}^{-1})^2}$$

$$= 4.57 \times 10^{-11} \text{ gram}$$

The best analytical balances have a precision of about 1 part in 10^7, and this is insufficient, by a factor of about 10^4, to measure the loss of mass in such a chemical reaction.

The **law of conservation of mass** is often stated as:

In any chemical reaction the initial mass of the reactants is equal to the final mass of the products.

The preceding calculation shows that this law is true within the limits of experimental precision available at the present time. In this sense, the law of conservation of mass, like its counterpart, the law of conservation of energy, is a *limiting* law—a law that is true only under certain extreme conditions. The extreme condition in this case is that the amount of energy involved must be relatively small. These two laws are actually parts of the more general law expressed in Einstein's mass-energy equation.

EXERCISES

1. From the data given in Sec. 9.1, find the formula for mercuric oxide.
2. A sample of an oxide of gold weighing 2.212 grams was decomposed by heat. The metallic gold obtained weighed 1.972 grams.

Find the percentage of oxygen in the compound. Find the simplest formula for the oxide.

3. Find the simplest formula for the compound containing 36.5 percent sodium, 25.4 percent sulfur, and 38.1 percent oxygen.

4. A compound contains 22.9 percent sodium, 21.5 percent boron, and 55.7 percent oxygen. Find the simplest formula.

5. Find the weight of 1 liter of carbon tetrachloride, CCl_4, vapor at 150° C and 1 atm pressure.

6. A compound of carbon gave, on analysis, the following percentages: C, 30.45; H, 3.83; Cl, 45.69; O, 20.23. The density of the compound was 7.06 grams/liter (STP). What was the molecular formula of the compound?

7. A compound analyzes as follows: C, 37.2 percent; H, 7.8 percent; Cl, 55.0 percent; and 934 ml of the dry vapor, measured at 25° C and 740 mm, weigh 2.4 grams. Find the molecular formula of the compound.

8. Express in percentages by weight the composition of the compound hexammineplatinum (IV) chloride, the formula for which is $[Pt(NH_3)_6]Cl_4$.

9. What weight of aluminum must be used per kilogram of iron oxide, Fe_3O_4, in the reaction to form aluminum oxide, Al_2O_3, and metallic iron?

10. Metallic copper reacts with moderately dilute nitric acid as follows:

$$3Cu + 8HNO_3 \rightarrow 3Cu(NO_3)_2 + 2NO + 4H_2O$$

What weight of nitric oxide, NO, is obtainable from 100 grams of copper plus excess (more than enough) nitric acid?

11. Find the volume of nitrous oxide, N_2O, obtainable at 25° C and 720 mm from 100 grams of ammonium nitrate heated to decompose as follows:

$$NH_4NO_3 \rightarrow N_2O + 2H_2O$$

12. What weight of potassium permanganate, $KMnO_4$, is needed to obtain 825 ml of oxygen as measured over water at 23° C and 746 mm pressure. The equation is

$$2KMnO_4 \rightarrow K_2MnO_4 + MnO_2 + O_2$$

13. What volume of dry oxygen measured at 20° C and 740 mm pressure is needed to burn 5.0 liters of acetylene, C_2H_2, the acetylene being measured at STP? The products of combustion are carbon dioxide and water.

14. Aluminum reacts with sodium hydroxide and water as follows:

$$2Al + 2NaOH + 6H_2O \rightarrow 3H_2 + 2NaAl(OH)_4$$

What volume of hydrogen could be obtained as measured over water at 29° C and 855 mm pressure by the use of 115 grams of aluminum plus excess sodium hydroxide solution?

15. Zinc sulfide reacts with nitric acid as follows:

$$3ZnS + 8HNO_3 \rightarrow 3Zn(NO_3)_2 + 3S + 2NO + 4H_2O$$

If 400 grams of ZnS is treated with 400 grams of HNO_3, which reagent and what weight of it is present in excess?

16. In an attempt to prepare xenon tetrafluoride, XeF_4, according to the equation

$$Xe + 2F_2 \rightarrow XeF_4$$

43.5 ml (STP) of Xe was mixed with 100 ml of F_2 and then heated. The solid product was found to weigh 0.389 gram. What was the percentage yield of XeF_4, that is, the actual yield divided by the maximum theoretical yield?

17. A sample of carbon weighing 3.00 grams was burned to carbon dioxide in a calorimeter containing 2000 grams of water. The water present, originally at 20° C, rose 11.0° C in temperature. The heat capacity of the calorimeter itself was found to be 139 cal deg^{-1}. Find the heat of combustion per gram-atom of carbon.

18. From the following two reactions,

$$CO_2 + Ca(OH)_2 \rightarrow CaCO_3 + H_2O + 30.5 \text{ kcal}$$

and

$$CaO + H_2O \rightarrow Ca(OH)_2 + 11.5 \text{ kcal}$$

find the heat of reaction for

$$CaO + CO_2 \rightarrow CaCO_3$$

19. Given that

$$2Cu + O_2 \rightarrow 2CuO + 69.8 \text{ kcal}$$

and

$$2CO + O_2 \rightarrow 2CO_2 + 135 \text{ kcal}$$

find the heat of reaction for the reduction of cupric oxide, CuO, to copper metal by carbon monoxide, the by-product being carbon dioxide.

20. Over a period of years between 1893 and 1908, H. Landholt subjected the law of conservation of mass to a searching test. He found no deviation from the law within a possible error of 1 part in 10,000,000. How large a release (or absorption) of energy would have been required for him to detect the mass change?

10

Reaction Velocity

10.1   Rate of Chemical Change

Some chemical reactions, such as the explosion of dynamite, proceed at very high speed, and others, such as the rusting of iron, usually take place so slowly as to be scarcely perceptible. The detailed study of reaction velocity and of the factors that influence it constitutes the branch of chemistry known as *chemical kinetics.*

The rate at which a chemical reaction takes place may be expressed in terms of moles of reactant converted in unit time or of moles of product formed in unit time. More frequently, *reaction velocity* is expressed as the change of concentration in unit time. Concentration is generally expressed as moles per liter, so that if, say, the decomposition of ammonia to nitrogen and hydrogen were being studied, it would be convenient to say that the ammonia was disappearing at the rate of a certain number of moles per liter per second. But it will be clear that if several reactants were involved, the complete statement of the reaction velocity might become quite complicated.

There is the further complication that chemical reactions almost never proceed by the route suggested by the equation. The actual mechanism of even the simplest reaction is likely to consist of several steps, some of which may be very difficult to identify. A chemical equation ordinarily gives merely the initial reactants and the final products. It is with these that we shall be chiefly concerned in this book.

The rates of some transformations of matter, such as those radioactive changes described in Chapter 7, are virtually independent of all external conditions. But the rates of chemical transformations may in general be changed more or less at will. The chief factors that determine chemical reaction velocity are four in number:

1. Nature of the reactants
2. Concentration of the reactants
3. Temperature of the reactants
4. Presence of catalysts

The nature of the reactants is of prime importance in determining reaction velocity. Magnesium burns vigorously in air, but iron ordinarily will not burn at all. Having chosen our reactants, we shall find it possible to exercise considerable control over the reaction velocity. How this may be done will be described in the succeeding sections, but first a few remarks will be made about methods for studying reaction velocity.

A comparatively simple chemical process is the exchange reaction of hydrogen with its isotope deuterium. Writing the symbol D for ^2_1H, we have

$$H_2 + D_2 \rightarrow 2HD$$

A possible procedure in studying the rate of this reaction is to place measured volumes of hydrogen and of deuterium together in a container of known volume, under appropriate conditions of temperature and pressure. At certain intervals of time, a small portion of the gas mixture is removed for analysis in the mass spectrometer. The result observed will be a progressive increase of molecules of mass 3 amu (HD) and a decrease of molecules of masses 2 (H_2) and of 4 (D_2). The rates at which these changes occur may be expressed mathematically and used to help interpret the mechanism by which the reaction takes place.

Another experimental procedure in studying reaction velocity could be applied to a reaction such as the decomposition of ammonia:

$$2NH_3 \rightarrow N_2 + 3H_2$$

It will be noted that, as the ammonia decomposes, 1 mole of nitrogen plus 3 moles of hydrogen are formed for every 2 moles of ammonia used. This means that in a container of fixed volume, there will be a progressive increase of pressure, and from this increase it will not be difficult to find and express in appropriate terms the rate at which the ammonia is decomposing.

Some chemical substances are strongly colored. Potassium permanganate is a rich purple color, and this color is discharged as permanganate undergoes reaction with sulfur dioxide in dilute acid solution.

The rate at which the color disappears may be related to the change in concentration of the permanganate.

Still another method is applicable to a reaction such as that of copper oxide with hydrogen to yield copper metal and water:

$$CuO + H_2 \rightarrow Cu + H_2O$$

The rate of this reaction could be studied from the rate at which weight is lost by the copper oxide, by the loss in pressure of the hydrogen, or by the rate at which water collects as, for instance, by absorption in a drying agent, of which calcium chloride is one kind. It is clear that the number of methods available for studying reaction velocities is almost as great as the kinds of reactions to be studied.

10.2   Law of Mass Action

For some chemical reactions, such as the decomposition of ammonia mentioned above, all reactants and all products are present in one and the same state of matter. In the example given, the ammonia, the nitrogen, and the hydrogen are all gases. Such a reaction is said to be *homogeneous.* Homogeneous reactions may occur in gases, in liquids, and (possibly) even in solids, but in each case only one phase (Sec. 4.3) may be present. By contrast, the reaction of hydrogen with copper oxide, also mentioned above, is a *heterogeneous* reaction. The hydrogen is in the gas phase and the water is probably also in the gas phase at the temperature of reaction, but the copper oxide and the copper are in solid phases. Attention in this section will be confined to homogeneous reactions.

For a given set of reactants at constant temperature, it is in general found that the reaction velocity is proportional to the concentration of the reactants. This statement is the **law of mass action,** formulated by C. M. Guldberg and P. Waage in 1864.

The law of mass action may be stated in terms of a mathematical equation. Suppose that there is a hypothetical reaction as follows:

$$A + B \rightarrow C + D$$

Then, according to the law of mass action, the rate of reaction of A and B to form C and D is given by

$$Rate = k[A][B] \tag{10.1}$$

where k is called the *rate constant* and [A] and [B] are the concentrations of A and B, respectively, expressed in moles per liter. This clearly states that if the concentration of A or of B, or of both, is increased, the rate at which A and B react will also increase.

There is, however, a further complication because the rate at which reactant A disappears may not necessarily be the same as that at which reactant B disappears. This difficulty may be resolved by specifying which reactant is meant by symbols such as Rate$_A$ and Rate$_B$. But a more generally useful symbol, borrowed from differential calculus, is $d[A]/dt$ and $d[B]/dt$. These symbols have the meanings: "the rate at which the concentration of A changes," and "the rate at which the concentration of B changes." Equation 10.1 may then be rewritten as

$$- \frac{d[A]}{dt} = k[A][B] \tag{10.2}$$

The minus sign shows that the *decrease* of [A] is observed. A similar equation with different k may be written for [B]. Equation 10.2 is a differential equation, and rate processes will be written in this form throughout the remainder of this book.

Now, while the law of mass action as stated above is applicable to an idealized homogeneous reaction, and while its development marked a milestone in the study of chemical reactivity, it is true that there are few reactions to which it may be applied without modification. The difficulty arises because, as stated in the preceding section, few reactions proceed by the simple mechanism suggested by the equation, which gives only initial reactants and final products. If a reaction actually proceeds through several steps, then it is obvious that the slowest of the several steps will be the one that determines the rate of the overall reaction. If this slowest reaction step can be identified, it is referred to as the *rate-determining* step.

The influence of reactant concentration on reaction velocity can be determined only by experiment. Often an increase of reactant concentration increases the reaction velocity; sometimes it has no effect; and sometimes the velocity is decreased. It is possible to summarize this statement in a more general expression of the law of mass action, as follows:

$$- \frac{d[A]}{dt} = k[A]^a[B]^b \tag{10.3}$$

where a and b are exponents that are generally either whole numbers or reciprocals of whole numbers but which may even be negative. In case there are three (or even more) reactants, they may all be represented in the rate equation, thus:

$$- \frac{d[A]}{dt} = k[A]^a[B]^b[C]^c \cdots \tag{10.4}$$

The decomposition of dinitrogen pentoxide is an example of a reaction in which only one reactant is present:

$$2N_2O_5 \rightarrow 4NO_2 + O_2$$

and in which the reaction velocity is found experimentally to depend on the first power of the concentration. For this reaction the law of mass action may be written as

$$-\frac{d[N_2O_5]}{dt} = k[N_2O_5]$$

An equation of this kind is called the *rate law* for this particular reaction, and if, as in this case, the concentration is raised only to the first power (the exponent a in Eq. 10.3 is equal to 1), then the reaction is said to be a *first-order reaction*. The exponents a, b, c, in Eqs. 10.3 and 10.4 are called the *reaction order*, which is unity in this example.

An example of a *second-order* reaction is the dimerization (doubling up) of aluminum chloride:

$$2AlCl_3 \rightarrow Al_2Cl_6$$

The rate law for this reaction is found experimentally to be

$$-\frac{d[AlCl_3]}{dt} = k[AlCl_3]^2$$

and this, consequently, is a second-order reaction.

This reaction of nitric oxide with oxygen to form nitrogen dioxide,

$$2NO + O_2 \rightarrow 2NO_2$$

follows the rate law:

$$-\frac{d[NO]}{dt} = k[NO]^2[O_2]$$

(A similar law, with a different constant k, may be written for the disappearance of the oxygen.) This reaction is therefore second order with respect to NO and first order with respect to O_2. In such a case the over-all rate is said to be third order. In general, whenever the rate-determining step is known, it will be found that the rate law follows the pattern given above for the reaction of nitric oxide and oxygen, each concentration being raised to a power equal to the prefix in the balanced chemical equation. If the rate-determining step in a homogeneous gas reaction is known to be

$$2A + 3B \rightarrow C$$

then the rate law is

$$-\frac{d[A]}{dt} = k[A]^2[B]^3 \tag{10.5}$$

or, in general, if the rate-determining step is

$$aA + bB \rightarrow C$$

the law is

$$-\frac{d[A]}{dt} = k[A]^a[B]^b \tag{10.6}$$

The law of mass action is one of the most useful in chemistry. Although its applications are often obscure, the underlying basis for the law is clear. Two molecules, A and B, cannot be expected to react unless they come in contact with each other. Molecular collisions are certainly a requirement for chemical reactivity, and the more molecules there are per unit volume, the more collisions will occur. But what fraction of these collisions may be effective in producing chemical change is another matter to which our attention will be directed in the next section.

10.3   Effect of Temperature

For almost all chemical reactions, the velocity is increased as the temperature increases, and this is in sharp contrast to reactions involving nuclear disintegration. This increase of velocity means that the rate constant becomes larger at higher temperatures. It is often found that the reaction velocity doubles or triples for each 10 deg rise of temperature, but this is not valid for all reactions, and it is not valid at very high temperatures.

The effect of increased temperature in accelerating chemical reactions makes it clear why exothermic reactions tend to go to completion, often with increasing violence. When a reaction gives off heat, that heat goes to warm the products, the surroundings, and any remaining reactants. Consequently the reaction velocity increases, producing an even more rapid evolution of heat. The reaction is self-sustaining in the sense that once it has started, no more heat need be applied from an external source. This effect is only too obvious when a house burns down—the heat emitted serves only to hasten the complete destruction of the house. The cooking of an egg is also a chemical reaction, but it is endothermic and consequently slows and stops if the external source of heat is removed. In general it may be said that exothermic reactions and mildly endothermic reactions may be made to take place with ease. But strongly endothermic reactions require the addition of large quantities of heat and so are correspondingly difficult.

It may be thought that the increase of reaction velocity generally observed with increasing temperature is related to the fact that molecules move more rapidly and hence collide more vigorously at higher temperatures. But in Chapter 2 it was stated that the average velocity of the molecules is proportional to the square root of the absolute temperature. It is difficult, therefore, to see why a 10 degree increase of temperature of from, say, 300° K to 310° K should double the reaction velocity. A possible explanation is as folows: At any temperature the molecules are not all moving at the same velocity. As shown in Fig. 2.8 some molecules are moving rapidly, some slowly. Probably only the faster-moving mole-

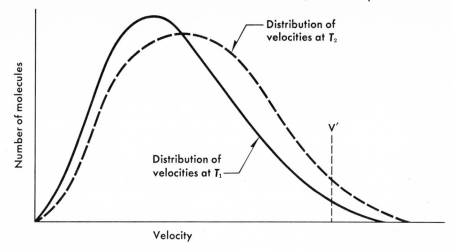

Fig. 10.1 Raising the temperature from T_1 to T_2 (say from 300 to 310° C) may increase the average molecular velocity only a few percent. But the number of molecules moving fast enough (V^-) to react chemically has been doubled.

cules collide with energy sufficient to bring about an effective collision, a collision resulting in a chemical change. As shown in Fig. 10.1, a temperature increase of a few degrees may cause only a small increase in the average kinetic energy of all the molecules, but there may be a large increase in the number of molecules that now have sufficient energy to make an effective collision.

Many chemical reactions show the effect already described in Sec. 7.6 for nuclear fusion reactions, namely, some energy must be put *into* the system before reaction takes place, even though the reaction may be strongly exothermic. Figure 7.6 may serve for such a chemical reaction, as well as for a nuclear reaction, except that the energies involved in the former are very much smaller than those in the latter. The activation energies for chemical reactions are defined by an equation derived by S. Arrhenius:

$$k = Ae^{-E/RT} \tag{10.7}$$

where k is the rate constant referred to in the preceding section, A is the frequency factor (a measure of the number of effective collisions in unit time), e is the base of the natural system of logarithms, E is the activation energy, R is the gas constant (Sec. 5.3), and T is the absolute temperature.

Equation 10.7 is useful in calculating activation energies for many homogeneous reactions, but various complications make it less useful in calculating reaction rates. We shall, therefore, not use the Arrhenius equation for any problems in this book. Nevertheless, it is quite clear that if the activation energy for a reaction is low, the reaction may proceed with high velocity. If the activation energy is high, then the reaction may be quite slow even though other circumstances are favorable. In the latter case it would be justifiable to investigate the possibility of catalysis.

10.4   *Catalysis*

The rate at which a chemical reaction proceeds is often changed to a remarkable degree by the presence of foreign substances that do not themselves appear in the final product or products. Hydrogen peroxide, for instance, normally decomposes slowly into oxygen and water,

$$2H_2O_2 \rightarrow 2H_2O + O_2$$

but in the presence of even a trace of finely powdered platinum, the decomposition may become violent or even explosive. Similarly, the temperature at which potassium chlorate decomposes,

$$2KClO_3 \rightarrow 2KCl + 3O_2$$

at an appreciable velocity may be many degrees lower if there is added to the potassium chlorate a relatively small quantity of manganese dioxide. The platinum and the manganese dioxide as used in these two reactions are called catalysts. They do not appear in the formulas of the products of reaction and they may, for the most part, be recovered unchanged at the end of the experiment.

Some catalysts increase the velocity of a reaction, whereas others appear to decrease the velocity and are sometimes called negative catalysts. But many authorities believe that a so-called negative catalyst is rather an agent, better called an *inhibitor,* that somehow destroys catalysts which may be present accidently. In any event, a *catalyst* is properly defined as a substance that alters the rate of a chemical reaction without appearing as part of the final product. Catalysts are often altered, or even destroyed, during the course of a reaction.

Catalysis may occur in systems in which all reactants, all products, and the catalyst itself are in the same phase. This is called *homogeneous* catalysis. An example of liquid phase homogeneous catalysis is the inversion of the sugar sucrose dissolved in water. This reaction, which yields a mixture of glucose and fructose, is catalyzed by a drop of two of any strong acid such as sulfuric acid. On the other hand, if the catalyst is in a state of matter different from that of the reactants, the process is called *heterogeneous* catalysis. An example is the formation of ammonia from nitrogen and hydrogen under the catalytic influence of iron:

$$N_2 + 3H_2 \rightarrow 2NH_3$$

Catalysis is often characterized by the astonishingly large amounts of reactants that may be converted under the influence of small amounts of catalyst. In the synthesis of ammonia, as above, it is not unusual for millions of moles of ammonia to be formed for each mole of catalyst present. But sometimes the usefulness of the catalyst is lost slowly or rapidly as the case may be. Catalysts are often subject to poisoning; for instance, the action of powdered nickel in catalyzing the conversion of a vegetable oil to a fat is destroyed by a comparatively small quantity of hydrogen sulfide. Some significance may be attached to the fact that many catalyst poisons are also poisons for animal organisms. Many arsenic compounds are in this class. Catalysts that have suffered poisoning may sometimes be reactivated, but causes other than poisoning are known for loss of activity. Sometimes mere excess heating of the catalyst destroys its usefulness.

Catalysis is also often characterized by an astonishing degree of specificity. This is to say, a catalyst for the synthesis of ammonia may be worthless in the production of sulfuric acid, and vice versa.

Many chemical elements and compounds exhibit catalytic activity. Not infrequently it is found that small amounts of still another substance added to a catalyst may increase its activity. Such substances are called *promoters,* an example being the small amount of potassium which, added to iron, notably increases its activity for the synthesis of ammonia. Catalysts are often used on "supports"; that is to say, the active catalyst, which may be platinum, is prepared intimately mixed with and "supported" by silica gel. But in many such cases there is evidence that the support itself plays an essential part in the catalysis. Catalysis, whatever its importance, is as much an art as a science.

A few examples of catalysts that are of major importance in the chemical industry are as follows: Nickel, iron, and platinum are used to accelerate reactions in which hydrogen is added to another atom or compound. The synthesis of ammonia is one such reaction, the treatment of cottonseed oil to yield edible fats is another. Platinum, vanadium pentoxide, and manganese dioxide are used to catalyze the union of oxygen with sulfur dioxide in the manufacture of sulfuric acid. Metal halides, such as aluminum chloride or cuprous chloride, are used to rearrange organic compounds, or to add a halogen, or to remove a hydrogen. Aluminum oxide may be used to remove the elements of water from alcohol to form ethylene, or conversely, water may be added to ethylene to form alcohol. Chromium sesquioxide may be used to convert a hydrocarbon such as heptane into toluene, used for making TNT.

In spite of these examples, and many more, it must be admitted that the mechanism by which catalysts work remains one of the major unsolved problems in chemistry. All the resources of modern science have been applied to this problem. These include chemical analysis, x-ray diffraction, surface area studies, and electric and magnetic properties, but

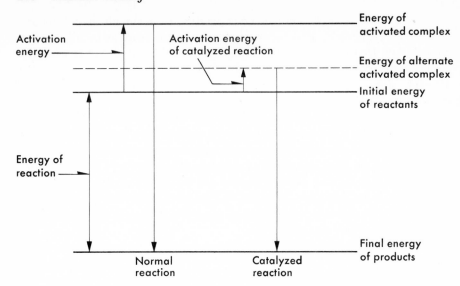

Fig. 10.2 This diagram illustrates a possible difference between a catalyzed reaction and one which is not catalyzed. The catalyst may provide an alternate reaction mechanism and this alternate mechanism may
have a lower activation energy even though the overall energy of reaction
remains the same. According to one theory of reaction kinetics the reactants first form an activated complex which then decomposes to the
final products.

there is no single chemical reaction for which the catalytic mechanism
is completely understood. In general the action of a catalyst seems to be to
lower the activation energy, as shown in Fig. 10.2. This is done, presumably,
by providing an alternative path, or mechanism, which does not involve
such a high energy barrier. In some catalytic reactions, it seems reasonably certain that an intermediate compound may be formed. Thus
reactant A, instead of changing directly to B, first unites with catalyst
C to form AC, which in turn decomposes, regenerates the catalyst, and
forms the desired product B. In heterogeneous catalysis especially, there
is evidence for the formation of "surface" compounds between reactant
and catalyst. Some aspects of this phenomenon will be discussed in the
following section.

10.5   Adsorption

If the surface of a solid is exposed to a gas, it is observed that
molecules of the gas tend to adhere to the surface. To a degree this is
true also at the surfaces of liquids and at solid-liquid interfaces. This

phenomenon is called *adsorption.* The solid or liquid of which the surface is part is called the *adsorbent*; the substance that adheres to that surface is called the *adsorbate.* Adsorption has an important relationship to heterogeneous catalysis and to heterogeneous reactions in general. Adsorption occurs for all gases, irrespective of their chemical inertness, and it occurs on all solids. Sometimes the binding forces between adsorbent and adsorbate are so weak and transient that the steady-state concentration of molecules on the surface is scarcely perceptible, but sometimes the binding is so strong that it becomes easier to vaporize the solid itself rather than to destroy the adsorbent-adsorbate bonds.

The quantity of adsorbate that can be held on the surface of a solid is directly proportional to the accessible surface of the solid. The surface of a given mass of a solid is related to the size of the particles of solid. This may be shown as follows:

Consider a cube of solid adsorbent 1 cm on an edge. There being six faces to a cube, the surface of the cube is 6 cm². Now let this cube be broken up into little cubes of only 10^{-3} cm on an edge. There will be 10^9 of these little cubes, and each one will have a surface of 6×10^{-6} cm², giving a total surface of 6×10^3 cm² for all. The effect of subdividing the original cube in this way has been to increase the surface area by a factor of 10^3. This is the principal reason why a finely powdered solid dissolves more readily, reacts chemically more readily, and appears to exhibit greater catalytic activity than does the same substance before powdering.

Solids may be prepared with surprisingly large surfaces. It is convenient to give the surface per gram of adsorbent, and this is called the *specific surface.* Charcoal is one solid, and silica another, that may easily be prepared with specific surfaces well in excess of 1000 m². Some charcoals have surfaces of nearly an acre per gram. The specific surface is obviously of major importance in determining the properties of a solid. A solid that may appear to be virtually inert in massive form may become highly reactive in finely divided form. This is shown by iron, a solid mass of which is scarcely attacked by air, but in finely divided form iron catches fire in air. The specific surface of a solid may be estimated in various ways, one of the most useful being the Brunauer-Emmett-Teller (BET) method, by which a quantity of a relatively inert gas, such as nitrogen, just sufficient to cover the surface of the solid with a single layer of molecules is found. From a knowledge of the dimensions of a nitrogen molecule, the specific surface of the solid is readily found.

In many cases the process of adsorption is quite similar to the condensation of a gas to a liquid. Molecules of the gas are held to the surface of the adsorbent by weak forces identical with, or similar to, the van der Waals forces referred to in Chapter 2. The process of adsorption is generally exothermic, and the heat liberated per mole of adsorbate is about the same as the heat of condensation. This process is called *physical adsorption.* On a solid of high specific surface (provided the temperature is not too much above the normal boiling point of the adsorbate) the quantities of gas that can be physically adsorbed can be surprisingly large. This is the basis of the use of charcoal as the active material in certain kinds of gas masks; the charcoal adsorbs and holds some classes of poisonous gases, such as chlorine.

One reason why high surface area solids seem to show enhanced chemical and catalytic activity is simply that the concentration of the reacting molecules is increased in the layer of molecules held at the surface. Then, in accordance with the law of mass action, the velocity of any reaction that may normally occur is increased correspondingly. But this is not the only reason for enhanced activity.

There is abundant evidence that many molecules are adsorbed at surfaces with the formation of true chemical bonds. When this occurs, it is called *chemisorption.* Evidence that chemical bonds may be formed is as follows: Nearly all true examples of chemisorption are exothermic, and the heat liberated is often many times greater than that observed in the phase transition of the adsorbate from gas to liquid. If the molecules that have been adsorbed can be removed (that is, desorbed), they are often found to have undergone chemical change. Hydrogen and nitrogen, for example, when chemisorbed on iron can be desorbed as ammonia. The properties of the chemisorbed molecules, as observed spectroscopically, are often radically different from those of the same molecules in physical adsorption.

In favorable cases it is possible to prove that electrons in the adsorbent undergo the pairing characteristic of the formation of true chemical bonds. Chemisorption does not occur on all solids, and it does not occur with all adsorbates. Physical adsorption occurs for all solids under appropriate conditions, but chemisorption requires a specific inter-action between adsorbent and adsorbate. Hydrogen is readily chemi-sorbed on nickel metal, but not on copper. Oxygen is chemisorbed on chromium sesquioxide, but apparently not on silicon dioxide. Both gases may be physically adsorbed on all four adsorbents mentioned. Chemi-sorption has been studied by many methods, of which one of the most impressive is an adaptation of the field emission microscope (Sec. 5.6), by which adsorbed molecules on metal surfaces have been observed directly on the microscope screen.

The importance of chemisorption in heterogeneous chemical reactions and in catalysis is that it represents the first step in many such reactions. In the case of powdered iron catching fire in air, the first step is obviously the chemisorption of oxygen molecules on the surface of the iron. This process is strongly exothermic, and the liberated heat raises the temperature of the iron particle and of the reacting oxygen to a degree such that the reaction proceeds with increasing velocity until the whole particle is converted to iron oxide. Similar reactions in science, in industry, in corrosion, and in space re-entry are almost infinite in number and in variety.

In heterogeneous catalysis, the only difference is that the reactant molecules leave the solid unchanged after they themselves have suffered some change. A good example is the hydrogen-deuterium exchange reaction to which reference was made above. This reaction is strongly catalyzed by nickel metal. The implication is clear that hydrogen molecules are dissociated into hydrogen atoms, which combine chemically with

$$\text{Ni Ni Ni Ni} + \text{H}_2 \rightarrow \overset{\displaystyle \text{H} \quad \text{H}}{\underset{\displaystyle \text{Ni Ni Ni Ni}}{|\quad\quad|}}$$

nickel atoms on the metal surface. Deuterium molecules undergo a similar reaction, but now, instead of all the nickel being converted to a nickel-hydrogen compound, the hydrogen atoms unite in part with deuterium atoms to form molecules of HD, which are desorbed from the surface, leaving the nickel unchanged. In such a case we say that the nickel has acted as a catalyst.

EXERCISES

1. Suppose that in a homogeneous gas reaction the rate-determining step is $A(g) + B(g) \rightarrow 2C(g)$ — heat. Give four ways in which the velocity of the reaction may be increased.

2. To burn sugar in air requires a fairly high temperature, but sugar undergoes essentially the same reaction in a human body at 98.6° F. Suggest a reason.

3. Sketch a simple apparatus and suggest experimental procedure that can be used to measure the rate of the following homogeneous gas reaction, $2CO(g) + O_2(g) \rightarrow 2CO_2 (g)$.

4. What explanation may be offered for the fact that the velocity of a chemical reaction generally increases very rapidly as the temperature is raised? What increase of reaction velocity is not infrequently found if the temperature is raised from 0° C to 100° C?

5. Draw a diagram showing the possible effect of a catalyst on the activation energy of an endothermic reaction.

6. A reaction $A \rightarrow B$ has an activation energy of 13 kcal/mole of A and an energy of reaction (exothermic) of 44 kcal. Find the activation energy for the reverse reaction, $B \rightarrow A$.

7. Assuming that the rate-determining step in the union of hydrogen

and iodine is represented by the equation $H_2(g) + I_2(g) \rightarrow$ $2HI(g)$, what effect on the reaction rate will be caused by doubling the concentration of hydrogen and tripling that of iodine?

8. Assume that the reaction between nitric oxide and oxygen proceeds as follows: $2NO(g) + O_2(g) \rightarrow 2NO_2(g)$. Into a container there is placed 2 moles of nitric oxide and 1 mole of oxygen. After a certain interval of time it is found that 1 mole of nitric oxide and $\frac{1}{2}$ mole of oxygen remain in the container. How will the rate of reaction at this stage compare with that at the beginning of the experiment? Assume that the temperature remains the same.

9. A certain homogeneous gas reaction is found to have a rate law: $-d[A]/dt = k[A]^{1/2}[B]^{3/2}$. In what units is the rate constant properly expressed.

10. A series of three experimental runs was made on a reaction $A(g) + B(g) \rightarrow C(g)$, the initial concentrations of A and B being different in each run. The initial rate of formation of C was found at the start of each run, before any appreciable change in the concentrations of A and B had occurred. The accompanying table gives the data obtained.

Run	Initial [A]	Initial [B]	Initial C Formation Rate
1	$0.10M$	$0.10M$	2.0×10^{-3} mole liter^{-1} min^{-1}
2	$0.20M$	$0.20M$	8.0×10^{-3} mole liter^{-1} min^{-1}
3	$0.20M$	$0.10M$	8.0×10^{-3} mole liter^{-1} min^{-1}

(a) Write the rate law for this reaction.
(b) What may be said about the order of the reaction?
(c) At what initial rate would C have been formed if the initial concentration of A had been 0.10M; and B, 0.20M?
(d) At what initial rate would C have been formed if the initial concentrations of both A and B had been 0.40M?

11. Consider the first-order homogeneous gas reaction $A(g) \rightarrow B(g)$, for which the rate law is necessarily

$$-\frac{d[A]}{dt} = k[A]$$

The integrated form of this equation (assuming that no decomposition of A has occurred at time zero, is

$$[A]_0 - [A] = [A]_0(1 - e^{-kt})$$

where $[A]_0 = [A]$ at $t = 0$; that is to say, $[A]_0$ is the initial concentration of A.

Another way of writing this relationship is

$$\ln \frac{[A]_0}{[A]} = kt$$

or

$$\log \frac{[A]_0}{[A]} = \frac{kt}{2.3}$$

This last equation should be familiar from our discussion of half-life in Sec. 7.2.

If $[A]_0 = 1.00$ mole liter^{-1} and if $k = 0.1$ mole liter^{-1} sec^{-1}, find and plot $\log [A]_0/[A]$ at 5-sec intervals from $t = 0$ to $t = 60$ sec.

12. Replot the data of Exercise 10 as $[A]$ against t. (This is a logarithmic decrement curve. It illustrates one of the most frequently observed rate processes in science.)

13. Radioactive decay rates are given as dn/dt or as dm/dt, where n and m are the number of atoms and mass, respectively. Chemical rates are generally given in terms of concentration, but otherwise their treatment is much the same. What is the *order* of a radioactive decay process?

14. The reaction $(A \rightarrow)$ is known to be first order. If in 20 min the concentration of A has diminished by 38 percent, what is the half-life of this reaction, that is, the time until $[A] = [A]_0/2$?

15. In a study of the decomposition of ammonia on a tungsten catalyst at 1000° K, it was found that the rate of the reaction was *independent* of the concentration of ammonia. Write an expression for the rate law of this reaction. (Such a reaction is said to be a zero-order reaction. Suggest a reason why such a condition could occur.)

16. On a sample of silica gel it was found that a monolayer (a single layer of molecules) of nitrogen adsorbed on the surface was reached at 116 ml(STP) per gram of silica. It is estimated that the cross-sectional area per molecule of nitrogen is 16.2 Å^2 (square angstrom units.) Calculate the specific surface of the silica gel sample.

11

Chemical Equilibrium

If a sample of radioactive matter (not subject to regeneration from another source) is observed for a time sufficiently long in comparison with its half-life, it will be found that the last detectable portion has finally undergone disintegration. The original atoms are all destroyed, and it may be said that the reaction has gone to completion. Radioactivity is, in this sense, an irreversible transformation of matter.

If some ammonia is placed in contact with a catalyst under appropriate conditions, it will be found in due course that some of or all the ammonia has decomposed to nitrogen and hydrogen. But, in sharp contrast to the case of radioactive decay, if nitrogen and hydrogen are mixed under appropriate conditions in the presence of the same catalyst, it will be found in due course that some ammonia has been formed. Such a reaction is called a *reversible reaction.* If the decomposition of the ammonia is written

$$2NH_3 \rightarrow N_2 + 3H_2$$

and the synthesis of ammonia as

$$N_2 + 3H_2 \rightarrow 2NH_3$$

then the fact that this reaction is reversible is designated by a double-arrow notation; thus,

$$N_2 + 3H_2 \rightleftharpoons 2NH_3$$

in which case convenience will dictate whether the nitrogen and hydrogen or the ammonia should be put on the left of the equation, as written.

A chemical reaction is said to have gone to completion when one or more of the reactants may no longer be detected in the system. The fact that a reaction may have gone to completion does not in itself prove that the reaction is irreversible. Most chemical reactions may be caused to approach completion by appropriate adjustment of the reaction conditions, as will be described below. In one sense, all chemical reactions are, in theory, reversible. But some reactions, such as the burning of wood, are effectively irreversible in that the wood cannot be formed again, although a very similar process is commonplace in growing vegetation.

11.2   Equilibria in Reacting Systems

The existence of reversible reactions gives rise to chemical equilibria. Consider a hypothetical reversible reaction

$$A + B \rightleftharpoons C + D$$

in which all reactants and all products are gases. Quantities of A and B are placed in a container under conditions such that a reaction proceeds with measurable velocity. The rate of reaction between A and B will, according to the law of mass action, be proportional to the concentration of A multiplied by the concentration of B. At the start of the experiment, the rate of the reverse reaction will be zero because the concentrations of C and D are zero.

As the reaction proceeds, the concentrations of both A and B will become progressively less, and the rate of the reaction between these substances will diminish. At the same time, however, the concentrations of C and D will increase as these substances are formed through the reaction of A and B. The rate of reaction between C and D will continue to increase as long as the concentrations of C and D increase. Sooner or later the increasing rate of reaction between C and D will equal the diminishing rate of reaction between A and B. After the opposing rates have become equal, the concentrations of all four substances will remain constant, and equilibrium will have been reached.

At *equilibrium* the concentrations of all reactants and products will remain constant, and if the forward reaction (the one written toward the right) happens to be exothermic, the reverse reaction will be endothermic. At equilibrium the heat liberated by the forward reaction will be absorbed by the reverse reaction, as a consequence of which the temperature of the reacting system will also remain constant, provided there is no loss or gain of heat from the surroundings.

These outward evidences of inertness must not obscure the fact that both forward and reverse reactions are continuing, even though equilibrium has been reached and the concentrations of reactants and products do not change. Proof that the forward and reverse reactions continue at equilibrium may be obtained with the aid of hydrogen isotopes. Suppose the reaction

$$N_2 + 3H_2 \rightleftharpoons 2NH_3$$

has reached equilibrium and that now a little deuterium gas, $\dot{D}_2$, is added to the system. Almost at once it will be found that the hydrogen in the reaction mixture consists of H_2, D_2, and HD molecules and that the ammonia consists of NH_3, NH_2D, NHD_2, and ND_3 molecules. These several molecular species could not have been formed if all chemical reaction had stopped. It will be noted that chemical equilibrium bears some resemblance to the processes that establish equilibrium vapor pressure (Sec. 3.4).

It is not to be supposed that equilibrium is reached when all substances are present in equal concentration. The relative amounts and concentrations of each substance present at equilibrium may be very different for different reactions and for the same reaction under different conditions. It may also be mentioned that just as it is possible to have metastable states such as that which occurs in a supercooled liquid (Sec. 4.1), it is possible to have metastable equilibria in chemical reactions. The reaction between hydrogen and oxygen offers an example of this effect. These two gases may be kept mixed together without detectable reaction for an indefinite time, provided the temperature is not raised and no catalyst is present to help surmount or lower the activation energy barrier. Under the circumstances it might be concluded erroneously that equilibrium had been reached. But let a spark reach the mixture, or let a few specks of powdered platinum be introduced, and the mixture will approach the true equilibrium in a fraction of a second, and it will do so with explosive violence. The true equilibrium for this reaction at room temperature lies so far in the direction of the product water that the reaction may be said to go effectively to completion. One criterion of a true chemical equilibrium is that it may be approached from either side. One may, for instance, start with nitrogen and hydrogen, or one may start with ammonia. If a true equilibrium rather than a false or metastable equilibrium has been reached, it will be found that the relative concentrations of all reactants and all products are the same in either case, provided, of course, all conditions are maintained the same.

11.3   Le Châtelier's Principle

If a system (a set of reacting substances) at equilibrium is subjected to a stress (a change of conditions), the equilibrium will shift in such direction as to diminish the stress (it will tend to restore the original conditions).

The statement above is **Le Châtelier's principle,** enunciated in the year 1885. It is the basis for procedures used to obtain more or less product, as may be desired, from all reversible chemical reactions. The stresses that may be applied to a reacting system are:

1. Change of pressure, and its corollary
2. Change of concentration of one or more reactants
3. Change of temperature

To these stresses will be added the effect of adding a catalyst, although a catalyst is not a stress in the sense intended by Le Châtelier. All examples will be chosen from homogeneous gas reactions, heterogeneous reactions being deferred until a later section.

Consider a reaction in which gas molecules of one, and only one, substance A are being converted reversibly into B:

$$A \rightleftharpoons B$$

The rate of conversion of $A \rightarrow B$ will presumably be dependent on some power of the concentration of A, and the rate of conversion $B \rightarrow A$ will be dependent, at equilibrium at least, on the same power of the concentration of B. This statement must be true because it is found experimentally in a system such as that postulated, that increasing or decreasing the pressure at constant temperature, which must of necessity mean increasing or decreasing the concentration, has no effect on the *relative* velocities of forward and reverse reactions at equilibrium. This may be expressed in another way: It is found that for a reaction in which each reactant molecule is converted into one, and only one, product molecule, a change of pressure has no effect on the equilibrium; that is to say, the *relative* concentrations of A and B remain unchanged.

There are not many actual homogeneous gas reactions such as that described above. One important reaction of this kind, involving molecular hydrogen, will be described in Chapter 17. But there are many reactions in which two or more molecules are transferred into the same *number* of other molecules. Some examples of this are the reaction of hydrogen and bromine (at moderately elevated temperatures) to form hydrogen bromide:

$$H_2 + Br_2 \rightleftharpoons 2HBr$$

the decomposition of nitric oxide:

$$2NO \rightleftharpoons N_2 + O_2$$

and the water-gas shift reaction[1]:

$$CO_2 + H_2 \rightleftharpoons CO + H_2O(g)$$

[1] The designations (g), (l), or (s) refer to the states: gas, liquid, solid.

In these reactions, and in all similar reactions in which the number of gas molecules is the same on both sides of the arrows, it is found that change of pressure has no effect on the relative concentrations of reactants and products at equilibrium.

There are many reactions in which the numbers of molecules represented on each side of the arrows are not the same. Two examples are, first, the synthesis of ammonia:

$$N_2 + 3H_2 \rightleftharpoons 2NH_3$$

and, second, the decomposition of nitrous oxide:

$$2N_2O \rightleftharpoons 2N_2 + O_2$$

In the first of these reactions, 4 moles of nitrogen plus hydrogen react to form 2 moles of ammonia. According to the gas laws, 2 moles of any gas will exert less pressure than 4 moles, *provided conditions are the same*. If, therefore, a given volume of nitrogen plus hydrogen were to be converted to ammonia, the pressure in the system would be diminished. An increase of pressure applied to the system at constant temperature *after equilibrium has been reached,* will result in a shift of the equilibrium to the right. This is what is found experimentally to be true, and it is the reason that the industrial synthesis of ammonia is commonly operated at several hundred atmospheres of pressure, in order to increase the yield of ammonia. In terms of Le Châtelier's principle, under the influence of the applied stress (which in this case is an increase of pressure) the equilibrium shifts in such direction as to form a smaller total number of moles of gas.

For the second reaction given above, namely, the decomposition of nitrous oxide, an increase of pressure at constant temperature would diminish the number of moles of nitrogen plus oxygen present at equilibrium because in this reaction, as written to the right, 3 moles are formed for every 2 that decompose. Conversely, a *decrease* of applied pressure will increase the equilibrium number of moles of nitrogen and oxygen.

A change of pressure applied to a mixture of gases must, of necessity, be applied to all gases present. But it is possible to change effectively the partial pressure of one or more of the gases present by the simple device of forcing more of one or more substances into the container. If, in the reaction of nitrogen and hydrogen to form ammonia, more nitrogen is added, at constant temperature and volume, to the system at equilibrium, it will be found that the equilibrium shifts in such a direction as to use more nitrogen, plus some of the hydrogen present, and to form more ammonia. The same change occurs if the concentration of hydrogen is increased. But if the concentration of ammonia is arbitrarily increased, the equilibrium will shift somewhat in the direction of decomposing ammonia.

This effect of changing concentration on a system at equilibrium may be used effectively in forcing a reaction to completion, or nearly so. If, in the synthesis of ammonia, the concentration of ammonia is deliberately lowered, then the equilibrium will shift in the direction of generating more ammonia until all the nitrogen or hydrogen, or both, are used. The ammonia concentration may conveniently be kept low by permitting it to dissolve in water, in which ammonia is very soluble. This procedure effectively removes the ammonia from the reacting gas mixture.

The third stress to be considered is the effect of changing temperature. If an exothermic reaction proceeds with measurable velocity, the reactants, the products, and the container all become warm or hot, as the case may be:

$$A \rightleftharpoons B + \text{heat}$$

If such a reaction has reached equilibrium, then any shift to a new equilibrium farther to the right, as written, will liberate more heat. If, therefore, the temperature is raised by the application of heat from an external source, the equilibrium will shift in such a direction as to cool the system; namely, to the left.

The synthesis of ammonia is an exothermic reaction:

$$N_2 + 3H_2 \rightleftharpoons 2NH_3 + 21.9 \text{ kcal}$$

If the temperature is raised on the system at equilibrium, the result will be a shift to the left, and the concentration of ammonia, at constant temperature and pressure, will be diminished. But for an endothermic reaction such as the synthesis of nitric oxide,

$$N_2 + O_2 \rightleftharpoons 2NO - \text{heat}$$

an increase of temperature will increase the equilibrium concentration of the product at the right.

From what has been said above it should be clear that the yield of ammonia obtainable from the reaction of nitrogen and hydrogen is increased by operating the reaction at high pressure, but that the yield is decreased by high temperature. This poses a problem: The velocity of almost all reactions is increased by raising the temperature. By mixing nitrogen and hydrogen under high pressure at low temperature, it would be possible to obtain a high yield of ammonia, but equilibrium might not be reached for millions of years. It is necessary to distinguish clearly between the condition of equilibrium, which is related to the relative concentrations of reactants and products, and to the rate at which that equilibrium is attained. Useful reactions almost always require a favorable equilibrium and a reasonably satisfactory velocity. A low temperature defeats the purpose of the ammonia synthesis, although it does in principle ensure a favorable equilibrium yield of ammonia.

Under the circumstances described, it is fortunate that catalysts have been found that will greatly accelerate the velocity of reaction between nitrogen and hydrogen. It is therefore important to consider whether a catalyst may have any influence on the equilibrium as well as on the velocity. Many experimental investigations have been made on this subject, but no effect of a catalyst on a system at equilibrium has ever been found. A catalyst may, and often does, hasten the attainment of equilibrium; but no catalyst has been found able to change the relative concentrations of reactants and products at equilibrium, and there are sound theoretical reasons for believing that no such catalyst ever will be found.

The usefulness of Le Châteliers principle is such that it is applied in every branch of science. This must not conceal the fact that the principle will yield only qualitative predictions concerning the direction in which an equilibrium may be shifted. Quantitative predictions are possible, but they are beyond the scope of this book. It must also be pointed out that consideration must be given to the conditions of the experiment. If a system involving a homogeneous gas reaction at equilibrium,

$$A(g) + B(g) \rightleftharpoons C(g) + \text{heat}$$

were to be subjected to an increase of pressure at constant volume, then this could be achieved only by raising the temperature. The increase of pressure would tend to shift the equilibrium to the right, but the increase of temperature would shift it to the left. In such a case an accurate prediction of the net result would require a more advanced study than that presented here.

11.4   Equilibrium Constant

For a homogeneous, gas phase reaction

$$A \rightleftharpoons B$$

it is found by experiment that at equilibrium the concentrations of A and B are related as follows:

$$\frac{[B]}{[A]} = K$$

when the brackets, [ ], designate concentration in moles per liter, and K is called the *equilibrium constant*.

For a more general reaction,

$$aA + bB \rightleftharpoons cC + dD$$

the equilibrium constant has the form

TABLE 11.1 EXAMPLES OF GAS PHASE REACTIONS AND
EQUILIBRIUM EXPRESSIONS

Reaction	K
$CO_2(g) + H_2(g) \rightleftharpoons CO(g) + H_2O(g)$	$\dfrac{[CO][H_2O]}{[CO_2][H_2]}$
$H_2(g) + Br_2(g) \rightleftharpoons 2HBr(g)$	$\dfrac{[HBr]^2}{[H_2][Br_2]}$
$N_2(g) + 3H_2(g) \rightleftharpoons 2NH_3(g)$	$\dfrac{[NH_3]^2}{[N_2][H_2]^3}$

$$\frac{[C]^c[D]^d}{[A]^a[B]^b} = K$$

each concentration being raised to the power corresponding to the appropriate coefficient in the chemical equation.

The equilibrium constant is one of the most useful concepts in chemistry. Application to specific problems will, for the most part, be deferred until Chapter 14, but some derivations and general properties of the constant will be presented in this section. It will be noted that by convention the reaction products at the right in the equation are placed in the numerator of the equilibrium constant expression. A large value for K shows, therefore, that the reaction will go to near completion toward the right. A few examples of equilibrium constant expressions are shown in Table 11.1. Some experimental data showing that the equilibrium constant is independent of the concentrations of the individual reactants are shown in Table 11.2.

It is possible to derive the equilibrium constant expression on a theoretical basis. This will be done for a very simple, idealized case in which the rate-determining steps are assumed to be

$$A + B \rightleftharpoons C + D$$

TABLE 11.2 SOME EQUILIBRIUM CONCENTRATIONS (MOLE LITER^1) AND
CONSTANTS FOR THE REACTION
$$CO_2(g) + H_2(g) \rightleftharpoons CO(g) + H_2O(g)$$

CO_2	H_2	CO	$H_2O(g)$	K
0.54	0.34	0.65	0.46	1.6
0.12	0.10	0.087	0.22	1.6
0.95	0.13	0.51	0.39	1.6
0.18	1.05	0.80	0.38	1.6

The rate of disappearance of A is, according to the law of mass action,

$$-\frac{d[A]}{dt} = k_1[A][B]$$

Similarly, the rate of disappearance of C is given by

$$-\frac{d[C]}{dt} = k_2[C][D]$$

At equilibrium, by definition, the rate of the forward reaction is equal to the rate of the reverse reaction; hence,

$$k_1[A][B] = k_2[C][D]$$

and rearranging,

$$\frac{[C][D]}{[A][B]} = \frac{k_1}{k_2} = K$$

The equilibrium constant of a reaction is independent of pressure, concentration, and the presence or absence of a catalyst. The constant does, however, depend on temperature, as must be obvious from Le Châtelier's principle. For a reaction that is exothermic, as written,

$$H_2 + Br_2 \rightleftharpoons 2HBr + heat$$

an increase of temperature decreases the equilibrium constant, and for an endothermic reaction,

$$N_2 + O_2 \rightleftharpoons 2NO - heat$$

an increase of temperature increases the equilibrium constant. The mathematical expressions that relate the equilibrium constant to the heat of reaction lie beyond the scope of this book. A change of pressure (at constant temperature) will, of course, alter the relative concentrations of any gaseous reactants and products, except in those cases where the number of moles of gas is independent of any shift in the equilibrium.

While the equilibrium constant may be derived (in an elementary fashion) by equating reaction velocities as above, it in itself tells nothing concerning the velocity with which equilibrium may be attained.

This section will be concluded with some simple problems related to equilibrium constants in gas phase reactions.

PROBLEM: Starting with a moles per liter of A, find the concentration of B after equilibrium has been reached for the homogeneous gas reaction:

$$A \rightleftharpoons B$$

SOLUTION: The equilibrium constant is given by

$$K = \frac{[B]}{[A]}$$

where [A] and [B] are the concentrations of A and B respectively at equilibrium. For this reaction at constant volume $[A] = a - [B]$ because 1 mole of A is decomposed for every mole of B formed. Hence:

$$K = \frac{[B]}{a - [B]}$$

and

$$[B] = \frac{aK}{1 + K}$$

PROBLEM: The equilibrium constant for the homogeneous gas reaction

$$H_2 + I_2(g) \rightleftharpoons 2HI$$

is $K = 45.9$ at 490° C. If the concentrations of both hydrogen and iodine at equilibrium are both 0.1 mole liter^{-1}, find the concentration of hydrogen iodide.

SOLUTION: The expression is:

$$\frac{[HI]^2}{[H_2][I_2]} = 45.9$$

substituting:

$$\frac{[HI]^2}{0.1 \times 0.1} = 45.9$$

hence:

$$[HI]^2 = 45.9 \times 10^{-2}$$

and

$$[HI] = (45.9 \times 10^{-2})^{1/2} = 0.68 \text{ mole liter}^{-1}$$

11.5   Equilibria in Heterogeneous Systems

Many chemical reactions involve reactants or products, or both, in two or more phases. A few examples of such heterogeneous reactions are as follows:

$$CaCO_3(s) \rightleftharpoons CaO(s) + CO_2(g)$$
$$NaCl(s) + H_2SO_4(l) \rightleftharpoons 2HCl(g) + Na_2SO_4(s)$$
$$NH_3(g) + HCl(g) \rightleftharpoons NH_4Cl(s)$$
$$Fe_3O_4(s) + 4H_2(g) \rightleftharpoons 3Fe(s) + 4H_2O(l) \text{ or } (g)$$

There are also known reactions in which all reactants and products are solids, but the laws describing reaction velocity and equilibrium in such systems are not yet adequately formulated.

It was indicated in the preceding chapter that the rate of a heterogeneous reaction may depend on the surface area of the solid reactants. A finely divided solid will certainly almost always react more rapidly than the same solid in massive form. Equilibrium is thus more rapidly attained by the use of finely powdered reactants, but the final equilibrium concentrations cannot be changed in this way. Furthermore, the equilibrium constant establishes a relation, not between total masses but between the relative *concentrations* of reactants and products. It is certainly possible to change the *mass* of a solid reactant, but it is impossible to make an appreciable change in the *concentration* of a solid or a liquid by adding more reactant.

Consider, then, the reversible, heterogeneous reaction between solid sulfur and gaseous oxygen to form gaseous sulfur dioxide:

$$S(s) + O_2(g) \rightleftharpoons SO_2(g)$$

In this reaction the concentration of sulfur is necessarily a constant, and it may therefore be ignored in writing the expression for the equilibrium constant, which becomes

$$\frac{[SO_2]}{[O_2]} = K$$

This procedure is valid for the solid and liquid phases present in any heterogeneous system at equilibrium. In the decomposition of calcium carbonate, for which the equation is given above, the only gas present is carbon dioxide. The equilibrium constant expression thus becomes

$$[CO_2] = K$$

At 1000° C, the pressure of carbon dioxide in equilibrium with calcium carbonate and calcium oxide, as shown, is 1.05 atm, and because the pressure of a gas is directly proportional to the number of moles of gas present, it is convenient to use the pressure (or partial pressure as the case may be) instead of converting to moles per liter. The equilibrium constant expression for this reaction may therefore be written as

$$P_{CO_2} = K$$
$$= 1.05 \text{ atm} \quad \text{(at 1000° C)}$$

and this is the manner in which equilibrium constants involving gases are often expressed.

PROBLEM: In a 5.0 liter container, what is the minimum weight of calcium carbonate necessary to establish equilibrium at 1000° C?

Heated Fe₃O₄ undergoing reduction

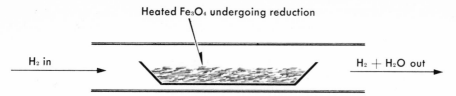

H₂ in →   H₂ + H₂O out →

Fig. 11.1 *Quantitative reduction of an oxide by forcing the reaction to completion through continuous displacement of the equilibrium.*

SOLUTION: First find from the perfect gas law the number of moles of carbon dioxide present at equilibrium:

$$n = \frac{PV}{RT}$$

$$= \frac{1.05 \text{ atm} \times 5.0 \text{ liters}}{8.21 \times 10^{-2} \text{ liter atm mole}^{-1} \text{ deg}^{-1} \times 1273 \text{ deg}}$$

$$= 5.01 \times 10^{-2} \text{ mole}$$

One mole of calcium carbonate is required for every mole of carbon dioxide formed. Hence, equilibrium under these conditions will require 5.0×10^{-2} mole of $CaCO_3$, and this is

$$5.0 \times 10^{-2} \text{ mole} \times 100.09 \text{ grams moles}^{-1} = 5.01 \text{ grams } CaCO_3$$

A very familiar type of reaction is that shown above for the reduction of magnetite (Fe_3O_4) by hydrogen to yield metallic iron and water. In a closed container this reaction will reach equilibrium as represented by the expression

$$\frac{[H_2O(g)]^4}{[H_2]^4} = K$$

It is impossible to convert all the magnetite to metallic iron in this way, but if the magnetite is heated in a stream of flowing hydrogen, then the reaction will go to completion readily. The reasons for this are twofold. First, the concentration of hydrogen is kept high by the continuous flow of fresh hydrogen into the system, and second, the water-vapor concentration is kept low because the flowing hydrogen sweeps the steam out of the system. In this way the system is never permitted to reach equilibrium, and the magnetite may be easily reduced quantitatively to metallic iron. This procedure, one of the commonest in chemistry for forcing a reversible reaction to completion, is shown diagrammatically in Fig. 11.1.

EXERCISES

1. Select three familiar reactions which normally proceed so far in one direction that they may be said to be irreversible.

2. What evidence is available to show that chemical reaction continues even though equilibrium may have been reached?

3. For the reaction

$$A(g) + B(g) \rightleftharpoons C(g)$$

draw a graph, plotting concentration vertically and time horizontally, to show how the concentrations of A, B, and C change.

4. Consider the following five systems at equilibrium (all substances are gases):

(1) $2NO + O_2 \rightleftharpoons 2NO_2 + heat$
(2) $N_2 + O_2 \rightleftharpoons 2NO - heat$
(3) $N_2 + 3H_2 \rightleftharpoons 2NH_3 + heat$
(4) $H_2 + I_2 \rightleftharpoons 2HI - heat$
(5) $2CO + O_2 \rightleftharpoons 2CO_2 + heat$

(a) List those systems in which increase of pressure (at constant temperature) has no effect on the equilibrium.
(b) List those in which an increase of temperature has no effect on the equilibrium.
(c) List those in which addition of a catalyst has no effect on the equilibrium.

5. State the principle of Le Châtelier.

6. If an increase of temperature can increase the rate of a reaction, and addition of a catalyst can do the same, is it possible to say that the effect of a catalyst is the same as the effect of raising the temperature?

7. Three different reactions have the following equilibrium constants: 10^{12}, 1, and 10^{-28}, respectively. State if these reactions at equilibrium have yielded (a) scarcely any product, (b) virtually all reactant has been used up, or (c) reactant and product are present in roughly equal proportions.

8. Consider the following system at equilibrium:

$$2SO_2(g) + O_2(g) \rightleftharpoons 2SO_3(g) + 45.2 \text{ kcal}$$

If the temperature is raised, will the equilibrium constant be expected to increase, decrease, or remain the same?

9. For the following system at equilibrium,

$$N_2(g) + 3H_2(g) \rightleftharpoons 2NH_3(g) + 22 \text{ kcal}$$

what will be the effect of adding some of the inert gas helium, temperature and volume remaining constant?

10. Derive from fundamental principles an expression for the equilibrium constant for the hypothetical reaction:

$$A(g) + B(g) \rightleftharpoons C(g) + D(g)$$

11. Write expressions for the equilibrium constants for the following reactions:

   (a) $N_2O_4(g) \rightleftharpoons 2NO_2(g)$
   (b) $2H_2(g) + O_2(g) \rightleftharpoons 2H_2O(g)$
   (c) $2H_2O(g) + Cl_2(g) \rightleftharpoons 4HCl(g) + O_2(g)$
   (d) $ZnO(s) + CO(g) \rightleftharpoons Zn(s) + CO_2(g)$
   (e) $P_4(s) + 5O_2(g) \rightleftharpoons P_4O_{10}(s)$

12. For the system

$$A(g) + 3B(g) + 2C(g) \rightleftharpoons 4D(g)$$

   at equilibrium it is found that in a 5.0-liter container, there are present 2.0 moles of A, 2.0 moles of B, 1.0 mole of C, and 3.5 moles of D. Calculate the equilibrium constant.

13. In the water-gas reaction

$$C(s) + H_2O(g) \rightleftharpoons CO(g) + H_2(g)$$

   what will be the effect of blowing a large excess of preheated steam over the heated coke (C)?

14. Under certain conditions of temperature and pressure, it is found that at equilibrium for the reaction.

$$N_2 + 3H_2 \rightleftharpoons 2NH_3$$

   the following concentrations are present: nitrogen, 1.0 mole/liter; hydrogen, 3.0 moles/liter; and ammonia, 0.45 mole/liter. Find the equilibrium constant.

15. At elevated temperature the equilibrium constant for the reaction

$$N_2(g) + O_2(g) \rightleftharpoons 2NO(g)$$

   is 6.0×10^{-4}. If the concentration of nitrogen is 0.10 mole/liter and the concentration of oxygen is 0.020 mole/liter, what is the equilibrium concentration of nitric oxide?

16. The following substances are found to be present in a reaction at equilibrium: $CaO(s)$, $Fe(s)$, $Br_2(g)$, and $H_2(g)$. Of these substances, which, if any, may be omitted from the expression for the equilibrium constant?

17. For the reaction

$$A(s) + 2B(g) \rightleftharpoons 2C(g)$$

   it is found that the equilibrium constant at a certain temperature is 0.46. If the mass of A present is 1.0 mole and the concentration of B is 0.50 mole/liter, what concentration of C will be present?

18. For the reaction

$$A(g) \rightleftharpoons B(g)$$

starting with 1.0 mole/liter of A, what concentration of B will be present at equilibrium if the equilibrium constant under the condition of the experiment is 1.3×10^{-2}?

19. If, for the reaction

$$CaCO_3(s) \rightleftharpoons CaO(s) + CO_2(g)$$

the equilibrium constant at 1000° C may be written

$$P_{CO_2} = 1.05 \text{ atm}$$

(a) what pressure will be developed at equilibrium in a 5.0-liter container if the calcium carbonate originally added weighed 1.0 gram?

(b) what pressure will be developed under the same conditions if the calcium carbonate originally added weighed 100 grams?

12

Solutions

12.1 Properties of Solutions

An absolutely pure chemical element or compound exists only in the imagination. Chemistry is concerned chiefly with mixtures. A mixture may be heterogeneous, and the individual components be recognizable—if not by the naked eye, then by a microscope of moderate resolving power; or the mixture may be optically homogeneous, as in air and sea water, where the components of the mixture are not so readily identified. Homogeneous mixtures are called *solutions,* and the general relationship between elements, compounds, mixtures, and solutions is shown in the accompaning illustration.

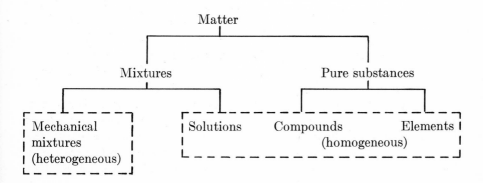

A *solution* may be defined as a homogeneous mixture of one phase but of two or more components. There are many different types of solutions. Gases may dissolve in other gases. Air, which may be thought of principally as oxygen dissolved in nitrogen, is an example of a gas dissolved in a gas. It is, however, true that a solution of a gas in a gas differs from other types of solutions—the molecules collide with each other, but they are not in effective contact with each other as is the case, for instance, in a solution of alcohol in water. Gases dissolve in liquids to form true solutions. Air dissolves to some extent in water, and carbon dioxide readily dissolves in water under pressure.

In some cases, gases dissolve in solids. Hydrogen can dissolve to a considerable extent in the metal palladium. Liquids dissolving in other liquids form one of the commonest classes of solutions. Alcohol in water, acetic acid in water, mixtures of hydrocarbons in gasoline are all examples of liquid-liquid solutions. Solids dissolved in liquids form another important class of solutions. Salt in water, sugar in water—we shall present many examples of such solutions in later chapters. Solutions of solids in solids are also well known. Alloys, consisting of two or more metals, often are formed by a process of solid solution. Brass, for instance, is a solution of copper and zinc.

When a substance such as sugar is dissolved in, say, water, it is customary to refer to the water as the *solvent*. The sugar is called the *solute*. These terms are convenient, and in many cases there is no ambiguity as to which substance is the solute and which the solvent. But water may be dissolved in alcohol, or alcohol in water, in any proportion. Under such circumstances the terms solute and solvent tend to lose their meanings.

Solutions have various properties in common, of which optical homogeneity is one and variable composition is another. But solutions may be formed under widely different conditions. The simplest kind of solution from the point of view of molecular interactions is one of, say, liquid argon dissolved in liquid neon. These two elements consist of molecules containing one atom only, and as far as is known, they are chemically inert. In the dissolving of liquid argon as solute in liquid neon as solvent, the principal change that occurs is that each argon molecule becomes surrounded by neon molecules instead of by argon molecules. The molecules of a solute in such a case are not unlike the molecules of a gas in that they move more as individuals than as groups of molecules of the same kind.

But such simple processes of solution are comparatively rare. In most cases, and this is especially true of inorganic solutes, the solvent molecules tend to cluster around the solute ions, or molecules, as the case may be. These clusters may have definite compositions, or they may not, but they resemble true chemical compounds to such a degree that consideration of them will be deferred until later chapters. The same is true of such obvious chemical processes as occur when, say, copper metal is dissolved in nitric acid. Here the reaction is one of conversion of copper to copper nitrate, and it is the copper nitrate that remains in solution.

Whenever solutions are formed, the specific properties of solvent and solute are modified to a degree that depends on to what extent a true chemical transformation may have taken place. This is true of even such a process as that of alcohol dissolving in water. The density of an alcohol-water solution is greater than the average density that might have been expected from the relative proportions. This may be expressed in another way: A pint of alcohol dissolved in a pint of water yields somewhat less than a quart of solution.

The process of solution has a further resemblance to true chemical reaction in that there is always some heat effect observed. When alcohol is dissolved in water, there is an appreciable evolution of heat, and sulfuric acid dissolving in water is dangerously exothermic. Endothermic solution processes are also well known.

12.2   Concentration

The properties of solutions depend upon the relative proportions of solvent and solute present. A solution in which the proportion of solute is large is said to be a *concentrated* solution; one in which the concentration of solute is small is said to be *dilute*. There are many different methods for expressing the concentration of a solution. Several of these methods will be given, but attention will be directed chiefly at the two methods that will prove to be of most service in later pages. These are the systems known as *molarity* and *molality*.

The *molarity* of a solution is the number of moles of solute per liter of solution. A 1-molar solution contains 1 mole of solute per liter of solution, and is designated $1M$.

PROBLEM: What weight of sugar, $C_{12}H_{22}O_{11}$, is required to prepare 1 liter of $1M$ sugar solution?

SOLUTION: The weight of a mole of sugar is the formula weight expressed as grams. The formula weight is 342. A mole of sugar therefore weighs 342 grams. It requires 342 grams of sugar to prepare 1 liter of $1M$ sugar solution.

It is particularly important to note that molarity means moles of solute per liter of solution and that this is not the same as moles of solute per liter of solvent. A liter of sugar solution does not necessarily contain a liter of water, just as a quart of alcohol-water solution is not

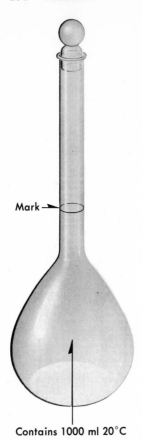

Mark →

Contains 1000 ml 20°C

Fig. 12.1 Volumetric flask.

formed by mixing a pint of alcohol and a pint of water. To make a liter of 1*M* solution of sugar or of other solute, use is made of a volumetric flask (Fig. 12.1). A volumetric flask has a rather large body and a narrow neck. On the neck of the flask there is etched ·a mark such that when the flask is filled to the mark, the amount of liquid contained in the flask is a definite volume; say, 1 liter. To make a liter of 1*M* sugar solution, weight out 342 grams of sugar and place this in a 1 liter volumetric flask. Fill the flask about three-quarters full of water and then shake the flask until all the sugar is dissolved. Add more water, with frequent shaking, until the solution reaches the mark on the neck of the flask. You then have 1 liter of 1*M* sugar solution, but this operation is not the same as weighing out 342 grams of sugar and adding 1 liter of water to it.

The importance of the molarity concept is such that it will be illustrated by several more problems.

PROBLEM: What weight of sodium chloride is required to prepare 1 liter of $1M$ NaCl solution?

SOLUTION: It will be recalled that a mole is, strictly speaking, 6.02×10^{23} molecules, but that it is convenient (as described in Sec. 8.3) to refer to the weight of a mole as a formula weight expressed in grams. The formula weight of NaCl being 58.5 grams, the answer to this problem is simply that it requires 58.5 grams of NaCl to prepare 1 liter of $1M$ NaCl solution. But some authorities prefer not to use the word "mole" in such a loose sense, and in preference use a system called *formality*, with the symbol F. One liter of $1F$ NaCl contains 58.5 grams of NaCl.

     The formality system is used for all substances that (for example, sodium chloride) do not form particulate molecules. Formality is identical with molarity in the way the latter is defined in this book.

PROBLEM: What weight of magnesium nitrate, $Mg(NO_3)_2$, is contained in 1.8 liter of $0.63M$ solution?

SOLUTION: The formula weight of $Mg(NO_3)_2$ is 148. Therefore, 1 liter of $1M$ $Mg(NO_3)_2$ would contain 148 grams. Then 1.8 liter of $1M$ $Mg(NO_3)_2$ would contain 1.8×148 grams, and 1.8 liter of $0.63M$ solution would contain 1.8×148 grams $\times 0.63 = 168$ grams.

PROBLEM: What is the molar concentration of a solution that contains 200 grams of HCl in 6.5 liters of solution?

SOLUTION: A mole of HCl weighs 36.5 grams. In 6.5 liters of $1M$ HCl there would be 6.5×36.5 grams. Then 200 grams of HCl in 6.5 liters of solution is only

$$\frac{200 \text{ grams}}{6.51 \text{ liters} \times 36.5 \text{ grams mole}^{-1}} = 0.84 \text{ mole/liter}$$

The concentration of the solution is $0.84M$.

PROBLEM: There is available a quantity of $6.0M$ H_2SO_4. What volume of this acid must be taken to prepare 10 liters of $2.5M$ H_2SO_4?

SOLUTION: A 10 liter volume of $2.5M$ H_2SO_4 would contain 10×2.5 moles of H_2SO_4. This number of moles must therefore be taken from the $6M$ solution.

     By definition, 6 moles of H_2SO_4 are contained in 1 liter of $6M$ solution. Hence, 10×2.5 moles would be contained in

$$10 \times 2.5 \times 1/6 \text{ liter} = 4.2 \text{ liters}$$

The desired 10 liters of 2.5M H_2SO_4 may then be made by taking 4.2 liters of 6M H_2SO_4 and diluting this with water until the volume is 10 liters.

The second important method for expressing the concentration of a solution is the molality system. *Molality* is the number of moles of solute per kilogram of solvent. Note that molality and molarity are not the same, even for water as solvent, in spite of the fact that 1 liter of water weighs approximately 1 kg. Use of the molality system may be illustrated by the following problem.

PROBLEM: How would one proceed to prepare a 0.129-molal solution (often abbreviated as 0.129m) of $KClO_3$ in 345 ml of water?

SOLUTION: The formula weight of $KClO_3$ is 122.6. A 1m solution would contain 122.6 grams of $KClO_3$ dissolved in 1000 grams H_2O. Hence, a 0.129m solution in 345 grams of water would require

$$122.6 \text{ grams} \times 0.129 \times 0.345 = 5.46 \text{ grams } KClO_3$$

The 5.46 grams of $KClO_3$ should be weighed out and dissolved completely in 345 ml (345 grams) of water.

PROBLEM: A solution contains 7.80 grams of glucose, $C_6H_{12}O_6$, dissolved in 83.5 grams of water. What is the molal concentration of this solution?

SOLUTION: The formula weight for $C_6H_{12}O_6$ is 180; hence 1 mole weighs 180 grams. The concentration of the solution is

$$\frac{7.80}{180} \text{ moles in 83.5 grams of solvent}$$

or

$$\frac{7.80}{180} \times \frac{1}{83.5} \text{ moles/gram solvent}$$

or

$$\frac{7.80}{180} \times \frac{1000}{83.5} = 0.518 \text{ moles/kg solvent}$$

The concentration is 0.518m.

Other methods for expressing the concentration of a solution will be considered only briefly. The mole-fraction method gives the number of moles of one component (solute or solvent) divided by the total number of moles (solute plus solvent) present in the solution. This method is applicable to multicomponent systems. The normality method gives the number of gram-equivalents of solute present per liter of solution. The concept of gram-equivalents will be discussed in the next chapter. The percentage method gives the percent by weight of

TABLE **12.1** SUMMARY OF METHODS USED IN EXPRESSING THE CONCENTRATION OF A SOLUTION

Name	Symbol	Solute units	Solvent units	Definition
Molarity	M	gram-mole	liter solution	$\dfrac{\text{moles solute}}{\text{liter solution}}$
Formality	F	gram-formula weight	liter solution	$\dfrac{\text{formula-wt solute}}{\text{liter solution}}$
Molality	m	gram-mole	kg solvent	$\dfrac{\text{moles solute}}{\text{kg solvent}}$
Mole fraction	x	mole	mole solution	$\dfrac{\text{moles solute}}{\text{total moles}}$
Normality	N	gram-equivalent weight	liter solution	$\dfrac{\text{equiv-wt solute}}{\text{liter solution}}$

solute in the solution, or alternatively, the percent by volume, or sometimes even the weight of solute per 100 grams of solvent. Several of these systems are summarized in Table 12.1.

12.3 *Solubility*

Experience tells that there is a limit to the quantity of sugar that can be dissolved in water. After this limit has been reached, it is not possible to force more sugar into solution, no matter how long the mixture is stirred, unless the temperature is changed. Additional sugar simply lies undissolved at the bottom of the container. The sugar is said to have a definite solubility in water. The term solubility will be defined more precisely below.

Some substances such as sugar, are highly soluble in water—large quantities of sugar may be dissolved in moderate quantities of water. Other substances, such as barium sulfate, are soluble to such an exceedingly slight degree that they are commonly said to be insoluble, although a truly insoluble substance probably does not exist. Degree of solubility is determined not only by the nature of the solute but also by the solvent. Sulfur readily dissolves in carbon disulfide, but it is practically insoluble in water. Furthermore, the solubility of most substances depends on the temperature and, especially for gases, on the pressure.

A solution that has been shaken with excess solute until no further apparent dissolving takes place is said to be a saturated solution. The *solubility* of a solute is defined as the concentration of a saturated solution of solute at the particular temperature employed. A condition of saturation implies the existence of a physical equilibrium not unlike that already described for the pressure exerted by a vapor in contact with its liquid phase. When a solution is saturated, particles of the excess solute are continually going into the solvent, but particles are also crystallizing from solution to become solid again. When these opposing processes take place at equal rates, the condition of equilibrium has been reached, and the solution is said to be saturated. A *saturated solution* is defined as one in which the dissolved solute is in equilibrium with excess undissolved solute.

The solubility of one substance in another may be determined by chemical analysis of a saturated solution. One very simple example will suffice for the present. If it is desired to measure the solubility of, say, sodium chloride in water at room temperature, it would first be necessary to prepare a saturated solution of sodium chloride under the desired conditions. A quantity of the saturated solution, free from excess solute, would then be removed and accurately measured by weight or by volume. In this example it would now be possible to obtain the weight of sodium chloride present by permitting the water to evaporate, perhaps at somewhat elevated temperature, or under partial vacuum. The dry sodium chloride would then be weighed. The solubility of the sodium chloride in water could be expressed as grams of solute per 100 grams of solvent, or in any other desired manner. At 25° C the solubility of sodium chloride is thus found to be 36.1 grams NaCl per 100 grams H_2O. The solubility of barium sulfate under the same conditions is only 2.22×10^{-4} gram $BaSO_4$ per 100 grams H_2O. Note that a saturated solution is by no means necessarily a concentrated solution.

With a few exceptions, most solids become more soluble as the temperature is raised. This effect results from the fact that most solution processes are endothermic:

$$solute + solvent \rightleftharpoons solution - heat$$

(If, for instance, potassium nitrate is dissolved in water, the solution feels cold.) Then, by application of Le Châtelier's principle, it is seen that the equilibrium will be shifted to the right by an increase of temperature. The solubility of potassium nitrate is 13.3 grams KNO_3 per 100 grams H_2O at 0° C, but rises to 246 grams per 100 grams at 100° C.

The solubility of a gas in a liquid (or in a solid) appears always to be decreased by increase of temperature. This is a natural consequence of the increasing kinetic energy (and thus of the escaping tendency) of a gas as the temperature is raised. But the solubility of most gases is increased by increasing the pressure in accordance with **Henry's law** which may be stated as:

The solubility of a gas dissolved in a liquid at constant temperature is directly proportional to the partial pressure of the gas.

It will be noted from the statements made above that a solution which is saturated at room temperature may often dissolve more solute if the temperature is raised; in the case of a gas, a solution that is saturated at one pressure may dissolve more solute if the pressure is raised. These effects give rise to the phenomenon of *supersaturation.* Sodium thiosulfate (photographer's hypo) is much more soluble at high temperature than at low. If a saturated solution of this compound is prepared at, say, 100° C, there will be in solution several times as much solute as could be present in a saturated solution at room temperature. Now let this saturated solution at 100° C be freed from all excess solute and then allowed to cool to room temperature. It might be expected that, under these circumstances, excess solute would crystallize from the solution, but this is not necessarily the case. Careful cooling, in the absence of shaking or of dirt particles, often results in the solution reaching room temperature (or lower) before any crystallization takes place. The solution in this condition contains more (often much more) solute than does a saturated solution at the same temperature. Such a solution is said to be *supersaturated.*

Supersaturation is not an equilibrium condition; it resembles the condition called *supercooling.* Such states are said to be metastable. If to the supersaturated solution there is added a single tiny crystal of the solute, the crystal will grow rapidly, and in a few seconds all the excess solute will have crystallized. Supersaturation is a common phenomenon and one that may occur in solid-solid solutions, as of one metal dissolved in another.

12.4 Molecular Weights in Solution

It will be recalled that the molecular weights of gases may be obtained from the gas density under standard conditions. Another method is applicable to many substances that can be obtained in solution.

In Fig. 3.4 there was shown the equilibrium vapor pressure for a liquid, plotted against the temperature. The boiling point was indicated as the temperature at which the vapor pressure becomes equal to the atmospheric pressure. In Fig. 12.2 there is shown the vapor pressure plot for both a pure solvent and a solution. The plot has been extended to include the freezing-point region as well as the boiling point. It will be noted that at any given temperature, the vapor pressure of the solution is less than that of the pure solvent. This is true of any solution except one in which the volatility of the solute is comparable with, or greater than, that of the solvent.

The lowering of the vapor pressure of a solution relative to that of the pure solvent depends on the number of moles of solute present, and it may be used to find the molecular weight of a dissolved substance,

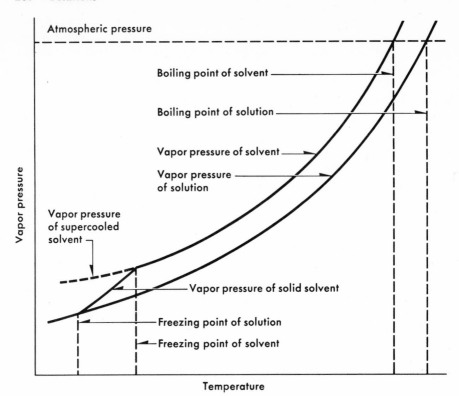

Fig. 12.2 *Vapor pressure plotted against temperature for a pure solvent, for supercooled solvent, and for solid solvent. The vapor pressure for a solution is also shown. It will be noted that the vapor pressure of the solution is less than that of the pure solvent at any given temperature, and that this results in the solution having a lower freezing point and a higher boiling point. The curves are exaggerated a little for the sake of clearness.*

but this method is somewhat complicated and more convenient methods are available. It will be seen from Fig. 12.2 that, because of the lowering of the equilibrium vapor pressure, the boiling point of a solution is higher and the freezing point is lower than those of the pure solvent. Both the elevation of the boiling point and the depression of the freezing point have been found to be related to the molecular weight of the solute, and constitute important methods for finding molecular weights.

It has been found by experiment that, for a dilute solution of a solute of low volatility, the elevation, ΔT, of the boiling point is given by

$$\Delta T = k_b m \tag{12.1}$$

where k_b is the *molal boiling-point constant*, and m is the molal concentration of the solution. The quantity k_b is characteristic of the particular solvent used. The important relationship given in Eq. 12.1 states that the elevation of the boiling point is directly proportional to the molality of the solution. Use of this relationship in finding molecular weights will be illustrated by the next problem.

PROBLEM: The normal boiling point of carbon disulfide is 46.13° C, but when 2.83 grams of sulfur are dissolved in 63.0 grams of carbon disulfide, the boiling point is raised by 0.41 degrees. Find the molecular weight of sulfur dissolved in carbon disulfide. The molal boiling-point constant for carbon disulfide is 2.34.

SOLUTION: From Eq. 12.1, the molality of the solution is

$$m = \frac{\Delta T}{k_b}$$

Molality is defined as the number of moles of solute per kilogram of solvent; and the number of moles of solute is the mass in grams of solute divided by the mass in grams of 1 mole of solute.

Let w be the mass in grams of solute and W the mass in kilograms of solvent. Then

$$\frac{\Delta T}{k_b} = \frac{w}{(\text{grams per mole solute}) \times W}$$

and rearranging,

$$\text{grams per mole solute} = \frac{wk_b}{\Delta TW}$$

$$= \frac{2.83 \text{ grams} \times 2.34 \text{ deg mole}^{-1}\text{ kg}}{0.41 \text{ deg} \times 0.0630 \text{ kg}}$$

$$= 257 \text{ grams mole}^{-1}$$

A mole of sulfur dissolved in carbon disulfide weighs 257 grams and, as the atomic weight of sulfur is 32.1, it appears that the formula for sulfur under these conditions is S_8.

The determination of molecular weights from freezing-point depression is very similar, it being found that the depression of the freezing point is directly proportional to the molal concentration, or

$$\Delta T = k_f m \qquad\qquad (12.2)$$

The molal freezing-point constant, k_f, is, of course, different from k_b, and it refers to a depression rather than an elevation. Table 12.2 give k_b and k_f, together with normal boiling and freezing points for several useful solvents.

TABLE 12.2   SOME MOLAL BOILING- AND FREEZING-
POINT CONSTANTS

Solvent	Normal bp, °C	k_b	Normal fp	k_f
Water	100	0.5	0.0	1.85
Benzene	80.15	2.53	5.45	5.1
Camphor	......	....	178.4	40.0
Barium chloride	......	....	962	108

PROBLEM: A solution contains 25.0 grams of solute in 298 grams of water. The freezing point is −3.0° C. Find the molecular weight of the solute. (The lowering of the freezing point is obviously 3.0 degrees.)

SOLUTION: From Eq. 12.2, rearranged as for the previous problem,

$$\text{Grams per mole solute} = \frac{wk_f}{\Delta TW}$$

$$= \frac{25.0 \text{ grams} \times (1.85 \text{ deg mole}^{-1} \text{ kg})}{3.0 \text{ deg} \times 0.298 \text{ kg}}$$

$$= 52 \text{ gram mole}^{-1}$$

The molecular weight of the solute is 52.

The constants k_b and k_f may be used to calculate the change of boiling and freezing points, respectively for substances of known molecular weight. The elevation of the boiling point or depression of the freezing point from normal may also be used to determine the purity of a compound, provided a pure sample is available for comparison. It may interest the reader to know that the constants k_b and k_f are related to the heats of vaporization and fusion, respectively. For instance, $k_f = RT^2/\Delta Hn$, where R is the gas constant, T the normal (°K) freezing point, ΔH the heat of fusion per mole, and n the number of moles in 1 kg of solvent.

The several properties of a solution, such as vapor-pressure lowering, that depend on the number of dissolved particles are called *colligative* properties. In addition to those colligative properties already mentioned, another will be described briefly. This is *osmotic pressure*.

If a piece of animal membrane or of uncoated cellophane is placed so that one side is in contact with a solution and the other with a pure solvent, it will be found that solvent molecules diffuse through the membrane in the direction toward the solution, thus tending to dilute the solution. A convenient demonstration of this phenomenon, called *osmosis*, is shown in Fig. 12.3. A considerable hydrostatic pressure may be built up in

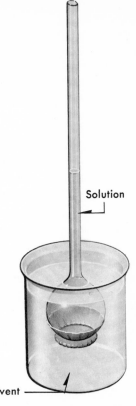

Solution

Fig. 12.3 Osmosis experiment. The osmotic pressure is in-dicated by the height to which the solution rises in the tube.

Solvent

this way, and when the system has reached equilibrium, the pressure developed is the osmotic pressure.

The popular explanation for osmosis is that, the vapor pressure of the pure solvent being greater than that of the solution, the solvent mole-cules simply "evaporate" through the membrane. It is, however, probable that purely mechanical considerations, such as the diameter of the pores in the membrane, play a part in the effect. Whatever may be the basic reason for osmosis, it is important in the transfer of fluids through cell walls in living matter; and, the osmotic pressure being related to the molecular weight of the solute, use is made of osmosis in finding the molecular weights of very large molecules to which the vapor density or freezing point depression methods are not applicable.

12.5 Colloids

True solutions are optically homogeneous; the extent to which the solute may settle is almost always imperceptible, and the freezing point and other properties show characteristic changes. Mechanical suspensions, on the other hand, settle rapidly, as does sand from water; the individual particles are readily discerned; and the freezing point and other properties are generally those of the pure liquid.

There is a borderline between these two categories of mixtures. The particles may be too small to settle out or to be visible, but they may be too large for the mixture to be considered a true solution. Matter in this condition is said to be in the colloidal state, and such mixtures are called *colloids.* Particles forming colloids average from 10 to 10,000 Å in diameter and may contain from one to a few million molecules, depending on their size. Elements and compounds form colloids, and they are found in all states of matter.

Colloid particles are not visible to the unaided eye, but they may be made visible by the ultramicroscope. A beam of light shining through a true solution, free from dust particles, is practically invisible, but a beam of light shining through a colloid is clearly visible because the colloidal particles, although themselves invisible, reflect light to the observer. This effect is often seen when sunlight enters a darkened room through a small hole in a shade. This property of colloids is known as **Tyndall effect.** If the beam of light is focused by a lens and a microscope is placed directly above the focal point, then the colloidal particles become visible as tiny dancing specks of light. This arrangement is called an *ultramicroscope.* The movement of the particles is, of course, the Brownian movement. The fact that colloids show the Brownian movement is a further distinction between colloids, true solutions, and mechanical mixtures.

It might be expected that, in time, colloids would settle; and, for one reason or another, some of them do. But colloidal gold prepared by Michael Faraday over a hundred years ago is still in the colloidal state. There appear to be at least three reasons why colloidal particles do not settle out. First, the particles are small enough to show the Brownian movement. This continued erratic motion prevents the particles from collecting in aggregates and from falling, under the influence of gravity, to the bottom of the container. Second, the colloidal particles are electrically charged, and all the particles of a given colloid have the same charge. Like electric charges repel each other; the particles are thus prevented from collecting in large aggregates. Third, not infrequently is it found that films form around the colloidal particles. These films may, for instance, be of gelatin, which acts to prevent coagulation of the particles. Prevention of coagulation is one of the principal factors tending to keep the colloidal particles from settling out. If the particles can grow by one particle adhering to another, then the particles will soon be too large for the Brownian movement, and once the Brownian movement stops, settling will be rapid.

Substances may be prepared in the colloidal state by several methods. Such substances must, of course, be relatively insoluble in the mixture that is to be used. Otherwise, the colloid will simply pass into true solution. Colloids may be prepared either by breaking down or dispersing massive portions of matter to the dimensions where colloidal effects appear, or they may be prepared by starting with dissolved substances and building up or condensing colloidal particles from the individual atoms or ions of which they are composed.

Dispersion, as a method of preparing colloids is often practiced with a colloid mill, a mechanical device that grinds particles to colloidal size. Another way of doing this, especially for the preparation of colloidal metals, is to take two wires of the substance (say, gold or platinum), connect them to an electric circuit, and bring the wires in momentary contact under water. The electric arc that forms tears little particles of the metal away, and some of these are of the proper dimensions to form a colloid. The method is referred to as the Bredig arc.

Many substances go into the colloidal condition when placed in contact with appropriate agents such as water. Glue, for instance, is often said to dissolve in water, but actually it forms a colloid rather than a true solution. The water is said to act by a process of peptization, and is spoken of as a peptizing agent. Sodium hydroxide acts as a peptizing agent on many substances. In the ceramic industry, the manufacture of chinaware and porcelainware, small amounts of sodium hydroxide keep the clays in a fluid, colloidal condition without the use of excess water. The clays may thus conveniently be molded for firing without the shrinkage and distortion attendant upon the use of much water.

Colloids of one liquid in another, such as oil and water, are generally difficult to keep any length of time. But they may be stabilized by the use of emulsifying agents. Such agents form a protective film over the colloidal particles. Soap will emulsify a mixture of oil and water, and yolk of egg will emulsify a mixture of olive oil and vinegar, as in mayonnaise.

The condensation methods for colloid preparation involve starting with a solution. Gold colloid may be prepared by addition of a mild reducing agent, such as tannin, to a dilute gold chloride solution. A beautiful red-gold or blue-gold colloid results. The color depends on the size of the particles, which in turn depends on the conditions under which the reduction is carried out. Colloidal arsenic sulfide is prepared by adding hydrogen sulfide to arsenous oxide, As_2O_3, suspended in water:

$$As_2O_3 + 3H_2S \rightarrow As_2S_3 + 3H_2O$$

Colloidal ferric hydroxide is made by hydrolyzing ferric chloride. A dilute solution of ferric chloride in water is simply boiled for a few moments. The red colloid resuts[1]:

$$FeCl_3 + 3H_2O \rightarrow Fe(OH)_3 + 3HCl$$

[1] Some authorities write the red substance as $Fe_2O_3 \cdot xH_2O$ instead of $Fe(OH)_3$.

It is sometimes necessary to break down the colloidal state in order to separate the constituents. The principles involved are not entirely clear, but it appears that this may be done by neutralizing the electric charges that normally aid in preventing settling. Suppose the particles are all negatively charged. This charge may be neutralized by adding to the colloid an ion carrying a strong positive charge. Barium chloride, containing the ion Ba^{2+}, for instance (or even better, aluminum sulfate, containing Al^{3+}), would be effective in breaking down a negative colloid. If, on the other hand, the charge on the colloid is positive, then an ion with a strong negative charge should be added. Such ions are SO_4^{2-} contained in sodium sulfate, Na_2SO_4 (or better, PO_4^{3-}, as in sodium phosphate). A negative colloid will neutralize a positive colloid.

The principle of neutralizing the electric charges on colloids is applied in the Cottrell precipitator. Smokes are examples of colloids formed in air. These are called *aerosols.* In various industries, smokes produced incidental to chemical operations may be objectionable or may carry away valuable by-products. Such smoke particles may be recovered by having the flue gases pass through chambers containing highly charged wires or chains. The smoke particles collected on these wires fall to the floor of the chamber.

A few varied colloidal systems known are as follows: (1) gas in liquid: foams, beer, whipped cream; (2) gas in solid: air in minerals such as meerschaum; (3) liquid in gas: fogs, aerosal sprays; (4) liquid in liquid: emulsions, mayonnaise; (5) liquid in solid: gels, gelatin; (6) solid in gas: smokes; (7) solid in liquid: many, as described above; (8) solid in solid: some colored glass and minerals.

EXERCISES

1. In what ways do solutions resemble, and differ from, true compounds?
2. With the aid of a simple experiment show that the vapor pressure over a sugar solution is less than that over pure water.
3. Show diagrammatically the relationship between vapor pressure and temperature for (a) a pure solvent and (b) a solution.
4. List at least six possible methods for finding molecular weights.
5. State Henry's law.
6. How would one prepare a supersaturated solution of a substance that is less soluble hot than cold?
7. Why do not colloids settle out?
8. A solution contains 83.8 grams of solute dissolved in 391 grams of solvent. Express the concentration in parts by weight of solute per 100 grams of solution (that is, in weight percent).

9. What weight of magnesium perchlorate, $Mg(ClO_4)_2$, is required for 300 ml of 1.8M solution?
10. What volume of 12M H_2SO_4 is required for the preparation of 15 liters of 0.10M solution?
11. How many moles of solute are present in each of the following solution: (a) 240 ml of 3.5M $BaCl_2$; (b) 240 ml of 3.5M HNO_3; (c) 240 ml of 3.5M of an unknown solute?
12. What volume of 3.35M Na_2SO_4 contains the same weight of solute as 125 ml of 1.25M solution?
13. What volume of 2.60M $BaCl_2$ contains the same number of moles of solute as 2.10 liters of 1.75M LiCl solution?
14. To what volume must 25 ml of 6.0M HCl be diluted in order for the solution to be 0.85M?
15. What volume of 4.5M H_2SO_4 must be diluted to prepare 100 ml of 1.00M solution?
16. What weight of glucose, $C_6H_{12}O_6$, is required to make a 0.733M solution in 445 grams of water?
17. Find the molecular weight of a substance, 3.2 grams of which dissolved in 65 grams of water lowers the freezing point to $-1.05°$ C.
18. What freezing-point lowering would be produced by 200 grams of methyl alcohol, CH_3OH, that is dissolved in 1000 grams of water?
19. What is the molecular weight of a nonelectrolyte, 3.25 grams of which dissolved in 50 grams of water depresses the freezing point to $-2.90°C$?
20. What is the concentration of a water solution of sugar ($C_{12}H_{22}O_{11}$) that boils (1 atm) at 100.38° C?
21. What weight of benzene as solvent would be required to dissolve 10 grams of naphthalene ($C_{10}H_8$) so that the solution would freeze at $+1.0°$ C? Molal freezing-point constant for benzene is 5.12° C. Normal freezing point is 5.4° C.
22. The molal freezing-point constant for naphthalene is 6.9° C. When 0.154 gram of acetanilide is dissolved in 9.83 grams of naphthalene, the freezing point of the solvent is lowered 0.805 degree. What is the molecular weight of acetanilide?
23. Pure cyclohexane freezes at 6.0° C; 20 grams of benzene (C_6H_6) in 1.0 kg of cyclohexane freezes at 1.0° C. What would be the freezing temperature of a solution containing 1.3 moles of benzene in 500 grams of cyclohexane?
24. What is the molar concentration of water in pure water if the density of water (at 25° C) is 0.997 gram/ml.
25. To a liter of water is added 84.5 grams of ethanol, C_2H_5OH. What is the mole fraction of ethanol present?

26. In using the expression $k_f = RT^2/\Delta Hn$ to relate the molal freezing-point constant to the heat of fusion, it is necessary to express the gas constant, R in the same units, namely, temperature degrees (K), calories, and moles as used for the other quantities in the equation. The gas constant in these units is $R = 1.986$ cal mole^{-1} deg^{-1}. Determine if k_f calculated in this way is the same as the experimentally found k_f for water.

13

Acids, Bases, Salts, and Solvents

13.1 Electrolytes

All true metals show a good conductivity for electricity. This conductivity appears to result from a more or less free movement of electrons within the metal, and it is not associated with any chemical change in the metal. Sodium chloride is not a metal, and it is a poor conductor of electricity as a solid. It does, however, become a good conductor when it is heated above the melting point or when it is dissolved in water. The electrical conductivity of sodium chloride under these conditions is always associated with a physical transport of matter and with chemical changes. Fused (melted) sodium chloride carries electricity, but in so doing, it undergoes decomposition into sodium metal and chlorine. In water solution, sodium chloride conducts electricity, but in so doing, the sodium chloride and the water are converted into hydrogen, sodium hydroxide, and chlorine. A substance that conducts electricity with simultaneous chemical change is called an *electrolyte*. This chapter will be concerned with solutions of electrolytes.

The electrical conductivity of a solution may easily be demonstrated by connecting an electric-light bulb in series with two strips of metal,

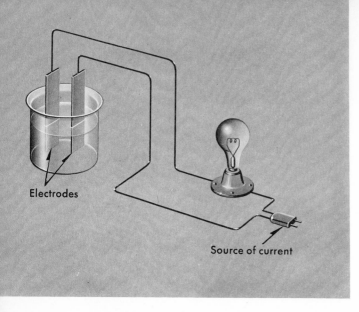

Fig. 13.1 Apparatus for testing the electrical conductivity of solutions.

Source of current

preferably of nickel or platinum, as shown in Fig. 13.1. These metal strips are dipped into a beaker containing the solution under investigation. If the solution conducts electricity, the lamp will light up. A very rough estimate of the electrical conductivity may be made from the brightness of the lamp, but appropriate meters must be used, under standardized conditions, to obtain quantitative measures of the conductivity.

Some substances dissolve in water to form solutions that exhibit excellent electrical conductivity. These are called *strong electrolytes*. Sodium chloride, hydrogen chloride, sulfuric acid, and potassium nitrate are typical examples of strong electrolytes. Our attention in this chapter will be directed chiefly toward strong electrolytes.

Some substances such as boric acid or ammonium hydroxide may be quite soluble in water, but they form only moderate to poor electrically conducting solutions. Such substances are called *weak electrolytes*, and they will be discussed in the next chapter.

An explanation for the behavior of electrolytes in solution was advanced in 1884 by S. Arrhenius. Although his theory has undergone considerable revision, it is still regarded as a basically correct view. Arrhenius' proposal was that such solutions contain ions; that is, they contain the charged particles that we now know to be formed from atoms by loss or gain of electrons. In the case of sodium chloride the ions present in the solid become surrounded by solvent molecules and drift apart. Under the influence of an electric field these ions migrate, the positive ions toward the negative electrode and the negative ions toward the positive electrode. In due course it will be found that the positive sodium ions have increased in concentration in the neighborhood of the negative electrode, and the negative chloride ions have increased in concentration around the positive electrode. The electricity is carried through the solution to the appropriate electrode by the drift of oppositely charged ions. This effect of ionic migration may be demonstrated by using copper permanganate, $Cu(MnO_4)_2$, as electrolyte as shown in Fig. 13.4. The copper ion is blue and the permanganate ion is purple. After migration under the influence of an electric field has proceeded for some time, it will be found that the blue copper ion has collected around the negative electrode and the purple permanganate around the positive electrode.

By definition, a *strong electrolyte* is one that provides a high concentration of ions per mole of solute. It follows, therefore, that the conductivity of such a solution should be proportional to the concentration. This is found to be true for dilute solutions of solutes such as sodium chloride, although at higher concentrations there are complications, which will be briefly described below. If, therefore, one has prepared, say, a $0.01M$ solution of NaCl in water, it is corrected to say that the concentration of Na^+ ions is $0.01M$ and also that the concentration of Cl^- ions is $0.01M$. If the concentration of NaCl is $0.02M$, then the concentrations of both Na^+ and Cl^- become $0.02M$ and the conductivity of the solution is approximately doubled.

Fig. 13.2 Diagrammatic representation of how a crystal of sodium chloride may dissolve in water. The ions of sodium and of chlorine in the crystal attract water molecules which have the effect of reducing the electrical attraction between adjacent, oppositely charged ions. These ions then drift away independently under the influence of the Brownian movement.

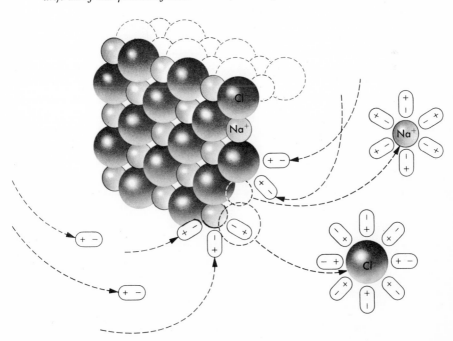

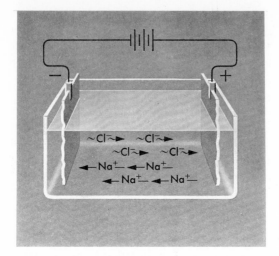

Fig. 13.3 Under the influence of an electric current, a solution of sodium chloride soon is found to have sodium ions collecting around the negative pole, while chlorine ions collect around the positive pole. Some chlorine may actually bubble off from the surface of the positive pole.

The concentration of ions in solution depends also on the nature of the solute. Some solutes, of which barium sulfate is an example, are soluble in water to such a slight degree that they are often said to be insoluble. Nevertheless it is found that all the barium sulfate that does dissolve in water is present as the ions Ba^{2+} and SO_4^{2-}. The concentration of a saturated solution of $BaSO_4$ is only $1 \times 10^{-5}M$, and such a solution obviously contains too low a concentration of ions to be a good conductor of electricity.

Some solutes possess various degrees of covalency and of bond strength between the several atoms that might be expected to dissociate

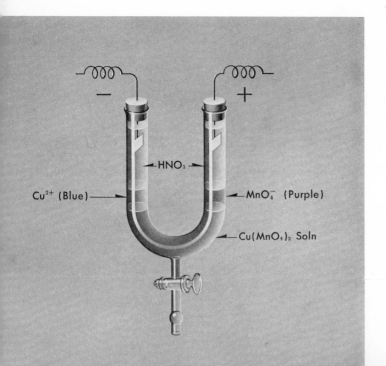

Fig. 13.4 Migration of ions demonstrated by the electrolysis of copper permanganate solution. The blue copper, Cu^{2+}, ions migrate toward the negative pole and the purple permanganate, MnO_4^-, ions toward the positive pole.

TABLE 13.1   Dielectric constants of some solvents

Solvent	Formula	Dielectric constant at 21° C
Hydrogen cyanide	HCN	95.4
Sulfuric acid	H_2SO_4	84
Water	H_2O	80
Sulfur dioxide	SO_2	15.6
Ammonia	NH_3	15.5
Benzene	C_6H_6	2.3

to ions in solution. Mercuric chloride, $HgCl_2$, is one of the rather small number of salts that is a true weak electrolyte. Although $HgCl_2$ is quite soluble in water, the electrical conductivity of the solution remains comparatively low. Many acids and bases exhibit similar effects. It is also true that many solutes react chemically with water. Phosphorus trichloride, PCl_3, is scarcely to be considered an electrolyte, but it reacts with water, forming hydrochloric acid. The solution thus becomes an excellent conductor of electricity.

The concentration of ions in a solution depends not only on the concentration and nature of the solute, but also on the nature of the solvent. Hydrogen chloride is a typical strong electrolyte dissolved in water, but it forms a nonconducting solution in benzene. Apart from specific reaction between solute and solvent, the chief property of a solvent that leads to a high concentration of ions is the dielectric constant.[1] In general, polar molecules (Sec. 8.6) form liquids of high dielectric constant. Table 13.1 gives dielectric constants for a few typical solvents. Solvents of high dielectric constant are often referred to as *ionizing solvents.*

The electrical conductivity is not the only property that may be used to estimate the concentration of ions in solution. It will be recalled that the freezing point depression is one of several properties proportional to the molal concentration of a solution. If a $0.1m$ solution of NaCl in water

---

[1] If two parallel metal plates are arranged as shown with an electric potential across

them, the capacitance C_0 is the ratio of quantity of electricity accumulated on the plates to the potential across them. If the space between the plates is filled with some nonconducting substance, it will be found that the capacitance is changed to C. The dielectric constant $E = C/C_0$.

contains $0.1m$ Na^+ and $0.1m$ Cl^-, then the total concentration of solute particles is $0.2m$ and the freezing point of the water should be

$$0.2 \times -1.85 \text{ deg} = -0.37° \text{ C}$$

The experimental freezing point of such a solution is about $-0.35°$ C, a deviation of 0.02 deg. A more complicated example is calcium chloride, $CaCl_2$, in which a $0.1m$ solution of $CaCl_2$ might be expected to yield $0.1m$ Ca^{2+} plus $0.2m$ Cl^- (because there are two Cl^- ions for each Ca^{2+} ion) for a total particle concentration of $0.3m$. The freezing point observed for such a solution should be $0.3 \times -1.85 \text{ deg} = -0.56 \text{ deg}$, whereas it is actually $-0.49°$ C, a deviation of 0.07 deg.

It appears, therefore, the freezing point lowering may be used for a very rough estimate of the number of gram-ions[2] from one mole of solute.

PROBLEM: A $0.1m$ water solution of nickel chloride, $NiCl_2$, freezes at $-0.54°$ C. How many ions are present in the formula $NiCl_2$?

SOLUTION: A $0.1m$ solution in water would freeze at $-0.185°$ C, provided no dissociation takes place. If the actual freezing point is $-0.54°$ C, the molal concentration of particles must have been about $(-0.54/-0.185) \times 0.1m = 0.29m$. The ions present in the formula $NiCl_2$ are then, presumably, one Ni^{2+} plus two Cl^-.

While the kind of calculation shown above is often useful, it must be admitted that it lacks something of expected accuracy; but this is also true of estimates of ion concentration in strong electrolytes as derived from electrical conductivity measurements. This section will be concluded with some remarks concerning possible reasons for these discrepancies.

As described in Sec. 8.6, each ion in a crystal of sodium chloride has six nearest neighbor ions of opposite charge, and all these neighbor ions remain, except for vibration, in the same relative positions with respect to each other. But if the sodium chloride is dissolved in water, the high dielectric constant of the water and the effects of molecular motion lower the attractive forces between the oppositely charged ions. At infinite dilution it might be supposed that the ions would be completely free of each other, but of course in contact with and to some degree attracted to molecules of the solvent.

At ordinary concentrations there must be attractive forces between the oppositely charged ions so that (while the various neighboring ions will be able to move with respect to each other) at any given instant each

---

[2] The gram-ion is often used in the same sense as gram-atom. A *gram-ion* is the mass in grams of 6.02×10^{23} ions.

positive ion will be associated with some loosely attracted negative ions, and vice versa. In this way the mobility of both positive and negative ions will be diminished and the electrical conductivity will be lowered. Similarly, the effective concentration of the ions will be somewhat less than those estimated in the problem given above, the decrease being due to this lack of complete freedom from oppositely charged ions and from solvent molecules.

These ideas were developed in 1923 by P. Debye and E. Hückel into the **interionic attraction theory,** which, with later developments, is an important correction and extension of the **Arrhenius theory of electrolytic dissociation.** The Debye-Hückel theory lies beyond the scope of this book. We shall therefore content ourselves by stating that it gives a reasonably satisfactory explanation for the effects observed, provided the concentrations are very low.

The concept of *effective* concentration of an ionic species in solution has found considerable use. It is defined as

$$a = \gamma m \tag{13.1}$$

where a is the effective molal concentration, m is the molality, and γ is the *activity coefficient*. The activity coefficient is a measure of the deviation from ideal behavior, such as would be the case if, say, NaCl gave a freezing-point lowering of exactly 2×1.85 deg per mole of solute per kilogram of water. The activity coefficient depends on the concentration. For instance, at $0.0001m$, the activity coefficient of KCl is 0.982; at $0.1m$, it is 0.977. We shall have some further reference to activity coefficients in Chapter 15.

In the Appendix there will be found a table of various positive and negative ions and some remarks concerning the solubilities of the salts formed from these ions.

13.2   Self-ionization of Solvents

The purest water that may be prepared has a small, but measurable, electrical conductivity. This conductivity is not due to any dissolved electrolytes accidentally present in trace amounts, but is rather an inherent property of water itself. The property is believed to be due to the ability of water molecules to react with each other to form ions. The reaction is reversible, and may be represented as follows:

$$2H_2O \rightleftharpoons H_3O^+ + OH^-$$

the ion H_3O^+ being commonly called the *hydronium ion*. This reaction, which is sometimes called autoprotolysis, is a transfer of a proton from one water molecule to another. Representing the molecules in structural form, we have

$$H—\overset{..}{\underset{|}{O}}: + H—\overset{..}{\underset{|}{O}}: \rightleftharpoons \left[H—\overset{..}{\underset{|}{O}}—H \right]^{+} + \left[:\overset{..}{\underset{..}{O}}—H \right]^{-}$$
$$HHH$$

the line between atoms representing, as before, an electron-pair bond. The ability of the water molecule to undergo this reaction is made possible by the pairs of electrons present in this molecule but unused in bond forma-tion, and the reaction is doubtless aided by the high dielectric constant of water, although this is not the only requirement for self-ionization.

A molecule that readily gives up a proton is sometimes said to be *protogenic;* one that readily accepts a proton is sometimes said to be *protophilic.* (We shall examine such substances and give them simpler names in the next section.) A molecule like that of water which, as shown above, may either give up or accept a proton is said to be *amphiprotic.* It is this remarkable property that accounts for many of the unique chemical reactions of water.

The hydronium ion is simply a water molecule attached to a proton. In view of this, many authors omit the water in writing the formula for the hydronium ion, and we shall follow this custom. The self-ionization reaction for water then becomes

$$H_2O \rightleftharpoons H^+ + OH^-$$

and the expression for the equilibrium constant is

$$\frac{[H^+][OH^-]}{[H_2O]} = K$$

Now, in water, the degree of self-ionization that takes place is very small and, water being a liquid, the concentration of water (the number of moles per liter) is a constant. We may, then, with only negligible error, multiply both sides of the equation by $[H_2O]$, to obtain

$$[H^+][OH^-] = K_w$$

The constant K_w is called the *dissociation constant,* or the *ion product,* for water.

At 25° C, $K_w = 1 \times 10^{-14}$ mole^2 liter^{-2}, and as one proton and one hydroxide ion are produced from each dissociating water molecule, it follows that in pure water,

$$[H^+] = [OH^-] = (1 \times 10^{-14} \text{ mole}^2 \text{ liter}^{-2})^{1/2}$$
$$= 1 \times 10^{-7} \text{ mole liter}^{-1}$$

The ion product for water is one of the most useful concepts in chemistry. The numerical value given has been derived from careful

TABLE 13.2 SELF-IONIZATION PROCESSES AND CONSTANTS FOR
SOME SOLVENTS

Solvent	Reaction	Ion product
Water	$2H_2O \rightleftharpoons H_3O^+ + OH^-$	10^{-14}
Ammonia	$2NH_3 \rightleftharpoons NH_4^+ + NH_2^-$	10^{-23}
Sulfuric acid	$2H_2SO_4 \rightleftharpoons H_3SO_4^+ + HSO_4^-$	10^{-4}
Hydrogen fluoride	$2HF \rightleftharpoons H_2F^+ + F^-$	very small
Benzene	$2C_6H_6 \rightleftharpoons C_6H_7^+ + C_6H_5^-$	zero

measurements of electrical conductivity on the purest water obtainable. It is to be noted that the ion product of water increases with increasing temperature, becoming, for instance, 9.6×10^{-14} at 60° C. Note also that in water at 25° C, only 1 molecule in 500,000,000, on the average, has undergone self-ionization.

Water is not the only liquid that undergoes self-ionization. A few other examples are given in Table 13.2.

It is not essential that the molecule exhibiting self-ionization should contain hydrogen. Bromine trifluoride shows some conductance and is presumably self-ionized as follows:

$$2BrF_3 \rightleftharpoons BrF_2^+ + BrF_4^-$$

13.3 *pH*

The concentration of positive hydrogen ions in solution is often represented by a convention known as *pH*. This term is defined as the logarithm of the reciprocal of the hydrogen ion concentration. Thus,

$$pH = \log \frac{1}{[H^+]} = - \log [H^+]$$

where $[H^+]$ stands, as before, for the hydrogen ion concentration expressed in moles per liter. It then follows that

$$[H^+] = 10^{-pH} = \frac{1}{10^{pH}}$$

For *pH* 8, $[H^+] = 10^{-8}M$, or 0.00000001 mole/liter; for *pH* 2, $[H^+] = 0.01M$; and for *pH* 0, $[H^+] = 1M$ because 10 raised to the zero power equals 1.

PROBLEM: The *pH* of a solution is 2.6. Find the hydrogen ion concentration.

SOLUTION: The numerical value of $[H^+]$ is the number whose logarithm is -2.6; that is, the antilog of -2.6. Proceed as follows:

$$\text{Antilog } (-2.6) = \text{antilog } (0.4 - 3.0) = 2.5 \times 10^{-3}$$

Hence $[H^+] = 2.5 \times 10^{-3}M$. (The antilog -3.0 is obviously 10^{-3}, and the antilog of 0.4 is 2.5, as may be found from log tables or slide rule.)

PROBLEM: The hydrogen ion concentration of a solution is $3.5 \times 10^{-4}M$. Find the pH.

SOLUTION: By definition, $p\text{H} = -\log [H^+]$; hence, for this solution,

$$
\begin{aligned}
p\text{H} &= -\log (3.5 \times 10^{-4}) \\
&= -(\log 3.5 + \log 10^{-4}) \\
&= -(0.54 - 4) \\
&= 3.5
\end{aligned}
$$

Values of pH are seldom given beyond one decimal place.

The pH method for representing hydrogen ion concentration is a convenience, and it is widely used. If, in pure water at $25°$ C, $[H^+] = 10^{-7}M$, then it is obvious that the pH of pure water under these conditions is 7. The pH of blood is normally about 7.4, that of the gastric fluid in the stomach about 3 to 4, and of sea water, 8.2. Note that as the hydrogen ion concentration rises, the pH falls.

13.4   Acids and Bases

There are three classes of electrolytes. These are known as acids, bases, and salts, respectively. This section will be devoted to general definitions and to properties associated with acids and bases. The historical development of modern concepts concerning acids and bases included a long period in which water was the only important known ionizing solvent. Definitions that were applicable to water solutions have proved to be too narrow for application to nonaqueous solutions. For this reason, there have been developed successively broader definitions of acids and bases; we shall present three of these, starting with the classical.

The classical definition of an acid is: An *acid* is a substance that will increase the hydrogen ion, H^+, concentration of water. A *base* is a substance that will increase the hydroxide ion, OH^-, concentration of water. Inasmuch as, in water, the ion product is always 1×10^{-14} at $25°$ C, regardless of the presence of solutes, it follows that an acid will *decrease* the hydroxide ion concentration, and a base will *decrease* the hydrogen ion concentration of water.

PROBLEM: Acid is added to water until the hydrogen ion concentration is $0.01M$. What is the hydroxide ion concentration?

SOLUTION: In water,

$$[H^+][OH^-] = 1 \times 10^{-14} \text{ mole}^2 \text{ liter}^{-2}$$

Solving for $[OH^-]$ and substituting for $[H^+]$,

$$[OH^-] = \frac{1 \times 10^{-14} \text{ mole}^2 \text{ liter}^{-2}}{1 \times 10^{-2} \text{ mole liter}^{-1}}$$
$$= 1 \times 10^{-12} \text{ mole liter}^{-1} \quad \text{or} \quad 1 \times 10^{-12}M.$$

Acids have the properties of sour taste; of reaction with certain organic substances called indicators, causing them to change color; of catalyzing certain reactions such as the inversion of sucrose; and of reacting with many (but not all) metals, with the liberation of hydrogen gas. Bases in solution feel soapy, have a bitter taste, and affect indicators in a manner opposite to those for acids. Most important, acids and bases are able to react with each other by a process called *neutralization*, which will be described in the following section. Many acids and bases are corrosive and potentially dangerous.

Some acids and some bases are strong electrolytes, and are called strong acids or strong bases, respectively. In water, they exist almost exclusively as ions. Other acids and bases are weak electrolytes that exist in solution mostly as undissociated molecules. Weak acids and bases will be treated in the next chapter. A few examples of strong acids are hydrochloric, HCl; nitric, HNO_3; and perchloric, $HClO_4$. Examples of strong bases are sodium hydroxide, $NaOH$; potassium hydroxide; KOH; and tetramethylammonium hydroxide, $N(CH_3)_4OH$. The mere presence of hydrogen in the formula of a compound is no proof of acidic properties; methane, CH_4, is by no means an acid. Similarly, a compound such as hypochlorous acid, $HClO$, may actually contain $-OH$ groups and may be better written as $ClOH$, but it is not a base. The only true test of acidic or basic properties is the experimental test; of these, the effect on selected indicators is the most convenient.

Some acids, such as sulfuric, H_2SO_4, have two hydrogen atoms in the formula. In this, but not in all such cases, both hydrogen atoms may form ions; thus,

$$H_2SO_4 \rightarrow H^+ + HSO_4^-$$
$$HSO_4^- \rightleftharpoons H^+ + SO_4^{2-}$$

but the second hydrogen atom does not contribute much to the total hydrogen ion concentration; H_2SO_4 is a strong acid; HSO_4^- is a moderately weak acid.

It will be noted that the dissolving of an acid in water may, in every case, be represented as a chemical reaction in which the acid reacts with the water to raise the hydrogen ion concentration, with due regard for the fact that the hydrogen ion is invariably hydrated (that is, attached to one and possibly to more than one water molecule). Thus,

$$HX + H_2O \rightleftharpoons H_3O^+ + X^-$$

Bases react with the dissociated hydrogen ions present in water; thus, we have

$$OH^- + H_3O^+ \rightleftharpoons 2H_2O$$

If the concentration of hydrogen ions is greater than that of hydroxide ions, the solution is said to be *acidic;* if the concentration of hydroxide ions is greater than that of hydrogen ions, the solution is said to be *basic.* In pure water, the concentration of hydrogen ions is equal to the concentration of hydroxide ions, namely $1 \times 10^{-7}M$, at 25° C. Pure water is therefore said to be *neutral;* water provides the dividing line between acids and bases.

It will also be noted that both equations given immediately above may be considered as transfers of a proton. The reaction of a classical acid with water is a proton transfer from an acid molecule to a water molecule, with the formation of H_3O^+. The reaction of a base in water is a proton transfer from a hydronium ion to a hydroxide ion, with formation of a water molecule. These considerations led to the development of the *Brönsted-Lowry* definition of acids and bases. These are: An *acid* is a substance that can give up a proton; a *base* is a substance that can accept a proton. In these definitions the word "substance" is interpreted very broadly to mean any species of molecule or ion capable of undergoing reaction.

With the aid of the Brönsted-Lowry definition, it is possible to reinterpret the behavior of the several molecules and ions mentioned above. Hydrochloric is obviously a Brönsted-Lowry acid, as are nitric and sulfuric. But the ion HSO_4^-, as previously indicated, is also a Brönsted-Lowry acid. Other examples of negative ions acting as acids are dihydrogen orthophosphate, $H_2PO_4^-$, and bicarbonate ion, HCO_3^-. Furthermore, some positive ions may act as Brönsted-Lowry acids. Examples of these are hydronium, H_3O^+, and ammonium, NH_4^+. Examples of Brönsted-Lowry bases are hydroxide, OH^-, and the amide ion, NH_2^-. Water may act as an acid, giving up a proton, or it may act as a base, accepting a proton; hence, as stated in a previous section, water is properly said to be amphiprotic. But a protogenic substance (Sec. 13.2) is more often and more conveniently said simply to be an acid; and a protophilic substance, a base.

It will be observed that whenever an acid (in this sense) gives up a proton, the residue of the acid becomes itself capable of accepting a proton. For instance, if the acid HSO_4^- gives up a proton reversibly, as it does, then

$$HSO_4^- \rightleftharpoons H^+ + SO_4^{2-}$$

But the sulfate ion, SO_4^{2-}, is capable of accepting a proton to form HSO_4^- and is therefore properly considered to be a base. In such a case the SO_4^{2-} is called the *conjugate base* of the acid HSO_4^-.

The Brönsted-Lowry definition makes it possible to extend acid-base considerations to a wide variety of nonaqueous solutions. Liquid ammonia will serve as an example. It has already been stated that the self-ionization of ammonia is similar to that of water, although it has a lower ion product constant. Ammonia is therefore amphiprotic—the conjugate base being the amide ion, NH_2^-, and the conjugate acid the ammonium ion, NH_4^+:

$$2NH_3 \rightleftharpoons NH_2^- + NH_4^+$$

Potassium amide (potassamide), KNH_2, is therefore a base in liquid ammonia; and ammonium chloride, NH_4Cl, is an acid. These two compounds will neutralize each other:

$$KNH_2 + NH_4Cl \rightarrow KCl + 2NH_3$$

or, omitting the ions that take no part in the reaction,

$$NH_2^- + NH_4^+ \rightarrow 2NH_3$$

Many other parallel reactions are known in the ammonia system and in other solvent systems.

An even more generalized concept of acids and bases is found in the Lewis definitions. Lewis defined an acid as an electron-pair acceptor and a base as an electron-pair donor. The implications of these definitions are most clearly seen by reference to a substance such as boron trifluoride, BF_3, which has the ability to combine with other substances through acceptance of a pair of electrons. A typical Lewis base is ammonia, which can supply an electron pair. The neutralization of boron trifluoride and ammonia may be represented as follows:

Lewis acid   Lewis base   salt

The Lewis concept is a rather formal one, but one that has considerable applicability in nonaqueous systems and especially in the area of reactions between solids and in fused salts.

13.5   *Neutralization*

Suppose that to a dilute aqueous solution of a strong acid, there is added, progressively, portions of a strong base. The base will neutralize the acid according to the general equation

$$HX + MOH \rightleftharpoons H_2O + MX$$

There are various reasons why any reversible reaction may, or may nearly, go to completion. One reason is that one or more of the products may be only slightly ionized. This is the case above, where, as already described, the product water has the low ion product of 10^{-14} moles^2 liter^{-2}. A typical example is the neutralization of hydrochloric acid with sodium hydroxide:

$$HCl + NaOH \rightleftharpoons H_2O + NaCl$$

which, as far as any real change occurs, is simply the union of a hydrogen (or hydronium) ion with a hydroxide ion:

$$H^+ + OH^- \rightleftharpoons H_2O$$

Another reason that may tend to force a reversible reaction to near completion is that a precipitate may form, thus effectively lowering the concentration of the products. This occurs in, for instance, the neutralization of sulfuric acid with the base barium hydroxide, the product barium sulfate being virtually insoluble in water:

$$H_2SO_4 + Ba(OH)_2 \rightleftharpoons 2H_2O + BaSO_4$$

In all such neutralizations of Brönsted-Lowry acids and bases, the products are water plus a salt. The latter may or may not remain in solution as ions.

In the discussion that follows, it will be assumed that both acid and base are strong electrolytes and that, to simplify the calculations, the acid is in dilute aqueous solution and the base is added as a solid. This procedure avoids a correction for the change in total volume, which would occur if the base were to be added in the form of a solution.

Let us say that the initial concentration of hydrochloric acid in a beaker is $0.10M$ and that the volume is 100 ml. Then, to this beaker there are added 20 successive portions of solid sodium hydroxide, each containing 0.0010 mole of NaOH and therefore weighing 0.040 gram. After each addition of base, the solution is stirred until reaction is complete; then the hydrogen ion concentration is determined. The result obtained is shown in Table 13.3, which also shows the pH of the solution at each step. If the hydrogen ion concentration is known in any aqueous solution, it is possible to find the hydroxide ion concentration also

TABLE 13.3 PROGRESSIVE ADDITION OF 0.0010 MOLE PORTIONS OF
NaOH TO 100 ml OF 0.10*M* HCl

Portions of NaOH added	$[H^+]$, *M*	*p*H	$[OH^-]$, *M*
0	1×10^{-1}	1	1.0×10^{-13}
1	9×10^{-2}	1.05	1.1×10^{-13}
2	8×10^{-2}	1.1	1.25×10^{-13}
3	7×10^{-2}	1.16	1.4×10^{-13}
4	6×10^{-2}	1.22	1.7×10^{-13}
5	5×10^{-2}	1.3	2.0×10^{-13}
6	4×10^{-2}	1.4	2.5×10^{-13}
7	3×10^{-2}	1.53	3.3×10^{-13}
8	2×10^{-2}	1.7	5.0×10^{-13}
9	1×10^{-2}	2	1.0×10^{-12}
10	1×10^{-7}	7	1×10^{-7}
11	1.0×10^{-12}	12	1×10^{-2}
12	5.0×10^{-13}	12.3	2×10^{-2}
13	3.3×10^{-13}	12.5	3×10^{-2}
14	2.5×10^{-13}	12.6	4×10^{-2}
15	2.0×10^{-13}	12.7	5×10^{-2}
16	1.7×10^{-13}	12.8	6×10^{-2}
17	1.4×10^{-13}	12.9	7×10^{-2}
18	1.25×10^{-13}	12.9	8×10^{-2}
19	1.1×10^{-13}	12.96	9×10^{-2}
20	1.0×10^{-13}	13	1×10^{-1}

because the ion product for water at 25° C is 1×10^{-14} mole² liter⁻². The hydroxide ion concentration so obtained is also shown in Table 13.3.

It will be seen that the hydrogen ion concentration of the solution falls during each addition of the base, that $[H^+]$ decreases by a factor of one trillion, and that $[OH^-]$ increases by the same factor. These changes are more conveniently represented graphically if the *p*H rather than $[H^+]$ is plotted against the moles of base added, as shown in Fig. 13.5.

From Fig. 13.5 it is clear that at one point during addition of the base, all the acid has been neutralized, but no excess base has been added. At this point, called the *neutral point*, the *p*H of the solution is that of pure water, namely, 7. It is possible to recognize the neutral point by making electrical measurements on the solution; these measurements will be described in Chapter 15. It is also a convenient circumstance that certain complex organic substances have the property of changing color at the neutral point. These substances are called *indicators*—one of them is litmus, which turns red in acid and blue in base; another is bromothymol

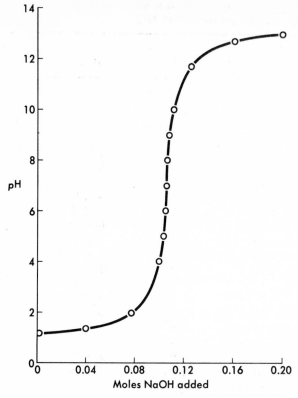

Fig. 13.5 The progressive change of pH as 0.001 mole portions of NaOH are added to 100 ml of 0.10M HCl. The pH changes abruptly at the equivalence point.

blue, which turns yellow in acid and blue in base. There are many other indicators known, of which phenolphthalein is one of the most useful, but they do not all change color at *p*H 7 as do litmus and bromothymol blue. Further remarks concerning indicators will be made in Chapter 14.

Ability to determine the neutral point (sometimes called the *end point*) of a neutralization reaction makes possible the titration of an acid with a base, or vice versa, so that if the concentration of one is known, that of the other may be found. This is part of the branch of chemistry known as volumetric quantitative analysis. It will be illustrated by the following two problems.

PROBLEM: What weight of sodium hydroxide will be required to neutralize 25 ml of 0.50M sulfuric acid?

SOLUTION: Always write a balanced equation for the reaction

$$2NaOH + H_2SO_4 \rightarrow Na_2SO_4 + 2H_2O$$

Fig. 13.6 A burette. This simple device makes it convenient to transfer a measured volume of an acid or base (or any other liquid reagent.)

If the acid is 0.50M, then 1000 ml contains 0.50 mole of H_2SO_4, so that 25 ml would contain $25/1000 \times 0.50$ mole of H_2SO_4.

According to the equation, 1 mole of H_2SO_4 neutralizes 2 moles of NaOH; therefore $25/1000 \times 0.50$ mole of acid would neutralize $25/1000 \times 0.50 \times 2$ mole of NaOH. As 1 mole of NaOH is equal to $(23 + 16 + 1)$ grams = 40 grams, the weight of NaOH required to neutralize 25 ml of 0.50M H_2SO_4 is

$$\frac{25}{1000} \times 0.50 \times 2 \times 40 \text{ grams} = 1.0 \text{ gram of NaOH}$$

In a titration such as that indicated, it is not necessary that acid and base be strong electrolytes.

PROBLEM: What is the molar concentration of a nitric acid solution, 75 ml of which neutralizes 30 ml of 1.2M $Ca(OH)_2$ solution?

SOLUTION:

$$Ca(OH)_2 + 2HNO_3 \rightarrow Ca(NO_3)_2 + 2H_2O$$

The amount of $Ca(OH)_2$ reacting is

$$\frac{30}{1000} \times 1.2 \text{ mole}$$

According to the equation, 1 mole of $Ca(OH)_2$ neutralizes 2 moles of HNO_3. The amount of nitric acid required to neutralize $30/1000 \times 1.2$ mole of calcium hydroxide is, then,

$$\frac{30}{1000} \times 1.2 \times 2 \text{ moles of } HNO_3$$

This number of moles of HNO_3 is contained in 75 ml of acid solution; therefore 1000 ml of acid solution would contain

$$\frac{1000}{75} \times \frac{30}{1000} \times 1.2 \times 2 \text{ moles} = 0.96 \text{ mole of } HNO_3$$

If 0.96 mole is contained in 1000 ml, then the concentration of the solution is $0.96M$.

It has been noted that the formulas of some acids such as hydrochloric, HCl, have only one hydrogen atom that ionizes and which consequently takes part in a neutralization reaction. Other acids such as sulfuric, H_2SO_4, have two such hydrogen atoms, and some, such as phosphoric, H_3PO_4, have three. Similarly, some bases such as sodium hydroxide, NaOH, provide one hydroxide ion, and others, such as calcium hydroxide, $Ca(OH)_2$, provide two.

This distinction is the basis of another method for describing the concentration of acids, bases, and salts. The formula weight of an acid, divided by the number of reactive hydrogen atoms in the formula, is called the *equivalent* weight of the acid. Similarly, the formula weight of a base, divided by the number of hydroxide ions in the formula, is called the equivalent weight of the base. Examples of equivalent weights of some acids and bases are given in the accompanying table.

Substance	Formula	Formula weight	Equivalent weight
Hydrochloric acid	HCl	36.5	36.5
Sulfuric acid	H_2SO_4	98.1	49.0
Phosphoric acid	H_3PO_4	98.0	32.6
Sodium hydroxide	NaOH	40.0	40.0
Calcium hydroxide	$Ca(OH)_2$	74.1	37.0

Just as the weight of a mole is the formula weight expressed as grams, a *gram-equivalent weight* is the equivalent weight expressed as grams. A *normal* solution is one that contains 1 gram-equivalent weight of solute per liter of solution. It will be clear that for hydrochloric acid and for sodium hydroxide, a molar (*M*) solution and a normal (*N*) solution are exactly the same, but that a one-molar sulfuric acid solution is twice as concentrated as a one-normal sulfuric acid solution.

Normal solutions are convenient for persons having to do large numbers of titrations. The convenience will be illustrated by the following problem.

PROBLEM: What volume of 0.30N acid is required to neutralize 10 ml of 2.5N base?

SOLUTION: The base is 2.5/0.30 times as concentrated as the acid. Therefore it will require (2.5/0.30) × 10 ml = 83 ml of acid to neutralize the base.

Notice that in the above problem the answer is the same, no matter what acid or what base is under consideration.

The idea of normal solutions may also be applied to salts and to reactions involving oxidation and reduction, but the method is less used now than formerly. Do not confuse normal solutions with a normal saline solution, which is a solution (much used in biology) containing about 1 percent of sodium chloride in water.

EXERCISES

1. What is the difference between the conduction of electricity by a metal as contrasted with conduction by a solution of an electrolyte?
2. What is the difference between a strong acid and a weak acid?
3. Using electron dot symbols, show the difference between sodium atom and sodium ion, aluminum atom and ion, bromine atom and bromide ion, sulfur atom and sulfide ion, sulfide ion and sulfate ion.
4. Write formulas for the following salts: ammonium chloride, barium sulfate, calcium oxalate, chromic sulfate, cupric sulfide, ferrous sulfate, potassium permanganate, silver nitrate, sodium hypochlorite, sodium bicarbonate, strontium nitrate.
5. Name each of the following: $Al_4(SiO_4)_3$, $SbCl_3$, $Ba(NO_2)_2$, Bi_2S_3, CaF_2, $CuCl_2$, $PbBr_2$, MgI_2, $Hg(NO_3)_2$, Ag_2S, AgI, $NaHCO_3$, $NaClO_3$, $Zn(NO_3)_2$.
6. What is the dielectric contant?

7. A solution containing 2.94 grams of $Mg(NO_3)_2$ dissolved in 100 grams of H_2O starts to freeze at $-0.96°$ C. Approximately how many ions are indicated per formula?

8. Show that for pure water, for every molecule dissociating to H^+ and OH^-, about 5×10^8 molecules remain undissociated.

9. The concentration of hydroxide ions may be represented by the expression pOH, which has a meaning exactly analogous to pH. If in a water solution the pH is 9, what is the pOH?

10. Find the pH of the following solutions:
   (a) A solution containing 0.0001 mole/liter of hydrogen ion.
   (b) A $0.00015M$ solution of the strong base $Ca(OH)_2$.
   (c) A $0.3M$ solution of the strong acid HCl.

11. Give the hydrogen ion concentration in moles per liter for solutions having a $pH = 3$; $pH = 8.5$.

12. A $0.1M$ acid solution is reported as having a pH of 3. What explanation may be offered?

13. What weight of potassium hydroxide will be needed to neutralize 50 ml of $0.65M$ nitric acid?

14. What volume of $0.30M$ sodium hydroxide solutions will be needed to neutralize 10 ml of $0.18M$ sulfuric acid?

15. If 23.2 ml of sodium hydroxide solution is needed to neutralize 10 ml of $0.44M$ hydrochloric acid, what is the molar concentration of the base?

16. It requires 18.5 ml of NaOH solution to neutralize 10 ml of $0.55M$ HCl solution. What is the concentration of the base in (a) moles per liter, (b) grams per liter?

17. It requires 17.6 ml of $1.12M$ H_3PO_4 to neutralize 50 ml of $Ca(OH)_2$ solution. What is the concentration of the base in (a) moles per liter, (b) grams per liter?

$$3Ca(OH)_2 + 2H_3PO_4 \rightarrow Ca_3(PO_4)_2 + 6H_2O$$

18. How many grams of KOH are required to neutralize 22 ml of oxalic acid that contains 0.95 mole of $C_2O_4H_2$ per liter?

$$2KOH + H_2C_2O_4 \rightarrow K_2C_2O_4 + 2H_2O$$

19. What volume of $0.50M$ $AgNO_3$ is required to precipitate as AgCl all the chlorine in 1.0 gram of NaCl?

20. What volume of $1.05M$ $Ba(OH)_2$ solution is required to neutralize 50 ml of $0.75M$ H_2SO_4? What weight of $BaSO_4$ will be formed?

21. How many liters of dry carbon dioxide at standard conditions will be liberated by the action of 150 ml of $1.5M$ HCl on excess limestone?

$$2HCl + CaCO_3 \rightarrow CO_2 + CaCl_2 + H_2O$$

22. A solution is made up by mixing 50 ml of 0.75M KOH and 33 ml of 0.65M H$_2$SO$_4$. The solution is then diluted to 1000 ml. What is the molar concentration of acid (or of base) that remains not neutralized?

23. What volume of 1.15N sulfuric acid is needed to neutralize 23.3 ml of 1.88N potassium hydroxide solution?

24. Whenever a strong acid is neutralized by a strong base, it is found that the heat liberated in the exothermic reaction is either 13.8 kcal/mole of reactant or some small, whole number multiple of 13.8 kcal. Suggest a reason for this.

14

Ionic Equilibria

It has previously been mentioned that a chemical reaction between ions in solution may be expected to go to completion, or nearly so, under certain conditions. These conditions are: (1) one of the products is only slightly soluble and thus tends to form a precipitate; (2) one of the products is a gas, which is allowed to escape; (3) one of the products is, as is water, only slightly dissociated into ions. To these we may add (4) certain reactions between oxidizing and reducing agents, including those in which relatively large amounts of energy are involved.

In the present chapter some of these topics will be considered on a quantitative basis. The examples chosen will be some ionic reactions involving substances that are only slightly dissociated and some reactions in which a precipitate is formed. Ionic reactions in general lend themselves to relatively simple treatment by the law of mass action. One reason for this is that the volume of a solution suffers only negligible change during an ionic reaction, and this minimizes the complicated computations that are often necessary in connection with reactions involving gases. Another reason is that ionic reactions are often very rapid, or even appear to be instantaneous. There is, consequently, rarely much waiting for equilibrium to be reached. And finally, the behavior of solutions of weak electrolytes is described by the law of mass action with considerable accuracy.

14.1 *Weak Acids, Weak Bases*

Strong acids are substantially completely dissociated to ions in water, and their behavior is not readily predictable by the law of mass action. Weak acids—those in which dissociation is slight—dissociate reversibly as follows:

$$HA \rightleftharpoons H^+ + A^-$$

For such a system at equilibrium, it is found that

$$\frac{[H^+][A^-]}{[HA]} = K_i$$

where the square brackets imply, as before, the concentration in moles per liter, and where K_i is called the *ionization constant*. More precisely, the concentrations should be corrected for the activity (Sec. 13.1) of the several dissolved species, but this correction will be ignored. It will be realized that K_i incorporates an expression for the concentration of water involved in the reaction. This procedure is justifiable because the concentration of water remains virtually constant during a reaction. Ionization constants for a number of weak acids and weak bases at room temperature are given in Table 14.1.

Uses of ionization constants will be illustrated by some problems.

PROBLEM: Find the molarity of hydrogen ions in 0.10M acetic acid solution.

SOLUTION: Acetic acid is CH_3CO_2H, abbreviated to HAc in Table 14.1. There is only one ionizable hydrogen atom in the molecule. The ionization constant is 1.8×10^{-5}. Then

$$\frac{[H^+][Ac^-]}{[HAc]} = K_i = 1.8 \times 10^{-5}$$

It is clear that $[H^+] = [Ac^-]$ because the ionization of acetic acid produces one, and only one, hydrogen ion for every acetate ion. It is also clear that $[HAc] = 0.10 - [H^+]$ mole liter^{-1} because the total concentration of acetic acid (both molecular and dissociated) is 0.10M, and dissociation has lowered this by an amount equal to $[H^+]$. However, $[H^+]$ will be very small because acetic acid is a weak acid and hence, by definition, only slightly dissociated. Without introducing much error, we may say that $0.10 - [H^+] = 0.10$. Then, letting $[H^+] = [Ac^-] = x$, we have

$$\frac{x^2}{0.10} = 1.8 \times 10^{-5}$$

TABLE 14.1   IONIZATION CONSTANTS FOR SOME WEAK ACIDS AND BASES
IN AQUEOUS SOLUTION AT ROOM TEMPERATURE

Acid or Base	Reaction	K_i
Acetic	$HAc \rightleftharpoons H^+ + Ac^-$	1.8×10^{-5}
Boric	$H_3BO_3 \rightleftharpoons H^+ + H_2BO_3^-$	5.8×10^{-10}
Carbonic	$H_2CO_3 \rightleftharpoons H^+ + HCO_3^-$	4.3×10^{-7}
bicarbonate ion	$HCO_3^- \rightleftharpoons H^+ + CO_3^{2-}$	4.7×10^{-11}
Formic	$HCO_2H \rightleftharpoons H^+ + HCO_2^-$	2×10^{-4}
Hydrazoic	$HN_3 \rightleftharpoons H^+ + N_3^-$	1.9×10^{-5}
Hydrocyanic	$HCN \rightleftharpoons H^+ + CN^-$	4×10^{-10}
Hydrofluoric	$HF \rightleftharpoons H^+ + F^-$	7.2×10^{-4}
Hydroselenic	$H_2Se \rightleftharpoons H^+ + HSe^-$	1.7×10^{-4}
Hydrosulfuric	$H_2S \rightleftharpoons H^+ + HS^-$	1×10^{-7}
hydrosulfide ion	$HS^- \rightleftharpoons H^+ + S^{2-}$	1×10^{-14}
Hypochlorous	$HClO \rightleftharpoons H^+ + ClO^-$	9.6×10^{-7}
Nitrous	$HNO_2 \rightleftharpoons H^+ + NO_2^-$	4.5×10^{-4}
Phosphoric(ortho)	$H_3PO_4 \rightleftharpoons H^+ + H_2PO_4^-$	7.5×10^{-3}
dihydrogen phosphate ion	$H_2PO_4^- \rightleftharpoons H^+ + HPO_4^{2-}$	2×10^{-7}
(mono)hydrogen phosphate ion	$HPO_4^{2-} \rightleftharpoons H^+ + PO_4^{3-}$	1×10^{-12}
Silicic	$H_4SiO_4 \rightleftharpoons H^+ + H_3SiO_4^-$	1×10^{-10}
Ammonium hydroxide	$NH_4OH \rightleftharpoons NH_4^+ + OH^-$	1.8×10^{-5}
Hydrazinium hydroxide	$N_2H_5OH \rightleftharpoons N_2H_5^+ + OH^-$	1×10^{-6}
Hydroxyaluminum ion	$AlOH^{2+} \rightleftharpoons Al^{3+} + OH^-$	7.1×10^{-10}

whence $x^2 = 1.8 \times 10^{-6}$ and $x = 1.3 \times 10^{-3}$ mole liter^{-1}. The concentration of hydrogen ions in this solution is $1.3 \times 10^{-3}M$.

PROBLEM: What is the percentage dissociation of the acetic acid solution referred to in the preceding problem?

SOLUTION: If 0.10 mole/liter of acetic acid was originally present and if 1.3×10^{-3} mole of the acid dissociated, then the fraction of the acid dissociated is

$$\frac{1.3 \times 10^{-3}}{0.10} = 1.3 \times 10^{-2}$$

That is to say, the acid is 1.3 percent dissociated.

PROBLEM: What is the pH of the above solution?

SOLUTION: The hydrogen ion concentration is 1.3×10^{-3} mole liter^{-1}, and pH is defined as the negative logarithm of the hydrogen ion concentration.

Then

$$pH = - \log (1.3 \times 10^{-3})$$
$$= - (\log 1.3 + \log 10^{-3})$$
$$= - (0.11 - 3.0)$$
$$= 2.89$$

The pH of a solution is rarely meaningful beyond the first decimal; hence the answer to the problem may be written pH 2.9.

If a solution of a weak acid or a weak base in water is further diluted with more water, it will be found that as the electrolyte becomes more dilute, it also becomes more highly dissociated. This effect will be illustrated by the following problem.

PROBLEM: Referring once more to the preceding problem, let us dilute a sample of the 0.10M HAc with water until the volume of the solution has been doubled (say, of 100 ml to 200 ml). Then the concentration of the acid must be 0.05M. Find the percentage dissociation.

SOLUTION: As before, letting $[H^+] = [Ac^-] = x$, we have

$$\frac{x^2}{0.05} = 1.8 \times 10^{-5}$$

whence

$$x = 9.5 \times 10^{-4} \text{ mole liter}^{-1}$$

Then the fraction of the acid dissociated is

$$\frac{9.5 \times 10^{-4}}{0.05} = 1.9 \times 10^{-2}$$
$$= 1.9 \text{ percent}$$

This is compared with only 1.3 percent dissociation when the acid concentration was 0.10M.

One further problem of this type will show how, given the percentage dissociation, to calculate the ionization constant.

PROBLEM: Hydrocyanic acid dissociates according to the equation

$$HCN \rightleftharpoons H^+ + CN^-$$

A 0.050M HCN solution is found to be 0.009 percent dissociated. Find the ionization constant for this acid.

SOLUTION: At equilibrium,

$$\frac{[H^+][CN^-]}{[HCN]} = K_i$$

The concentration of HCN molecules is essentially 0.050M. The concentration of hydrogen ions is the same as the concentration of cyanide ions and is equal to 0.009 percent of 0.050M. Hence,

$$[H^+] = [CN^-] = 5 \times 10^{-2} \times 0.9 \times 10^{-4} = 4.5 \times 10^{-6}$$

Then

$$K_i = \frac{(4.5 \times 10^{-6})^2}{5 \times 10^{-2}} = 4 \times 10^{-10}$$

Similar problems may be encountered for weak bases such as ammonium hydroxide, for which at equilibrium,

$$\frac{[NH_4^+][OH^-]}{[NH_4OH]} = 1.8 \times 10^{-5}$$

It should be remembered that sodium hydroxide, calcium hydroxide, and the like are strong bases that do not lend themselves to calculations such as those given above.

The reader may notice that there is a certain similarity between the effect produced by progressive dilution with solvent of a weak acid or base, and the effect produced by increasing the volume at constant temperature for a homogeneous gas reaction. If the volume of an acetic acid solution is so increased, dissociation of the acid is increased. If the volume of ammonia gas in equilibrium with nitrogen and hydrogen is increased, dissociation of the ammonia is increased.

14.2 *Common-Ion Effect*

If to an acetic acid solution there is added some sodium acetate, the result will be to repress the ionization of the acid. The equilibrium involved is as above,

$$HAc \rightleftharpoons H^+ + Ac^-$$

Sodium acetate, like almost all salts, may be considered to be completely in the form of ions that are, in this case, Na^+ and Ac^-. The increase of acetate ion concentration caused by the addition of sodium acetate will force acetate ions to combine with hydrogen ions to form more molecules of acetic acid. This statement follows from a consideration of the expression

$$\frac{[H^+][Ac^-]}{[HAc]} = 1.8 \times 10^{-5}$$

where it is clear that an increase of $[Ac^-]$ must be matched by a decrease of [H⁺] or an increase of [HAc], or both, if the expression at the left, above, is to remain equal to a constant.

The effect described is known as the *common-ion effect*. In the example given, the ion that is common to both acetic acid and sodium acetate is the acetate ion. The common-ion effect will be illustrated by the following problem.

PROBLEM: What is the molar concentration of hydrogen ions in a 0.10M acetic acid solution that also contains 0.05M sodium acetate?

SOLUTION: As was done in one of the problems above, the concentration of acetic acid molecules, [HAc], may be taken as substantially 0.10M. The concentration of acetate ions, [Ac⁻], is only negligibly greater than that of the added sodium acetate, namely, 0.05M. Hence we write

$$\frac{[H^+] \times 0.05}{0.10} = 1.8 \times 10^{-5}$$

and

$$[H^+] = \frac{1.8 \times 10^{-5} \times 10^{-1}}{5 \times 10^{-2}} = 3.6 \times 10^{-5}M$$

The effect of adding a small concentration (0.05M) of sodium acetate to a 0.10M acetic acid solution is therefore to lower the hydrogen ion concentration from $1.3 \times 10^{-3}M$ to $3.6 \times 10^{-5}M$, nearly a forty-fold decrease.

14.3 *Buffered Solutions*

The acetic acid and sodium acetate mixture will serve to illustrate another related effect. Suppose that to such a mixture there is added a drop of a strong acid, such as hydrochloric. The hydrogen ions so introduced will combine with the acetate ions from the sodium acetate to form acetic acid molecules. The solution will not become nearly so strongly acid—that is, [H⁺] will remain much lower—than if the same quantity of hydrochloric acid had been added to pure water. On the other hand, suppose a drop of strong base, such as sodium hydroxide, is added to the acetic acid and sodium acetate mixture. Then the hydroxide ions from the base will combine with hydrogen ions from the acetic acid, but this will cause more acetic acid molecules to ionize, and the final result will be only a slight change in the hydrogen ion concentration.

A solution such as acetic acid plus sodium acetate to which moderate amounts of acid or base may be added without greatly changing the *p*H of the solution is said to be a *buffered* solution. The acid-salt mixture is called a *buffer*.

PROBLEM: A solution contains 1.0M HAc and 1.0M NaAc. To 1.0 liter of this solution there is added 1 ml of 12M HCl. What change of pH is caused by the addition of this quantity of the strong acid?

SOLUTION: The hydrogen ion concentration prior to addition of the HCl is obviously $1.8 \times 10^{-5}M$, and the pH is therefore 4.7.

The reaction that occurs during addition of the HCl is

$$H^+ + Ac^- \rightarrow HAc$$

The amount of HAc so formed is equal to the moles of H^+ added, namely, 1.2×10^{-2} mole. This gives a total $[HAc] = 1.012M$ and a residual $[Ac^-] = 0.988M$. Then

$$[H^+] = \frac{1.8 \times 10^{-5} \times 1.012}{0.988} = 1.84 \times 10^{-5}M$$

and the pH is now still about 4.7.

Thus, although 1.2×10^{-2} mole of hydrogen ion was added (in the form of hydrochloric acid) and although this, if added to a liter of pure water, would have changed the pH of the water from 7 to 1.9, the presence of the buffer caused the change of pH to be negligible.

PROBLEM: What weight of sodium acetate must be dissolved in 1 liter of 0.2M acetic acid to buffer the solution at pH 5?

SOLUTION: A pH 5 is equivalent to $[H^+] = 1 \times 10^{-5}M$. Then, solving for $[Ac^-]$ in the ionization constant expression,

$$[Ac^-] = \frac{K_i[HAc]}{[H^+]} = \frac{1.8 \times 10^{-5} \times 0.2}{1 \times 10^{-5}}$$
$$= 0.36M$$

This is the concentration of acetate ions required to achieve the desired result. As the complete formula for sodium acetate is $NaC_2H_3O_2$, the formula weight is 66.0, so that 0.36 mole of acetate ions will be obtained from 0.36×66 grams = 24 grams NaAc. As the volume of the solution is 1 liter, it will suffice to dissolve 24 grams of sodium acetate.

There are many substances that may serve as buffers. They are particularly important in the chemistry of living matter. Blood is, normally, buffered at about pH 7.4 by the various salts and organic compounds present.

14.4 Hydrolysis

The neutralization of a Brönsted acid by a Brönsted base invariably produces water plus a salt. A salt derived from a strong acid and a strong base may be dissolved in water to form a neutral solution. This is true of sodium chloride, in the case of which, although water molecules doubtless cluster around the Na^+ and Cl^- ions, the water does not suffer any decomposition and the normal slight dissociation of the water to H^+ and OH^- ions is not unbalanced. But if either the acid or the base, or both, are weak electrolytes, complications arise.

An example of a salt formed from a strong acid and a weak base is ammonium chloride. Such a salt gives a slightly acid reaction in water. An example of a salt formed from a weak acid and a strong base is sodium acetate. Such a salt gives a slightly basic reaction in water. An example of a salt formed from a (moderately) weak acid and a weak base is lead tetrafluoride, which reacts in water almost completely to form lead dioxide and hydrogen fluoride. A reaction such as any of these, in which a compound is partially or completely decomposed by interaction with water, is called *hydrolysis*. Most reactions of hydrolysis are reversible, but many tend, for one reason or another, to go virtually to completion. This section will be restricted to calculation of the change of hydrogen ion concentration for a relatively simple case of basic hydrolysis.

The reason that sodium acetate dissolved in water gives a basic reaction may be found by considering the behavior of the sodium and acetate ions in the presence of water. The sodium ions undergo no reaction, but the acetate ions tend to unite with the hydrogen ions formed from the water, and form molecules

$$Ac^- + H^+ \rightleftharpoons HAc$$

of acetic acid. This reaction lowers the hydrogen ion concentration and therefore causes a moderate increase of hydroxide ion in the solution. This is true because, in any such reaction involving water, the ion product $[H^+][OH^-]$ must remain the same, namely, 1×10^{-14}.

The reason ammonium chloride dissolved in water gives an acid reaction is very similar. The chloride ions have no effect on the water, but the ammonium ions tend to react as follows:

$$NH_4^+ + OH^- \rightleftharpoons NH_4OH$$

thus lowering the hydroxide ion concentration and leaving a moderate excess of hydrogen ions in the solution. It will be clear that both reactions above could be written in the form

$$Ac^- + H_2O \rightleftharpoons HAc + OH^-$$

and

$$NH_4^+ + H_2O \rightleftharpoons NH_4OH + H^+$$

without much real change in meaning, and this is the form in which hydrolysis reactions are generally written.

For acetic acid at equilibrium,

$$\frac{[H^+][Ac^-]}{[HAc]} = K_i = 1.8 \times 10^{-5}$$

and the ion product for water is

$$[H^+][OH^-] = K_w = 1 \times 10^{-14}$$

By dividing one expression by the other, we have

$$\frac{[H^+][OH^-]}{[H^+][Ac^-]/[HAc]} = \frac{K_w}{K_i}$$

from which

$$\frac{[HAc][OH^-]}{[Ac^-]} = \frac{1 \times 10^{-14}}{1.8 \times 10^{-5}}$$
$$= 5.5 \times 10^{-10}$$
$$= K_h$$

The quantity $K_w/K_i = K_h$ is called the *hydrolysis constant*.

The hydrolysis constant may be used to find the hydrogen ion concentration of a salt solution, as in the following problem.

PROBLEM: Find the hydrogen ion concentration in a 0.020M solution of sodium acetate.

SOLUTION: The reaction is essentially this:

$$Ac^- + H_2O \rightleftharpoons HAc + OH^-$$

The expression given above for the hydrolysis constant includes the (constant) concentration of the water. Every acetate ion undergoing hydrolysis yields one molecule of acetic acid and one hydroxide ion; hence [HAc] = [OH$^-$]. We may then write

$$\frac{[OH^-]^2}{2 \times 10^{-2}} = 5.5 \times 10^{-10}$$

It is true that [Ac$^-$] is less than 0.02M by the fraction used to form HAc, but this fraction is small and may be neglected. Therefore

$$[OH^-]^2 = 5.5 \times 10^{-10} \times 2 \times 10^{-2}$$
$$= 11 \times 10^{-12}$$

and

$$[OH^-] = 3.3 \times 10^{-6}M$$

Then, as

$$[H^+][OH^-] = 1 \times 10^{-14}$$
$$[H^+] = \frac{1 \times 10^{-14}}{3.3 \times 10^{-6}}$$
$$= 3 \times 10^{-9} M$$

The solution is therefore quite definitely basic, the hydrogen ion concentration being about 33 times lower than that in pure water.

14.5 *Indicators*

In Sec. 13.5 it was stated that certain organic compounds, of which litmus is one, may be used to identify the neutral point during the titration of an acid with a base. Indicators are weak acids (or weak bases) and, as such, lend themselves to treatment by the theory developed in Sec. 14.1.

An indicator may be represented by the formula HIn,[1] and its reversible dissociation to ions is as follows:

$$HIn \rightleftharpoons H^+ + In^-$$
(one color)   (another color)

from which it follows that

$$\frac{[H^+][In^-]}{[HIn]} = K_{In}$$

If the ion In$^-$ is one color, and the molecule HIn another, then the color will be half changed when $[In^-] = [HIn]$. When an indicator is used during titration, the condition of half change from one color to another is called the *end point*. With proper selection of an indicator, the end point should be the same, or very nearly the same, as the *equivalence point*, namely, the point at which acid and base have been mixed in stoichiometrically equivalent proportions. But neither end point nor equivalence point need be the same as the neutral point, which is the point at which $[H^+] = [OH^-] = 1 \times 10^{-7} M$.

If the color is half changed when $[In^-] = [HIn]$, then at the end point,

$$[H^+] = K_{In}$$

That is to say, at the end point, the hydrogen ion concentration is equal to the ionization constant for the indicator. If the hydrogen ion concentration is expressed as *p*H, then it is convenient to express the ionization

---

[1] The actual formula for the indicator phenolphthalein is $C_{20}H_{14}O_4$.

constant by a similar convention, namely pK which is defined as the negative logarithm of the ionization constant. Then *at the end point* for any indicator, $pH = pK$.

Consideration of the expression for the ionization constant will show that the color of an indicator cannot change abruptly at a certain pH, but that it must change progressively as the pH changes. That this is true will be shown by the following problem.

PROBLEM: The ionization constant for a certain indicator is 1×10^{-7}; hence, at pH 7, the concentration of In^- is equal to that of HIn. What will be the ratio $[In^-]/[HIn]$ at pH 6?

SOLUTION: At pH 6, $[H^+] = 1 \times 10^{-6} M$, so that

$$\frac{[In^-]}{[HIn]} = \frac{1 \times 10^{-7}}{1 \times 10^{-6}} = 10^{-1}$$

It may be seen that there is still present one part of In^- for every ten parts of HIn, even though the hydrogen ion concentration has been changed by a factor of 10. But the change of color caused by a change in concentration ratio from 1:1 to 1:10 is generally readily perceptible to the eye. The end point during a titration is, as a rule, recognizable within a pH change of 1 unit, and this change can be caused by less than one drop of a typical strong acid or base. This is the basis for the great convenience of indicators in titrations.

Various indicators do not all change color at the same pH; to

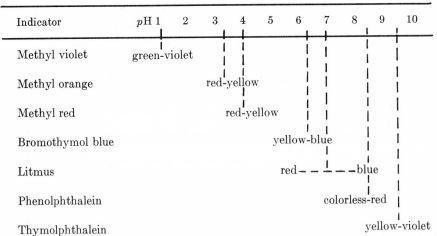

TABLE 14.2   SOME ACID-BASE INDICATORS

Indicator	pH 1	2	3	4	5	6	7	8	9	10
Methyl violet	green-violet									
Methyl orange			red-yellow							
Methyl red				red-yellow						
Bromothymol blue						yellow-blue				
Litmus						red – – – – – blue				
Phenolphthalein								colorless-red		
Thymolphthalein										yellow-violet

express it another way, they do not all have the same ionization constants. Table 14.2 shows a number of useful indicators, their colors in acid and base, and the pH at which the indicator is half changed.

The titration of a strong acid with a strong base offers no particular problem. When a quantity of acid added is just sufficient to react with the base present, with no excess of either, the solution is neutral or very nearly so. The equivalence point is then at the neutral point, and the only problem is to select an indicator that will change color reasonably close to pH 7. There are several possible choices, but methyl violet would change color too soon.

The titration of a weak acid with a strong base, or vice versa, is a more difficult problem. If, to acetic acid (a weak acid) there is added a strong base such as sodium hydroxide, the products of reaction are water and sodium acetate. Sodium acetate, as described in Sec. 14.4, is a typical example of a salt that hydrolyzes in water, giving a basic reaction. The result of this is that, at the equivalence point, the pH will be considerably higher than 7; or, to express it another way, during addition of a strong base to a weak acid, the neutral point (pH 7) will be reached *before* the quantity of base added is stoichiometrically equivalent to the amount of acid present. For this reason, in such a case it is necessary to choose an indicator that has an end point near the higher pH actually present at the equivalence point. Phenolphthalein would be acceptable for this purpose, but for the titration of a strong acid with a weak base, it would be necessary to use an indicator such as methyl orange. By suitable choice of indicators it is even possible to titrate a strong acid and a weak acid present together in a mixture.

14.6   Solubility Product

A saturated solution of silver chloride in water contains a very small amount of dissolved silver chloride—this compound being commonly, though not quite accurately, described as being insoluble. Although the solubility of silver chloride is very low, this compound, as are almost all salts, is a strong electrolyte in the sense that all the dissolved silver chloride is present as ions. We may then write

$$AgCl(s) \rightleftharpoons Ag^+ + Cl^-$$

For such a solution of a very slightly soluble salt, it is almost always found that the product of the two ion concentrations is a constant; that is,

$$[Ag^+][Cl^-] = K_{sp}$$

where $[Ag^+]$ and $[Cl^-]$ represent the molar concentrations of silver ions and chloride ions, respectively, and K_{sp} is called the *solubility product*.

For the more general case, any slightly soluble salt B_mA_n yields m positive ions of B and n negative ions of A; thus

$$B_mA_n(s) \rightleftharpoons mB^{pos} + nA^{neg}$$

and the expression for the solubility product is

$$[B]^m[A]^n = K_{sp}$$

the concentration of each ion being raised to the power represented by the subscript following it in the formula. For instance, for arsenic sesquisulfide the reaction is

$$As_2S_3(s) \rightleftharpoons 2As^{3+} + 3S^{2-}$$

and the solubility product is given by

$$[As^{3+}]^2[S^{2-}]^3 = K_{sp}$$

Use of the solubility product make it possible to predict whether or not a given system will produce a precipitate. In the case of silver chloride

TABLE 14.3   SOLUBILITY PRODUCTS AT ROOM TEMPERATURE

Compound	Equilibrium	K_{sp}
Silver chloride	$AgCl(s) \rightleftharpoons Ag^+ + Cl^-$	1.7×10^{-10}
Silver bromide	$AgBr(s) \rightleftharpoons Ag^+ + Br^-$	3.3×10^{-13}
Silver iodide	$AgI(s) \rightleftharpoons Ag^+ + I^-$	8.5×10^{-17}
Lead chloride	$PbCl_2(s) \rightleftharpoons Pb^{2+} + 2Cl^-$	1.7×10^{-5}
Mercurous chloride	$Hg_2Cl_2(s) \rightleftharpoons Hg_2^{2+} + 2Cl^-$	1.1×10^{-18}
Lead chromate	$PbCrO_4(s) \rightleftharpoons Pb^{2+} + CrO_4^{2-}$	1.8×10^{-14}
Barium chromate	$BaCrO_4(s) \rightleftharpoons Ba^{2+} + CrO_4^{2-}$	8.5×10^{-11}
Magnesium hydroxide	$Mg(OH)_2(s) \rightleftharpoons Mg^{2+} + 2OH^-$	8.9×10^{-12}
Calcium hydroxide	$Ca(OH)_2(s) \rightleftharpoons Ca^{2+} + 2OH^-$	1.3×10^{-6}
Aluminum hydroxide	$Al(OH)_3(s) \rightleftharpoons Al^{3+} + 3OH^-$	1×10^{-33}
Ferrous hydroxide	$Fe(OH)_2(s) \rightleftharpoons Fe^{2+} + 2OH^-$	1.6×10^{-15}
Cupric hydroxide	$Cu(OH)_2(s) \rightleftharpoons Cu^{2+} + 2OH^-$	6×10^{-20}
Calcium sulfate	$CaSO_4(s) \rightleftharpoons Ca^{2+} + SO_4^{2-}$	2.4×10^{-5}
Barium sulfate	$BaSO_4(s) \rightleftharpoons Ba^{2+} + SO_4^{2-}$	1×10^{-10}
Calcium carbonate	$CaCO_3(s) \rightleftharpoons Ca^{2+} + CO_3^{2-}$	4.8×10^{-9}
Calcium fluoride	$CaF_2(s) \rightleftharpoons Ca^{2+} + 2F^-$	3.4×10^{-11}
Silver sulfide	$Ag_2S(s) \rightleftharpoons 2Ag^+ + S^{2-}$	1.0×10^{-51}
Cupric sulfide	$CuS(s) \rightleftharpoons Cu^{2+} + S^{2-}$	4×10^{-38}
Ferrous sulfide	$FeS(s) \rightleftharpoons Fe^{2+} + S^{2-}$	1×10^{-19}
Nickel sulfide	$NiS(s) \rightleftharpoons Ni^{2+} + S^{2-}$	3×10^{-21}
Mercuric sulfide	$HgS(s) \rightleftharpoons Hg^{2+} + S^{2-}$	3×10^{-53}
Lead sulfide	$PbS(s) \rightleftharpoons Pb^{2+} + S^{2-}$	1.0×10^{-28}
Zinc sulfide	$ZnS(s) \rightleftharpoons Zn^{2+} + S^{2-}$	4.5×10^{-24}

referred to above, if in the solution the product of the silver ion concentration multiplied by the chloride ion concentration exceeds the solubility product for silver chloride, then a precipitate may form.

Table 14.3 gives solubility products for some commonly encountered salts. Use of these data will be illustrated by the following problem.

PROBLEM: In a liter of water there is dissolved 2.3 mg of silver ion (added in the form of some soluble salt such as silver nitrate) and then there is added 8.5 mg of chloride ion (possibly in the form of sodium chloride). Will a precipitate of silver chloride be formed?

SOLUTION: The ion concentrations must first be expressed in moles per liter:

$$[Ag^+] = \frac{2.3 \times 10^{-3}}{107.9} = 2.13 \times 10^{-5} M$$

and

$$[Cl^-] = \frac{8.5 \times 10^{-3}}{35.5} = 2.4 \times 10^{-4} M$$

The product of these two is

$$[Ag^+][Cl^-] = 2.13 \times 10^{-5} \times 2.4 \times 10^{-4} \text{ mole}^2 \text{ liter}^{-2}$$
$$= 5.1 \times 10^{-9} \text{ mole}^2 \text{ liter}^{-2}$$

The solubility product for silver chloride, from Table 14.3 is 1.7×10^{-10} mole^2 liter^{-2}. The solubility product is smaller than 5.1×10^{-9}, and hence a precipitate will form.

PROBLEM: The solubility product of lead chloride, $PbCl_2$, is 1.7×10^{-5} at room temperature. Find the solubility of lead chloride in grams of lead ion per liter of solution. (Hereafter we shall omit solubility product units unless there is some particular reason for retaining them.)

SOLUTION: Since

$$PbCl_2(s) \rightleftharpoons Pb^{2+} + 2Cl^-$$

by definition,

$$[Pb^{2+}][Cl^-]^2 = K_{sp} = 1.7 \times 10^{-5}$$

Let x be the concentration of lead ions in a saturated solution of lead chloride. Then

$$[Pb^{2+}] = x$$

and

$$[Cl^-] = 2x$$

this last statement being true because, according to the equation, there are two chloride ions for every lead ion. Hence

$$x \times (2x)^2 = 1.7 \times 10^{-5}$$
$$4x^3 = 1.7 \times 10^{-5}$$

and

$$x = 1.6 \times 10^{-2}M$$

To convert to grams per liter multiply by the atomic weight of lead, which is 207. Then a saturated solution of lead chloride in water at room temperature contains

$$1.6 \times 10^{-2} \text{ mole liter}^{-1} \times 207 \text{ gram mole}^{-1} = 3.3 \text{ gram liter}^{-1} \text{ of } Pb^{2+} \text{ ion}$$

The common ion effect may be applied to slightly soluble salts to alter their solubility. This is illustrated by the following problem.

PROBLEM: What is the solubility of lead chloride, at room temperature, expressed as grams of lead ions per liter of solution which also contains $2.0M$ hydrochloric acid?

SOLUTION: As in the preceding problem the solubility product expression is

$$[Pb^{2+}][Cl^-]^2 = 1.7 \times 10^{-5}$$

but now virtually all the chloride ion concentration is supplied by the strong acid HCl. With only negligible error it may be assumed that

$$[Cl^-] = 2.0M$$

Then

$$[Pb^{2+}] \times (2.0)^2 = 1.7 \times 10^{-5}$$

and

$$[Pb^{2+}] = \frac{1.7 \times 10^{-5}}{4.0} = 4.2 \times 10^{-6}M$$

Expressed as grams, the concentration of lead ions is

$$4.2 \times 10^{-6} \text{ mole liter}^{-1} \times 207 \text{ gram mole}^{-1} = 8.7 \times 10^{-4} \text{ gram liter}^{-1}$$

The addition of a moderate amount of hydrochloric acid has therefore lowered the concentration of lead ions in solution by about five thousandfold.

14.7   Simultaneous Equilibria

Frequently two or more equilibria may be present simultaneously in a chemical system. Such a system was described in Sec. 14.3, in which use was made of the ionization constant of a weak acid and of the ion product of water to find the hydrolysis constant of a salt. In the present section, simultaneous use will be made of the ionization constant of a weak acid and of the solubility product of a sparingly soluble salt to find the equilibrium concentration of metal ions in solution under various conditions of hydrogen ion concentration. This calculation will serve both as an illustration of how simultaneous equilibria may be handled and as a review of some topics already covered in this chapter. The particular examples chosen will be to find the equilibrium concentration of lead ions in a dilute solution of hydrochloric acid that has been saturated with hydrogen sulfide gas, and then to do the same for zinc ions.

PROBLEM: Find the weight of Pb^{2+} ions that may remain in 100 ml of solution which is 0.3M in HCl and is saturated at room temperature and 1 atm with H_2S.

SOLUTION: The approach to this problem will be through the solubility product of PbS, but first it will be necessary to find the equilibrium concentration of sulfide ions under the conditions stated.

Hydrogen sulfide dissociates in two steps:

$$H_2S \rightleftharpoons H^+ + HS^-$$
$$HS^- \rightleftharpoons H^+ + S^{2-}$$

The ionization constants are not known with great accuracy, but the values given in Table 14.1 will serve our purpose:

$$\frac{[H^+][HS^-]}{[H_2S]} = 1 \times 10^{-7}$$

$$\frac{[H^+][S^{2-}]}{[HS^-]} = 1 \times 10^{-14}$$

These two equations may be combined by multiplying one by the other as follows:

$$\frac{[H^+][HS^-]}{[H_2S]} \times \frac{[H^+][S^{2-}]}{[HS^-]} = 1 \times 10^{-7} \times 1 \times 10^{-14}$$

from which

$$\frac{[H^+]^2[S^{2-}]}{[H_2S]} = 1 \times 10^{-21}$$

It so happens that, for a saturated solution of hydrogen sulfide at room temperature and 1 atm pressure, $[H_2S] = 0.10M$. Hence, in such a solution,

$$[H^+]^2[S^{2-}] = 1 \times 10^{-22}$$

The next step in solving the problem is to find $[S^{2-}]$ under the stated conditions, namely, in the presence of 0.30M HCl. As HCl is a strong acid, it follows that $[H^+] = 0.30M$. Therefore

$$[S^{2-}] = \frac{1 \times 10^{-22}}{[H^+]^2}$$

$$= \frac{1 \times 10^{-22}}{(0.30)^2}$$

$$= 1.1 \times 10^{-21}M$$

The final step in the problem involves calculation of $[Pb^{2+}]$ from $[S^{2-}]$, as found above, and the solubility product of lead sulfide. From Table 14.3:

$$[Pb^{2+}][S^{2-}] = 1 \times 10^{-28}$$

and

$$[Pb^{2+}] = \frac{1 \times 10^{-28}}{[S^{2-}]}$$

$$= \frac{1 \times 10^{-28}}{1.1 \times 10^{-21}}$$

$$= 1 \times 10^{-7}M$$

The problem given was to find the weight of lead ions that could remain in 100 ml of solution under the stated conditions. The weight is

$$1 \times 10^{-7} \text{ mole liter}^{-1} \times 207 \text{ gram mole}^{-1} \times 0.10 \text{ liter} = 2 \times 10^{-6} \text{ gram}$$

The answer is: only 2 micrograms of lead remain in solution.

This same calculation will now be repeated for zinc sulfide under identical conditions. The purpose of this is to show a striking difference between the solubility of lead sulfide and that of zinc sulfide in dilute acid solution.

PROBLEM: Find the weight of Zn^{2+} ions that may remain in 100 ml of solution which is 0.3M in HCl and is saturated at room temperature and 1 atm with H_2S.

SOLUTION: From the preceding problem we already have $[S^{2-}]$ under these conditions, namely, $[S^{2-}] = 1.1 \times 10^{-21}M$. Then, from the solubility product for ZnS,

$$[Zn^{2+}][S^{2-}] = 4.5 \times 10^{-24}$$

and

$$[Zn^{2+}] = \frac{4.5 \times 10^{-24}}{1.1 \times 10^{-21}} = 4.1 \times 10^{-3}M$$

the weight of zinc ions remaining in 100 ml of solution is

4.1×10^{-3} mole liter$^{-1} \times 65.4$ gram mole$^{-1} \times 0.10$ liter $= 2.7 \times 10^{-2}$ gram

Both lead sulfide and zinc sulfide are virtually insoluble in pure water. But in the presence of dilute hydrochloride acid, an appreciable weight of zinc will remain in solution, whereas the lead sulfide remains almost completely insoluble. The difference in concentrations of zinc and lead in solution exceeds 10,000. This difference is due to the action of the hydrogen ions from the hydrochloric acid in lowering the sulfide ion concentration, and also to the difference in solubility products of the zinc sulfide and the lead sulfide. Use of the effect described has often been made in the analytical separation of zinc from lead and other metal ions.

EXERCISES

1. Illustrate with appropriate examples the several reasons why an ionic reaction may go to completion, or nearly so.
2. (a) A drop of hydrochloric acid added to a liter of water increases the conductivity, but only moderately so. Does this mean that hydrochloric is a weak acid? (b) Hydrofluoric acid is able to dissolve glass; hydrochloric cannot do so. Does this mean that hydrofluoric acid is stronger than hydrochloric?
3. Write expressions for the ionization constants of the following:
   (a) Ionization of bicarbonate ion, HCO_3^-
   (b) Ionization of silicic acid, H_4SiO_4 (first ionization stage only)
   (c) Ionization of the weak base silver hydroxide, $AgOH$ ($AgOH$ probably does not exist as such, but its action is simulated by moist Ag_2O)
4. (a) Calculate the hydrogen ion concentration in a $0.01M$ H_3BO_3 (boric acid) solution.
   (b) What is the percentage ionization of the boric acid in this solution?
   (c) What is the pH of the solution?
5. In venous blood the following equilibrium is set up by the carbon dioxide:

$$H_2CO_3 \rightleftharpoons H^+ + HCO_3^-$$

If the pH of blood is buffered at 7.4, what percentage of the total carbon dioxide is actually present as bicarbonate ions?
6. If freshly distilled water is allowed to stand exposed to the atmosphere, it will be found that the pH falls slightly. Why should this be so?
7. The pH of beer is about 4.5. What concentration of carbon dioxide would be sufficient to give this degree of acidity?

8. A $0.20M$ solution of formic acid, HCO_2H (only one ionizable hydrogen), is 3.2 percent dissociated to formate ions and hydrogen ions. What is the ionization constant for this acid?

9. The ionization constant for phenol, C_6H_5OH (only one ionizable hydrogen), is 1.3×10^{-10}. Why is it incorrect to say that $[H^+]$ in a $0.0001M$ phenol solution is $1.1 \times 10^{-7}M$?

10. (a) Find the hydrogen ion concentration in a solution that contains $1M$ HCN plus $0.5M$ NaCN.
    (b) Find the hydroxide ion concentration in a solution that contains $0.5M$ NH_4OH plus $1M$ NH_4Cl.

11. To 10 ml of $1.0M$ HNO_2 there is added 10 ml of $3.0M$ $NaNO_2$ and the solution is diluted with water to 100 ml. Find the pH of the solution.

12. A buffered solution contains 1 mole of acetic acid plus 1 mole of sodium acetate per liter.
    (a) Calculate the pH of this solution.
    (b) 4.0 grams of NaOH is dissolved in 1 liter of the solution. Find the pH.

13. Calculate the hydrolysis constant for NH_4Cl.

14. Find the pH of each of the following solutions:
    (a) $0.3M$ sodium azide, NaN_3
    (b) $0.1M$ KF; $0.1M$ KNO_3

15. Find the resultant hydrogen ion concentration for each of the following situations:
    (a) 25 ml of $0.1M$ HCl is added to 25 ml of $0.1M$ NaOH.
    (b) 25 ml of $0.1M$ HCN is added to 25 ml of $0.1M$ NaOH.
    (c) 25 ml of $0.1M$ HCl is added to 25 ml of $0.1M$ NH_4OH.

16. Find the pH of the solution resulting from mixing 50 ml of $0.1M$ HCN with 25 ml of $0.1M$ NaOH.

17. The ionization constant for phenolphthalein is 2.0×10^{-10}. Find the pH at which phenolphthalein will be half changed from colorless to red.

18. The ionization constant for methyl red is 5×10^{-6}. What fraction of the methyl red molecules will remain red at pH 7?

19. Select suitable indicators for each of the following titrations:
    (a) $HNO_3 + Ba(OH)_2$; (b) $H_2SO_4 + N_2H_5OH$; (c) $HN_3 + KOH$.

20. Write solubility product expressions for following:
    (a) $Ni(OH)_2$
    (b) Ag_2SO_4
    (c) Hg_2I_2 (contains the ion Hg_2^{2+})

21. To 500 ml of water containing 7.2 mg of barium nitrate, $Ba(NO_3)_2$, there is added 500 ml of water containing 3.3 mg of sulfuric acid. Will a precipitate of barium sulfate be formed? (Note that the total volume becomes virtually 1000 ml).

22. The solubility of silver chromate, Ag_2CrO_4, is about 0.030 grams/liter. Find the solubility product.

23. Find the weight in milligrams per liter of silver ion that will remain in solution if to 0.0025M silver nitrate solution there is added sodium bromide to make the solution 0.30M in bromide ion.

24. The solubility product of lead fluoride, PbF_2, is 3.2×10^{-8}. Find the solubility of lead fluoride in milligrams per liter.

25. Fluorine is sometimes added to water in the form of sodium fluoride because it has a therapeutic action in preventing dental caries. The concentration added is generally one part by weight of fluoride ion per million parts of water. If the water supply is hard water with a calcium ion concentration $1.6 \times 10^{-5}M$, is there not some possibility of precipitating calcium fluoride?

26. Considering the solubility product of $BaSO_4$ and the hydrolysis of the SO_4^{2-} ion, is it correct to say that the dissolved sulfate part of $BaSO_4$ is present as SO_4^{2-} rather than as HSO_4^-?

27. A solution contains 0.02M concentrations of the following ions: Pb^{2+}, Cu^{2+}, and Fe^{2+}. The pH is adjusted to 2, and the solution is then saturated with hydrogen sulfide. Find the concentration in milligrams per liter of each ion that remains in solution.

28. A solution contains 0.05M zinc chloride, 1M acetic acid, and 2M sodium acetate. The solution is now saturated with hydrogen sulfide. Find the weight in milligrams of zinc ions remaining in solution.

29. A solution prepared by saturating water with carbon dioxide gas at 25° C and 1 atm has a concentration of about 0.034M. What pH would be necessary to prevent the precipitation of barium carbonate from a 0.02M barium nitrate solution saturated with carbon dioxide? For $BaCO_3$, $K_{sp} = 5.1 \times 10^{-9}$.

15

Oxidation and Reduction

15.1 Reactions of Oxidation and Reduction

The products of a chemical reaction may in general be found only by experiment. Valuable new reactions are not infrequently discovered by accident. Nevertheless, it is possible to classify the myriad reactions known in inorganic chemistry and in many cases to predict the products. There appear to be only a few main classifications of inorganic reactions. One of these is direct combination, or addition, of elements or compounds to form new substances. This process may be considered together with the reverse process, namely, decomposition. For instance, sulfur dioxide may be prepared by the direct union of sulfur and oxygen:

$$S + O_2 \rightarrow SO_2$$

Boron trifluoride unites with ammonia:

$$BF_3 + NH_3 \rightarrow H_3NBF_3$$

Nitrogen dioxide unites with itself:

$$2NO_2 \rightleftharpoons N_2O_4$$

An example of the reverse (decomposition) type of reaction occurs when mercuric oxide is heated:

$$2HgO \rightleftharpoons 2Hg + O_2$$

or when ammonium nitrate is heated:

$$NH_4NO_3 \rightarrow N_2O + 2H_2O$$

Another class of reaction involves substitution, or a change of partners. A familiar example of this is a typical neutralization in which a hydroxide ion takes the place of a water molecule associated with a proton:

$$H_3O^+ + OH^- \rightleftharpoons H_2O + H_2O$$

This kind of reaction occurs also during the precipitation of silver chloride from a solution containing silver ions, to which chloride ions have been added. In the preceding chapter, the water molecules associated with ions in solution were in general ignored. But if these molecules are shown in the formula, then the precipitation reaction is seen as a substitution of Cl^- for H_2O; thus

$$[Ag(H_2O)_2]^+(aq) + Cl^- \rightarrow AgCl(s) + 2H_2O$$

Another substitution reaction involves the exchange of carbonate ion for hydroxide ion in the precipitation of calcium carbonate:

$$Ca(OH)_2 + H_2CO_3 \rightarrow CaCO_3 + 2H_2O$$

Reactions such as those given above are generally fairly simple, and no particular difficulty need be encountered in writing and balancing the equations for these reactions, provided the formulas for the reactants and products are known.

Attention will now be directed to certain kinds of reaction which take place in aqueous solution. If, to a solution containing cupric, Cu^{2+}, ions there is added a piece of zinc metal, it will soon be found that the blue (hydrated) cupric ions have been transformed into metallic copper and that the zinc metal has been transformed into zinc, Zn^{2+}, ions which have gone into solution. The change may be represented as follows:

$$Cu^{2+} + Zn \rightarrow Cu + Zn^{2+}$$

It will, of course, be understood that some negative ions, such as SO_4^{2-}, must be present in the solution, but they appear to take no part in the change shown.

For Cu^{2+} ions to change to Cu metal it is clear that the ions must have gained electrons:

$$Cu^{2+} + 2e^- \rightarrow Cu(s)$$

and it is similarly clear that the Zn must have lost electrons:

$$Zn(s) \rightarrow Zn^{2+} + 2e^-$$

Any reaction involving a loss of electrons is called an *oxidation,* and any reaction involving a gain of electrons is called a *reduction.* In the reaction of Cu^{2+} ions with metallic Zn, the Cu^{2+} ions are reduced, the Zn metal is oxidized. The Cu^{2+} ions are said to be the oxidizing agent, and the Zn metal the reducing agent. In this example the electrons are transferred from the zinc to the cupric ions.

The formation of the ionic solid sodium chloride from sodium metal and chlorine gas is an example of oxidation and reduction, the electron being transferred from the sodium to the chlorine, as described in Sec. 8.5. Oxidation and reduction applies to covalent compounds, but the idea of electron transfer is less applicable to such substances. For that reason, there has been devised a rather arbitrary concept called the *oxidation state*[1] and this concept is applicable to most kinds of chemical substances. Oxidation state is defined by the following rules:

1. The algebraic sum of the oxidation states in any formula must equal zero.

2. The oxidation state for an element not combined with a different element is zero.

3. The oxidation state of oxygen in compounds is 2—, except in peroxides (1—) and in superoxides (½—) or when the oxygen is in combination with fluorine (2+).

It will be a convenience if it is pointed out that hydrogen has an oxidation state of 1+ in all compounds except true hydrides. In a true (saltlike) hydride, of which LiH is an example, the oxidation state of hydrogen is 1—. Such hydrides will be further described in Chapter 22. Furthermore, elements of Group IA in the Periodic Table (Chapter 16) show an oxidation state of 1+ in all their compounds.

Then, for sulfur in SO_3, the oxidation state is 6+; for carbon in CO_2, it is 4+; for aluminum in Al_2O_3, it is 3+; and for phosphorus in P_2O_5, it is 5+. The oxidation states defined as above should not be confused with the electric charges on the ions. When an ion is derived from a single atom, as Cl^-, Na^+, Al^{3+}, and S^{2-}, the charge on the ion is the same as the oxidation state. But in sulfate ion, SO_4^{2-}, the oxidation state of the sulfur is 6+. Two other examples are: nitrogen in HNO_3, 5+; and manganese in $HMnO_4$, 7+. The oxidation states do not necessarily have a direct significance as far as atomic or molecular structure is concerned, but their usefulness will become increasingly evident.

Equations that do not involve oxidation and reduction rarely offer difficulty in balancing, but when oxidation and reduction occur, the equation may be very troublesome. Two examples will be given of a useful method.

The first example will be the catalytic oxidation of ammonia by oxygen to form nitric oxide and water. Proceed as follows:

---

[1] Some authors call this the *oxidation number.*

1. Show oxidation states of all elements taking part in the reaction

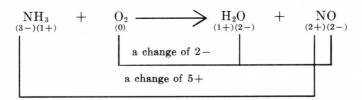

It will be noted that only nitrogen and oxygen undergo a change of oxidation state in this reaction. The hydrogen remains unchanged.

2. The nitrogen is oxidized from 3— to 2+, a change of 5+. The oxygen is reduced from 0 to 2—, a change of 2—.

3. Oxidation must always be accompanied by, and equal to, reduction. The gain by the nitrogen must equal the loss by the oxygen. The least common multiple of 5 and 2 is 10. It is therefore necessary to take two nitrogen atoms, each going from 3— to 2+, to balance five oxygen atoms, each going from 2— to 0. Provisionally, the equation is

$$2NH_3 + 2\tfrac{1}{2}O_2 \rightarrow 2NO + 3H_2O$$

4. The equation may be cleared of the fraction by multiplying everything by 2:

$$4NH_3 + 5O_2 \rightarrow 4NO + 6H_2O$$

The second example will be the production of chlorine from hydrochloric acid and potassium permanganate.

1. Show the oxidation states of all elements that undergo oxidation or reduction. In the following example, these elements are chlorine and manganese.

$$\underset{(1-)}{HCl} + \underset{(7+)}{KMnO_4} \rightarrow \underset{(0)}{Cl_2} + \underset{(1-)}{KCl} + \underset{(2+)}{Mn} \underset{(1-)}{Cl_2} + H_2O$$

2. The chlorine is oxidized from —1 to 0, a net change of 1+, but it will be noted that some of the chlorine undergoes no oxidation and is merely used as Cl- to form KCl and $MnCl_2$.

3. The manganese is reduced from 7+ to 2+, a net change 5—.

4. The total gain of oxidation states must equal the total loss; hence it will be necessary to take 5 chlorines, in the form of HCl, and 1 manganese, in the form of $KMnO_4$. As a tentative equation we then have:

$$5HCl + KMnO_4 \rightarrow 2\tfrac{1}{2}Cl_2 + ?KCl + ?MnCl_2 + ?H_2O$$

But this involves $2\tfrac{1}{2}Cl_2$, which may be cleared to a whole number by taking 10HCl and $2KMnO_4$:

$$10HCl + 2KMnO_4 \rightarrow 5Cl_2 + ?KCl + ?MnCl_2 + ?H_2O$$

5. Now note that $2KMnO_4$ will yield $2KCl + 2MnCl_2$, for which a total of 6 chlorines will be required. These 6 chlorines undergo no oxidation. We add these 6 chlorines to the 10 chlorines that do undergo oxidation, and the complete balanced equation is then

$$16HCl + 2KMnO_4 \rightarrow 5Cl_2 + 2KCl + 2MnCl_2 + 8H_2O$$

It will be most useful if we now redefine oxidation and reduction. *Oxidation* is an algebraic increase of oxidation state; *reduction* is a decrease.

15.2   Voltaic Cells

Any metal placed in an ionizing solvent such as water has a tendency to dissolve with the formation of ions. This reaction is reversible:

$$M \rightleftharpoons M^{n+} + ne^-$$

For active metals such as sodium, it is easy to cause the reaction to go to completion to the right, as indicated above, but for inactive metals such as platinum, the tendency is so slight that perceptible formation of ions may be brought about only with difficulty.

If a strip of metallic zinc is placed in a solution of zinc sulfate, some of the zinc dissolves, forming zinc ions. The electrons liberated in this process remain in the metallic zinc, imparting a negative charge to the metal strip. Normally, the process stops at this point, but arrangements may be made to have the reaction proceed until all the zinc has been dissolved.

Now, if a strip of metallic copper is placed in a solution of copper sulfate, the same type of reaction will tend to occur, but the tendency of copper to go into solution, its *solution pressure,* is less than that of zinc. Copper is commonly said to be a metal less active than zinc.

Now let the zinc, zinc sulfate, copper sulfate, copper system be combined as shown in Fig. 15.1. The zinc metal dips into the zinc sulfate

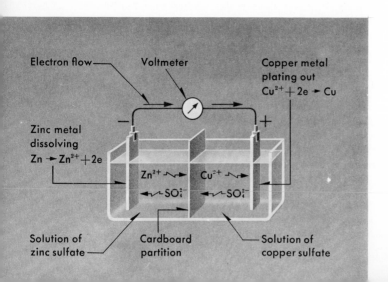

Fig. 15.1   A   zinc-copper voltaic cell.

solution; the zinc sulfate and copper sulfate solutions are separated by a sheet of cardboard or other porous partition. The partition prevents gross mixing of the solutions, but permits diffusion of ions either way. The copper metal dips into the copper sulfate solution.

As a result of the different solution pressures exerted by the zinc and the copper, the zinc metal strip will acquire a charge that is negative with respect to that on the copper metal strip. This arrangement constitutes a *voltaic cell* (sometimes called a *galvanic* cell) for the generation of electricity. Current may be taken off by appropriate connections to the zinc and copper. The reaction taking place at the surface of the zinc metal is an oxidation:

$$Zn \rightleftharpoons Zn^{2+} + 2e^-$$

the reaction going to the right as written. The reaction taking place at the surface of the copper metal is a reduction:

$$Cu^{2+} + 2e^- \rightleftharpoons Cu$$

the reaction going to the right as written. The *overall* reaction is

$$Zn + Cu^{2+} \rightleftharpoons Zn^{2+} + Cu$$

and this proceeds spontaneously to the right, but the zinc and the copper reactions are unique in that they do not occur at the same place.

The electrode at which oxidation takes place is called the *anode;* the electrode at which reduction takes place is called the *cathode.* In a voltaic cell, the anode is negative with respect to the cathode. Electrons flow in the external circuit from anode to cathode. Within the cell, the electric current is carried by a migration of zinc and copper ions in one direction and of sulfate ions in the other.

Such an arrangement, in which one or the other of the electrodes is actually used up, is called a primary cell. The particular cell described is known as the Daniell cell. The total quantity of electricity obtainable from a voltaic cell depends on the quantities of reactants present. Quantity of electricity is expressed in coulombs, and 1 mole of electrons (6.02×10^{23} electrons) carries a charge of 96,500 coulombs.

PROBLEM: A voltaic cell is made up with a zinc anode weighing 100 grams. Assuming that all other reactants are present in excess, what is the maximum quantity of electricity that may be obtained from this cell?

SOLUTION: The equation is

$$Zn \rightleftharpoons Zn^{2+} + 2e^-$$

A gram-atom of zinc weighs 65.4 grams; hence 100 grams of zinc will liberate

$$\frac{100}{65.4} \times 2 \times 9.65 \times 10^4 \text{ coulombs} = 2.96 \times 10^5 \text{ coulombs}$$

The charge carried by 1 mole of electrons (namely, 96,500 coulombs) is called a *faraday* of electricity. The answer to the problem above might have been expressed as 3.06 faradays of electricity or (inasmuch as coulombs = amperes × seconds) the problem could have required the maximum length of time a current of 0.10 amp could have been drawn from the cell. The time would have been

$$\frac{2.96 \times 10^5 \text{ coulombs}}{1 \times 10^{-1} \text{ amp}} = 2.96 \times 10^6 \text{ sec}$$

$$= 34 \text{ days, 6 hr}$$

The voltage, or rather the electromotive force (emf), produced by a voltaic cell is, of course, quite different from the quantity of electricity. Voltage is a measure of electrical intensity (or pressure) rather than of quantity. This will be discussed in the following section.

15.3   Oxidation Potentials

Every reaction of oxidation and reduction may be thought of as the sum of two separate reactions, one an oxidation or loss of electrons, and the other a reduction or gain of electrons. In a voltaic cell, these reactions take place at the anode and cathode, respectively. Similarly, the electromotive force produced in a voltaic cell may be thought of as the sum of the emf produced at the cathode and that produced at the anode. For the zinc-copper cell described in the preceding section, one may refer to the *half cell* consisting of zinc metal in contact with a solution containing zinc ions and to the half cell consisting of copper metal in contact with a solution containing copper ions. The overall reaction in the complete cell is

$$Zn + Cu^{2+} \rightarrow Zn^{2+} + Cu$$

but the *half reactions* taking place at anode and cathode, respectively, are

$$Zn \rightarrow Zn^{2+} + 2e^-$$

and

$$Cu^{2+} + 2e^- \rightarrow Cu$$

The emf associated with a half reaction is called the *oxidation potential*. The voltage that is measured for the complete voltaic cell is approximately the sum of the oxidation potentials for the two half reactions.

In a voltaic cell, it is not difficult to measure the voltage with a voltmeter or potentiometer and to find which electrode is positive with

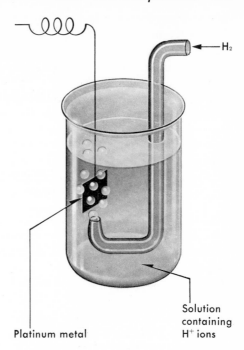

Fig. 15.2 *Hydrogen electrode (half cell). The platinum is inert except as a collector and transmitter of electrons.*

H₂ (as labeled)

Platinum metal

Solution
containing
H⁺ ions

respect to the other. It is also easy to compare one oxidation potential with another, but there is no known method for deciding the *sign* of an oxidation potential, and there is no known method for measuring the actual emf for any half cell by itself. For this reason, it has been necessary to adopt the quite arbitrary method of comparing oxidation potentials with that of the hydrogen half cell. A *hydrogen electrode* consists of a piece of roughened platinum foil surrounded by hydrogen gas and immersed in dilute acid. This arrangement, shown in Fig. 15.2, behaves not unlike a half cell consisting of a metal in contact with a solution containing ions of the metal, the half reaction in this case being

$$H_2 \rightleftharpoons 2H^+ + 2e^-$$

A standard hydrogen electrode is one in which the hydrogen gas surrounding the platinum is at 1 atm pressure, and in which the effective concentration of the positive hydrogen ions is 1 molal,[2] and at 25° C.
A standard hydrogen electrode is arbitrarily assumed to have an emf of zero. This serves as a standard for comparing other half-reaction potentials.

If now a complete voltaic cell is made up of, say, zinc metal in contact with 1*m* ZnSO₄ solution as one half cell and a standard hydrogen

---

[2] We say *effective* concentration because here and elsewhere the molality of the solution must be corrected for the activity (Sec. 13.1) of the ions. We shall ignore this correction.

electrode as the other half cell, then the voltage for the complete cell is the sum of the oxidation potential for the half reaction at the zinc half cell plus that at the hydrogen half cell. If it is assumed that the potential of the standard hydrogen electrode is zero, then the measured voltage of the complete cell must be the emf of the zinc half cell. In this particular case the emf happens to be 0.76 volt, and the hydrogen electrode is positive with respect to the zinc electrode.

In the manner described for the zinc half cell, it is possible to find

TABLE 15.1   HALF REACTIONS AND OXIDATION POTENTIALS AT ROOM TEMPERATURE FOR ELEMENTS IN CONTACT WITH 1-MOLAL SOLUTIONS OF THEIR IONS

Half reaction	E_0 volts
$Li \rightleftharpoons Li^+ + e^-$	3.04
$K \rightleftharpoons K^+ + e^-$	2.92
$Ca \rightleftharpoons Ca^{2+} + 2e^-$	2.87
$Na \rightleftharpoons Na^+ + e^-$	2.71
$Mg \rightleftharpoons Mg^{2+} + 2e^-$	2.34
$Al \rightleftharpoons Al^{3+} + 3e^-$	1.67
$Zn \rightleftharpoons Zn^{2+} + 2e^-$	0.76
$Cr \rightleftharpoons Cr^{3+} + 3e^-$	0.74
$Fe \rightleftharpoons Fe^{2+} + 2e^-$	0.44
$Ni \rightleftharpoons Ni^{2+} + 2e^-$	0.25
$Sn \rightleftharpoons Sn^{2+} + 2e^-$	0.14
$Pb \rightleftharpoons Pb^{2+} + 2e^-$	0.13
$H_2 \rightleftharpoons 2H^+ + 2e^-$	0.00
$Sn^{2+} \rightleftharpoons Sn^{4+} + 2e^-$	−0.15
$Cu \rightleftharpoons Cu^{2+} + 2e^-$	−0.34
$2I^- \rightleftharpoons I_2 + 2e^-$	−0.54
$H_2O_2 \rightleftharpoons O_2 + 2H^+ + 2e^-$	−0.68
$Fe^{2+} \rightleftharpoons Fe^{3+} + e^-$	−0.77
$2Hg \rightleftharpoons Hg_2^{2+} + 2e^-$	−0.79
$Ag \rightleftharpoons Ag^+ + e^-$	−0.80
$Hg \rightleftharpoons Hg^{2+} + 2e^-$	−0.85
$2Br^- \rightleftharpoons Br_2(l) + 2e^-$	−1.06
$Pt \rightleftharpoons Pt^{2+} + 2e^-$	−1.2?
$2H_2O \rightleftharpoons O_2 + 4H^+ + 4e^-$	−1.23
$2H_2O + Mn^{2+} \rightleftharpoons MnO_2 + 4H^+ + 2e^-$	−1.23
$7H_2O + 2Cr^{3+} \rightleftharpoons Cr_2O_7^{2-} + 14H^+ + 6e^-$	−1.33
$2Cl^- \rightleftharpoons Cl_2 + 2e^-$	−1.36
$4H_2O + Mn^{2+} \rightleftharpoons MnO_4^- + 8H^+ + 5e^-$	−1.52
$Au \rightleftharpoons Au^+ + e^-$	−1.68
$2H_2O \rightleftharpoons H_2O_2 + 2H^+ + 2e^-$	−1.77
$2F^- \rightleftharpoons F_2 + 2e^-$	−2.87

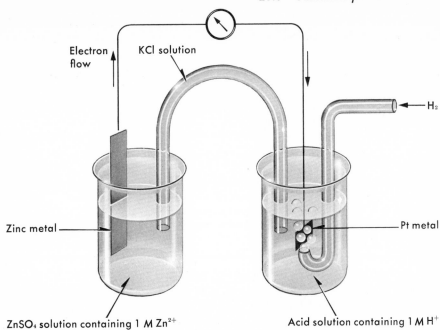

Fig. 15.3 *Complete for measuring the EMF of the* $Zn \rightleftarrows Zn^{2+} + 2e^-$ *half cell by coupling it with a standard hydrogen electrode. The inverted U tube containing a conducting solution, such as KCl in water, serves the same purpose as the cardboard partition shown in Fig. 15.1.*

the electrode potential for any reaction involving oxidation and reduction. Table 15.1 gives a list of half reactions and their oxidation potentials. As these are for $1m$ solutions (corrected for activity) at $25°$ C and, where gases are involved, at 1 atm, these oxidation potentials are called *standard oxidation potentials*. They are often designated E_0.

There is no known way to tell the signs of the potential between metal and solution. This ambiguity is resolved arbitrarily in Table 15.1; those reactants that are more readily oxidized than hydrogen are said to have a positive oxidation potential. This is in accordance with current practice among American physical chemists, but many authors (especially in Europe) use the opposite convention. Notice in Table 15.1 that in every case the half reaction is written as one of oxidation, which would take place at an anode. Consequently, the electron or electrons appear as products of the half reaction at the right of the equation, as written. It follows, therefore, that the reverse of any half reaction shown in Table 15.1 would be a reduction, occurring as a cathode reaction, and that the sign of the potential would therefore be reversed.

The table of oxidation potentials, which is often called the *electro-*

motive series, is useful in predicting the voltage of any voltaic cell, as shown in the following problem.

PROBLEM: Find the voltage of a zinc-copper cell, assuming all concentrations to be $1m$.

SOLUTION: Such a cell is often designated

$$Zn|Zn^{2+}||Cu^{2+}|Cu$$

According to Table 15.1, the half reaction and their standard oxidation potentials are

$$Zn \rightleftharpoons Zn^{2+} + 2e^- \qquad E_0 = 0.76 \text{ volt}$$

and

$$Cu \rightleftharpoons Cu^{2+} + 2e^- \qquad E_0 = -0.34 \text{ volt}$$

But it must be remembered that the half reaction that takes place at the cathode is the reverse of that written, with reversed sign of emf:

$$Cu^{2+} + 2e^- \rightleftharpoons Cu \qquad E_0 = 0.34 \text{ volt}$$

The voltage of the complete cell is simply the sum 0.76 volt + 0.34 volt = 1.10 volts. The zinc metal becomes negative with respect to the copper, and electrons flow in the *external* circuit from zinc to copper.

PROBLEM: Find the voltage for the cell

$$Cu|Cu^{2+}||Ag^+|Ag$$

SOLUTION: If the concentrations are $1m$, the voltage is -0.34 volt $+ 0.80$ volt $= 0.46$ volt, and the copper metal becomes negative with respect to the silver.

The potentials given in Table 15.1 are for half cells containing $1m$ water solutions. If the concentration of the solution is varied, the electrode potential will vary in a manner predictable from Le Châtelier's principle. For the half reaction $Cu \rightleftharpoons Cu^{2+} + 2e^-$, making the solution more concentrated (that is to say, raising the concentration of the Cu^{2+} ions) will force the equilibrium toward the left, as written. This has the effect of moving the half reaction to a lower position in the electromotive series; the reaction has less tendency to go to the right, as written, and the oxidation potential becomes less. Consequently, if there is set up a voltaic

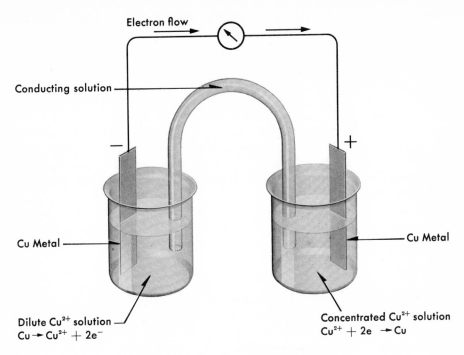

Electron flow

Conducting solution

−

+

Cu Metal

Cu Metal

Dilute Cu²⁺ solution
$Cu \rightarrow Cu^{2+} + 2e^-$

Concentrated Cu²⁺ solution
$Cu^{2+} + 2e \rightarrow Cu$

Fig. 15.4 A copper concentration cell.

cell of which one half cell consists of copper metal in contact with dilute copper sulfate solution and the other half cell of copper metal in contact with concentrated copper solution, as follows:

$$Cu|Cu^{2+}(dil)||Cu^{2+}(conc)|Cu$$

then the complete cell will yield a small but measurable voltage. Such a voltaic cell is called a *concentration cell*. The experimental arrangement is shown in Fig. 15.4. In this cell the copper metal in contact with the more dilute solution is negative with respect to the other.

This effect of changing the emf with changing concentration applies to all half cells. For a hydrogen electrode it is common to use the effect to measure hydrogen ion concentration. Thus, if a standard hydrogen electrode in which $[H^+] = 1m$ is said arbitrarily to have $E_0 = 0$, then a half cell in which $[H^+]$ is not $1m$ will have a definite emf that is not zero. Instruments for measuring hydrogen ion concentrations in this way are widely used in scientific laboratories and in industry. They have definite advantages in precision and convenience over the use of indicators. Such instruments are called pH *meters*.

The reader who examines a table of standard oxidation potentials, such as Table 15.1, may wonder why the potentials given, and even the order in which they occur, are so different from the ionization potentials given in Table 8.1. The reason for the differences is that the ionization potential and the standard oxidation potential do not refer to the same thing. The ionization potential represents the energy necessary to remove an electron from an isolated (gas state) atom; thus

$$M(g) \rightarrow M^+ + e^-$$

It is true that the oxidation potentials are commonly written as referring to half reactions that seem, superficially, to be the same as that given for the ionization potential; but, in fact, the oxidation potential half reactions are made up of several processes, of which the ionization potential represents only one. Consider an atom that is part of a piece of metal, such as might be used as the electrode in a half cell. One step in converting this atom to an ion in solution must be the breaking of the metallic valence bonds which bind the atoms together in a metal. This step may be represented as

$$M(s) \rightarrow M(g)$$

and the energy necessary to do this is the heat of vaporization (or of sublimation, as the case may be).

The second step will be analogous to the ionization potential, namely,

$$M(g) \rightarrow M^+ + e^-$$

but there is now a third step in which the ion formed becomes surrounded by, and attached to, solvent molecules. If the solvent is water, then

$$M^+ + nH_2O \rightarrow M^+(aq) \text{ or } M^+(H_2O)_n$$

The energy involved here is the energy of hydration, and this is generally opposite in sign to the sublimation energy and the ionization potential. Still other processes, such as the "dissolving" of the electron in the metal, may take part. We see, therefore, that the oxidation potential is a complex quantity, of which the ionization potential is an important but not necessarily the largest part.

15.4   Displacement Reactions

The oxidation potentials shown in Table 15.1 may be related to the equilibrium constants for the complete reactions that take place between oxidizing and reducing agents. The relationship is

$$\ln K = \frac{nFE_0}{RT} \tag{15.1}$$

where $\ln K$ is the natural logarithm of the equilibrium constant; n, the number of electrons involved in the oxidation-reduction step; F, the faraday of electricity; E_0, the standard oxidation potential; R, the gas constant; and T, the absolute temperature. For $1m$ solutions at $25°$ C, the emf of a zinc-copper voltaic cell is 1.10 volts, and Eq. 15.1 becomes

$$\log K = 16.9 \times 2 \times 1.10$$

there being two electrons transferred from each atom of zinc to each ion of copper. The quantity K is then 1.5×10^{37}, and the equilibrium constant is

$$\frac{[Zn^{2+}]}{[Cu^{2+}]} = K = 1.5 \times 10^{37}$$

In other words, the reaction goes (as is well known) virtually to completion.

Standard oxidation potentials are convenient for predicting the course of a chemical reaction, provided oxidation and reduction are possible. Distinguish between the reduced form of the half reaction and the oxidized form. In the half reaction,

$$Li \rightleftharpoons Li^+ + e^-$$

The reduced form is Li and the oxidized form is Li^+. In the half reaction,

$$2H_2O \rightleftharpoons O_2 + 4H^+ + 4e^-$$

the reduced form is $2H_2O$ and the oxidized form is $O_2 + 4H^+$. In all the half reactions given in Table 15.1, the reduced form is at the left.

Now, in general, it may be said that at standard concentrations, *the reduced form in any half reaction will reduce the oxidized form in any half reaction for which the oxidation potential is algebraically less.* Thus potassium metal, K, will reduce aurous ion, Au^+, in aqueous solution. The complete reaction is

$$K + Au^+ \rightleftharpoons K^+ + Au$$

and the voltage of the complete cell is $2.92 + 1.68 = 4.60$ volts. This is a typical displacement reaction in which a more active metal (one with a higher oxidation potential) displaces a less active metal from solution. Another displacement reaction is that of a more active halogen displacing one that is less active, as in the displacement of iodine from iodide ion solution by the more active chlorine:

$$Cl_2 + 2I^- \rightleftharpoons 2Cl^- + I_2$$

In this case the two half reactions and their respective oxidation potentials are as follows:

$$2Cl^- \rightleftharpoons Cl_2 + 2e^- \qquad E_0 = -1.36 \text{ volts}$$
$$2I^- \rightleftharpoons I_2 + 2e^- \qquad E_0 = -0.53 \text{ volt}$$

The voltage of the cell in this reaction is $+0.83$ volt.

In Table 15.1, lithium metal is the most powerful reducing agent; fluoride ion, F^-, the weakest. Those reduced forms lower than about silver are seldom, if ever, referred to as reducing agents. Similarly, fluorine, F_2, is the most powerful oxidizing agent shown; lithium ion, Li^+, the weakest. Those oxidized forms above cupric ion, Cu^{2+}, are not often referred to as oxidizing agents.

As is obvious from Eq. 15.1, the expectation of an oxidation-reduction reaction going to completion, or nearly so, is greater the larger the voltage for the complete reaction. Thus the reaction between potassium metal and aurous ion will go effectively to completion, but that between tin and plumbous ion,

$$Sn + Pb^{2+} \rightleftharpoons Sn^{2+} + Pb$$

with an emf of $0.14 - 0.13 = 0.01$ volt, will not normally go to completion. A supposed displacement reaction of aluminum ion by nickel,

$$3Ni + 2Al^{3+} \rightleftharpoons 3Ni^{2+} + 2Al$$

yields a negative emf of $0.25 - 1.69 = -1.44$ volts, and hence cannot possibly proceed to the right as written, but may proceed to the left, aluminum displacing nickel ions.

Application of oxidation potentials to reactions such as these may be complicated if one or more ionic products happens to be insoluble or happens to form a complex compound. Both contingencies shift the equilibrium by lowering the concentration of one or more ions present. One example of this effect will suffice. According to the rule given above, any metal with a positive oxidation potential will displace hydrogen ions from solution. This is simply another way of saying that the more active metals dissolve in acids. At the other extreme, gold has such a low oxidation potential that it could not possibly undergo the reaction

$$2Au + 2H^+ \rightarrow 2Au^+ + H_2$$

Nevertheless, a mixture of nitric and hydrochloric acids, called *aqua regia*, will dissolve the king of metals, although no hydrogen is liberated. This reaction occurs because the gold forms a complex ion, $AuCl_4^-$, the effect of which is to lower the concentration of Au^+ ions until it is virtually zero. This in turn shifts the equilibrium to a degree sufficient to permit the gold to go into solution.

This section will be completed with a description of how half reactions may be used in an alternative method for balancing equations of oxidation and reduction.

PROBLEM: Aluminum metal will displace iron from a solution containing ferrous, Fe^{2+}, ions. The two half reactions are

$$Al \rightleftharpoons Al^{3+} + 3e^-$$

and

$$Fe^{2+} + 2e^- \rightleftharpoons Fe$$

write a balanced equation for the reaction.

SOLUTION: The only difficulty here is to make sure that the number of electrons lost by the aluminum is equal to the number gained by the ferrous ions. The numbers lost and gained in the two half reactions are 3 and 2, for which the least common multiple is 6. Then, multiplying the first equation by 2 and the second by 3, we have

$$2Al \rightleftharpoons 2Al^{3+} + 6e^-$$

and

$$3Fe^{2+} \rightleftharpoons 3Fe + 6e^-$$

The addition of these two half reactions gives the balanced equation:

$$2Al + 3Fe^{2+} \rightleftharpoons 2Al^{3+} + 3Fe$$

It will, of course, be realized that the positive ions in solution must be electrically balanced by an appropriate number of negative ions, of which sulfate, SO_4^{2-}, would serve. The negative ions take no part in the reaction and may therefore be omitted unless there is some reason for wanting to know, for instance, the weight of ferrous sulfate necessary to react with a given weight of aluminum. A complete equation written for such a purpose would be as follows:

$$2Al(s) + 3FeSO_4(aq) \rightleftharpoons 2Al_3(SO_4)_3(aq) + 3Fe(s)$$

PROBLEM: Write a balanced equation for the reduction of cobaltic, Co^{3+}, ion to cobaltous, Co^{2+}, ion by water.

SOLUTION: The half reactions are

$$Co^{3+} + e^- \rightleftharpoons Co^{2+}$$

and

$$2H_2O \rightleftharpoons 4H^+ + O_2 + 4e^-$$

Multiplying the first equation by 4, and adding:

$$4Co^{3+} + 2H_2O \rightleftharpoons 4Co^{2+} + 4H^+ + O_2$$

PROBLEM: The oxidation of metallic copper by dilute nitric acid yields cupric ions, nitric oxide, and water. Write the balanced equation.

SOLUTION: The half reactions must be,

$$Cu \rightleftharpoons Cu^{2+} + 2e^-$$

and

$$NO_3^- + 4H^+ + 3e^- \rightleftharpoons NO + 2H_2O$$

Then

$$3Cu \rightleftharpoons 3Cu^{2+} + 6e^-$$

and

$$2NO_3^- + 8H^+ + 6e^- \rightleftharpoons 2NO + 4H_2O$$

Adding,

$$3Cu + 2NO_3^- + 8H^+ \rightleftharpoons 3Cu^{2+} + 2NO + 4H_2O$$

It is particularly important to note that in combining half reactions to give a complete equation, the electrons involved must cancel out, and that this is done by multiplying the half reactions to obtain the least common multiple. But in finding the emf of a complete voltaic cell, the oxidation potentials given in Table 15.1 are added without being multiplied by the number of electrons present. For instance, in the example given above of aluminum metal displacing iron from ferrous sulfate solution, the E_0 values are 1.67 volts for the aluminum half reaction and 0.44 volt for the iron half reaction. The voltage produced in a voltaic cell from these half reactions at 25° C and $1m$ concentration would be (with due regard for signs) $1.67 - 0.44 = 1.23$ volts.

15.5   Practical Voltaic Cells

In this section we shall describe two familiar voltaic cells: the dry cell, used in flashlights and portable radios, and the lead storage battery, used in automobiles. The dry cell is an example of a primary cell; the lead storage cell, an example of a secondary cell. Primary cells are voltaic cells in which the chemical changes occurring are, for practical purposes, irreversible. Secondary cells are those that may be recharged an indefinite number of times. A battery is, strictly speaking, several voltaic cells connected together.

The dry cell is dry only by comparison; it would not operate if it were free of moisture. The active material consists of a moist paste rather than of a liquid. The cell consists of a carbon rod that serves as the positive electrode; this is surrounded by a mixture of manganese dioxide and graphite, which is in turn surrounded by a wet paste of ammonium chloride, often mixed with flour or starch. The whole is enclosed in a zinc container that serves as the negative electrode. Zinc chloride and mercuric chloride are added to the paste to improve the operation and life of the cell. The

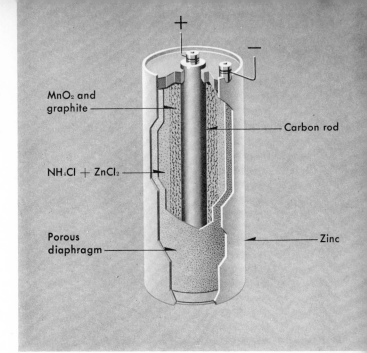

MnO$_2$ and
graphite

Carbon rod

NH$_4$Cl + ZnCl$_2$

Fig. 15.5 Dry cell.

Porous
diaphragm

Zinc

graphite serves to increase the electrical conductivity of the manganese dioxide mixture.

The chemical reactions taking place during operation of the dry cell are not perfectly understood, but are believed to be approximately as follows: Zinc goes into solution, the liberated electrons imparting a negative charge to the zinc metal container:

$$Zn \rightleftharpoons Zn^{2+} + 2e^-$$

The ammonium ions react with the manganese dioxide, yielding ammonia and leaving the manganese with an oxidation state of 3+, perhaps in the form of MnOOH, or possibly as ZnMn$_2$O$_4$:

$$2NH_4^+ + 2MnO_2 + 2e^- \rightleftharpoons 2NH_3 + 2MnOOH$$

The electrons necessary for this reaction come from the carbon rod, which thereby acquires a positive charge. The ammonia may combine with zinc ions, forming the complex ion Zn(NH$_3$)$_4^{2+}$.

The voltage delivered by a dry cell of the above type is about 1.5 to 1.6 volts. Owing to an effect known as polarization, the voltage drops rapidly if large currents are withdrawn from the cell, but the cell recovers its voltage if allowed to stand. Dry cells are, therefore most satisfactory for intermittent use. Other types of dry cells are known. One of the most popular is the mercury cell, which is widely used in hearing aids and in electronic equipment.

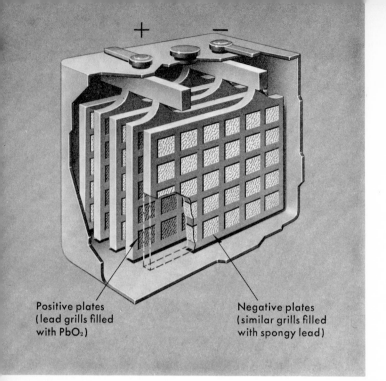

Negative plates
(similar grills filled
with spongy lead)

Fig. 15.6 Storage cell.

In its simplest form, the lead storage cell (Fig. 15.6) consists of a sheet of lead dioxide, PbO_2, placed in moderately dilute sulfuric acid. In practice, the lead dioxide is supported on a sheet or grid of lead. In most commercially available cells there are several layers of lead and of lead dioxide, kept apart by insulating strips called separators.

During discharge of the cell, the lead electrode tends to form lead ions, the electrons liberated in this process imparting a negative charge to the remaining lead. This forms the negative pole of the cell:

$$Pb \rightleftharpoons Pb^{2+} + 2e^-$$

In the presence of sulfuric acid, the lead ions form insoluble lead sulfate, which deposits in part as a white substance on the metallic lead:

$$Pb^{2+} + SO_4^{2-} \rightarrow PbSO_4$$

At the lead dioxide electrode, the lead with an oxidation state of 4+ is reduced to 2+:

$$PbO_2 + 2e^- + 4H^+ \rightarrow Pb^{2+} + 2H_2O$$

The hydrogen ions shown in this reaction come, of course, from the sulfuric acid. The electrons necessary to reduce Pb^{4+} to Pb^{2+} come from the lead dioxide electrode, imparting to it a positive charge. In the reaction at this electrode, the lead ions formed also combine with sulfate ions from the sulfuric acid to form lead sulfate, as above.

By combining these equations, we may write for the reaction taking place at the negative pole during discharge:

$$Pb + H_2SO_4 \rightarrow PbSO_4 + 2H^+ + 2e^-$$

and at the positive pole,

$$PbO_2 + 2e^- + H_2SO_4 + 2H^+ \rightarrow PbSO_4 + 2H_2O$$

The reaction at the negative pole gives up electrons; that at the positive pole takes up electrons.

We may now write one equation to represent the overall reaction in the lead storage cell during discharge. This equation is as follows:

$$Pb + PbO_2 + 2H_2SO_4 \rightarrow 2PbSO_4 + 2H_2O$$

To recharge a secondary cell, an external source of electricity is connected with negative pole to negative electrode and positive to positive. Electrons flow into the cell in the opposite direction from that during discharge. The chemical reactions taking place are exactly the opposite of those occurring during discharge. The lead ions at the negative pole are reduced to metallic lead. Those at the positive pole are oxidized to lead dioxide. The overall equation for charging is exactly the reverse of that for discharge. We therefore write

$$Pb + PbO_2 + 2H_2SO_4 \underset{\text{charge}}{\overset{\text{discharge}}{\rightleftharpoons}} 2PbSO_4 + 2H_2O$$

for the complete reaction, although this may be a rather oversimplified representation. When fully charged, a cell of the type described delivers slightly over 2 volts. The total quantity of electricity obtainable may be quite large.

Reactions of oxidation and reduction are almost infinite in their variety, and each such reaction lends itself, in principle, to the generation of electricity. Attention has recently been directed to the direct conversion to electricity of the energy derivable from the union of some combustible substance like gasoline or carbon monoxide with oxygen. A voltaic cell for achieving this purpose is called a *fuel cell*.

One kind of fuel cell utilizes the reaction between hydrogen and oxygen:

$$2H_2 + O_2 \rightleftharpoons 2H_2O$$

the half reactions being the ones that should already be familiar:

$$H_2 \rightleftharpoons 2H^+ + 2e$$

and

$$O_2 + 4H^+ + 4e^- \rightleftharpoons 2H_2O$$

Figure 15.7 shows, diagrammatically, a cell for obtaining electricity directly from the reaction above. The hydrogen and oxygen gas are admitted to compartments separated by a porous membrane coated on each

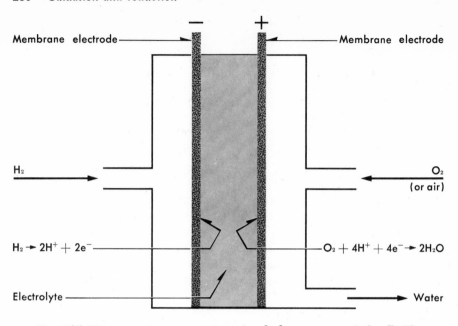

Fig. 15.7 Diagrammatic representation of a hydrogen-oxygen fuel cell. The overall reaction is $2H_2 + O_2 \rightarrow 2H_2O$.

side with a substance that serves the double purpose of catalyzing the half reactions involved and conducting the electron flow to the external circuit. The water formed is evaporated or discharged. Voltaic cells of this kind, using a variety of fuels cheaper than hydrogen, appear at this writing to be reaching a satisfactory stage of engineering development.

EXERCISES

1. Show oxidation states for elements in black letters in each of the following formulas: **Ca**O, **Ti**O₂, **Sb**₂O₃, **W**O₃, H**I**, **Ge**H₄, H₂**Se**, H₂**Se**O₃, **Zn**(OH)₂, H₃**P**O₄, **Y**(OH)₃, **K**, **S**₂, **Cl**₂, **Cl**O₄⁻, **Cr**O₄²⁻, **N**H₄⁺, **Pb**O₂ (a dioxide), Ba**O**₂ (a peroxide), K**O**₂ (a superoxide), **H**₄P₂O₇, Ca**H**₂ (a true hydride),

2. In the equation

$$Cu_2S + 2Cu_2O \rightarrow 6Cu + SO_2$$

the copper is reduced. What is the reducing agent?

3. In the reaction

$$PbS + PbSO_4 \rightarrow 2Pb + 2SO_2$$

what atom or atoms are reduced? What atom or atoms are oxidized? What is the reducing agent? What is the oxidizing agent?

4. Consider the following:

(a) $CuO + H_2 \rightarrow Cu + H_2O$
(b) $Cl_2 + 2Br^- \rightarrow Br_2 + 2Cl^-$
(c) $Ag^+ + Zn \rightarrow Zn^{2+} + Ag$
(d) $H_2SO_4 + NaNO_3 \rightarrow HNO_3 + Na_2SO_4$
(e) $KMnO_4 + MnSO_4 + H_2O \rightarrow MnO_2 + K_2SO_4 + H_2SO_4$
(f) $CuSO_4 + NaOH \rightarrow Cu(OH)_2 + Na_2SO_4$
(g) Na_2O_2 (a peroxide) $+ CrCl_3 + NaOH \rightarrow$
$$Na_2CrO_4 + NaCl + H_2O$$
(h) $Al + Cl_2 \rightarrow Al_2Cl_6$
(i) $Pb(NO_3)_2 + H_2S \rightarrow PbS + HNO_3$
(j) $FeS + O_2 \rightarrow Fe_2O_3 + SO_2$

Show oxidation states for all atoms in the above, indicate which reactions involve oxidation and reduction, and balance all equations.

5. Balance the following:

(a) $HNO_3 + KI \rightarrow KNO_3 + NO + I_2 + H_2O$
(b) $PbO_2 + Pb + H_2SO_4 \rightarrow PbSO_4 + H_2O$
(c) $NH_4NO_2 \rightarrow N_2 + H_2O$
(d) $Sn^{2+} + Fe^{3+} \rightarrow Fe^{2+} + Sn^{4+}$
(e) $PbO_2 + H^+ + Mn^{2+} \rightarrow Pb^{2+} + MnO_4^- + H_2O$

6. In some of the above reactions (Exercise 5), an element acts in more than one way as far as oxidation or reduction is concerned. Point out in which reactions this is true, and list: (a) what is oxidized, (b) what is reduced, (c) the oxidizing agent, and (d) the reducing agent.

7. With the aid of a labeled diagram, describe (a) a zinc half cell, (b) a hydrogen half cell, (c) a complete zinc-hydrogen cell, and show direction of electrons in the external circuit.

8. What general type of chemical reaction can be used for the production of electricity? Take an example, other than one of those described in the text, and show how it can be utilized.

9. In a zinc-copper cell, the copper is positive, but in a copper-gold cell, the copper is negative. Explain.

10. Having available the four metals, iron, nickel, copper, and silver, construct the voltaic cell having the maximum emf.

11. (a) Between which of the following pairs may an oxidation-reduction reaction be expected to take place: Sn^{2+} and Br^-; Sn^{2+} and Br_2; Sn^{4+} and Br_2; Sn^{4+} and Br^-?
(b) Diagram a voltaic cell(s) for the reaction labeling all

parts and solutions, directions of electron flow in the external circuit, and emf for $1m$ solutions at 25° C.

12. Define anode and cathode.
13. Hydrogen is being supplied to a fuel cell at the rate of 1 ml/min (at STP), all other reactants being present in excess. What is the maximum theoretical current that may be drawn from this cell?
14. When oxygen is bubbled through a solution of ferrous, Fe^{2+}, ions in water, the iron is oxidized to ferric, Fe^{3+}, ions. What are the half reactions involved? Write a balanced ionic equation for this reaction, and state what happens to the pH of the solution.
15. Find the voltage developed in each of the following voltaic cells (all solutions being $1m$):

    (a) $Mg|Mg^{2+}||Zn^{2+}|Zn$
    (b) $Cu|Cu^{2+}||Au^+|Au$
    (c) $Fe|Fe^{2+}||Ag^+|Ag$
    (d) $H_2|H^+||Hg_2^{2+}|Hg$

16. Write half reactions for each of the cells in Exercise 15. Write complete reaction equations, and state which electrode is positive.
17. A voltaic cell is constructed as follows:

$$Ni|Ni^{2+}||Ag^+|Ag$$

all solutions being $1m$.
    (a) Diagram the cell and show direction of electrons in the external circuit.
    (b) Write equations for the two half reactions.
    (c) State the emf for the complete cell.
    (d) State the effect on the emf of lowering the nickel ion concentration.
    (e) State the effect on the emf of lowering the silver ion concentration.
18. A voltaic cell is made up of manganese metal in contact with Mn^{2+} ions, and chlorine gas in contact with Cl^- ions.
    (a) Diagram the cell, showing which direction the electrons flow in the external circuit, and write equations for the half reactions.
    (b) Write an equation for the complete reaction and show the cell voltage. $Mn \rightleftharpoons Mn^{2+} + 2e^-$, $E_0 = 1.18$ volts.
    (c) Indicate the effect on the cell voltage of lowering the Mn^{2+} ion concentration.
    (d) Indicate the effect on the cell voltage of lowering the Cl^- ion concentration.
    (e) Indicate the probable effect of raising the chlorine gas pressure.

(f) Indicate the effect of substituting the (I^-, I_2) half cell for the (Cl^-, Cl_2) half cell on the cell voltage.

19. Two cells are made as follows:

$$Zn|Zn^{2+}||H^+|H_2$$

and

$$H_2|H^+||Ag^+|Ag$$

Predict the effect on the cell voltage in each of the two cells if the following changes are made: (a) the hydrogen ion concentration is increased; (b) the pressure of the hydrogen gas is increased.

20. When ammonia is added to a solution containing cupric ions, the ammonia combines with the copper as follows:

$$Cu^{2+} + 4NH_3 \rightleftharpoons Cu(NH_3)_4^{2+}$$

the equilibrium being quite far to the right, as written. What effect on the cell voltage will be caused by adding ammonia to the more concentrated half cell of a copper concentration cell?

21. It takes more energy to remove an electron from a lithium atom than from a potassium atom, but lithium has a higher oxidation potential. What are some possible reasons for this?

22. Of what two half reactions could each of the following be considered to consist?

(a) $2H_2O + 2Cl_2 \rightleftharpoons 4H^+ + 4Cl^- + O_2$
(b) $Zn + 2H^+ + 2Cl^- \rightleftharpoons Zn^{2+} + 2Cl^- + H_2$
(c) $Br_2 + 2K^+ + 2I^- \rightleftharpoons I_2 + 2K^+ + 2Br^-$

23. (a) Between which of the following pairs of substances may an oxidation-reduction reaction be expected to take place?

Mn and Hg^{2+}	I^- and Br_2
Mn and Mg^{2+}	K^+ and H^+
Ca and Zn	Fe and I_2
Ni and F^-	Pt and Ni^{2+}
Cl_2 and H_2O	H_2 and Cu^{2+}

(b) Write balanced ionic equations for those pairs that react, and show the emf produced in cells containing 1-molal solutions of the ions.

24. Under what conditions might the following reaction go to the right?

$$H_2 + Pb^{2+} \rightleftharpoons Pb + 2H^+$$

25. If a copper wire is placed in a solution of silver nitrate, there soon appear beautiful crystals of metallic silver. Explain?

26. Estimate the equilibrium constant for the following reaction:

$$Sn + Pb^{2+} \rightleftharpoons Sn^{2+} + Pb$$

27. Using the method of half reactions, complete and balance the following:

    (a) $MnO_4^- + H_2O_2 + H^+ \rightarrow$
    (b) $Cr_2O_7^- + I^- + H^+ \rightarrow$
    (c) $Sn^{2+} + Mg \rightarrow$
    (d) $Br_2 + Fe^{2+} \rightarrow$
    (e) $MnO_2 + H^+ + Cl^- \rightarrow$

28. Assuming that the zinc outer container (and electrode) in a small dry cell weighs 40 grams and that all other reactants are present in excess, what is the maximum, theoretical quantity of electricity obtainable from the cell?

29. A copper concentration cell is made up with the more concentrated half cell containing 1 liter of $2m$ Cu^{2+}, and the more dilute half cell containing 1 liter of $1m$ Cu^{2+}. Assuming that the copper metal electrodes are very large, find how much electricity could be drawn from the cell before the emf becomes zero.

16

The Chemical Elements

16.1 Natural Abundance of the Elements

The part of the universe most readily accessible to us is that part on, or near, the surface of the earth, namely, the earth's crust. Most of the known chemical elements may be found in the earth's crust, although the proportions in which they are found are very different for different elements. Some chemical elements do not occur naturally, but may be made artificially. Examples of processes for synthesizing elements will be described in Chapter 20. The synthesis of an element differs from a natural occurrence in that in nature the various isotopes are found mixed together, whereas in synthetic elements it often occurs that only one specific nuclide is prepared. It is probable that when the universe, as we know it, was created, all elements were made, but now most of the radioactive nuclides have decayed to the degree that they can no longer be detected in the earth's crust.

Considering the universe as a whole, it appears that the elements of lower atomic number are much more abundant than those of higher number. It has been estimated that 90 percent of the universe is hydrogen, with the possibility that many elements are still being created and continue to decay. But in the earth's crust the situation is quite different. Most of the hydrogen presumably present originally has escaped from the earth's gravitational field, and oxygen is the most abundant, followed by silicon and aluminum.

Table 16.1 shows some of the more abundant elements in the earth's crust and their relative abundances. In this connection it is significant that uranium should be found in the earth's crust. Uranium is radioactive and it is not being generated by the decay of some other element. This shows that the uranium must have been formed at some finite time in the past; otherwise, it would have all disappeared. The age of the universe, calculated on this basis, is estimated at about 4×10^9 years. Observations, as far as they have been made, of other planets and of distant stars show that the elements familiar on Earth are also found elsewhere in the universe, although the relative proportions may be quite different.

In any given sample of a natural element, it nearly always occurs that the several isotopes present are mixed in the same proportion. For instance, in magnesium, no matter from what natural source, the relative proportions of the three isotopes are: ^{24}Mg, 77.4%, ^{25}Mg, 11.5%; and ^{26}Mg, 11.1%. If one or more isotopes of an element should happen to be radioactive with a short half-life, then it is easy to see why the natural abundance of that nuclide should be vanishingly small. But why some stable nuclides should be much more abundant than others is harder to understand. Perhaps some nuclei were less readily formed than others in the processes that went on during creation of the universe, or perhaps some nuclei were used in forming other nuclei. Whatever processes may have been involved in synthesis of elements at the time of the creation may only be surmised.

TABLE 16.1   RELATIVE ABUNDANCES OF SOME ELEMENTS
IN THE EARTH'S CRUST (LITHOSPHERE
AND HYDROSPHERE)

Element	Symbol	Weight, percent
Oxygen	O	49.2
Silicon	Si	25.7
Aluminum	Al	7.5
Iron	Fe	4.7
Calcium	Ca	3.4
Sodium	Na	2.6
Potassium	K	2.4
Magnesium	Mg	1.9
Hydrogen	H	0.9
Titanium	Ti	0.6
All others		1

16.2 Natural Occurrence of the Elements

Any natural source of a chemical element is called a *mineral,* and any commercially useful source is called an *ore.* Minerals may include pure elements free from combination with other elements, elements in mixtures, elements in chemical combination, and virtually endless series of compounds and mixtures. The chemical composition and distribution of minerals is the science of geochemistry. This section will be devoted to describing how some of the more important elements occur in, or near, the earth's crust, and to presenting some general principles that determine whether elements occur uncombined or in compounds. An element that occurs free from chemical combination is said to be *native,* although this term is most frequently used in reference to metals such as native gold.

Chemical elements that occasionally, or always, are found to occur native include the six group zero gases, the six members of the palladium-platinum group, and the elements carbon, nitrogen, oxygen, sulfur, copper, silver, and gold. Iron is sometimes found native, but this is only in meteorites. Traces of other uncombined elements, of which hydrogen is one, are found in the atmosphere and elsewhere.

The Group Zero gases helium, neon, argon, krypton, xenon, and radon always occur in nature as the free elements. They are, however, found mixed with other elements and compounds present in the atmosphere or in natural gases. Separation and purification of these and other elements will be described in Chapter 21.

The element carbon occurs in nature principally combined with oxygen in the form of carbonates, of which calcium carbonate is one. But occasionally there are found deposits of almost pure carbon in the form either of diamond or of graphite crystals. Carbon is fairly readily formed by reduction of carbonates or by decomposition of living matter, in which it is always abundantly present. Having once been formed, the carbon is comparatively unreactive and may persist as the uncombined element unless it is heated in the presence of oxygen.

Nitrogen, on the other hand, is much less widely distributed in nature. It owes its presence as free nitrogen in air to the unusual stability of the N_2 molecule. Oxygen, by contrast, occurs chiefly combined with other elements in endless groups of minerals such as the silicates, oxides, carbonates, and phosphates. But oxygen is so abundant that there is some left over as the free element in the atmosphere. Oxygen is also released during the growth of vegetation. It is true that oxygen and nitrogen may combine chemically to form nitric oxide, but the equilibrium lies far in the direction of the free elements except at very high temperatures. Sulfur, as does oxygen, occurs principally in the form of compounds such as sulfates, but deposits of the free elements in a fairly high state of purity are found in various parts of the world. These may have been formed by reduction of sulfur-containing compounds.

In the absence of complications such as those mentioned above, the occurrence of an element free or in combination is fairly easily predicted. Those elements, such as potassium, with a high (algebraic) oxidation potential are never found as native metal. Such elements are, however, found in the *oxidized* state (which, for potassium, is the K^+ ion) in combination, of course, with some appropriate negative ion. Potassium and all other elements near the top of the electromotive series occur as positive ions in minerals, of which potassium chloride is a very simple example.

Those elements such as fluorine, with a low (algebraic) oxidation potential, are never found as the free element. Such elements are, however, found in the *reduced* state (which, for fluorine, is the F^- ion) in combination with some appropriate positive ion. Fluorine, occurs as the negative ion in minerals, of which calcium fluoride is one. If the reduced form of a half-reaction of low E_0 happens to be a metal, as is the case for the half-reaction

$$Au \rightleftharpoons Au^{3+} + 3e^- \qquad E_0 = -1.5 \text{ volts}$$

then the element is generally found in nature as the free metal.

TABLE 16.2 EXAMPLES OF IMPORTANT MINERALS

Formula	Chemical name*	Mineralogical name
H_2O	hydrogen oxide	water
CO_2	carbon dioxide	
Al_2O_3	aluminum oxide	corundum
Fe_2O_3	ferric oxide	hematite
TiO_2	titanium dioxide	rutile
MnO_2	manganese dioxide	pyrolusite
Fe_3O_4	(magnetite)	magnetite
SnO_2	stannic oxide	cassiterite
$FeCr_2O_4$	ferrous chromite	chromite
$CaCO_3$	calcium carbonate	calcite
HgS	mercuric sulfide	cinnabar
PbS	lead sulfide	galena
$CaSO_4 \cdot 2H_2O$	calcium sulfate dihydrate	gypsum
$CaWO_4$	calcium tungstate	scheelite
$NaCl$	sodium chloride	halite
$Be_3Al_2(SiO_3)_6$	beryllium aluminum silicate	beryl

*These are common names, but not necessarily the names based on modern nomenclature systems.

This section has concluded with Table 16.2 which lists a few important minerals for a few important elements. Formulas, chemical names as far as applicable, and mineralogical names are given. It should be understood that the compositions of minerals may be extremely complex and that they tend to merge into each other in a manner that can be confusing. A pure compound in the chemical sense is rare in nature.

16.3 Periodicity of the Elements

If the chemical elements are arranged in order of increasing atomic number, it will be found that most of the elements fall into groups characterized by "family" resemblances with respect to their chemical and physical properties. Sodium and potassium are much alike; carbon and silicon show resemblances; fluorine, chlorine, bromine, and iodine have many characteristic family properties.

The recurrent appearance of group characteristics in the elements is summarized in the following statement:

The properties of the chemical elements are periodic functions of their atomic numbers.

This is the **law of chemical periodicity**, first stated by D. Mendeleev in 1868.[1]

When it is said that the properties of the elements are a periodic function of their atomic numbers, it is meant that specific properties such as hardness or chemical reactivity, or oxidation states, change from element to element in a cyclic manner—certain similarities making their appearance at more or less regular intervals. For our purposes, the most useful properties are those related to the combining power, and these will be surveyed in the following section. One example of a periodic physical property is the melting point. Figure 16.1 shows melting points plotted against atomic number. The melting points start with extremely low temperatures for hydrogen ($-259°$ C) and helium ($-272°$ C at 26 atm), rise through lithium ($186°$ C), beryllium ($1284°$ C), boron ($2300°$ C), and carbon ($> 3500°$ C), then fall precipitously to nitrogen ($-210°$ C), oxygen ($-218°$ C), fluorine ($-223°$ C), and neon ($-249°$ C), then rise again through sodium ($97.5°$ C), magnesium ($651°$ C), and silicon ($1420°$ C). This cyclic or periodic variation is repeated through all the elements. The periodicity is not perfect—a few elements seem to be misplaced—but in general the periodicity is sufficient so that the melting point of an unknown element could be predicted with fair accuracy. It must be emphasized that nearly all specific physical and chemical properties show this periodicity.

[1] In 1868 atomic numbers were unknown. Mendeleev stated his law in terms of atomic weights.

TABLE 16.3 THE PERIODIC TABLE (SHORT FORM)

Series	Group 0	Group 1		Group 2		Group 3		Group 4		Group 5		Group 6		Group 7		Group 8
		A	B	A	B	A	B	A	B	A	B	A	B	A	B	
Series 1															$_1$H	
Series 2	$_2$He	$_3$Li		$_4$Be		$_5$B		$_6$C		$_7$N			$_8$O		$_9$F	
Series 3	$_{10}$Ne	$_{11}$Na		$_{12}$Mg		$_{13}$Al		$_{14}$Si		$_{15}$P			$_{16}$S		$_{17}$Cl	
Series 4	$_{18}$Ar	$_{19}$K	$_{29}$Cu	$_{20}$Ca	$_{30}$Zn	$_{21}$Sc	$_{31}$Ga	$_{22}$Ti	$_{32}$Ge	$_{23}$V	$_{33}$As	$_{24}$Cr	$_{34}$Se	$_{25}$Mn	$_{35}$Br	$_{26}$Fe $_{27}$Co $_{28}$Ni
Series 5	$_{36}$Kr	$_{37}$Rb	$_{47}$Ag	$_{38}$Sr	$_{48}$Cd	$_{39}$Y	$_{49}$In	$_{40}$Zr	$_{50}$Sn	$_{41}$Nb	$_{51}$Sb	$_{42}$Mo	$_{52}$Te	$_{43}$Tc	$_{53}$I	$_{44}$Ru $_{45}$Rh $_{46}$Pd
Series 6	$_{54}$Xe	$_{55}$Cs	$_{79}$Au	$_{56}$Ba	$_{80}$Hg	$_{57-71}$*	$_{81}$Tl	$_{72}$Hf	$_{82}$Pb	$_{73}$Ta	$_{83}$Bi	$_{74}$W	$_{84}$Po	$_{75}$Re	$_{85}$At	$_{76}$Os $_{77}$Ir $_{78}$Pt
Series 7	$_{86}$Rn	$_{87}$Fr		$_{88}$Ra		$_{89-103}$†										

* Rare earth elements 57–71: La, Ce, Pr, Nd, Pm, Sm, Eu, Gd, Tb, Dy, Ho, Er, Tm, Yb, Lu.

† Actinides 89–103: Ac, Th, Pa, U, Np, Pu, Am, Cm, Bk, Cf, Es, Fm, Md, —, Lw.

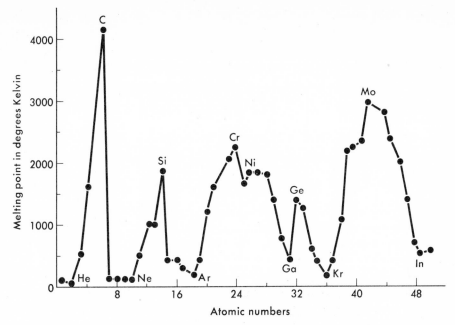

Fig. 16.1 *The periodic law illustrated by a plot of atomic numbers versus melting points of the elements, from atomic numbers 1 to 50.*

The periodicity of the elements could not arise accidentally; it is the result of an underlying fundamental recurring feature in the structure of the atoms. Reference to Table 6.3 will identify this recurring feature as the way in which electrons are distributed among the various energy levels. The similar elements sodium and potassium have in common that although the highest energy level normally containing electrons in sodium is the *L* shell, and the corresponding level for potassium is the *M* shell, yet one, and only one, electron is contained in each of these shells. The similar elements carbon and silicon each have four electrons in the *L* and *M* shells, respectively; and the family group consisting of fluorine, chlorine, bromine, and iodine is characterized by seven electrons in the highest occupied levels, which are the *L*, *M*, *N*, and *O* shells, respectively. This recurrent feature in the electron distribution is the principal reason why periodicity in properties is exhibited by the chemical elements.

Arrangement of the first few elements in order of increasing atomic number shows that they fall naturally into groups of eight.

$_2$He $_3$Li $_4$Be $_5$B $_6$C $_7$N $_8$O $_9$F
$_{10}$Ne $_{11}$Na $_{12}$Mg $_{13}$Al $_{14}$Si $_{15}$P $_{16}$S $_{17}$Cl

Disregarding hydrogen for the moment, we find that neon resembles helium, sodium resembles lithium (as well as potassium), and so on for each vertical pair of atoms shown.

But, if now the sequence of elements is continued, it will be found that the family resemblances rapidly break down. Chromium is only remotely like sulfur; iron is not at all like argon.

$$_{18}Ar \quad _{19}K \quad _{20}Ca \quad _{21}Sc \quad _{22}Ti] \quad _{23}V \quad _{24}Cr \quad _{25}Mn \quad _{26}Fe$$

Nevertheless, if the idea is pursued a little farther, it will be found that at element 32, germanium, a resemblance to silicon is noted.

$$_{27}Co \quad _{28}Ni \quad _{29}Cu \quad _{30}Zn \quad _{31}Ga \quad _{32}Ge \quad _{33}As \quad _{34}Se \quad _{35}Br$$

Arsenic definitely resembles phosphorus, selenium is much like sulfur, and bromine is very like chlorine.

It is not easy to arrange the elements so as to emphasize all the likenesses and unlikenesses among them, but this may be done fairly well if each vertical (family) group is divided into two subgroups, which may be called the A and B subgroups. Elements in the same group do not necessarily show very close resemblances unless they are also in the same subgroup. For instance, potassium and copper have few points of resemblance; they are therefore put in different subgroups, although they both belong in the same main group.

One form of the complete arrangement of the elements is shown in Table 16.3. This is a form of the Mendeleev *Periodic Table*. From this table it may be seen that when the elements are arranged in order of increasing atomic number, the elements with similar properties are found at recurrent, though not equal intervals. The intervals (or periods) are, disregarding hydrogen, made up of 8, 8, 18, 18, and 32 elements, plus a final incomplete period. Another form of the Periodic Table is shown on the inside back cover of this book.

16.4   Group Relationships in the Periodic Table

The family relationships referred to in the preceding section are found in the vertical arrangement of elements as shown in the two forms of the Periodic Table given in this book. The elements so arranged are said to be in groups. There are nine such groups, numbered 0 to VIII in Table 16.3, and there are seven horizontal series (or periods). It will be noted that in the long form of the table, given on the inside cover, the number of each series corresponds to the principal quantum number of the highest occupied energy level. Thus cesium, with atomic number 55, is in series 6, and reference to Table 6.3 will show that cesium has one electron in the O shell, for which the principal quantum number is 6.

In the preceding section it was pointed out that the group relationships among the elements arise from the fact that the elements in each group possess the same number of electrons in the highest normally occupied energy level. In Group IA the elements lithium, sodium, potassium, rubidium, cesium, and francium all have a single electron in the highest occupied level, although these elements have very different numbers of electrons in lower levels. In Group IIA the elements beryllium, magnesium, calcium, strontium, barium, and radium all have two electrons in the highest occupied level; and the elements of Group VIIB all have seven such electrons, as stated above. Because of this arrangement, all elements of a given group have similar electron dot symbols (Sec. 8.5), as is found in the following example from Group VIB:

$$:\overset{\cdot}{O}\cdot \quad :\overset{\cdot}{S}\cdot \quad :\overset{\cdot}{Se}\cdot \quad :Te\cdot \quad :Po\cdot$$

Inasmuch as the electrons in the valence shell are those that determine the oxidation states possible for an element, it is found that the maximum oxidation state for an element is equal to the number of the group in which the element belongs. This is shown clearly by the sequence of elements of atomic numbers 11 to 18, namely, sodium to argon.

Table 16.4 shows the Periodic Table group, the number of electrons in the valence shell, the maximum oxidation state, and the formula of the highest oxide, that is, the oxide with the largest proportion of oxygen. These relationships hold (with a few complications, to be mentioned below) throughout the Periodic Table; and this is generally true even though, as described in Chapter 8, those elements with only a few valence electrons tend to form compounds through positive ion formation, those with nearly eight valence electrons tend to form compounds by negative ion formation, and many elements unite by covalence rather than electrovalence.

TABLE 16.4

Element	Na	Mg	Al	Si	P	S	Cl	Ar
Group number	1	2	3	4	5	6	7	0
Valence electrons	1	2	3	4	5	6	7	8*
Maximum oxidation state	1	2	3	4	5	6	7	
Highest oxide	Na_2O	MgO	Al_2O_3	SiO_2	P_2O_5	SO_3	Cl_2O_7	

* Some authors refer to argon as having zero valence electrons. This depends largely upon one's point of view. Whether or not argon forms an oxide is uncertain at the time of writing.

It will be noted that six of the groups in the Periodic Table have A and B subgroups. The implications of this will also be discussed in the next section, as will the fact that Group VIII, insofar as it is filled, consists of nine elements arranged in three's, and that Group IIIA has, at two places, a large group of elements within a group, so to speak. There is the further difficulty that there is no satisfactory place for hydrogen. Some authors place hydrogen above lithium in Group I, others place it above fluorine in Group VII, and still others give it a special place of its own. But in spite of these and other peculiarities, the Periodic Table has proved to be one of the most useful concepts in chemistry, and it is complete at the present time except possibly for further additions at the end. But in Mendeleev's time there were many blanks in the table. These elements could scarcely have been discovered, nor could their existence have been surmised, before development of the Periodic Table.

16.5 Classification of the Chemical Elements

Arrangement in family groups related to the number of valence electrons present in the atom is by no means the only acceptable method for classifying the elements. One might, for instance, point out that 2 elements (bromine and mercury) are liquids at standard conditions, 11 (hydrogen, helium, neon, argon, krypton, xenon, radon, fluorine, chlorine, oxygen, and nitrogen) are gases, and the remaining 90 are solids. A more useful classification is in terms of the overall chemical and physical properties, with due regard for the obvious impossibility of meeting all needs, to best advantage, by any one system.

The chemical elements may be arranged in four classifications. These four are: hydrogen, which is the only member of its class; the Group Zero gases; the nonmetals; and the metals. There is no sharp dividing line between nonmetals and metals, as a consequence of which some authors add a borderline class of metalloids or semimetals. This procedure is not entirely satisfactory because some elements, of which tin is an example, are more like a metal in one crystalline phase, but more like a nonmetal in another phase.

In the Periodic Table on the inside cover of this book, the four classes of elements have been differentiated, as has the borderline region between nonmetals and metals. The element hydrogen is so important and has such unique properties that the whole of the following chapter will be devoted to it. The Group Zero gases—helium, neon, argon, krypton, xenon, and radon—will be described in the next section, but the nonmetals and the metals will be our principal concern throughout the remainder of this book.

The nonmetals are the following elements: boron, carbon, nitrogen, oxygen, fluorine, silicon, phosphorus, sulfur, chlorine, arsenic, selenium, bromine, tellurium, iodine, and (probably) astatine. All other elements (except hydrogen and the Group Zero gases) may be considered to be metals, with due regard for the difficulty of classifying elements near the borderline between nonmetals and metals. The nonmetals have, in general, the following properties, which differentiate them from metals: They readily accept electrons, thus acquiring a negative charge or entering into covalent bond formation. Such elements have, therefore, a high electron affinity and a high electronegativity. Nonmetals generally have low electrical and thermal conductivities—they tend to be insulators—and they are not malleable or ductile. Many (but not all) oxides of nonmetals form acids when dissolved in water; and most such oxides are volatile. Many hydrides of nonmetals are gases. It will be noted that the nonmetals are concentrated in one part of the Periodic Table, but they are not confined to any one group in the table.

The 81 metals in the Periodic Table have, in general, the following properties: They yield one or more electrons without too much difficulty and thus acquire a positive charge. Such elements have rather low ionization potentials and low electronegativity. Metals have high electrical and thermal conductivities, and they are generally malleable and ductile. A substantial number of metal oxides dissolve in water to form bases; very few metal oxides are volatile. No hydrides of metals are volatile.

There are so many metals that it is convenient to subdivide them further. One way of doing so is to list the more active metals, with high oxidation potentials, separately from the less active metals, with low oxidation potentials. The elements of Group IA of the Periodic Table are examples of very active metals; those of Group IB (often called the coinage metals) are, together with the six palladium-platinum group elements, examples of relatively inactive metals which, with the exception of copper, are often called the *noble* metals.

Another useful subclassification of the metals is on the basis of electron distribution in the various energy levels. Examination of Table 6.3 will show that in going from lithium (atomic number 3) to beryllium (atomic number 4) the extra electron needed is simply added to the lowest unfilled energy level, which in this case happens to be the 2*s* level. This is the pattern of energy level-filling throughout much of the Periodic Table, but there are some notable exceptions. In going from calcium (atomic number 20) to scandium (atomic number 21), the additional electron goes into the 3*d* level instead of, as might have been expected, the 4*p* level. It will be observed that this procedure of going into a lower, inner level is followed until copper (atomic number 29) is reached, when the inner 3*d* level is filled and the more normal filling of the 4*s* and 4*p* levels is resumed. This phenomenon is often called the *inner building*, and it is responsible for a number of unique properties of the elements in which it occurs. Some of these properties are variable oxidation states, strong color, attraction to a magnet, ability to enter into complex compound formation, and pronounced catalytic activity. We shall have much to say about these elements and their properties later; they are often called *transition* metals.

Because the energy level being filled is the 3d level, in the example given, these metals are sometimes said to belong to the 3d series, or are simply called d metals. Transition metals are as much or more like each other than they are like their neighbors in the vertical groups to which they belong in the Periodic Table. Thus chromium is more like manganese than it is like molybdenum, and nickel is more like cobalt than it is like palladium. There are in the Periodic Table three other transition series starting with yttrium (39), lanthanum (57), and actinium (89). These are known as the 4d, 5d, and 6d transition series, respectively, but the last two are complicated still further by an inner building within an inner building, so to speak.

In the series starting with lanthanum and called the *lanthanides*, or *rare earths*, electrons are also built into the 4f level, while in the series starting with actinium, called *actinides*, they appear to be built into the 5f level.

It may be wondered if the Periodic Table may now be considered complete. Certainly it appears to be so up to element 103. All the heaviest atoms have to be made artificially, and the difficulties of so doing increase as the atomic number goes up, while the half-life decreases. If element 104 is ever prepared, it will be, presumably, a member of Group IV in the Periodic Table, and resemble hafnium.

16.6   *Group Zero Gases**

The first five Group Zero gases—namely, helium, neon, argon, krypton, and xenon—all occur in the atmosphere. They were discovered by W. Ramsay and his associates in the period 1894–1898. The percentage abundances of these elements in the atmosphere are as follows:

He	5×10^{-4}
Ne	1.8×10^{-3}
Ar	0.93
Kr	1.1×10^{-4}
Xe	8×10^{-6}

With the exception of argon, which constitutes almost 1 percent of the atmosphere, all these gases are comparatively rare. Helium also

---

* Some authorities have recently reverted to an old practice of placing the noble gases in Group VIII.

occurs in certain natural gases, especially in parts of the United States, and in these gases the proportion of helium may reach several percent. Large quantities of helium, in the aggregate, are discharged to the atmosphere during the burning of natural gas. Helium, although not in itself radioactive, is a product of radioactive decay processes, being emitted in the form of alpha particles, as described in Chapter 7. The element radon, although present in trace amounts in the atmosphere, is in a somewhat different category because the most stable of its three principal isotopes has a half-life of only 3.8 days. Radon owes its occurrence in nature to a radioactive equilibrium. Radon-222 is formed from radium-226 and decays to polonium-218, as shown on Sec. 7.4.

Argon is a fairly important article of commerce, being used for filling electric light bulbs; while helium, neon, and (to a lesser degree) krypton have a variety of uses, none of which requires a very large tonnage. The production of these elements is essentially a problem in purification, which will be described in Chapter 21.

The element helium possesses some unique physical properties. The low density of helium (second in this respect only to hydrogen) combined with its safety in handling, makes helium useful for filling balloons. It is also useful in cases where a high diffusion rate, combined with safety, is required. Helium has the lowest boiling point of any known substance. Under 1 atm pressure, the boiling point is 4.2° K, and helium is apparently able to persist as a liquid down to absolute zero, although it may be solidified at 0.9° K under 26 atm pressure. Liquid helium is invaluable in the study of matter at very low temperatures. When helium is cooled to 2.18° K at 1 atm (called the *lambda* point), it undergoes a transition to a liquid called helium II. Helium II is certainly one of the most remarkable substances known. It has a heat conductivity that is 600 times greater than that of metallic copper at room temperature; it has a viscosity that is about 1000 times lower than that of hydrogen gas. If helium II is placed in a container, it will flow up the inner surface, down the outer surface, and will drip off the bottom. The isotope helium-3, which is present in natural helium to the extent of about 1.4×10^{-3} percent, does not show this helium II effect.

All the Group Zero gases have an electron distribution characterized by a filled valence shell, as follows:

	He	Ne	Ar	Kr	Xe	Rn
Configuration	$1s^2$	$2s^2\,2p^6$	$3s^2\,3p^6$	$4s^2\,4p^6$	$5s^2\,5p^6$	$6s^2\,6p^6$

The two valence electrons in helium, and the eight in each of the five other Group Zero gases, represent very stable configurations. No more electrons may be added without starting a new electron shell; or, to put it another way, the electron affinity of the inert gases is low. On the other hand, the ionization potential for each element is high, and electrons are not readily lost. In other words, these elements have no tendency to gain and a diminished tendency to share, or to lose electrons. As a consequence, they are chemically relatively unreactive.

This stability of a completed electron shell is also demonstrated in other ways. The chlorine atom, with seven electrons in its valence shell, lacks only one of achieving the same electron configuration as the nearest Group Zero gas, namely, argon. The electron affinity of chlorine is high, and this extra electron is easily acquired, the chlorine then becoming the negatively charged chloride ion, which is certainly far more stable than the isolated chlorine atom. Similarly, potassium has one electron in excess of the argon configuration. Potassium has a low ionization potential; it readily loses an electron to become the comparatively stable potassium ion, which also possesses the argon electron configuration. It will be noted that the three species Cl^-, Ar, and K^+ all have the same number of electrons. Atoms or ions of which this is true are said to be *isoelectronic*.

In an electric discharge tube, or in the ionization chamber of a mass spectrometer, it is possible to remove an electron from a Group 0 gas atom. When this is done, there may be a transitory formation of molecule-ions such as He_2^+, $NeHe^+$, and Ar_2^+. Other ion-molecule species that have been identified are ArH^+, and possibly $XeCH_3^+$, but all these species are so lacking in stability that they are thought to exist for only an extremely small fraction of a second.

The substance quinol, or hydroquinone, which has the formula $C_6H_4(OH)_2$, has the peculiar property that when it crystallizes, there are formed between each three quinol molecules small openings, or cavities, in the crystal lattice. These cavities are just large enough to accommodate one molecule of average size, and if quinol is allowed to crystallize in the presence of, say, argon under about 40 atm pressure, it will be found that argon molecules have been trapped in these cavities. The argon is released if the quinol is melted or dissolved in water. There is one argon atom trapped for every three quinol molecules, so that it is possible to write a formula, $[C_6H_4(OH)_2]_3Ar$, for the substance formed, if it may be called a substance. These products are given the general name of *clathrates*. Clathrates are formed by other crystallizable solids, of which an ammino-nickel cyanide, $Ni(CN)_2NH_3$ is one; and not only Group Zero gas molecules, but other substances such as hydrogen chloride, carbon dioxide, and benzene may be trapped. Clathrates are often found to have definite compositions, and in this they are similar to true chemical compounds. But there is, apparently, no true electronic interaction between the cage and the trapped molecule, and in this sense no valence bond has been formed. The argon in the clathrate may be captive, but it is not chemically combined.

The Group Zero elements of higher molecular weight do, however, form true chemical compounds. The first such compound was prepared by N. Bartlett in 1962. This compound is xenon hexafluoroplatinate (V), which was formed by heating xenon with platinum hexafluoride:

$$Xe + PtF_6 \rightarrow XePtF_6$$

Subsequently it was found that both xenon and radon form stable binary compounds with fluorine. Among those that have been prepared are the difluoride and the tetrafluoride. These and the corresponding radon compounds may be obtained by heating the Group Zero gas with fluorine at 400° C:

$$Xe + F_2 \rightarrow XeF_2$$
$$XeF_2 + F_2 \rightarrow XeF_4$$

The tetrafluoride is a colorless, crystalline solid melting at about 90° C. Although it hydrolyzes in water, it is otherwise a stable compound. Krypton also forms fluorides, although these are less stable, and xenon has been reported to form a trioxide, XeO_3.[2]

EXERCISES

1. Name the three most abundant chemical elements in the lithosphere (earth's crust) and give their approximate abundance.
2. The distribution of isotopes is almost always very nearly the same in all samples of elements found in nature. But there is a notable exception to this rule, namely, that lead in radioactive minerals often has a very different distribution of isotopes (and hence of atomic weight) as compared with lead from nonradioactive minerals. Explain this difference.
3. Some elements always occur in nature mixed with other elements and compounds but never in chemical combination. Name them.
4. Some elements occur uncombined in nature, but also may occur combined. Other elements virtually never occur free. Name several examples of the first class.
5. It often occurs that if a radioactive mineral is crushed and heated or dissolved in acid, some helium may be obtained. Why is this so?
6. Classify the following as to those species (elements or ions)

---

[2] The study of the Group Zero elements and their compounds is being vigorously pursued as this book is written. Many other reactions and compounds will doubtless soon be found. For over half a century these elements have been characterized as "inert" gases. The fact that some of them appear to be as reactive as gold or platinum is a sobering lesson in the necessity, in science, of questioning every statement of fact or theory, no matter how distinguished the authority and no matter how nearly universally accepted the statement may be.

that may be found in nature and those that are never found, as such, in nature.

$$Mg^{2+}, \; Ca, \; Mn, \; Zn^{2+}, \; Cl^-, \; Cl_2, \; Cu, \; Cu^{2+}$$

7. To the ionization potentials in electron volts given on Sec. 8.6, the following may be added: argon, 15.8; beryllium, 9.3; helium, 24.6; lithium, 5.4; neon, 21.6; and potassium, 4.3. By plotting atomic number horizontally and ionization potential vertically on graph paper, determine if the ionization potential is a periodic property through the first 20 elements.

8. How is the distribution of electrons in the various energy levels related to position in the Periodic Table?

9. By reference to the Periodic Table, list two pairs of elements in which the order of increasing atomic number is not the order of increasing atomic weight.

10. How is it possible for an element to have a higher atomic number but a lower atomic weight than a neighboring element?

11. Give probable electron dot formulas for the atoms nitrogen, phosphorus, arsenic, antimony, and bismuth.

12. List by symbol several elements (X) that may be expected to form oxides of the formulas X_2O_5, X_2O_7, X_2O_3, XO, and X_2O.

13. Write formulas for some probable compounds formed by oxygen with bismuth, barium, niobium, hafnium, actinium, rubidium, neon, and manganese.

14. At one time the determination of atomic weights was aided by the discovery by Dulong and Petit that the specific heat multiplied by the atomic weight is approximately a constant for many solid elements.

    (a) Find, if this is true for the metals gold, iron, and zinc, the specific heats of which are 0.0306, 0.108, and 0.0928 cal/gram/degree, respectively.

    (b) From the atomic weight of silver find its approximate specific heat. The experimental value is 0.0565.

15. Name the elements that are liquids at STP.

16. Name the elements that are gases at STP.

17. Name the important nonmetals.

18. (a) List those properties, some of which are characteristic of all metals, and all of which are characteristic of some metals.

    (b) Do the same for the nonmetals.

19. What electronic distribution factor determines whether an element belongs to a transition series?

20. Are there any transition metals that are also active metals in the sense of having fairly high oxidation potentials?

21. What is the difference between a transition series such as that starting with scandium and ending with copper, and that starting with lanthanum and ending with lutetium?
22. If element 104 is ever made, where will it go in the Periodic Table?
23. What is the structure of the nucleus of $^3_4$He?
24. What is helium II and what are its unique properties?
25. What volume of argon could be obtained from 100 grams of quinol-argon clathrate as measured at 25° C and 730 mm pressure?
26. Name five ions that are isoelectronic with neon.
27. Xenon hexafluoroplatinate (V) undergoes hydrolysis to yield xenon, oxygen, platinum dioxide, and hydrogen fluoride. Write a balanced equation for this reaction.

17

Hydrogen

17.1 Isotopes of Hydrogen

There are three known isotopes of hydrogen. These are characterized by mass numbers 1, 2, and 3. All have, of course, the atomic number 1. The symbols for the isotopes are, then, $_1^1H$, $_1^2H$, and $_1^3H$, but in view of the importance of these individual nuclides, they are given special names, as shown in Table 17.1. (The isotopes of other chemical elements are not, in general, given special names, but are identified merely by their mass numbers; for instance, uranium-235.)

TABLE 17.1 ISOTOPES OF HYDROGEN

Common designation	$_1^1H$	$_1^2H$	$_1^3H$
Names	hydrogen*	deuterium	tritium
Alternative symbols		$_1^2D$	$_1^3T$
Name of nucleus	proton	deuteron	triton
Composition of nucleus	(1p)	(1p 1n)	(1p 2n)

* The name "protium" is sometimes used for $_1^1H$ when it is desired to emphasize that a sample under consideration consists of this isotope only.

All hydrogen atoms are considered to have one proton in the nucleus, but deuterium and tritium have, in addition, one and two neutrons, respectively, in their nuclei as shown. It follows that the atomic masses of pure deuterium and pure tritium are slightly in excess of 2 and 3 amu, respectively.

In spite of these differences in their nuclei, the normal atoms of all hydrogen isotopes have one, and only one, orbital electron, as already indicated in Chapter 6, and the energy levels available to the electron are substantially the same in all three isotopes. The spectroscopic notation for the ground state of all hydrogen atoms is therefore 1s.

It was stated in Chapter 16 that approximately 0.9 percent by mass of the earth's crust consists of hydrogen, most of which is combined with oxygen in the form of water. Of this hydrogen, about 1 atom in every 6500 is a deuterium atom, and no more than 1 in 10^{18} is a tritium atom. Deuterium is therefore comparatively rare, and the fraction of tritium in the earth's crust is almost vanishingly small. Deuterium occurs in ordinary water in molecules that consist of 1 atom of ^1_1H and 1 atom of ^2_1D united with oxygen, as in H-O-D, rather than the more familiar H_2O. Tritium occurs, presumably, in a similar manner, but very little is known about naturally occurring tritium.

Ordinary hydrogen, ^1_1H, and deuterium, ^2_1D, are stable elements as far as radioactive decay is concerned. But tritium is radioactive, being a beta-ray emitter, with a half-life of 12.3 years. The product of disintegration is therefore helium-3, according to the nuclear reaction

$$^3_1H \xrightarrow{\text{12.3 years}} {}^3_2He + e^-$$

The above reaction is believed to be responsible for the minute amount of helium-3 found in the atmosphere.

Tritium would not now be found to occur naturally in the earth's crust or atmosphere, even in trace amounts, if it were not being regenerated through some process of radioactive transmutation. A possible source of tritium is the reaction of neutrons with nitrogen-14 to yield tritium and carbon-12. The neutrons could come from the reaction of cosmic rays with oxygen or with nitrogen molecules in the atmosphere. Tritium may also be produced synthetically, as will be described in Chapter 20.

17.2   Preparation of Hydrogen

Except for a trace of free hydrogen in the atmosphere, this element always occurs naturally in chemical combination with other elements, of which by far the most familiar is oxygen. The oxidation state of hydrogen in naturally occurring compounds is invariably 1+. In view of this circumstance, the preparation of hydrogen involves a reduction of oxidation state from 1+ to zero, as in molecular hydrogen H_2. To achieve this reduction, and hence to achieve the preparation of hydrogen, it is therefore necessary to use either a chemical reducing agent or, alternatively, to make use of electric energy in bringing about the reduction. The principles involved in these processes are fundamental in the preparation of many chemical elements; they will be described in detail.

It will be recalled (Sec. 15.4) that the reduced form in any half reaction will reduce the oxidized form in any half reaction of lower oxidation potential. The half reaction

$$Na \rightleftharpoons Na^+ + e^- \qquad E_0 = 2.7 \text{ volts}$$

has a higher potential than the appropriate half reaction for the decomposition of water, namely,

$$H_2 + 2OH^- \rightleftharpoons 2H_2O + 2e^- \qquad E_0 = 0.83 \text{ volt}$$

Sodium metal will therefore react with water to yield hydrogen, sodium ions, and hydroxide ions, as follows:

$$2Na + 2H_2O \rightleftharpoons H_2 + 2Na^+ + 2OH^-$$

the hydrogen emerging as bubbles of gas, and the remaining water

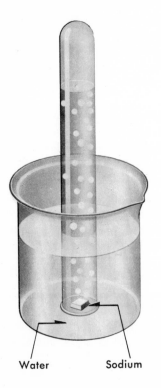

Fig. 17.1 *Hydrogen collected by the action of sodium on water:* $2Na + 2H_2O \rightarrow 2NaOH + H_2$.

Water   Sodium

becoming a solution of sodium hydroxide. A simple experimental arrangement for demonstrating this reaction is shown in Fig. 17.1. Many metals (above hydrogen in the electromotive series) will reduce water in a manner similar to that shown for sodium; but some of these metals react so slowly that scarcely any perceptible evolution of hydrogen occurs. Consideration of the oxidation potentials will establish whether or not a reaction is theoretically possible; but they tell nothing concerning the rate.

Water is not the only source of hydrogen, and some (though not all) acids provide a convenient reaction for the preparation of small quantities of hydrogen. The relative oxidation potentials may be somewhat more favorable in these cases than they are for water as the hydrogen source; consequently many dilute acids will react vigorously with metals of oxidation potential considerably lower than sodium. A typical example is the reaction of zinc on hydrochloric acid, the half reactions being as follows:

$$Zn \rightleftharpoons Zn^{2+} + 2e^- \qquad E_0 = 0.76 \text{ volt}$$
$$H_2 \rightleftharpoons 2H^+ + 2e^- \qquad E_0 = 0 \text{ volt}$$

(As hydrochloric is a strong acid, it is not necessary to consider the chloride ion in writing the half reactions above.) The complete equation for the preparation of hydrogen by the reaction of zinc metal on dilute hydrochloric acid is, then,

$$Zn + 2H^+ \rightarrow H_2 + Zn^{2+}$$

the chloride ion merely remaining in solution. An experimental arrangement for carrying out this reaction is shown in Fig. 17.2.

In a manner very similar to that shown above, aluminum metal is

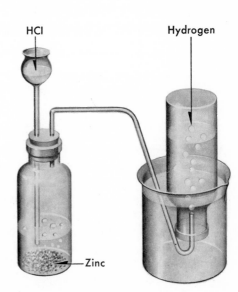

Fig. 17.2 Hydrogen prepared by the action of zinc on hydrochloric acid: $Zn + 2HCl \rightarrow ZnCl_2 + H_2$.

(owing to a superficial coating of aluminum oxide) almost inert to water under normal circumstances; but aluminum will vigorously reduce the hydrogen from dilute hydrochloric or sulfuric acids:

$$2Al + 6H^+ \rightarrow 3H_2 + 2Al^{3+}$$

Aluminum will also reduce the hydrogen in water, provided a strong base such as sodium hydroxide is present. The reaction that occurs is thought to produce the tetrahydroxyaluminate ion, $Al(OH)_4^-$, as a by-product:

$$2Al + 6H_2O + 2OH^- \rightarrow 3H_2 + 2Al(OH)_4^-$$

A somewhat similar reaction is found with several other metals of moderate activity.

Among other reducing agents that may be used for the preparation of hydrogen, an unusually effective one is hydrogen itself in the form of the negative hydride ion H^-. This ion is present in compounds such as lithium hydride, LiH, which are available commercially, although they do not occur in nature. The hydride ion will reduce the positive hydrogen in water, liberating hydrogen gas, as follows:

$$LiH + H_2O \rightarrow H_2 + Li^+ + OH^-$$

This method is useful for emergency inflation of small balloons by personnel of planes forced down at sea.

Hydrogen is produced for a variety of purposes, including the manufacture of ammonia, the hydrogenation of vegetable oils, and as a fuel in space rockets. Methods used for the large-scale production of hydrogen include the reduction of steam by red-hot iron:

$$3Fe + 4H_2O(g) \rightleftharpoons 4H_2 + Fe_3O_4$$

or, alternatively, the reduction of steam by red-hot carbon:

$$C + H_2O(g) \rightleftharpoons H_2 + CO$$

to produce the gas mixture ($H_2 + CO$), known as *water gas*. A related reaction is that of hydrocarbons (of which propane, C_3H_8, will serve as an example) with steam:

$$C_3H_8 + 6H_2O(g) \rightleftharpoons 10H_2 + 3CO_2 \tag{17.1}$$

All the foregoing reactions are reversible, and appropriate means must be taken to ensure a satisfactory equilibrium yield of hydrogen. The steam-hydrocarbon reaction is one of the most important of these industrial processes. It takes place at elevated temperature in the presence of a catalyst.

In addition to the several chemical processes described above, two others will be mentioned. If pure ammonia is heated in the presence of a catalyst, it will decompose to yield nitrogen and hydrogen:

$$2NH_3 \rightleftharpoons 3H_2 + N_2$$

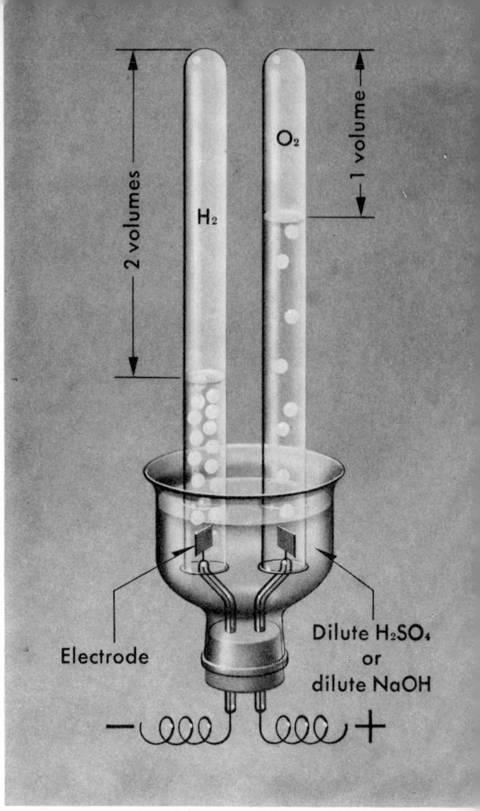

2 volumes

1 volume

O₂

H₂

Fig. 17.3 Electrolysis of water to yield hydrogen and oxygen.

Dilute H₂SO₄
or
dilute NaOH

Electrode

− +

This simple process is often used for the preparation of relatively small quantities of readily purified hydrogen. Another example of a decomposition reaction yielding hydrogen is the so-called thermal cracking (heating to decomposition) of hydrocarbons. There are many hydrocarbons in addition to propane mentioned above. A general formula for many of the hydrocarbons occurring in petroleum is C_nH_{2n+2}, where n may be any number from 1 to several hundred. Thermal cracking may be represented as:

$$C_nH_{2n+2} \rightarrow nC + (n+1)H_2$$

This reaction is also an important source of industrial hydrogen.

In a rather different category is the use of electricity to reduce the hydrogen in water. Pure water is not sufficiently ionized to conduct electricity very well, but the dissolving of certain acids, bases, or salts in water increases the conductivity greatly. Dilute sulfuric acid, sodium hydroxide, or sodium chloride are suitable reagents for the purpose. If a direct current of electricity is passed through a dilute solution of sulfuric acid, it will be found that bubbles of hydrogen emerge from the surface of the negative electrode, while bubbles of oxygen come from the surface of the positive electrode. An experimental arrangement for demonstrating the electrolysis of water is shown in Fig. 17.3. Both electrodes may be made of some relatively unreactive metal such as platinum, although iron may serve for the negative pole and carbon for the positive.

The reaction that takes place at the negative electrode is a reduction of the hydrogen ions (more properly hydronium ions), which are present at relatively high concentration in a water solution of any strong acid. The reduction of the hydrogen differs from the reactions presented above in that no chemical reducing agent such as metallic sodium or carbon is present. The reduction is brought about by the direct addition of electrons supplied by the electric current at the surface of the electrode. Such a process is called *electrochemical reduction*. At the positive electrode there is, of necessity, an electrochemical oxidation that, in the case illustrated in Fig. 17.3, produces gaseous oxygen.

The reduction of hydrogen ions at the negative electrode is followed by, or takes place virtually simultaneously with, combination of hydrogen atoms to form molecular hydrogen. The two-step process leads to the half reaction:

$$2H^+ + 2e^- \rightarrow H_2$$

In a solution of sodium hydroxide, or of sodium chloride, in water, the concentration of hydrogen ions is too low for the reaction given above to occur with appreciable velocity. The half reaction that takes place at the cathode (the electrode at which reduction occurs) may be represented as follows:

$$2H_2O + 2e^- \rightleftharpoons H_2 + 2OH^-$$

This reaction results in an accumulation of hydroxide ions around the negative electrode, causing the solution to become increasingly basic in this region.

The hydrogen produced by electrolysis is nearly pure, though rather more expensive than that obtained through chemical reduction. It is sold commercially as "electrolytic" hydrogen.

All the methods described above for producing hydrogen apply equally well for the less common isotopes, deuterium and tritium. One might, for instance, add sodium metal to deuterium oxide (heavy water):

$$2Na + 2D_2O \rightarrow D_2 + Na^+ + OD^-$$

or one might pass an electric current through T_2O, which has been acidified with a little sulfuric acid (made, of course, from tritium, and having the formula T_2SO_4):

$$2T^+ + 2e^- \rightarrow T_2$$

But the chief problems in dealing with deuterium and tritium are not so much how to prepare the gas from compounds, but rather how to prepare and keep these isotopes free from ordinary hydrogen. These problems, and their resolution, will be described in Chapters 20 and 21.

17.3 Faraday's Law of Electrolysis

The weight or the volume of hydrogen obtainable from a given weight of reactants may be readily calculated according to the method described in Chapter 8. One example will be given for purposes of review.

PROBLEM: What volume of hydrogen (STP) may be obtained by the reaction of 1.00 kg of propane, C_3H_8, with excess of steam, assuming that the reaction may be made to go to completion?

SOLUTION: Equation 17.1 states that 10 moles of hydrogen are obtainable from 1 mole of propane plus excess steam. The reaction of 1.00 kg of propane would therefore yield:

$$\frac{1000}{44} \times 10 \times 22.4 \text{ liters} = 5100 \text{ liters of } H_2 \quad (STP)$$

It is also possible to calculate the quantity of electricity associated with the chemical changes that occur during electrolysis. This calculation is possible because the reduction that takes place at the cathode (negative during electrolysis) and the oxidation that takes place at the anode involve a definite number of electrons per ion of reactant. This leads to **Faraday's law of electrolysis** which may be stated as follows:

The number of gram-equivalent weights of any substance deposited or evolved at an electrode is proportional to the quantity of electricity passing through the electrolyte.

This law may be tested by an experimental arrangement such as that shown in Fig. 17.4.

Fig. 17.4 A definite quantity of electricity is passed through each of several solutions. This may be done by connecting the cells in series as shown. It will be found that the actual weights of elements liberated at the electrodes vary greatly, but that the number of gram-equivalents of each is the same.

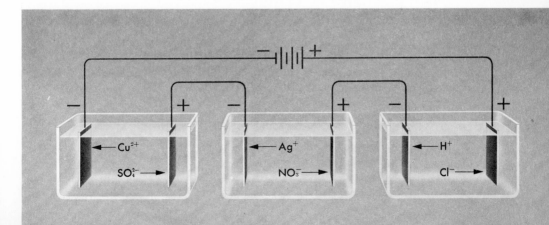

The term *equivalent weight* was used previously (Sec. 13.5) in defining normal solutions. In the present context involving reduction and oxidation, *gram-equivalent weight* may be defined as the gram-atomic weight divided by the number of electrons required per atom produced in the electrode reaction. For instance, a gram-atom of silver is 107.9 grams. The electrode reaction at the cathode during electrolysis of, say, silver nitrate solution is

$$Ag^+ + e^- \rightarrow Ag$$

that is to say, one electron is involved per atom of silver produced. Hence the gram-equivalent weight of silver is 107.9 grams, but for copper undergoing electrolysis from a copper sulfate solution, the electrode reaction is

$$Cu^{2+} + 2e^- \rightarrow Cu$$

so that the gram-equivalent weight of copper is $63.5/2 = 31.8$ grams. The gram-equivalent weight of hydrogen is obvious from the reaction

$$2H^+ + 2e^- \rightarrow H_2$$

namely, 1.0 gram.

It is found by experiment that to deposit or evolve 1 gram-equivalent weight of any element requires 96,500 coulombs of electricity. This quantity of electricity is called a *faraday*. *A faraday is a mole of electrons.* Faraday's law (first stated by Michael Faraday in the period 1832–1833) will be illustrated by two examples.

PROBLEM: What weight of copper could be deposited per hour by a current of 15.0 amp flowing through cupric sulfate solution?

SOLUTION: Recalling that coulombs = amperes $\times$ seconds, we find that 15.0 amp/hr gives 15.0 amp $\times$ 1 hr $\times$ 60 min hr^{-1} $\times$ 60 sec min^{-1} = 5.4×10^4 amp sec = 5.40×10^4 coulombs per hour.

The electrode reaction is

$$Cu^{2+} + 2e^- \rightarrow Cu$$

and 1 faraday of electricity will deposit 1 gram-equivalent weight of copper. Then 5.40×10^4 coulombs will deposit

$$\frac{5.40 \times 10^4}{9.65 \times 10^4} \times \frac{1}{2} \times 63.5 \text{ grams} = 17.8 \text{ grams}$$

PROBLEM: What volume (STP) of hydrogen may be evolved by a current of 100 amp flowing for 24 hr?

SOLUTION: As the electrode reaction is essentially

$$2H^+ + 2e^- \rightarrow H_2$$

the volume of hydrogen evolved will be

$$\frac{1.00 \times 10^2 \times 24 \times 60 \times 60}{9.65 \times 10^4} \times \frac{1}{2} \times 22.4 \text{ liters} = 1.0 \times 10^3 \text{ liters} \quad \text{(STP)}$$

It may be noted that the method of calculation described above was previously used (Sec. 15.2) for finding the maximum quantity of electricity that may be obtained from a galvanic cell by a process which is just the reverse of that taking place during electrolysis.

17.4   *Atomic Hydrogen*

The element hydrogen, unless combined with some other element, normally occurs as the diatomic molecule H_2; but under certain circumstances dissociation to atoms may take place. If gaseous hydrogen is very strongly heated or is irradiated with ultraviolet light, or is subjected to an electric discharge, some dissociation will occur, as follows:

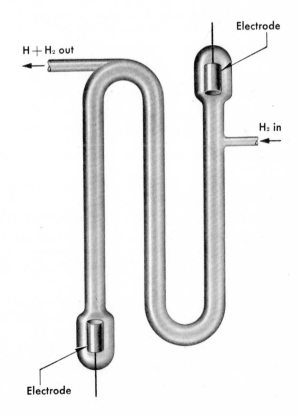

Electrode

H + H₂ out

H₂ in

Electrode

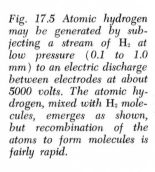

Fig. 17.5 Atomic hydrogen may be generated by subjecting a stream of H_2 at low pressure (0.1 to 1.0 mm) to an electric discharge between electrodes at about 5000 volts. The atomic hydrogen, mixed with H_2 molecules, emerges as shown, but recombination of the atoms to form molecules is fairly rapid.

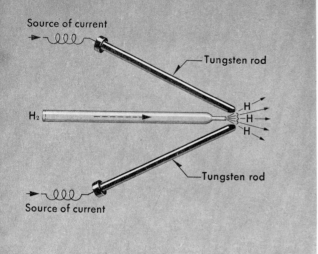

Fig. 17.6 The atomic hydrogen torch. Hydrogen gas is forced from the central tube through an electric arc where the hydrogen molecules are dissociated (broken up) into hydrogen atoms. As these hydrogen atoms recombine, $2H \rightarrow H_2$, they yield a large amount of heat. Tungsten rods are used to carry the electricity because tungsten can stand the intense heat without melting.

This reaction is conveniently produced in a gaseous discharge tube, as shown in Fig. 17.5.

While the equilibrium for the preceding reaction normally lies very far to the left, the rate of recombination of H atoms to form H_2 molecules may be slow in the absence of a catalyst. For this reason, it is possible to obtain a moderately high concentration of atomic hydrogen and to study its properties. Atomic hydrogen is characterized chiefly by being a powerful reducing agent, and by the strong evolution of heat that occurs when the atoms recombine. Atomic hydrogen will, for instance, reduce the sulfur in barium sulfate, as follows:

$$BaSO_4 + 8H \rightarrow BaS + 4H_2O$$

The preceding reaction does not occur with ordinary molecular hydrogen. The strongly exothermic recombination of atomic hydrogen is used in the so-called atomic hydrogen torch, the principle of which is shown in Fig. 17.6. One should not confuse this torch with the more familiar oxyhydrogen torch in which hydrogen is merely burned in an atmosphere of oxygen to yield water:

$$2H_2 + O_2 \rightarrow 2H_2O(g) + 116.4 \text{ kcal}$$

17.5 Molecular Hydrogen

Hydrogen in its usual form, H_2, of diatomic molecules has the distinction of having the lowest density of any known substance (under similar conditions of state, temperature, and pressure). The density of the gas at STP is only about 0.09 gram liter^{-1}, and hence, in accordance with

Graham's law, hydrogen has the highest diffusion rate of any known substance. The normal boiling and melting points are the second lowest of any known substance, only helium being lower. Hydrogen is a colorless, odorless gas; the liquid and the solid are also colorless. The gas is almost insoluble in water.

It will be recalled from the discussion in Sec. 8.5 that the union of two atoms of hydrogen to form a molecule constitutes a classical (and the simplest) example of covalent bonding between atoms. The distance between the centers of atoms in combination is called the *bond length,* and as two atoms are present in a molecule of hydrogen, one half of the bond length is called the *covalent radius* of hydrogen. It is necessary to include the word "covalent" in connection with this radius because the radius so obtained is different from the van der Waals radius described in Sec. 2.3, and is also different from the ionic radius to be discussed in a later chapter.

The covalent radius of hydrogen in H_2 molecules is 0.375 Å, but when hydrogen atoms are combined with atoms of other elements, the covalent radius of the hydrogen is about 0.28 Å. The van der Waals radius of hydrogen is 1.2 Å. The distance between atoms in covalently bonded molecules is usually measured by electron diffraction (Sec. 2.5), but for molecular hydrogen it is generally necessary to use spectroscopic methods.

The nucleus of a hydrogen atom, like that of many other atoms, spins on its axis. When two atoms of hydrogen are combined to form a molecule, there are presented two possibilities, in one of which the spins on the nuclei are parallel and in the other the spins are opposed, or anti-parallel. There are thus two possible modifications, or *isomers,* of hydrogen. These differ only in whether the nuclear spins are parallel or opposed. The two forms of hydrogen are called, respectively, *ortho-hydrogen* and *para-hydrogen,* and they constitute an example of isomerism; that is to say, a situation in which two molecules are identical except for some

ortho-hydrogen	*para*-hydrogen
parallel nuclear spins	antiparallel nuclear spins
(electrons not shown)	(electrons not shown)

internal structural difference, which in turn has an influence on certain properties of the substance.

The two isomers of hydrogen (not to be confused with the isotopes) normally exist in any sample of H_2, but one isomer may be readily converted into the other at elevated temperatures or under the influence of a catalyst. There is then an equilibrium set up, which may be represented as:

$$o\text{-}H_2 \rightleftharpoons p\text{-}H_2$$

At room temperature the equilibrium constant is as follows:

$$\frac{[p\text{-}H_2]}{[o\text{-}H_2]} \simeq 0.335$$

(the symbol $\simeq$ means "approximately equals"). From this it follows that hydrogen gas at equilibrium normally consists of about three parts *ortho*-hydrogen to one part of *para*-hydrogen. This is the ratio of the isomers as normally prepared at room temperature or higher, but the equilibrium shifts to form more *para*-hydrogen if the temperature is lowered. At the normal boiling point of hydrogen, the equilibrium concentration is about 99 percent *para*-hydrogen.

In recent years, interest in the isomers of hydrogen has increased because liquid hydrogen is used as a fuel for space rockets. This interest has led to an unusual situation. If hydrogen gas as prepared at room temperature or higher is converted to the liquid at $-252°$ C, the liquid will consist of the "high temperature" equilibrium concentration, namely, 3:1 *ortho* to *para* in a metastable equilibrium. But the liquid mixture will now slowly approach true equilibrium. At room temperature and higher, the reaction $o\text{-}H_2 \rightarrow p\text{-}H_2$ is neither exothermic nor endothermic, but as the temperature is lowered, it becomes exothermic. At the normal boiling point of hydrogen, $20.3°$ K, the reaction liberates about 339 cal/mole of H_2 converted. Although this is not a very large amount of heat, it so happens that the heat of vaporization of hydrogen is only about 216 cal/mole, so that the heat liberated during the *ortho* to *para* conversion is sufficient to boil off all the liquid hydrogen.

The solution to the difficulty presented above is to convert all the hydrogen to *para*-hydrogen during production of the liquid. At high temperatures the conversion appears to involve the formation of atomic hydrogen, which then recombines in the equilibrium concentration appropriate to the temperature. A similar mechanism apparently occurs over catalysts such as platinum or nickel, which are very effective at room temperature or higher. But at low temperatures the strength of the H—H bond (103 kcal/mole) is such that no formation of atomic hydrogen is probable, and a quite different catalytic mechanism is thus necessarily called for.

It so happens that the conversion of one hydrogen isomer to the other is catalyzed by any atom, ion, or molecule that is attracted to a magnet. Any so-called odd molecule, such as nitric oxide, NO, that possesses an odd number of electrons (Sec. 8.7) and is therefore attracted to a magnet, is capable of acting as a catalyst for the low-temperature isomerization of hydrogen. Other catalysts of this type are the cupric ion Cu^{2+} and molecular oxygen O_2, which although it has an even number of electrons, is nevertheless for a special reason attracted to a magnet. One

Gas out

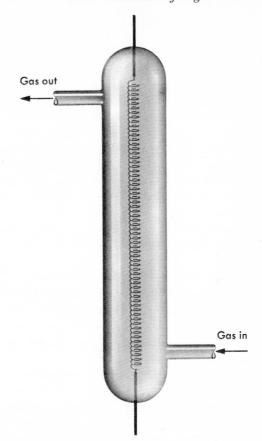

Gas in

Fig. 17.7 Thermal conductivity gauge. The wire is heated electrically, then its temperature is obtained indirectly by measuring its electrical resistance. The rate at which heat is lost from the wire depends on the composition of the gas surrounding the wire. In this way the gauge may be used to determine the composition of a gas mixture, as of ortho- and para-hydrogen.

of the catalysts used in the large-scale production of liquid hydrogen for rocket ships is iron oxide, in which the magnetic atom is the iron.

The reader may wonder what experimental arrangement may be used to distinguish the two isomers of hydrogen. This is readily done by a thermal conductivity measurement. The ability to conduct heat is moderately greater for *para*-hydrogen than for *ortho*. The measurement is conveniently made in a thermal conductivity gage, shown in Fig. 17.7.

All the material presented above has been in terms of the most abundant isotope, $_1^1H$. Deuterium also exhibits nuclear spin isomerization, but the *ortho* form is the more stable at low temperatures. The phenomenon described also occurs in a few other diatomic molecules, but is less important. It will be noted that the existence of isotopes makes possible six different kinds of molecular hydrogen—namely, H_2, HD, HT, D_2, DT, and T_2. All have some differences in properties, but only the symmetrical molecules H_2, D_2, and T_2 have nuclear spin isomers.

17.6   Chemical Properties of Hydrogen

Hydrogen forms compounds with nearly all the elements, and many of these compounds, such as water, ammonia, the hydrocarbons, and the carbohydrates, are substances of prime importance. Hydrogen forms more compounds than any other element.

A chemical property of a substance is a property that is characteristic of some chemical change; and a chemical change (Sec. 8.1) is a change involving rupture or formation of a bond between atoms. In this sense the *ortho- para*-hydrogen conversion may be less a chemical than a physical change, although it is often studied in the same manner as are chemical changes. A true example of a chemical change involving hydrogen (and a very simple one) is the isotopic exchange reaction between hydrogen (protium) and deuterium:

$$H_2 + D_2 \rightleftharpoons 2HD$$

This is a reaction that has been much investigated as a source of information concerning the mechanisms of chemical reactions in general, and the mode of action of catalysts (Sec. 10.4) in particular. If hydrogen and deuterium are mixed at room temperature, virtually no exchange reaction occurs. But if the temperature is raised above about 600° C, exchange takes place and equilibrium may be reached. The equilibrium constant for the reaction above, approaches 4 at higher temperatures, but is only about 3.3 at room temperature. (The reaction is slightly endothermic.) The fact that exchange does not take place at room temperature in the absence of a catalyst shows that an activation energy (Sec. 7.6) is necessary for this reaction. The source of this activation requirement is found readily if it is recalled (Sec. 17.4) that to break the H—H bond in H_2 (and the D—D bond in D_2) requires over 100 kcal/mole of hydrogen. Once this energy is supplied so that atomic hydrogen is produced, even in low concentration, then exchange may proceed rapidly by a *chain mechanism*, as follows:

$$H_2 \rightleftharpoons 2H$$
$$H + D_2 \rightleftharpoons HD + D$$
$$D + H_2 \rightleftharpoons HD + H$$

and so on until equilibrium is reached. A possible mode of catalytic activation for this exchange reaction was described in Sec. 10.5. The existence of this reaction implies also that in pure H_2 at elevated temperatures, or in the presence of a catalyst, the individual hydrogen atoms are constantly changing partners, although prior to the discovery of hydrogen isotopes there was no method for confirming this speculation.

Hydrogen enters into chemical combination primarily by three different electronic processes. Compounds formed by these processes will be described in detail in Chapter 22, but the nature of the processes and one or two examples of each process will be surveyed here.

First, the hydrogen atom may lose its electron to become a hydrogen ion, H^+. This is the only common ionization process in which the resulting ion possesses no electrons whatever. In other words, the loss of an electron from a hydrogen atom leaves merely the hydrogen nucleus, or proton. The proton is about 10,000 times smaller than an average atom, and for this reason, the proton never exists as such in chemical compounds (as, for instance, the Na^+ ion is able to exist). The proton always associates with other atoms or molecules. The hydronium ion, consisting of a proton plus a water molecule,

$$H_2O + H^+ \rightarrow H_3O^+$$

is an example of this process.

Second, the hydrogen atom may gain an electron to form the negative hydride ion, H^-. This process permits the hydrogen atom to attain the $1s^2$ electron configuration (Sec. 16.6) characteristic of the Group Zero gas helium. An example of this process is found in the reaction of hydrogen gas with lithium metal at somewhat elevated temperatures:

$$H_2 + 2Li \rightleftharpoons 2LiH$$

In this compound, lithium hydride, the hydrogen performs the same function as the chloride ion in, say, sodium chloride.

Third, hydrogen enters into innumerable compounds by the formation of an electron pair, covalent bond. Examples of this process are found in hydrogen chloride, HCl; in ammonia, NH_3; and in methane, CH_4.

In addition to the principal modes of combination outlined above, hydrogen is able to enter into other kinds of bond formation, which are unique to hydrogen. The more important of these will be presented in due course (Sec. 22.5).

Molecular hydrogen is often referred to as being a good reducing agent. Certainly it is effective in reducing the copper in cupric oxide:

$$CuO + H_2 \rightarrow Cu + H_2O$$

A similar reaction occurs for many other metal oxides, but the ability to reduce or to oxidize in a reaction depends on the relative reducibility (or oxidizability) of the several reagents present. Molecular hydrogen heated with calcium metal acts as an oxidizing agent, oxidizing the calcium from an oxidation state of zero to 2+. This diversity of action on the part of hydrogen is responsible for the difficulty in classifying hydrogen with other elements. Hydrogen is certainly not a metal, but because of its tendency to form a positive ion with a 1+ charge, it is often placed above lithium in the Periodic Table. On the other hand, because of its ability to form a negative ion with 1— charge, and its ability to form electron-pair bonds, hydrogen is often placed above fluorine, in Group VII of the Periodic Table, although hydrogen is certainly not a halogen. The only satisfactory solution to this problem is found in recognizing that hydrogen is unique and that there is no good place for it in any of the main groups of other elements.

This chapter will be concluded with a few comments concerning the reactions of deuterium and tritium. As might be expected, these isotopes enter into chemical combination by the same processes as does the more familiar hydrogen. Thus, compounds such as D_2O, ND_3, D_2SO_4, and T_2O are all known. The only differences, except the obvious differences in molecular weights and related properties, are that the rates of reaction may be somewhat slower for the heavier isotopes, and the equilibrium constants for various reactions may be moderately different. These phenomena are called *isotope effects*, and they are useful in the separation of one isotope from another, as will be described in Chapter 21.

EXERCISES

1. One liter (STP) of tritium, T_2, is allowed to stand for 40 yr. What volume (STP) of tritium will remain?
2. Assuming that the experiment could be performed without any loss of gas, what would be the pressure in the container at $0°$ C if 1 liter (STP) of T_2 is allowed to stand for 40 yr?
3. Of the various species of molecular hydrogen, H_2, HD, D_2, DT, and so on, several have very nearly the same mass. How could one distinguish between
   (a) a mixture of H_2 and D_2 as compared with pure HD
   (b) D_2 versus HT?
4. According to Table 16.1, hydrogen is only 0.9 percent by weight of the earth's crust. But what is the approximate abundance of hydrogen in terms of the relative numbers of atoms in the earth's crust?
5. What weight of magnesium will displace the same volume of hydrogen as 1 gram of aluminum, each metal being treated with excess acid?
6. The following equations represent reactions that might be used for emergency preparation of hydrogen:
   (a) $Na + H_2O \rightarrow$
   (b) $Zn + HCl \rightarrow$
   (c) $Al + NaOH + H_2O \rightarrow$
   (d) $LiH + H_2O \rightarrow$
   (e) $CaH_2 + H_2O \rightarrow$

Assuming that ample water is available but that all other reagents must be carried, find the reactions that will yield the most hydrogen per gram of reagent.

7. What current of electricity is required to produce hydrogen at the rate of 100 liters/min (STP)?

8. Compare the diffusion rates of H_2 and D_2.

9. The *ortho- para*-hydrogen conversion is one of the few reactions that involve the reaction of only one substance, and no change of volume. Suppose that 1 liter of p-H_2 (STP) is allowed to stand at room temperature in the presence of a catalyst until equilbrium is reached. What will be the concentration of o-H_2 formed? The answer may be expressed in moles per liter or in partial pressure. (See Sec. 11.5).

10. Hydrogen is able to attain the $1s^2$ helium electron distribution, but H^- is very active chemically and helium is inactive. Explain.

11. When sodium ionizes to form Na^+, the radius decreases moderately. But when hydrogen loses an electron, the decrease in radius is very nearly 100 percent. Explain.

12. When molten lithium hydride, LiH, is electrolyzed, lithium metal forms at the cathode, hydrogen at the anode. Explain.

13. What is the maximum volume (STP) of hydrogen that could be obtained by electrolyzing lithium hydride with a current of 5 amp for 30 min, assuming that no electricity is wasted?

14. In pure water the emf of the half reaction

$$H_2 \rightleftharpoons 2H^+ + 2e^-$$

is greater than zero. Explain.

15. The ion product (Sec. 13.2) for pure D_2O is 0.2×10^{-14}. Which has the higher pH (or pD), H_2O or D_2O? Does this mean that pure D_2O is not neutral?

16. Write an overall thermochemical equation for the union of hydrogen atoms followed by the burning of the hydrogen in oxygen. (This sequence of reactions actually may occur in use of the atomic hydrogen torch.)

17. The following reactions might be tried for the production of hydrogen. State which reactions have a chance of success and which reactions should be discarded. Give reasons for those reactions that would not be expected to yield hydrogen.

(a) $K + H_2O \rightarrow$

(b) $Pt + H_2O \rightarrow$

(c) $Au + H^+ \rightarrow$

(d) $Sn + H^+ \rightarrow$

(e) $Sn^{2+} + H^+ \rightarrow$

(f) electrolysis of Cu^{2+} solution in water

(g) electrolysis of Li^+ solution in water

(h) $H^- + H^+ \rightarrow$

18. Why should the van der Waals radius of hydrogen be larger than the covalent radius?

19. How would the radius of the H$^-$ ion compare with that of H$^+$, H, H in H$_2$?

20. Any substance that can catalyze the H—D exchange will catalyze the $o\text{-}pH_2$ reaction under the same conditions. But the reverse is not always true. Explain.

18

Preparation and
Physical Properties
of the Metals

18.1   Principles of Metallurgical Reduction

In Chapter 16 it was pointed out that some metals occur in nature as the free element. Purification procedures applicable to this group, and to others after the compounds in which they normally occur have been decomposed, will be described in Chapter 21. But most metals occur in chemical combination with other elements. This chapter will be devoted to the general principles involved in obtaining such metals from their ores and to about a dozen examples of such processes. These examples have been chosen to include the more important metals and especially to include illustrations of the various methods employed.

The whole sequence of procedures involved in the preparation of a pure metal from an ore of that metal is called *extractive metallurgy*. Extractive metallurgy consists, in part, of mechanical procedures for removing the ore from the ground, crushing it, and enriching it by methods collectively known as *beneficiation*. Beneficiation may consist of selecting valuable material by hand; more frequently, use is made of oil flotation, mechanical sorting devices, magnetic separators, and the like, all of which have as their purpose the elimination of worthless matter. The valuable ore is then ready for the principal chemical processes, which will result in the desired metal product.

Except for those few metals that occur native, all metals must be obtained by a process of reduction. This is true because all the metals form positive ions. The general process for obtaining a metal may therefore be indicated as an addition of electrons, that is to say, as reduction:

$$M^{n+} + ne^- \rightarrow M$$

We may then say that, in general, extractive metallurgy involves reduction of the metal ions to metal through the action of a chemical reducing agent or by electrochemical reduction. Some ions are easy to reduce. Another way of stating this is to say that weak reducing agents are effective for some metals. An example of such metals is mercury. Other metals, of which iron is an example, are less readily reduced and require more powerful reducing agents. Still other metals, such as aluminum, are quite difficult to reduce and require the most powerful reducing conditions.

It is frequently possible to predict whether a given reducing agent will be effective in producing metal. Some of the principles involved here have been touched upon briefly in Sec. 11.3 and Sec. 15.4. These principles will be reviewed and amplified slightly before we proceed to specific examples.

If a reaction is strongly exothermic, it is likely to proceed easily; if strongly endothermic, it is not likely to be successful. We shall take the reduction to cupric oxide by hydrogen as an example:

$$CuO + H_2 \rightleftharpoons Cu + H_2O$$

The heat of reaction for the decomposition of cupric oxide is as follows:

$$2CuO \rightarrow 2Cu + O_2 - 69.8 \text{ kcal}$$

(Data such as that given are obtainable from standard reference works, one of which is listed in the Appendix.) Similarly, the heat of formation of water from its elements is as follows:

$$2H_2 + O_2 \rightarrow 2H_2O(g) + 116.4 \text{ kcal}$$

The two equations above may be added to obtain a third equation, namely,

$$2CuO + 2H_2 + O_2 \rightarrow 2Cu + O_2 + 2H_2O - 69.8 \text{ kcal} + 116.4 \text{ kcal}$$

It will be noted that the O_2 may be canceled and that all quantities may be divided by two, thus leaving

$$CuO + H_2 \rightarrow Cu + H_2O + 23.3 \text{ kcal}$$

This reaction is seen to be fairly strongly exothermic. We may therefore expect to find that cupric oxide is reducible by hydrogen, and such is actually the case. But a similar calculation for aluminum oxide yields a quite different result. The heat of formation of aluminum oxide may be shown as follows:

$$2Al_2O_3 \rightarrow 4Al + 3O_2 - 798 \text{ kcal}$$

and adding this equation to that involved in the utilization of 3 moles of oxygen, namely,

$$6H_2 + 3O_2 \rightarrow 6H_2O + 349.2 \text{ kcal}$$

we obtain

$$2Al_2O_3 + 6H_2 \rightarrow 4Al + 6H_2O - 448.8 \text{ kcal}$$

which simplifies to

$$Al_2O_3 + 3H_2 \rightarrow 2Al + 3H_2O - 224.4 \text{ kcal}$$

This reaction is evidently strongly endothermic and, in consequence it would not be expected to proceed. Actually it is impossible to reduce aluminum oxide with hydrogen.

The examples above will serve to show how comparatively simple thermochemical calculations may save much experimental labor. It should be pointed out that the sign of the heat of reaction gives only a rough estimate as to whether the reaction will or will not proceed. In more advanced calculations a thermodynamic quantity called the "free energy" is used. Also, the calculations do not tell whether the reaction is likely to be fast or slow. Nevertheless, such examples as those given are among the most useful types of calculations made by chemists and chemical engineers. A few hours spent calculating heats of reaction may save very large sums in the design and construction of industrial-scale equipment.

Another criterion that may be used to predict the efficiency of a suggested reduction procedure is the standard oxidation potential for the half reaction involved. This is applicable only to aqueous solutions, but there are very real advantages in being able to handle solutions of metal ions in water. These advantages include especially the ability to apply purification procedures conveniently, as will be described in Chapter 21, and the general avoidance of high temperatures and of extremely corrosive substances. It is approximately correct to say that all metals that lend themselves to preparation in contact with water are so prepared or purified, even though other procedures are available.

It is obvious that a metal that stands so high in the electromotive series that it reduces water could not be readily prepared from a water solution. It would not, for instance, be feasible to prepare metallic sodium from an aqueous solution of sodium chloride because, even if sodium metal could be obtained in this way, it would immediately react with the water, liberating hydrogen. All metals below hydrogen in the electromotive series may be prepared from water solution; a few metals not too far above hydrogen may also be prepared in this way. Thus, zinc metal may, with certain precautions, be obtained from a water solution of zinc sulfate, as to be described in Sec. 18.3.

Furthermore, if the reduction process is one in which a chemical reducing agent is used, then consideration must obviously be given to whether the reducing agent will reduce the desired metal ion or whether it will reduce the water. Thus, copper metal is a satisfactory reducing agent for obtaining silver metal from a water solution containing silver ion, and zinc metal may be used to obtain copper from a copper sulfate solution. But sodium metal could not possibly be used to obtain metallic zinc from a zinc sulfate solution because the sodium would preferentially reduce the water, liberating hydrogen rather than reducing the zinc ions to form zinc metal.

With the above considerations in mind we shall now present metallurgical procedures for several metals. These will be grouped according to those that are quite easily obtained (and therefore have been for the most part known and used since ancient times), those that are somewhat more difficult to obtain as metals, and those that require strenuous reduction conditions (and therefore have been used in modern times only).

18.2 Easily Reduced Metals

Those elements most easily obtained from their compounds, namely, gold, platinum, and a few others, rarely occur in nature in any form other than as the free metal. Their production becomes, therefore, principally a problem in purification. Metals moderately more active, such as silver, mercury, copper, lead, and tin, generally occur in compounds (often as the sufide), but reduction to the metal is not difficult. The procedures used for mercury, copper, and lead will be described in detail in this section.

Mercury has been known since ancient times, probably because it is easily reduced from the mineral cinnabar (mercuric sulfide, HgS). In Spain, where it occurs, it is still treated by the method used by the Romans, namely, by simple heating. The reaction is as follows:

$$HgS + O_2 \rightarrow Hg + SO_2$$

It is sometimes said that mercuric oxide, HgO, is formed as an intermediate product in this reaction, and it is certainly true that the historically important reaction

$$2HgO \rightarrow 2Hg + O_2$$

takes place readily. But it is probable that the sulfide ion, which may act as a reducing agent, plays some part in the production of mercury metal from cinnabar.

Both copper and lead often occur in nature as the sulfides CuS (chalcocite) and PbS (galena). The reduction to metal in these cases is slightly more difficult. Chalcocite ore is first roasted strongly in air. This converts part, but not all, of the copper sulfide to copper oxide. The reaction, and those that follow, are complex, but are reasonably well represented by the following equation:

$$2Cu_2S + 3O_2 \rightarrow 2Cu_2O + 2SO_2$$

The next step in the reduction is a stronger heating of the mixture of un-oxidized Cu_2S plus the Cu_2O. This results in reduction of the copper to metal through the reducing action of the sulfide:

$$Cu_2S + 2Cu_2O \rightarrow 6Cu + SO_2$$

The impure copper so obtained is called *blister copper.*

The preparation of lead metal from the ore galena is quite similar, although sometimes carbon is added to aid in the reduction step:

$$2PbS + 3O_2 \rightarrow 2PbO + 2SO_2$$
$$PbS + 2PbO \rightarrow 3Pb + SO_2$$

or

$$2PbO + C \rightarrow 2Pb + CO_2$$

The last equation is similar to the process used by the ancient Phoenicians to obtain tin from the mineral cassiterite:

$$SnO_2 + C \rightarrow Sn + CO_2$$

Hydrogen may be used to reduce the oxides of all the metals mentioned above, and it is often so used to obtain relatively small quantities of nearly pure metal. It will also be noted that, in view of the fairly low oxidation potential shown by each of these metals in contact with their ions, it is possible to reduce them from aqueous solution through the action of a more active metal. Thus, zinc metal will reduce the ions of all metals lower than zinc in the electromotive series, but even milder reducing agents will suffice for elements like silver, which is readily displaced (in a striking experiment; see Fig. 18.1) by mercury. It is also possible to precipitate the less active metals from solutions of their ions by reducing agents other than metals. Silver mirrors are prepared in this way by treating an ammoniacal silver nitrate solution with a mild organic reducing agent such as the sugar glucose. Molecular hydrogen will also reduce some ions from solution, and if used under pressure, will even reduce lead from a lead ion solution:

$$Pb^{2+} + H_2 \rightleftharpoons Pb + 2H^+$$

although, owing to the relative positions of lead and hydrogen in the electromotive series, the equilibrium is not favorable for this reaction at 1 atm H_2 pressure.

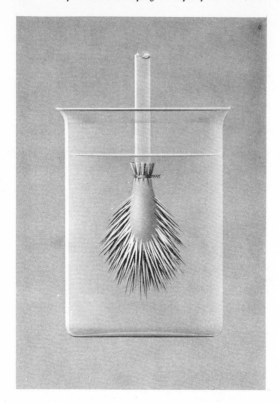

Fig. 18.1 A cloth bag containing some mercury is supported in a solution of silver nitrate. The displacement reaction

$$2Hg + Ag^+ \rightarrow Hg_2^2 + Ag$$

makes it appear that crystals of silver are growing out of the bag.

Electrolytic reduction is possible with all the metals mentioned above, and it is frequently used in the purification procedures to be described in Chapter 21. Under favorable conditions, the electrolytic reduction of silver proceeds with great reproducibility and precision and is an illustration of Faraday's law of electrolysis. In view of this, it is possible to measure a quantity of electricity by weighing the amount of silver that the electricity deposits on a cathode. Such a device is called a *coulometer*.

18.3 Less Easily Reduced Metals

As we ascend the electromotive series, we encounter elements that offer increasing difficulty of reduction to the metal. The two described in detail in this section are iron and zinc, with brief reference to a few others. Iron in the form of steel is the most important of all structural metals; it merits thorough study.

It is possible to reduce iron to the metal by electrolysis from aqueous solution, but the process is neither economical nor does it yield a satisfactory product. The principal ore of iron is hematite, which is essentially

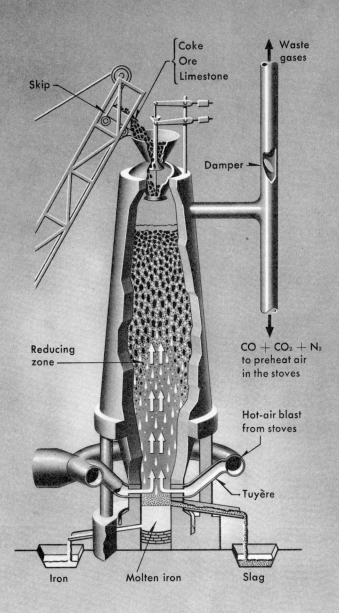

Fig. 18.2 Blast furnace.

ferric oxide, Fe_2O_3. After appropriate beneficiation, this and similar ores may be reduced by the action of carbon monoxide at a moderately high temperature. This reaction is carried out in large devices called blast furnaces. These are towers about 100 ft high and 25 ft wide (Fig. 18.2). The furnace is charged from the top with alternate layers of iron ore, coke, and limestone. Preheated air is forced into the furnace near the bottom. As soon as the heated air enters the blast furnace, the oxygen reacts with the coke and forms carbon dioxide, which in turn is reduced by coke to the monoxide:

$$C + O_2 \rightarrow CO_2$$
$$CO_2 + C \rightarrow 2CO$$

The carbon monoxide is an efficient reducing agent, and at temperatures ranging up to 1400° C the ferric oxide is reduced to metallic iron:

$$Fe_2O_3 + 3CO \rightarrow 2Fe + 3CO_2$$

Various equilibria are established in various portions of the furnace. The molten metallic iron containing some dissolved iron carbide, Fe_3C, runs to the bottom of the furnace, where it may be allowed to flow out and solidify in the form known as "pig iron." The overall process in obtaining pig iron is therefore not unlike the reduction of cassiterite with carbon except that the more easily reduced tin oxide does not need such a high temperature. The production of iron also involves elimination of impurities, of which ordinary sand is one. This is removed by the use of limestone, $CaCO_3$, which reacts with sand to form a slag consisting chiefly of calcium silicate, $CaSiO_3$:

$$CaCO_3 + SiO_2 \rightarrow CaSiO_3 + CO_2$$

Various types of iron ore may, of course, require some modification of the basic procedure outlined above. After the pig iron has been obtained, it is generally freed from virtually all impurities by strong heating in a specially designed furnace, after which measured quantities of carbon may be added to form steel of the quality desired.

Other metals that may be obtained by reduction with carbon or carbon monoxide at elevated temperatures include zinc, nickel, and tungsten, although both zinc and nickel occur most frequently as the sulfide and this must be converted to the oxide before reduction is attempted. Much zinc is made by electrolysis from aqueous solution. It may seem surprising that a metal standing as high as zinc in the electromotive series may be reduced from a water solution. The process does, in fact, require some care and the complete absence of catalysts that might promote the preferential liberation of hydrogen rather than zinc. Purified zinc oxide is dissolved in dilute sulfuric acid to form a solution of zinc sulfate. The solution is then fed to large tanks containing alternate rows of

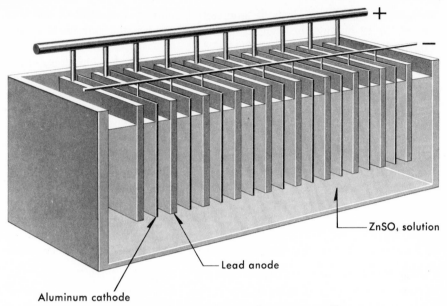

Fig. 18.3 *Cell for the electrolytic production of metallic zinc.*

aluminum cathodes and lead anodes (Fig. 18.3). During electrolysis the zinc deposits on the cathodes, from which it is stripped from time to time. While the zinc is being deposited, the concentration of hydrogen ions in the cell rises. Oxygen is liberated at the anode, and an equation for the overall reaction is as follows:

$$2Zn^{2+} + 2H_2O \rightarrow 2Zn + 4H^+ + O_2$$

The reason the reaction proceeds in this way rather than through the preferential liberation of hydrogen appears to be that on certain electrode surfaces, hydrogen requires a higher than normal potential for its reduction. The reason for this phenomenon, which is called *overvoltage*, is somewhat obscure. Traces of certain impurities added to the electrolyte cause an immediate and sometimes violent evolution of hydrogen, any zinc metal on the cathode being redissolved.

The quantity of electricity needed to deposit any given weight of zinc may be calculated from Faraday's law of electrolysis, as described previously. But in the electrodeposition of zinc and of many other elements, especially on a commercial scale, a further complication arises. It often happens that, owing to accidental leakages of electricity or to redissolving of the deposited element, the weight of the element finally collected on the electrode is somewhat less than that expected. The ratio of the actual to the theoretical yield in such a case is called the *current efficiency*. One example should suffice to make this clear.

PROBLEM: In the electrolysis of zinc sulfate solution, a current of 400 amp flowed for 12 hr, but the weight of zinc collected at the cathode was only 4.92 kg. What was the current efficiency?

SOLUTION: A current of 400 amp for 12 hr is $400 \times 12 \times 60 \times 60$ coulombs, and as the electrode reaction is

$$Zn^{2+} + 2e^- \rightarrow Zn$$

this quantity of electricity would theoretically produce

$$\frac{4.00 \times 10^2 \times 1.2 \times 10 \times 6.0 \times 10 \times 6.0 \times 10}{9.65 \times 10^4} \times \frac{1}{2} \times 65.38 \text{ grams}$$
$$= 5850 \text{ grams, or } 5.85 \text{ kg of zinc}$$

The current efficiency is then the ratio of the actual weight to the theoretical weight, namely,

$$\frac{4.92 \text{ kg}}{5.85 \text{ kg}} = 0.84, \text{ or } 84 \text{ percent}$$

18.4 Difficult Metals

Near the top of the electromotive series are to be found those metals most difficult to reduce from their compounds. Being themselves very powerful reducing agents, they require for their own reduction the strongest reducing conditions available. In general, neither chemical nor electrolytic reduction from aqueous solution is feasible for these metals because reducing agents strong enough to have the desired effect are also strong enough to reduce water. The attempted displacement of aluminum from a water solution of aluminum chloride by metallic sodium would produce only hydrogen. It might be thought that solvents less readily reducible than water could be found for these purposes, but none has proved very successful except as described below for aluminum.

The metals selected for detailed presentation in this section are sodium and aluminum, with briefer remarks concerning the preparation of magnesium, titanium, and uranium. The metals named are of great practical importance, and their reduction from compounds illustrates all the important principles involved in the preparation of metals that offer more than moderate difficulty.

Sodium metal may be obtained by chemical reduction, but electrolysis of a fused compound is the only practical method. If sodium chloride is heated until it melts, or fuses, it becomes a good conductor of electricity. (The normal melting point, 800° C, may be lowered, if it is so desired, by the addition of some solute, of which calcium chloride is one.) Now, on application of an electric current, sodium metal appears in the vicinity of the cathode:

$$Na^+ + e^- \rightarrow Na$$

and chlorine gas emerges from the neighborhood of the anode (Fig. 18.4):

$$2Cl^- \rightarrow Cl_2 + 2e^-$$

Notice that no water may be present in this process and that appropriate means must be taken to prevent subsequent mixing of the sodium and the chlorine, both of which are highly active elements. Other methods, related to that described, may be used to produce sodium. For instance, fused sodium hydroxide is a possible electrolyte. The use of a chloride electrolyte is, however, of very general applicability, and several other

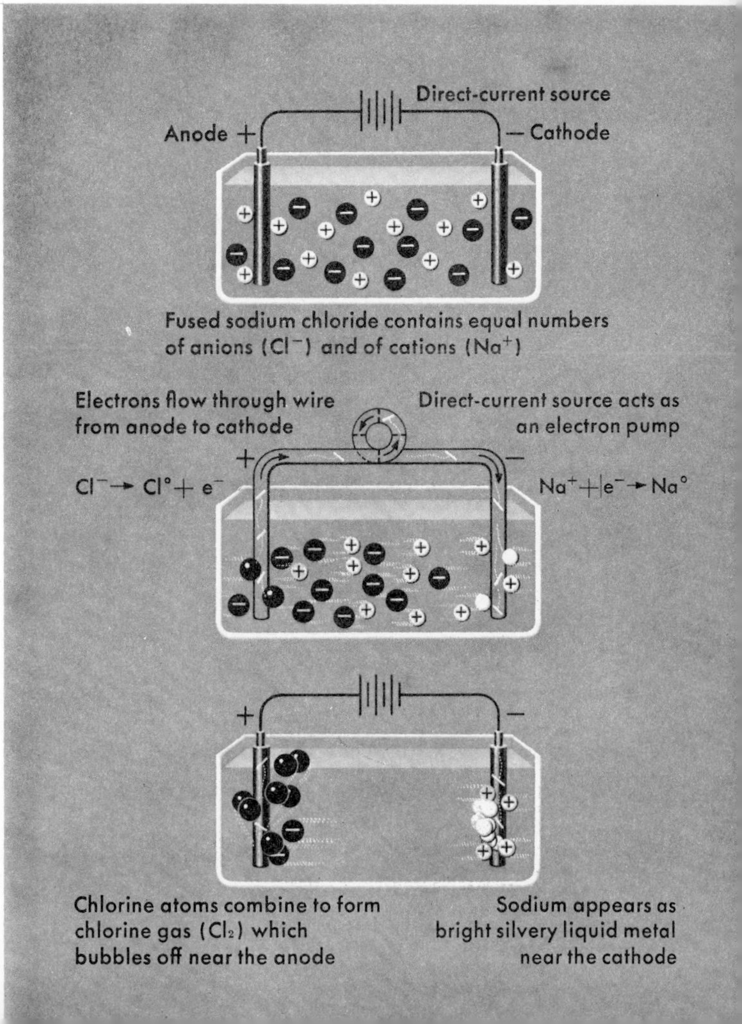

Fig. 18.4 Electrolysis of fused sodium chloride.

Direct-current source

Anode +   — Cathode

Fused sodium chloride contains equal numbers of anions (Cl$^-$) and of cations (Na$^+$)

Electrons flow through wire from anode to cathode

Direct-current source acts as an electron pump

$$Cl^- \rightarrow Cl° + e^-$$

$$Na^+ + e^- \rightarrow Na°$$

Chlorine atoms combine to form chlorine gas (Cl$_2$) which bubbles off near the anode

Sodium appears as bright silvery liquid metal near the cathode

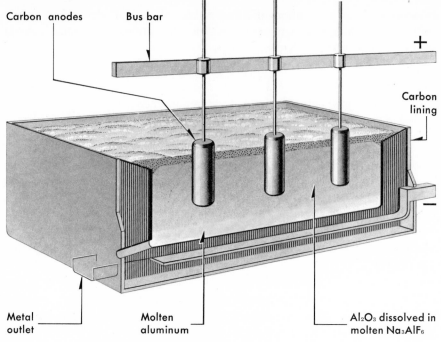

Carbon anodes   Bus bar   +

Carbon lining

Metal outlet   Molten aluminum Al_2O_3 dissolved in molten Na_3AlF_6

Fig. 18.5 Cell for electrolytic production of aluminum.

metals, of which magnesium is the most important, are prepared in this way.

Aluminum metal is produced by electrolysis of the oxide, Al_2O_3, which is dissolved in molten cryolite, Na_3AlF_6. This is the Hall-Héroult process. Purified aluminum oxide is dissolved in the cryolite at about 1000° C. The electrolytic cell consists of a graphite-lined box, which serves as the cathode. The anode is a series of large graphite rods dipping into the electrolyte. Liquid aluminum metal forms at the cathode,

$$Al^{3+} + 3e^- \rightarrow Al$$

and sinks to the bottom of the cell, from which it may be drained off, as shown in Fig. 18.5. The product at the anode is oxygen, part of which combines with the carbon to form carbon monoxide.

The direct chemical reduction of aluminum oxide is not possible because the formation of aluminum oxide from aluminum and oxygen is, as pointed out in Sec. 18.1, a strongly exothermic reaction. Consequently, the reverse process of decomposing aluminum oxide requires that a large amount of energy is used, and there is simply no chemical reducing half-reaction capable of supplying this energy. In fact this property of aluminum and its affinity for oxygen makes it possible to use aluminum as the reducing agent for several other metals. For instance, chromium metal may be obtained from chromium sesquioxide by mixing the oxide with powdered aluminum and then igniting the mixture. The exothermic reaction that takes place is as follows:

$$Cr_2O_3 + 2Al \rightarrow 2Cr + Al_2O_3$$

This kind of reaction is called *aluminothermy* or is known as the *Goldschmidt reaction.* Aluminothermy is also applicable to iron, manganese, and various other elements. The mixture of iron oxide and aluminum metal is called *thermite.* This reaction is so strongly exothermic that the reduced iron appears as a free-flowing liquid. Thermite is used for welding purposes. During World War II it was used in incendiary bombs.

Although aluminum cannot be obtained by chemical reduction of the oxide, it may be prepared through reduction of the chloride by metallic sodium:

$$AlCl_3 + 3Na \rightarrow Al + 3NaCl$$

This was at one time the only available method for obtaining metallic aluminum. While this reaction is not now used for the production of aluminum, a related reaction is used for several other metals. For instance, metallic titanium may be obtained by heating the tetrachloride with metallic magnesium, as follows:

$$TiCl_4 + 2Mg \rightarrow Ti + 2MgCl_2$$

Metallic uranium may be prepared by the analogous reaction of the tetrafluoride with magnesium:

$$UF_4 + 2Mg \rightarrow U + 2MgF_2$$

18.5   *Physical Properties of the Metals*

Those properties that are characteristic of all metals were presented in Sec. 16.5. A few physical properties of the more familiar metals are given in Table 18.1. The colors of the metals (omitted from Table 18.1) are all silver-gray (ranging from bright gray as in silver to dark gray as in lead) with the two exceptions, copper and gold. Copper is reddish-yellow; gold is pure yellow. The densities and the melting points need no further explanation. The structure column gives the arrangement of atoms in the unit cell (Sec. 4.5) as face-centered cubic (fcc), body-centered cubic (bcc), and so forth. Many metals are found to crystallize in two or more forms and are therefore said to be *polymorphic,* although the word "allotropic" is sometimes used in the same sense. Polymorphism is related to different arrangements of atoms in the unit cell. Where two or more such arrangements are common, all are shown.

Some further comment is called for concerning the column headed "metallic radius". The atoms adjacent to each other in a metal must, in a sense, be touching each other. This is obvious because high pressure has only a small effect on the density of a metal. This distance of nearest approach of two adjacent atoms in a metal is, then, a measure of the size of the atoms. The atoms in a metal are also obviously in some sort of chemical combination with each other. Absence of any valence forces would simply permit the atoms to fly apart; that is, the element would be a gas rather than a metal. In view of this, it has become the custom to take half the distance between centers of adjacent atoms in a metal as

TABLE 18.1   PHYSICAL PROPERTIES OF SOME COMMON METALS

Metal	Symbol	Density, gram cm^{-3}	Melting point, °C	Structure*	Metallic radius, Å
Aluminum	Al	2.70	933	fcc	1.43
Beryllium	Be	1.82	1533	hcp	1.12
Calcium	Ca	1.55	842	fcc, hcp	1.97
Chromium	Cr	7.19	1903	bcc	1.25
Cobalt	Co	8.9	1123	hcp, fcc	1.25
Copper	Cu	8.96	1083	fcc	1.28
Gold	Au	19.32	1336	fcc	1.44
Iron	Fe	7.87	1535	bcc, fcc	1.24
Lead	Pb	11.34	600	fcc	1.75
Lithium	Li	0.53	459	bcc, fcc, hcp	1.52
Magnesium	Mg	1.74	651	hcp	1.60
Mercury	Hg	13.55	−38.9	rho	1.50
Nickel	Ni	8.9	1728	fcc	1.24
Osmium	Os	22.50	2500	hcp	1.35
Platinum	Pt	21.45	2046	fcc	1.38
Silver	Ag	10.49	1233	fcc	1.44
Sodium	Na	0.97	371	bcc, fcc	1.85
Tin	Sn	7.30	504	dc, tet	1.5
Titanium	Ti	4.54	2193	hcp, bcc	1.5
Tungsten	W	19.3	3370	bcc, c	1.37
Uranium	U	18.7	1130	or, tet, bcc	1.50
Zinc	Zn	7.13	419.4	hcp	1.4

* The designations have the following meanings: fcc, face-centered cubic; hcp, hexagonal close-packed; bcc, body-centered cubic; rho, simple rhombohedral; dc, diamond cubic; tet, tetragonal; c, simple cubic, or orthorhombic. The structure hcp will be described in Chapter 24.

being the metallic radius of the atoms. The metallic radius is different from either the van der Waals radius (Sec. 2.3) or the covalent radius (Sec. 17.5), and it is also different from the ionic radius, to be described later. The metallic radius is useful in the study of metals, although it may vary somewhat in different polymorphic forms of a metal.

Metallic valence is less well understood than covalence or electrovalence. There is no general agreement as to the nature of the valence forces in metals, but two current ideas will be mentioned. One theory is based primarily on the fact that metals are all such good conductors of electricity. The idea is that the atoms in a metal are present as positive ions formed by the loss of electrons from the valence shell, but that these electrons are free to move in the metal and, being negative, act to bind the positive ions in position. This theory affords some explanation of why metals conduct electricity: The electrons, often said to be in the "conductivity band," are almost entirely free to move. At the same time it becomes less difficult to understand why metals are generally malleable; that is, metals may be distorted to a great degree without fracture. This must mean that no atom in a metal may be considered to be bonded exclusively to a given partner or set of partners, as in H_2 or (to a degree) in NaCl, but rather that the atoms may, under pressure, yield some partners and gain others, so that although each atom always has a complete coordination of partners, the partners are not always the identical atoms.

Another theory is that the atoms in metals actually form covalent bonds with each other, depending on the number of valence electrons possessed by each. The arrangement of atoms in metal is generally very simple. In sodium, as in many other metals, the atoms are arranged in the body-centered cubic pattern in which each atom has eight nearest neighbors; that is, its coordination number is 8. The idea is that sodium, having one electron in its valence shell, is able to form a covalent bond with another sodium atom (its actually does this to a degree in sodium vapor, which contains Na_2 molecules), but that this covalent bond is shared with each of the eight nearest neighbors. The element calcium has two valence electrons and so should have two covalent bonds shared among the eight neighbors (Ca is also bcc). The increased number of bonds should make calcium harder, denser, and with a higher melting point than that of sodium or potassium. This is actually the case, and similar relationships are found throughout the Periodic Table. But in spite of these successes it must be said that the valence forces in metals are still far from being understood.

Metals in general dissolve or combine with each other as well as with most other elements. Substances or mixtures retaining metallic properties, but formed from two or more different metals, are called *alloys*. Some alloys are merely mechanical mixtures, some are true solutions, but some are definite substances called *intermetallic compounds*. The valence forces operative in intermetallic compounds are obscure, and the law of definite proportions is often conspicuously ignored.

One further property will be mentioned. Some metals are slightly attracted to a magnet and others are slightly repelled. But three metals are very strongly attracted to a magnet. These three are iron, cobalt, and nickel. They are said to be *ferromagnetic*. A few other metals exhibit this property at low temperature.

18.6   *Corrosion*

Most metals have a tendency to react chemically with water, oxygen, carbon dioxide, or other substances found under atmospheric conditions. This process is called *corrosion*, and it involves oxidation and reduction. Iron, the commonest structural metal, is very subject to corrosion, and our discussion will be limited to it.

The products of iron corroding, or rusting, generally consist of oxides of iron, more or less hydrated. A popular theory of corrosion is that a voltaic cell action is set up on the surface of the metal (Fig. 18.6). Suppose that a sheet of iron has on its surface a speck of less active metal as impurity and that a drop of water lies over this region. The water, being exposed to air, will contain dissolved oxygen, carbon dioxide, and other impurities, some of which will make the water electrically conducting. These constitute all the essentials for a voltaic cell—namely, a more active metal, a less active metal, and a conducting solution. The iron, being more active, will dissolve, owing to the half reaction:

$$Fe \rightarrow Fe^{2+} + 2e^-$$

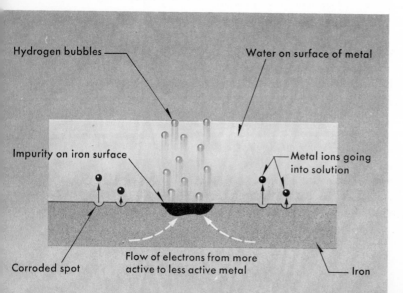

Hydrogen bubbles

Water on surface of metal

Impurity on iron surface

Metal ions going into solution

Corroded spot

Flow of electrons from more active to less active metal

Iron

Fig. 18.6 Schematic diagram showing how the presence of a speck of less active metal as an impurity can set up a voltaic cell on a moist iron surface. The reaction on the impurity is

$$2H^+ + 2e^- \rightarrow H_2$$

that on the iron surface is

$$Fe \rightarrow Fe^2 + 2e^-$$

This latter reaction leads to corrosion.

and will become the negative pole. The less active metal impurity will become positive by the reaction

$$2H^+ + 2e^- \rightleftharpoons H_2$$

and hydrogen will be liberated. Finally, in a subsequent reaction, the ferrous ion Fe^{2+} will be oxidized to ferric ion Fe^{3+} by the oxygen. A probable pair of half reactions for this change is as follows:

$$Fe^{2+} \rightleftharpoons Fe^{3+} + e^-$$

and

$$O_2 + 4H^+ + 4e^- \rightleftharpoons 2H_2O$$

the complete reaction being

$$4Fe^{2+} + O_2 + 4H^+ \rightleftharpoons 4Fe^{3+} + 2H_2O$$

but ferric ions, under these conditions, react with water to form the familiar reddish-brown rust, which is sometimes written $Fe(OH)_3$, but more properly, is $Fe_2O_3 \cdot xH_2O$.

Evidence that this overall view of corrosion is correct is shown by the rapid corrosion of pure iron in contact with metallic platinum when, of course, exposed to moist air. It is not necessary that a less active metal be present as impurity before corrosion can start. The metal in different portions of a single piece of iron may have slightly different activity. This difference may be very small, yet large enough for one part of the metal to become positive and the other negative so that corrosion may set in. Furthermore, if the oxygen concentration in different portions of the water is different, there may be set up a slight electrochemical action, as in a concentration cell. The same is true of other substances that may be present as impurities in the water.

Most efforts to control corrosion involve coating the metal with an inactive substance such as another metal or with a paint. Metals used to coat steel include zinc, tin, cadmium, copper, lead, chromium, and silver. Occasionally the more expensive noble metals such as gold and platinum are used. It may seem surprising that iron can be protected by a more active metal such as zinc; but certain metals, of which zinc is one, do not rapidly corrode, although they happen to be fairly high in the electromotive series. This is true of zinc and of aluminum because they become coated with a carbonate or oxide layer that protects against further corrosion. If steel is coated with zinc, the zinc mechanically protects the iron from the atmosphere, and the zinc itself has its carbonate coat.

But a zinc coating also acts in another way. Suppose a voltaic cell is set up between zinc and iron. Zinc is the more active of the two and therefore it, rather than the iron, becomes negative and tends to corrode. The zinc in a sense protects the iron both mechanically and electrochemically, a fact first reported by Michael Faraday in 1829. Until all the zinc coat has been destroyed, the iron will remain positive, and so has little tendency to lose electrons and go into solution. Zinc is inexpensive and is widely used for the protection of steel against corrosion. Galvanized iron is sheet steel coated thinly with zinc. Another widely used protective coating is tin. Tin is generally considered less active than iron. It was formerly thought to act solely as a mechanical coat, but later work indicates that its action may be not unlike that of zinc.

Other methods of corrosion resistance take advantage of the electrochemical nature of the process. For instance, suppose it is desired to protect a steel tank containing a water solution of salts or other electrolytes. Stainless steel bars are placed in the solution. A small electric current is made to flow from the bars, which are made positive, to the tank, which is made negative. This system is often used to protect boilers, tanks, and pipelines.

Still another method often used to protect pipelines is to connect the pipe through wires to bars of more active metals, such as magnesium. These active metal bars may be buried in the ground. The active metal corrodes fairly rapidly, but during this process, the pipeline is protected.

The use of paints and lacquers to protect metals is familiar to everyone. Steel bridges and ship hulls are constantly being painted against corrosion. The paints protect merely by mechanically preventing access of moisture and air to the metal surface.

One final method for protecting aluminum surfaces will be mentioned. The use of aluminum for naval construction, especially for naval aircraft, makes the corrosion of aluminum a major problem. It is found that aluminum may be given a heavy coat of aluminum oxide by making it the anode in an electrolytic cell. So-called anodized aluminum has remarkable corrosion-resistant properties.

EXERCISES

1. A solution contains ferrous, Fe^{2+}, ions, and cupric, Cu^{2+}, ions. Suggest a reducing agent that will have the effect of precipitating the copper as metal, but which will leave the iron in solution. Write a balanced equation for any reaction that occurs.

2. Metallic silver may be obtained by electrolysis of a water solution containing Ag^+ ions, but sodium may not. What is the reason for this difference?

3. The ground state of an element has the following electron distribution: $1s^2\ 2s^2\ 2p^6\ 3s^2\ 3p^6\ 3d^{10}\ 4s^2\ 4p^1$. What is likely to be the principal oxidation state of this element, other than zero? What methods of reduction to the metal are likely to be successful?

4. Describe three ways in which the rusting of iron may be inhibited.

5. One polymorphic form of lithium has the bcc structure. How many nearest neighbors is possessed by each lithium atom? If the lithium actually forms a kind of covalent bond with each of its nearest neighbors, how many electrons are supplied to each bond, on the average, by each atom?

6. A current of 1 amp passed through 1 liter of $1M$ $Cu(NO_3)_2$ solution for 1 hr. What is the molar concentration of the Cu^{2+} ions remaining in solution, assuming 100 percent current efficiency?

7. Given the half reaction for indium,

$$In \rightleftharpoons In^{3+} + 3e^- \qquad E_0 = 0.34 \text{ volt}$$

discuss the possibility of being able to deposit indium electrolytically from aqueous solution.

8. In a pipeline, iron pipe was connected directly to copper pipe. The iron corroded very quickly. Explain.

9. A dilute solution of sodium chloride is electrolyzed, and care is taken to prevent gross mixing of the cathode and anode products. If a current of 0.65 amp flows for 30 min, what volume of $1.00M$ H_2SO_4 will be required to titrate the base formed in the cathode compartment?

10. Given that

$$2Cu + O_2 \rightarrow 2CuO + 69.9 \text{ kcal}$$

and

$$2CO + O_2 \rightarrow 2CO_2 + 135 \text{ kcal}$$

find the heat of reaction for the reduction of cupric oxide to copper by carbon monoxide, and state whether the reaction may be expected to proceed.

11. Determine the feasibility of the following reaction:

$$Mn_3O_4 + 4H_2 \rightarrow 3Mn + 4H_2O$$

given that

$$3Mn + 2O_2 \rightarrow Mn_3O_4 + 325 \text{ kcal}$$

12. Some authorities claim that lead may be produced by the reaction

$$PbS + PbSO_4 \rightarrow 2Pb + 2SO_2$$

In this reaction, what atom or atoms are reduced? What atom or atoms are oxidized? What is the oxidizing agent or agents?

13. A zinc smelter (a place where metals are produced) uses 100,000 amp of electricity. Assuming 70 percent current efficiency, what is the daily output of zinc?

14. Compare the quantities of electricity necessary to deposit by electrolysis the *same weight* of iron in each of two cells, one of which contains dissolved ferrous sulfate, $FeSO_4$, and the other, dissolved ferric sulfate, $Fe_2(SO_4)_3$.

15. With the aid of a labeled diagram, show the half reactions and direction of electron flow when a steel pipeline is protected against corrosion by being connected by wires to magnesium bars buried in (moist) ground.

16. To deposit 1 gram-atom of silver requires 96,500 coulombs. The electric charge on a single electron is known from experiments in physics to be about 1.6×10^{-19} coulomb. With this information, calculate Avogadro's number.

17. The oxidation potential for the element lanthanum is as follows:

$$La \rightleftharpoons La^{3+} + 3e^- \qquad E_0 = 2.4 \text{ volts}$$

Design a method for the production of metallic lanthanum from its compounds. An available starting material is the oxide La_2O_3.

18. The oxidation potential for thallium is as follows:

$$Tl \rightleftharpoons Tl^+ + e^- \qquad E_0 = 0.34 \text{ volt}$$

Design a method for the production of metallic thallium.

19. The oxidation potential for metallic palladium is as follows:

$$Pd \rightleftharpoons Pd^{2+} + 2e^- \qquad E_0 = -0.83 \text{ volt}$$

Suggest possible procedures for obtaining palladium metal from palladous chloride, $PdCl_2$.

20. The following brief table gives the heat of formation of several metal oxides. The heat of formation is the heat evolved (exothermic) per mole of oxide formed.

Oxide	Formula	Heat of formation, kcal mole^{-1}
Cadmium oxide	CdO	65.2
Iridium dioxide	IrO$_2$	50.2
Molybdenum dioxide	MoO$_2$	131
Thorium dioxide	ThO$_2$	331

Propose reactions that might be feasible for reduction to the metal of each oxide given.

21. Compare the number of nearest atom neighbors possessed by each of the following three metals in their respective crystals: aluminum, chromium, tungsten (c), and zinc.

22. What differences are present in the number and arrangement

of electrons in copper metal, as compared with cupric ion? In aluminum metal as compared with aluminum ion, Al^{3+}?

23. Sodium forms an alloy (called an amalgam) with mercury. Suggest a method for removing the sodium.

24. What minimum weight of aluminum should be used for complete aluminothermic reduction of the manganese in 100 grams of Mn_3O_4?

19

Preparation and Physical Properties of Nonmetals

19.1 Introduction to the Nonmetals

Of the 15 nonmetals named in Sec. 16.5, in this chapter we shall consider in detail preparative methods for 6, namely: chlorine, fluorine, iodine, oxygen, phosphorus, and silicon. Briefer accounts will be given concerning arsenic, boron, bromine, carbon, nitrogen, selenium, and sulfur. Our reason for selecting the elements in this way is based on their importance for science and industry and because in each case some useful principle is presented or applied. It will soon be noted that the methods used in extracting nonmetals from their natural sources are often very similar to those used for metals. But the term "extractive metallurgy" is less appropriate for an element that is not a metal.

In Chapter 18 it was emphasized that metals invariably occur either native or with positive oxidation states. Some nonmetals, such as nitrogen, generally occur uncombined, and some such as sulfur often occur in a positive oxidation state. But most nonmetals occur in a negative oxidation state, and at least one (fluorine) occurs in no other way. Production of a nonmetal from a zero-valent state, as of nitrogen from air, involves solely a purification process. This and similar procedures will be described in

312

Chapter 21. Nonmetals such as phosphorus, which occur only in positive oxidation states, may be obtained by reduction, almost exactly as if they were metals. But elements that occur in negative oxidation states must be prepared by a process that is almost the reverse of that used for many metals, namely, a process of oxidation. It will be found, as is the case for metals, that both chemical and electrochemical oxidations are useful.

19.2   *The Halogens*

The difficulty in preparing the halogens decreases in the order fluorine, chlorine, bromine, and iodine. We shall start with iodine, which is the only one of the four to occur naturally in both negative and positive oxidation states. In Chile some iodine is found in the form of sodium iodate, $NaIO_3$, associated with sodium nitrate deposits. The chief chemical reaction in connection with the preparation of elementary iodine from this source is a reduction from the oxidation state of 5+ to zero. Inspection of a standard oxidation table shows for the half-reaction,

$$I^- + 3H_2O \rightleftharpoons IO_3^- + 6H^+ + 6e^- \qquad E_0 = -1.085 \text{ volts}$$

The iodate ion, IO_3^-, is therefore a reasonably strong oxidizing agent, and many reducing half-reactions are available. The reducing agent commonly used for this reaction is sodium bisulfite, $NaHSO_3$, which probably reacts in solution as sulfurous acid, H_2SO_3, being oxidized to sulfate, SO_4^{2-}, as follows:

$$H_2SO_3 + H_2O \rightleftharpoons SO_4^{2-} + 4H^+ + 2e^- \qquad E_0 = -0.20 \text{ volt}$$

From this, one may write the overall reaction as

$$IO_3^- + 3H_2SO_3 \rightleftharpoons 3SO_4^{2-} + 6H^+ + I^-$$

but this reaction leaves the iodine in too low an oxidation state for our purpose, which is to prepare free iodine. If now the solution containing iodide, I^-, ion is treated with a fresh portion of iodate, it is possible to take advantage of the two half-reactions:

$$2I^- \rightleftharpoons I_2 + 2e^- \qquad E_0 = -0.5345 \text{ volt}$$

and

$$I_2 + 6H_2O \rightleftharpoons 2IO_3^- + 12H^+ + 10e^- \qquad E_0 = -1.195 \text{ volts}$$

from which it is seen that the oxidation of iodide by iodate in acid solution to yield free iodine is possible:

$$5I^- + IO_3^- + 6H^+ \rightleftharpoons 3I_2 + 3H_2O$$

It will be noted from the oxidation potentials given above that almost any oxidizing agent will convert iodide ion to free iodine. Iodine is often found in a 1— oxidation state in oil-well brines, in seaweed, and elsewhere. The oxidation step may very conveniently be carried out with free chlorine, as already pointed out in Sec. 15.4. The reaction is a typical displacement, and one of the most familiar in chemistry:

$$2I^- + Cl_2 \rightleftharpoons I_2 + 2Cl^-$$

but if too high a concentration of chlorine is present, the iodine may be oxidized up to the iodate stage. Other oxidizing agents that may be used to obtain free iodine from an iodide include manganese dioxide in sulfuric acid solution:

$$2I^- + MnO_2 + 4H^+ \rightarrow I_2 + Mn^{2+} + 2H_2O$$

In fact, concentrated sulfuric acid alone will oxidize iodide ion, yielding free iodine, hydrogen sulfide, free sulfur, and sulfur dioxide, a rather unpleasant mixture.

The element bromine also forms compounds in which it has a positive oxidation state. For instance, bromine forms bromates of which sodium bromate, $NaBrO_3$, is an example. The bromate ion may be reduced to bromide ion in exactly the same manner as the iodate ion may be reduced to iodide ion; but bromine never occurs in nature in a positive oxidation state. The chief sources of commercial bromine are natural brines and sea water. The latter normally contains about 65 mg/liter of bromine as bromide ion. The preparation process involves the familiar one of oxidation with chlorine, after adjustment of the pH of the water by addition of a little sulfuric acid:

$$2Br^- + Cl_2 \rightleftharpoons Br_2 + 2Cl^-$$

Chlorine, like iodine and bromine, may also be prepared with a positive oxidation state, as in the hypochlorites, chlorates, and perchlorates, but chlorine never occurs in nature in any such form, and only under unusual circumstances would anyone want to prepare free chlorine from such a source. Chlorine is an industrially important element that occurs in abundance as the chloride ion Cl^- in rock salt and salt brines and, of course, in sea water. The principal step in the production of chlorine is therefore an oxidation of chloride ion to the free element:

$$2Cl^- \rightleftharpoons Cl_2 + 2e^- \qquad E_0 = -1.36 \text{ volts}$$

It will be noted that the half-reaction has a larger (negative) potential than the corresponding reaction for iodide or bromide ion. Consequently, fairly strong oxidizing conditions are required for this reaction.

It is quite possible to obtain free chlorine from a chloride by the use of a chemical oxidizing agent. On a small scale, this is often done by heating a mixture of sodium chloride and sulfuric acid with manganese

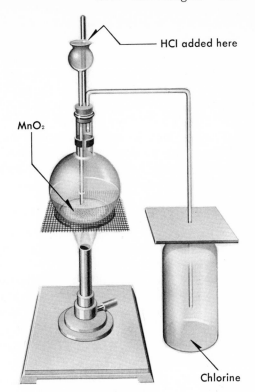

HCl added here

MnO₂

Chlorine

Fig. 19.1 Generation of chlorine:
MnO₂ + 4HCl → MnCl₂ + 2H₂O.

dioxide, as shown in Fig. 19.1. The sulfuric acid reacts with the sodium chloride to generate hydrogen chloride, which is then oxidized by the manganese dioxide as follows:

$$NaCl + H_2SO_4 \rightleftharpoons NaHSO_4 + HCl$$
$$4HCl + MnO_2 \rightleftharpoons MnCl_2 + Cl_2 + 2H_2O$$

At one time, chlorine was prepared over a catalyst by direct oxidation of hydrogen chloride by the oxygen in air. But this, the Deacon process, has long been obsolete:

$$4HCl + O_2(air) \rightleftharpoons 2Cl_2 + 2H_2O$$

At the present time, chlorine is prepared on a large scale chiefly by electrolytic oxidation. Two alternative systems are used. In one of these, sodium chloride is heated until it melts, and the melt is then electrolyzed to produce metallic sodium at the cathode (as described in Sec. 18.4) and free chlorine at the anode. Magnesium chloride, $MgCl_2$, may be similarly electrolyzed to yield magnesium and chlorine. The other system involves electrolysis of sodium chloride solution in water, as outlined in

Sec. 17.2 in connection with the electrolytic production of hydrogen. Here the by-product is sodium hydroxide. There are many designs of electrolysis cells in use for the production of chlorine. One class of cells uses mercury as the cathode. Under these circumstances the product at the cathode is a solution of sodium metal in mercury, namely a sodium-mercury alloy, or amalgam. This amalgam is allowed to react with water to yield hydrogen and sodium hydroxide, with recovery of the mercury for re-use.

The only oxidation states known for the element fluorine are 1— and zero. Fluorine never enters into compounds analogous to the chlorates, bromates, and iodates. Consequently, the preparation of the element fluorine always involves an oxidation:

$$2F^- \rightleftharpoons 2F_2 + 2e^- \qquad E_0 = -2.87 \text{ volts}$$

Furthermore, elementary fluorine is the most powerful oxidizing agent known, and it reacts violently with water. The only method thus far devised for producing fluorine is by electrolytic oxidation from a nonaqueous electrolyte.

Fluorine occurs in many minerals, of which fluorspar (calcium fluoride, CaF_2) is a convenient source. If this is treated with concentrated sulfuric acid, the fluorine is released as hydrogen fluoride:

$$CaF_2 + H_2SO_4(\text{conc}) \rightarrow 2HF + CaSO_4$$

Several systems of electrolytes have been devised for obtaining free fluorine. One system uses a solution of hydrogen fluoride dissolved in the acid salt KHF_2 at a temperature in the neighborhood of 100° C. The product at the cathode is hydrogen and, since hydrogen and fluorine recombine explosively, it is necessary to keep the products at anode and cathode separated.

The extremely corrosive nature of fluorine poses some problems in design of the electrolytic cells. Special grades of steel containers and cathodes are used commercially. The anode is carbon. As the fluorine is liberated, fresh anhydrous hydrogen fluoride is added to the cell. A cell design is shown in Fig. 19.2.

19.3   Oxygen, Sulfur, and Selenium

Most of the oxygen in the earth's crust is present as oxide ions or in combination with carbon, sulfur, phosphorus, and other elements. But the atmosphere is an inexhaustible source of uncombined oxygen which may be obtained by purification procedures to free the oxygen from nitrogen and other gases, which are mixed but not chemically combined

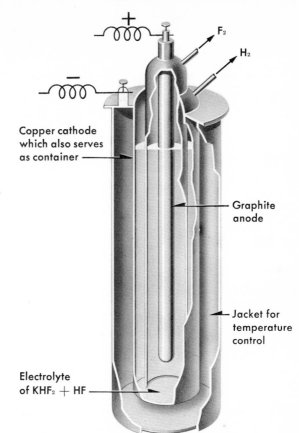

Fig. 19.2 Cell for the production of fluorine.

Copper cathode
which also serves
as container

F₂

H₂

Graphite
anode

Jacket for
temperature
control

Electrolyte
of KHF₂ + HF

with the oxygen. These purification procedures will be described in Chapter 21.

Although oxygen is almost always obtained directly from air, the importance of the element is such as to justify some descriptions of reactions by which oxygen may be obtained from compounds in which it occurs. It might be thought that the displacement reactions used for the production of bromine and iodine would also be effective for oxygen; in fact, chlorine is able to displace oxygen slowly from water,

$$2Cl_2 + 2H_2O \rightarrow 4Cl^- + O_2 + 4H^+$$

under the influence of sunlight, but the reaction is slow and of little practical importance as a production method. Fluorine is also able to displace oxygen from water, but because of the extreme reactivity of fluorine, the reaction not a popular one.

A more familiar procedure for the preparation of oxygen is to heat some compound that more or less readily gives up its oxygen. Reference has already been made to the historically important thermal decomposition of mercuric oxide:

$$2HgO \rightleftharpoons 2Hg + O_2$$

Similarly, barium peroxide, BaO_2, will yield part of its oxygen if it is heated under reduced pressure:

$$2BaO_2 \rightleftharpoons 2BaO + O_2$$

Another oxygen-rich compound that will decompose in part on heating is potassium permanganate:

$$2KMnO_4 \rightarrow K_2MnO_4 + MnO_2 + O_2$$

yielding potassium manganate, manganese dioxide, and oxygen. Still other substances in this category include sodium nitrate, lead dioxide, and potassium chlorate:

$$2NaNO_3 \rightarrow 2NaNO_2 + O_2$$
$$2PbO_2 \rightarrow 2PbO + O_2$$
$$2KClO_3 \rightarrow 2KCl + 3O_2$$

The last reaction is notorious for the way in which it is catalyzed by small amounts of certain metal oxides such as cupric oxide, ferric oxide, or (especially) manganese dioxide. It must not, however, be thought that all oxygen-rich compounds will decompose at elevated temperatures. Perhaps this would be true at extremely high temperatures, but for all practical purposes, a substance such as silicon dioxide, SiO_2, cannot be decomposed in this way.

Some compounds react with water to yield oxygen. One of these is barium peroxide, mentioned above:

$$2BaO_2 + 2H_2O \rightarrow 2Ba(OH)_2 + O_2$$

Another is potassium superoxide, KO_2:

$$4KO_2 + 2H_2O \rightarrow 4KOH + 3O_2$$

This latter reaction is used in some kinds of gas masks to provide oxygen for breathing, sufficient water being obtained from the exhaled breath.

The electrolysis of water to which some dilute sulfuric acid or some base has been added is another source of free oxygen, which is liberated at the anode surface, as described in Sec. 17.2, but the high cost of this method makes the oxygen product unable to compete with atmospheric oxygen.

No discussion of oxygen preparation is complete without some mention of the photosynthesis process by which growing vegetation takes carbon dioxide from the atmosphere and water (chiefly from the soil) and uses these compounds to generate the carbohydrates of plant tissue.

Oxygen is a by-product of this reaction, for which an overall equation may be written:

$$nCO_2 + nH_2O \rightarrow (CH_2O)_n + nO_2$$

where $(CH_2O)_n$ stands for a carbohydrate such as a sugar, starch, or cellulose. The reaction written above is actually extremely complicated. It takes place under the influence of sunlight and with chlorophyll, the green coloring matter in the leaves, as catalyst. The quantity of oxygen liberated to the atmosphere by growing vegetation is obviously very large.

The element sulfur, as does oxygen, occurs naturally as the free element, although it occurs even more abundantly in the form of sulfides and sulfates. Commercial sulfur is produced largely from the deposits of free sulfur and in part from sulfur compounds present in crude petroleum; it is also a byproduct of metal smelting operations on sulfide ores such as galena, PbS, and chalcocite, Cu_2S. The chief chemical reaction here is the obvious one of oxidation of the sulfur from an oxidation state of 2— to zero. In this connection it may be noted that, in the presence of water, hydrogen sulfide reacts with sulfur dioxide to form free sulfur:

$$2H_2S + SO_2 \rightarrow 3S + H_2O$$

This reaction may be responsible for the sulfur deposits found in certain volcanic regions. It may interest the reader to know that certain bacteria are able to oxidize hydrogen sulfide to free sulfur in somewhat the same manner as growing vegetation oxidizes hydrogen oxide (water) to free oxygen.

The element selenium is produced as a by-product, the chief reaction involving oxidation from the selenide, Se^{2-}, present in small quantities in sulfide ores.

19.4 *Phosphorus, Nitrogen, and Arsenic*

Phosphorus (as do most of the halogens, sulfur, and selenium) forms compounds in which the oxidation state of the phosphorus may be positive or negative, but the only natural sources of phosphorus are the phosphates such as calcium phosphate. Although these substances are found in rocks in seemingly endless variety, the only oxidation state in which the phosphorus occurs in nature is 5+. Production of the element phosphorus is therefore analogous to the production of iodine from an iodate, or of iron from iron oxide.

The reducing agent used for the preparation of phosphorus is carbon. If the raw material is calcium phosphate, as is generally the case, then some agent must be added to react with the calcium, which otherwise would tend to form calcium phosphate. To prevent this reaction, some sand (silicon dioxide) is added, and this reacts with the calcium, forming calcium silicate in a reaction reminiscent of the slag formation in the production of pig iron. The overall reaction may then be written:

$$2Ca_3(PO_4)_2 + 6SiO_2 + 10C \rightarrow 6CaSiO_3 + P_4 + 10CO$$

Actually, several reactions take place in the electric furnace used for phosphorus production (Fig. 19.3); the equation given above shows only the initial reactants and the final products. Phosphorus is a dangerous poison, and it catches fire spontaneously in air. The furnace and the containers for this element must be designed accordingly.

The element nitrogen occurs as such in inexhaustible supply in the atmosphere. Preparation of nitrogen is therefore primarily a problem in purification, to be discussed in Chapter 21. Nitrogen also occurs as sodium nitrate and as matter derived from living organisms, but these latter, while useful as a source of combined nitrogen, are not used as sources for free nitrogen. Occasionally, however, uncombined nitrogen is prepared for special purposes by the decomposition of ammonia or by heating ammonium nitrite:

$$NH_4NO_2 \rightarrow N_2 + 2H_2O$$

In the latter compound, the nitrogen is present in two different oxidation states, namely, 3— and 3+. The two nitrogen atoms mutually oxidize and reduce each other. There is some hazard in handling the compound, and

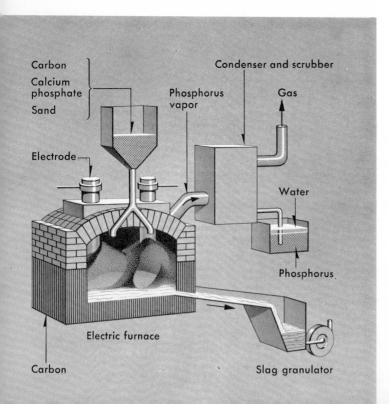

Carbon
Calcium phosphate
Sand

Condenser and scrubber

Phosphorus vapor

Gas

Electrode

Water

Phosphorus

Electric furnace

Carbon

Slag granulator

Fig. 19.3 Electric furnace for the production of phosphorus. The carbon, calcium phosphate, and sand are strongly heated. The products are phosphorus vapor and slag.

for that reason, it is generally prepared as required by the reaction of sodium nitrite and ammonium chloride:

$$NaNO_2 + NH_4Cl \rightarrow NH_4NO_2 + NaCl$$

Arsenic occurs in nature as the sulfide or as iron or nickel arsenide, generally mixed with other ores and obtained as a by-product in smelting operations as the sesquioxide, As_2O_3. Reduction to the element is then readily achieved by heating the oxide with carbon:

$$As_2O_3 + 3C \rightarrow 2As + 3CO$$

19.5 Silicon, Carbon, and Boron

The reaction of silicon with oxygen is strongly exothermic, and this is also true of boron with oxygen, but the oxidation of carbon to form carbon dioxide is somewhat less exothermic. In view of this, the reduction of silicon and of boron from their respective oxides is fairly difficult. Since these elements always occur with positive oxidation states in nature, their preparations require strong reducing conditions.

The only important source of silicon is ordinary sand, which may be obtained in the form of virtually pure silicon dioxide, SiO_2. The element silicon is obtained in the electric furance by reduction of silicon dioxide with carbon:

$$SiO_2 + 2C \rightarrow Si + 2CO$$

Some tendency to form silicon carbide, SiC, may be avoided by appropriate choice of conditions. The quantity of silicon produced is not very large, but it is important in the manufacture of various alloys and in electronic devices.

In view of the nearness of carbon to silicon in the Periodic Table and because of various similarities between these two elements, it might be thought that preparation of the element carbon would similarly be difficult. But this is not true; carbon occurs as such in nearly pure, and impure, forms in nature. It also occurs in abundance in the form of coal and in petroleum. Very large quantities of impure carbon are produced by heating coal in the absence of air. The product, called *coke,* is widely used for metallurgical reductions such as that of iron. Similarly, the strong heating of hydrocarbons causes decomposition, in part yielding hydro-carbons of lower molecular weight and in part yielding hydrogen and carbon.

Pure boron, as the element, may be obtained by electrolysis of fused potassium tetrafluoroborate, KBF_4. Reduction of the oxide with magnesium is also possible:

$$B_2O_3 + 3Mg \rightarrow 2B + 3MgO$$

as is thermal decomposition of diborane, B_2H_6,

$$B_2H_6 \rightarrow 2B + 3H_2$$

19.6   Allotropy and Physical Properties

Of the 15 nonmetals (Sec. 16.5), 6 normally exist in the elementary form as diatomic molecules. These are nitrogen, N_2; oxygen, O_2; fluorine, F_2; chlorine Cl_2; bromine, Br_2; and iodine, I_2. Some of the other nonmetals may exist as diatomic molecules at elevated temperatures; these include sulfur, S_2; selenium, Se_2; and carbon, C_2 (at very high temperatures). Under normal conditions of temperature and pressure the elements carbon, phosphorus, oxygen, sulfur, and selenium exhibit remarkable examples of allotropy. This phenomenon will be described first in this section.

In Chapter 18 it was stated that several metals occur in more than one crystal modification. These modifications reflect different arrangements of the atoms in the unit cell, and they are generally called *polymorphs*. Polymorphism means, literally, "many shapes," and it may therefore occur only in elements or compounds that are solids. Polymorphism certainly occurs in solid nonmetals such as carbon, but some nonmetals, of which oxygen is an example, exhibit two or more molecular forms even in the gaseous state. These two forms for oxygen are the diatomic molecule O_2 and the triatomic molecule O_3, called *ozone*. The term *allotropy* is applied to this phenomenon of elements that exhibit two or more molecular configurations, and in this sense, atomic hydrogen (Sec. 17.4) is an allotropic form of hydrogen. It is incorrect to use the term *polymorphism* in reference to liquid and gaseous examples of allotropy, but many authors use the word "allotropy" rather loosely in reference to any example of an element existing in two or more forms, whether it is a solid or not.

Carbon forms at least two crystalline allotropic modifications, graphite and diamond. If sugar, as an example, is heated excessively, it will be converted to a black substance called charcoal. Charcoal consists of minute, imperfect crystals of graphite, often characterized by an unusually high specific surface and therefore possessing strong adsorptive properties (Sec. 10.5). Graphite is a dark-gray substance with a greasy or unctuous feel. Studies of graphite crystals by x-ray diffraction show that the carbon atoms are arranged in layers, each atom closely bound to three others in the same plane so that the structure looks like a vast sheet of little hexagons (Fig. 19.4). The distance between neighboring atoms in the sheets is 1.42 Å,

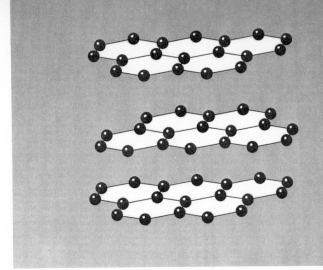

Fig. 19.4 Arrangement of carbon atoms in graphite.

and the bonds appear to be essentially covalent. The sheets of atoms are separated from each other by 3.40 Å, and the bonds appear to resemble van der Waals bonds. Graphite is a good conductor of electricity.

Graphite is found as such in some parts of the world. It is manufactured from coal, coke, or charcoal by the Acheson process, which consists of heating the carbon to about 3000° C in an electric furnace. Silica or iron oxide, or both, are added to catalyze the reaction.

Diamond, in sharp contrast to graphite, shares with one polymorph of boron nitride the distinction of being the hardest substance known. Diamond is transparent and colorless, and it is an electric insulator. The fact that diamond and graphite consist of nothing but carbon is demonstrated by burning a pure sample of each in oxygen. The product is nothing but carbon dioxide. The atoms in diamond are arranged so that each atom

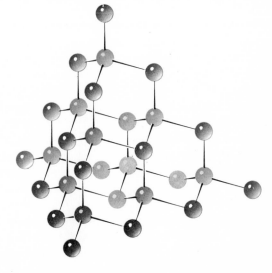

Fig. 19.5 Arrangement of carbon atoms in diamond.

is equidistant at 1.54 Å from each of four nearest neighbors. The whole crystal is then one vast structure in which each atom is held to four others by essentially covalent bonds (Fig. 19.5). The term *molecule* obviously loses its normal meaning in a system such as diamond. Diamonds, as is well known, are found sparingly distributed in various parts of the world. Graphite may be converted to diamond at high temperature and extremely high pressure.

Phosphorus is another element that exhibits an astonishing example of allotropy. There are at least four modifications, of which three will be mentioned. If phosphorus is condensed from the vapor, there is formed a white or yellow solid resembling wax. This substance, as does the vapor from which it is formed, consists of molecules containing four atoms of phosphorus, namely, P_4. The atoms are arranged at the corners of a tetrahedron, as shown in Fig. 19.6. The molecules in the solid are held to each other by weak van der Waals forces, while the bonds between the atoms in the molecule are covalent. White phosphorus is soluble in organic solvents, especially in carbon disulfide, from which octahedral crystals may be obtained. White phosphorus is extremely poisonous, and it ignites spontaneously in air.

If white phosphorus is heated to about 250° C in the absence of air, it changes into red phosphorus. This transformation is catalyzed by iodine. The structure of red phosphorus is not known, but this allotrope is insoluble in organic solvents, it is not poisonous, and it does not catch fire in air unless heated. Commercial red phosphorus often contains enough of the white allotrope to make it dangerous.

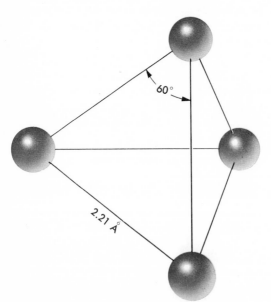

Fig. 19.6 Arrangement of atoms in phosphorus, P_4, molecule.

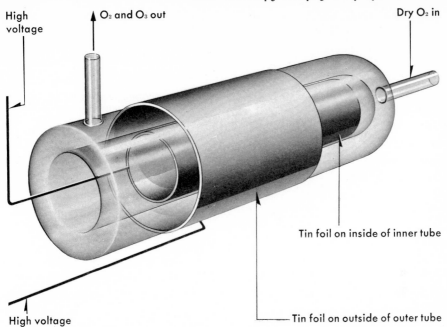

High
voltage

O₂ and O₃ out

Dry O₂ in

Tin foil on inside of inner tube

High voltage

Tin foil on outside of outer tube

Fig. 19.7 Ozonizer. Oxygen passes in the annular space between two glass tubes. The larger tube is covered on the outside with a conducting layer such as tinfoil; the inner tube is also covered on the inside. A high voltage source is connected across the tinfoil layers. The gas emerging is a mixture of oxygen (O₂), and ozone.

A third, black form of phosphorus is obtained by stronger heating of the white form under pressure or with an appropriate catalyst. The black allotrope is the most stable of all.

The allotropy of oxygen has already been mentioned. In addition to atomic oxygen, which may be prepared in an electric discharge at low pressure, oxygen forms the familiar O_2 molecules, it forms ozone, and it forms a rather unstable O_4 molecule. When ordinary oxygen gas is exposed to ultraviolet light or to certain forms of electric discharge, as shown in Fig. 19.7, it tends to absorb energy and to change to the allotropic modification ozone as follows:

$$3O_2 \rightleftharpoons 2O_3$$

Traces of ozone, produced by ultraviolet light from the sun, occur in the upper atmosphere. The ozone molecule consists of the three atoms arranged at a moderate angle to each other.

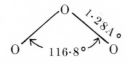

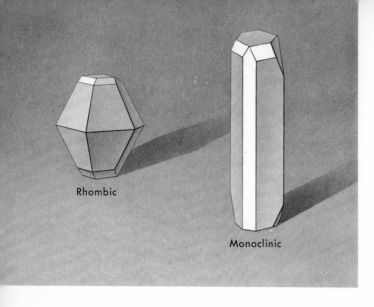

Rhombic

Monoclinic

Fig. 19.8 Two forms of crystal-line sulfur. The monoclinic form generally grows in long needles which are like the one in the drawing except that they are greatly extended along the vertical axis.

This substance is a pale-blue gas liquefying at $-112.3°$ C (O_2 boils at $-183°$ C) to a dark-blue liquid. Ozone is highly reactive and is dangerously explosive. It is a remarkably strong oxidizing agent, being exceeded in this respect only by fluorine, atomic oxygen, and oxygen difluoride, OF_2. Ordinary oxygen, although it has an even number of electrons, is attracted to a magnet and said to be *paramagnetic*. The reason for this is that, in O_2 molecules, two of the electrons present remain unpaired, a situation which is almost but not quite unique with this molecule. Ozone by contrast is, as are many substances, slightly repelled by a magnet and is said to be *diamagnetic*.

Sulfur is outstanding for the large number of allotropic forms in which it may be prepared. The stable form at room temperature is the rhombic (Fig. 19.8). This consists of S_8 molecules in which the eight atoms are arranged in puckered rings. Above $96°$ C the rhombic crystals slowly become needle-shaped in the monoclinic modification (Fig. 19.8). The molecules in monoclinic sulfur appear to be the same eight-membered rings as in rhombic, but they are arranged somewhat differently. This reversible transition is a true polymorphic change, with the transition point at $96°$ C.

Rhombic sulfur melts at $112.8°$ C, and monoclinic at $119.25°$ C, to a straw-colored liquid that may also contain S_8 molecules, but as the temperature is raised further, the liquid turns almost black and becomes so viscous that it will not pour out of an inverted vessel. As the temperature approaches the boiling point of sulfur, $444.6°$ C, the liquid becomes less viscous again, and if now it is poured into water, a peculiar rubber-like mass is formed. This is called *plastic sulfur* and it is thought to contain chains of S_8 and S_4 molecules derived from the breaking up of the S_8 rings. At still higher temperatures, sulfur vapor contains S_2 molecules, analogous to oxygen. A phase diagram showing some of the transitions observed in sulfur is given in Fig. 19.9.

The element selenium also exhibits allotropy. A red form consists of eight-membered rings, as does a gray form. The gray form has the property of becoming a better conductor of electricity when it is exposed to light.

Most of the remaining nonmetals occur in a less complicated series of structures, although boron is polymorphic and arsenic exhibits allotropy. Silicon takes on the same configuration as diamond. Nitrogen and all the halogens, as mentioned before, normally occur as diatomic molecules. It is true that all elements at elevated temperature will dissociate to form monatomic molecules, but for some, such as boron, carbon, and silicon, this takes place only at extraordinarily high temperatures. Molecular nitrogen shows a peculiar effect in that if nitrogen is exposed to an electric discharge, it dissociates to atoms, as does hydrogen (Sec. 17.4). If now the electric discharge is discontinued, it will be found that the gas continues to glow for several seconds or minutes. At one time it was thought that this was due to the slow recombination of the nitrogen atoms, but actually it is due to an unstable diatomic molecule reverting to the normal molecule, as follows:

$$2N \quad \rightarrow \quad N_2^* \quad \rightarrow \quad N_2$$

atomic	unstable	stable
nitrogen	molecule	molecule

In this sense, nitrogen may also be said to exhibit allotropy.

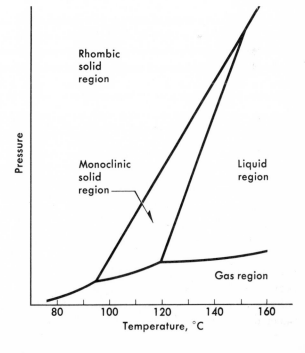

Fig. 19.9 Phase diagram for sulfur, slightly distorted for convenience. The high temperature region is not shown.

Rhombic solid region

Monoclinic solid region

Liquid region

Gas region

Pressure

Temperature, °C

80   100   120   140   160

Those properties that are characteristic of all nonmetals were described in Sec. 16.5. The physical properties which will be of most concern to us as we proceed to later chapters are given in Table 19.1. Some comment is called for in connection with two of these properties, namely, the covalent radius and the heat of dissociation.

TABLE 19.1   PHYSICAL PROPERTIES OF THE NONMETALS

Element	Formula*	Color	Melting point, °C	Boiling point	$\frac{1}{2}$ Inter-atom distance, Å	Heat of dissociation† kcal mole^{-1}
Boron	$\langle B \rangle_\infty$	black	2300	. . .	0.9	high
Carbon	$\langle C \rangle_\infty$	black or colorless	3500	. . .	1.5	83
Silicon	$\langle Si \rangle_\infty$	gray	1414	2355	1.2	42
Nitrogen	N_2	colorless	−210	−196	0.5	226
Phosphorus	P_4	white or red	44	280	1.1	51
Arsenic	$\langle As \rangle_\infty$	gray	874	610 (subl.)	1.2	32
Oxygen	O_2	colorless	−219	−183	1.2	118
Sulfur	S_8	yellow	119	444	1.0	51
Selenium	$Se_8(r)$	red or gray	217	685	1.2	44
Tellurium	$\langle Te \rangle_\infty$	gray	452	1390	1.4	33
Fluorine	F_2	pale yellow	−223	−187	0.7	37
Chlorine	Cl_2	yellow-green	−102	−34	1.0	58
Bromine	Br_2	red-brown	−7	59	1.1	46
Iodine	I_2	purple, black	114	183	1.3	36

* As pointed out in Sec. 8.3, the symbol $\langle \ \rangle_\infty$ will be used in this book to mean an infinite lattice of atoms, with no particulate molecule in the ordinary sense. Only the commonest forms, stable at room temperature, are shown.

† The heats of dissociation given are for the separation of two atoms. The large values for nitrogen and oxygen are explained in the text.

It will be recalled that half the distance between the centers of the two atoms in a hydrogen molecule is called the covalent radius of the hydrogen atom. (It was also pointed out that the covalent radius of hydrogen in a compound such as HCl is somewhat different from that in H_2.) The concept of the covalent radius may be applied to all the nonmetals; it is, for instance, found that half the distance between the two chlorine atoms in a Cl_2 molecule is a reasonable, accurate measure of the radius of the chlorine atom in all compounds in which chlorine is covalently bonded. The same is true of the other atoms that form diatomic molecules; but on the other hand, it has already been shown that the distance, for instance, between two adjacent carbon atoms may be different in the different allotropic modifications and different also in different directions in space (as in graphite) for the same allotrope. The *covalent radii* given in Table 19.1 are average values, but they are useful in estimation of the probable distance between atoms in a great variety of molecules, and also in leading to interpretations concerning the nature and strength of chemical bonds. Experimentally, the covalent radii are generally derived from x-ray or electron diffraction studies.

It may also be recalled that the strength of the H—H bond in the H_2 molecule was given as about 103 kcal/mole. This is the energy necessary to remove the two atoms in each molecule of hydrogen completely away from each other in a mole of hydrogen molecules. Bond strengths may also be found for all other diatomic molecules and also for other configurations as they occur. These data are found either by noting the temperature necessary to break the bond or by using spectroscopic or other methods. The column in Table 19.1, headed "heat of dissociation" gives the energy necessary to rupture the atom-to-atom bond in each of the nonmetals discussed in previous sections.

It will be clear that to dissociate I_2 into atoms is a much less complicated process than it is to dissociate diamond, in which each carbon atom is bonded to *four* other carbon atoms. Furthermore, some special comment is called for in connection with oxygen and nitrogen. In N_2 and O_2, the atoms are held together by more than one bond, or to put it another way, the bond in each of these two molecules is not the relatively simple single bond found in the H_2 molecule. This difference contributes to the large heats of dissociation shown by molecular nitrogen and oxygen. These elements do not show abnormally large bond strengths in single-bonded molecules such as hydrazine and hydrogen peroxide:

hydrazine

hydrogen peroxide

EXERCISES

1. Why cannot a chemical oxidation process be used for the preparation of fluorine?

2. Iodine, atomic number 53, has a lower atomic weight than tellurium, atomic number 52. What explanation may be offered?

3. What weight of potassium permanganate is needed to produce 285 ml of oxygen as measured over water at 20° C and 730 mm pressure?

4. In some of the following substances, the sulfur present may act only to be oxidized. In others, the reverse is true. In which of the following could the sulfur act only as a reducing agent, in which only as an oxidizing agent, and in which as both: H_2S, SO_3, SO_2, S, Na_2SO_3, H_2SO_4?

5. Show the oxidation state of each element in the following group of elements and ions: H_2, O_2, H_2O, HCl, HNO_3, $NaNO_3$, Na_2CO_3, CO_2, CS_2, Na_2SO_3, PbO_2, SO_4^{2-}, ClO_4^-, NH_4^+, NO_3^-, NH_4NO_2, $H_4P_2O_7$, Na_2MnO_4, $Zn(ClO_4)_2$, $Na_2Cr_2O_7$.

6. Write balanced equations for each of the following:

   (a) calcium nitride plus water
   (b) ammonium sulfate plus calcium hydroxide (a strong base)
   (c) $KOH + NO_2 \rightarrow KNO_3 + KNO_2 + ?$
   (d) $HI + HNO_2 \rightarrow NO + H_2O + ?$
   (e) $Br_2 + HNO_2 + H_2O \rightarrow HNO_3 + ?$
   (f) $NaI + H_3PO_4 \rightarrow NaH_2PO_4 + ?$
   (g) $As_2O_3 + Zn + H_2SO_4 \rightarrow AsH_3 + ZnSO_4 + H_2O$
   (h) $AsH_3 + O_2 \rightarrow As + H_2O$
   (i) $Bi(NO_3)_3(\text{in sol}) + H_2S \rightarrow$
   (j) $As_2O_3 + HNO_3(\text{conc}) + H_2O \rightarrow NO + ?$

7. Calculate the density of pure ozone gas at STP.

8. At 500° C and 760 mm pressure, 5 grams of sulfur vapor occupies 1.239 liters. What is the molecular formula of sulfur under these conditions?

9. The density of rhombic sulfur is 2.06 grams/ml and that of monoclinic is 1.96/ml. Discuss the effect of pressure on the rhombic $\rightleftharpoons$ monoclinic equilibrium.

10. From the phase diagram for sulfur, find (a) the line along which rhombic and monoclinic may exist in equilibrium; (b) the line along which liquid and gas are in equilibrium; (c) the line along which rhombic and gas are in equilibrium; and (d) the point at which monoclinic, liquid, and gas are in equilibrium.

11. From the phase diagram for sulfur, predict (a) the effect of starting at high pressure and 130° C, and slowly lowering the pressure at constant temperature; (b) the effect of starting at moderate (1 atm) pressure and low temperature, and slowly raising the temperature at constant pressure.

12. There are actually six known isotopes of oxygen. These have mass numbers 14 to 19 inclusive. Show the electronic and nuclear structure of each of these isotopes

13. What volume of chlorine (STP) may be obtained per day with a current of 1000 amp at 89 percent current efficiency?

14. Selenium is soluble in liquid sulfur. What information is necessary before the molecular weight of dissolved selenium can be obtained?

15. Compare sodium and fluorine with respect to number of electrons in the valence shell of the atoms, the radius of the atoms, the ionization potential, the electronegativity, the oxidation potential, the melting point, electrical conductivity, and oxidation states.

16. Chlorine and bromine are common impurities in iodine. The iodine may be purified by mixing it with potassium iodide and then heating. What is the basis for this purification process?

17. Iron is a metal: phosphorus, a nonmetal. The methods for obtaining these elements from their ores show an unusual similarity. Is this true of most metals and nonmetals, or is there something unique about this pair of elements?

18. The unit cell of solid molecular oxygen is simple cubic. Draw a diagram of this structure.

19. Compare the heat liberated for the recombination of a gram of nitrogen atoms with that for the recombination of a gram of iodine atoms.

20. Which requires the more energy, (a) dissociating a gram of fluorine to atoms or (b) dissociating a gram of chlorine to atoms?

21. In molecules of phosphorus, all the atoms are the same distance from each other. How does this preclude an arrangement in which the four atoms are at the corners of a square?

22. Sometimes it is convenient to prepare sulfur from a sulfide ore as a by-product instead of using native sulfur. Select a reasonably common sulfide ore and show by balanced equations how to obtain the free sulfur.

23. There is an appreciable quantity of ozone in the upper atmosphere. Why does it not sink to the surface of the earth?

24. Animals need oxygen for life, and they are able to obtain this from the atmosphere. Animals also need nitrogen (to build the proteins of their tissues), and the atmosphere contains abundant nitrogen. But animals cannot directly utilize atmospheric nitrogen. Comment on this anomaly.

25. Name some nonmetals that are conductors of electricity, and state the conditions under which this conductivity is exhibited.

20

Nuclear Synthesis

20.1 Isotopic Occurrence

The Table of Nuclides supplied with this book lists well over a thousand known nuclides. Of these, only about 300 occur in nature, and most of these are stable as far as radioactive decay is concerned. All the natural radioactive nuclides have either a very long half-life, as is the case for uranium-238, or are constantly being regenerated by a process of radioactive decay from some other element. Radium-226 is an example of this latter group. Some chemical elements have no stable isotopes and no radioactive isotopes that owe their existence to being part of a natural disintegration series. Such elements, of which technetium is one example, do not occur in nature. The general relationships that determine nuclear stability were surveyed in Chapter 7.

Nuclides that do not occur in nature must be prepared artificially. Most of the nuclides so prepared are radioactive, but this is not necessarily so; stable nuclides may also be prepared if there is any special reason for so doing. The difficulty in studying an isotope is obviously related to its half-life, and if this is very short, the experimental problems may prove to be too great. Major interest centers, of course, on the synthesis of those elements that do not occur in nature in appreciable concentrations. At the time of this writing, there appear to be 15 such elements. In the succeeding sections, we shall describe the general principles involved in nuclear synthesis and then discuss in more detail the synthesis and properties of several elements unknown in nature, and several new isotopes of naturally occurring elements. These examples will be chosen either because the syntheses involved illustrate important principles or because of some unusual interest attached to the element or nuclide concerned.

20.2   Principles of Nuclear Transmutation

The basic difference between one chemical element and another lies in the charge on the nucleus. Transmutation, the conversion of one element into another, must occur by addition to, or subtraction from, the nucleus of a net positive charge. The addition of a negative charge to the nucleus is hindered by the repulsion of the negative electron cloud. The addition of a positive charge is hindered by the repulsion of the positive nucleus itself. The natural radioactive changes described in Chapter 7 are, of course, examples of atomic transmutation, but these occur spontaneously. It is not possible to control such processes, and they occur with only relatively few kinds of atoms.

The first artificial atomic transmutation to be achieved was announced by Lord Rutherford in 1919. The alpha particles emitted by some of the decay products from radon are given off at high velocities. Rutherford bombarded nitrogen gas with these high-energy alpha particles. He was able to show that in a small fraction of the atomic collisions between the alpha particles and the nitrogen atoms, hydrogen atoms were produced. The nuclear equation for the reaction is

$$^{14}_{7}\text{N} + {}^{4}_{2}\text{He} \rightarrow {}^{1}_{1}\text{H} + {}^{17}_{8}\text{O}$$

Such an equation is often written in an abbreviated form:

$$^{14}\text{N}(\alpha,p)^{17}\text{O}$$

and is referred to as an α,p reaction. (The reader may wonder what has happened to the two positive charges on the alpha particle. Such charged particles, as they slow down as a consequence of collisions, quickly pick up electrons from external sources, and become neutral. Radium, for instance, emits alpha particles, but if radium is placed in an enclosed tube, the tube soon contains neutral helium atoms.)

Another example of an α,p reaction is the conversion of aluminum-27 to silicon-30:

$$^{27}\text{Al}(\alpha,p)^{30}\text{Si}$$

Bombardment by alpha particles does not necessarily yield a proton as one product. A famous reaction, which led J. Chadwick to the discovery of the neutron in 1932, was the α,n reaction of beryllium-9. If beryllium-9 is bombarded with high-energy alpha particles, the product is carbon-14 plus a neutron:

$$\_{4}^{9}\text{Be} + \_{2}^{4}\text{He} \rightarrow \_{6}^{12}\text{C} + \_{0}^{1}\text{n}$$

Still another famous alpha-induced reaction led Irène Curie and her husband F. Joliot to the discovery of artificial radioactivity in 1933. This was the α,n reaction of boron-10, in which boron-10 is converted to nitrogen-13 plus a neutron:

$$^{10}\text{B}(\alpha,\text{n})^{13}\text{N}$$

The artificial radioactivity arises from the nitrogen-13, which decays with positron emission and a half-life of 10 min.

Alpha particles are not the only projectiles that may be used to bring about nuclear changes. High-velocity protons may, for instance, cause the conversion of oxygen-18 to fluorine-18:

$$\_{8}^{18}\text{O} + \_{1}^{1}\text{H} \rightarrow \_{9}^{18}\text{F} + \_{0}^{1}\text{n}$$

and deuterons (deuterium nuclei) may cause changes such as the conversion of sodium-23 into another isotope of sodium:

$$\_{11}^{23}\text{Na} + \_{1}^{2}\text{H} \rightarrow \_{11}^{24}\text{Na} + \_{1}^{1}\text{H}$$

Sources of high-energy particles such as that used by Rutherford are rarely powerful enough to bring about the many nuclear transmutations now known. Methods are available for accelerating charged particles to very high velocities and energies. These will be described in the next section.

The neutron has unique advantages as a projectile for nuclear bombardment. Neutrons, having no charge, are repelled neither by the electron cloud surrounding the nucleus nor by the nucleus itself. Furthermore, neutrons are readily produced by the comparatively simple method of mixing beryllium with a little radium, which yields neutrons by the $^{9}\text{Be}(\alpha,\text{n})^{12}\text{C}$ reaction mentioned above. An abundant source of neutrons is the nuclear reactor to be described in Sec. 20.3.

Examples of nuclear reactions induced by neutrons include the following:

$$\_{47}^{107}\text{Ag} + \_{0}^{1}\text{n} \rightarrow \_{47}^{108}\text{Ag}$$
$$\_{15}^{31}\text{P} + \_{0}^{1}\text{n} \rightarrow \_{15}^{30}\text{P} + 2\_{0}^{1}\text{n}$$

Occasionally it is possible to use particles considerably heavier than those mentioned. For instance, the nucleus of the carbon atom has been used to produce elements of very high atomic number. It should also be recalled that the process of nuclear fission (Sec. 7.5) produces elements of medium atomic number. The fission product mixture is a source of many useful isotopes, some of which will be described later. It will be convenient to summarize and amplify the preceding discussion by a chart showing the changes produced in any nucleus by various kinds of bombardment. The changes are indicated by the change (gain or loss) of neutrons and the change (gain or loss) of atomic number. It will be recalled that the mass number is the sum of the atomic number plus the number of neutrons. These changes are shown in Table 20.1.

The precise way in which atomic transmutations occur under bombardment is still far from being understood, but two examples will be used to give some hint of the underlying mechanism involved. If a nitrogen-14 nucleus is hit by a neutron, the product is carbon-14 plus a proton:

$$^{14}_{7}\text{N} + ^{1}_{0}\text{n} \rightarrow ^{14}_{6}\text{C} + ^{1}_{1}\text{H}$$

What probably happens in this case is that the nitrogen-14 nucleus gains a neutron, becoming an unstable, transition-state nucleus containing 7 protons and 8 neutrons. It might be thought that the unstable $^{15}_{7}\text{N}$

TABLE 20.1 CHANGE OF ATOMIC NUMBER AND OF NUMBER OF NEUTRONS PRODUCED BY VARIOUS BOMBARDMENTS*

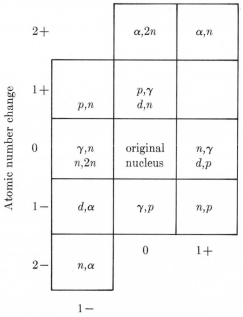

Atomic number change	Neutron change 1−	Neutron change 0	Neutron change 1+
2+		α,2n	α,n
1+	p,n	p,γ / d,n	
0	γ,n / n,2n	original nucleus	n,γ / d,p
1−	d,α	γ,p	n,p
2−	n,α		

* For instance, deuteron bombardment of a nucleus may liberate a neutron, giving a d,n reaction. This raises the atomic number by one unit, but makes no net change in the number of neutrons. The mass number is raised by one unit.

nucleus would re-eject the extra neutron, but what actually occurs is that a proton is ejected, leaving $^{14}_{6}C$. On the other hand, when sodium-23 is bombarded with neutrons, the produce is sodium-24:

$$^{23}_{11}Na + ^{1}_{0}n \rightarrow ^{24}_{11}Na + \gamma$$

In this case the transition nucleus is $^{24}_{11}Na$ plus an excess of energy. This energy is radiated as gamma rays. ($^{24}_{11}Na$ is itself radioactive, but this change is subsequent to that given.)

It will be clear that all atomic particles projected at a target will not cause nuclear transmutation. The fraction of collisions effective in bringing about the desired change is expressed as a hypothetical area, called the cross-section of the target nucleus. This cross-section varies from one nuclide to another, according to the energy of the projectile and the particular transmutation under consideration. The unit commonly used for expressing cross-sections (so defined) is the barn; 1 barn = 10^{-24} cm^2. For instance, the cross-section of nitrogen-14 for the $^{14}N(n,p)^{14}C$ reaction is 1.75 barns. (The term *cross-section* used in this way should not be confused with the actual physical size of the nucleus.) For the $^{14}N(n,\gamma)^{15}N$ reaction, the cross-section is only 80 *milli*barns.

20.3   Accelerators and Nuclear Reactors

This section will be concerned with methods for accelerating atomic particles to the velocities necessary for causing nuclear transmutations, and to methods for generating and controlling neutrons in quantities sufficient for the large-scale production of synthetic elements.

One of the earliest and most successful of the nuclear accelerators is the cyclotron, devised by E. O. Lawrence in 1932. The problem was to increase the velocity of a particle such as a proton, deuteron, or alpha ray until it approached the velocity of light. If a particle carrying an electric charge is caused to move in a magnetic field, the particle will be forced to move in a curved path. A proton moving in a magnetic field will go around in a circle. This is simply the normal action of a magnetic field on a moving electric charge. In the cyclotron, the charged protons or other particles are placed near the center of a strong magnetic field produced by a very large electromagnet. The region of the magnetic field is divided into two compartments shaped like the two halves of a pie cut across a diameter. The protons are placed at the center of the pie, and the whole pie is in the magnetic field. The upper and lower crusts of the pie consist of metal plates to which strong electric charges may be brought. The protons are free to move in an evacuated space between the upper and lower pie crusts. These two halves of the pie are more commonly referred to as the "dees" of the cyclotron, from their

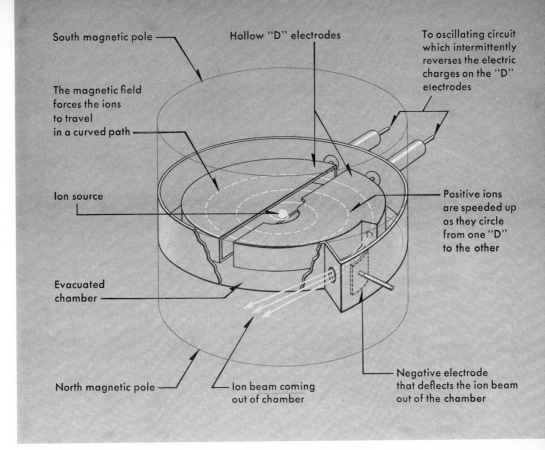

Fig. 20.1 Principal parts of the cyclotron. The magnetic field is produced by a very large electromagnet, the north and south poles of which are merely indicated in the drawing.

obvious resemblance in shape to the capital letter D. The arrangement is shown diagrammatically in Fig. 20.1.

One dee is first made positive; the other, negative. The proton moves in a curved path toward the negative side and thereby acquires some velocity. Just as the proton has completed a semicircle, the charges on the dees are reversed so that the proton receives a new impulse and hastens toward completion of a circular path. Each time the proton completes a semicircle, the charges on the dees are reversed, so that the proton goes faster and faster. As the velocity of the proton increases, it tends to fly away from the center of the magnetic field; hence, it actually spirals toward the outer circumference of the dees. All the while, the velocity keeps increasing until it is high enough to produce the desired nuclear changes. Then the proton beam is allowed to strike whatever target element is under study.

The cyclotron has been remarkably successful in the production of new elements and new isotopes of all elements. Other devices that similarly accelerate charged atomic particles to very high velocity are the betatron and the synchrotron. But in all these instruments the mass of new nuclide that can be produced is very small, in many cases being only a few atoms. For the large-scale production of new elements, it is necessary to use other methods.

In Sec. 7.5 it was shown how some of the nuclides of high atomic number undergo the nuclear fission reaction in which the nucleus is split to the accompaniment of a vast liberation of energy and a shower of excess neutrons. This liberation of neutrons may be controlled and utilized for nuclear transmutations in the nuclear reactor, the principal scientist responsible for this great development being E. Fermi.

A nuclear reactor may consist of a huge pile of graphite surrounded by massive concrete walls to prevent escape of the deadly radiation emitted. The graphite pile (shown in Fig. 20.2) has many holes through it. Into these holes there are inserted lumps of uranium metal encased in aluminum cans. Uranium normally contains 0.7 percent of the isotope uranium-235, which undergoes spontaneous fission. If the pile is large enough, the concentration of neutrons (half-life, 12 min) may be held at any desired level, and hence the rate at which the uranium-235 is used may be brought under effective control. Control is exercised by inserting into the reactor some substance that absorbs neutrons. Cadmium, or boron steel, serves this purpose. Rods of these metals are placed in slots in such a way that they may be moved in or out. The position of the rods is adjusted so that the reproduction factor (the number of fissions produced for every atom of uranium-235 undergoing fission) is less than 1. Then, as the reactor is set in operation, the control rods are slowly removed until the neutron intensity reaches the desired level, but not so high that the nuclear reaction becomes too violent.

The function of the graphite is in part to reflect, and so increase, the concentration of neutrons in the reactor; it also slows the neutron velocity. For most purposes of atomic transmutation, relatively slow neutrons are required. Another way of stating this is to say that the nuclear cross-section of the target isotope becomes larger for slow neutrons. This function of the graphite will be discussed further in the next section. A substance that slows neutrons is called a *moderator*. Heavy water, D_2O, is another substance that is effective as a moderator. Nuclides other than uranium-235 may be used as fuel in the reactor. Uranium-233 is another possibility, as is plutonium-239.

When the nuclear reactor is functioning, the irradiation of various isotopes to produce new elements and isotopes is simply a matter of inserting samples in holes in the reactor until the desired exposure to neutrons has been achieved.

It will be obvious from the discussion of nuclear fusion in Sec. 7.5 that the fusion of two atomic nuclei, of necessity, produces a different

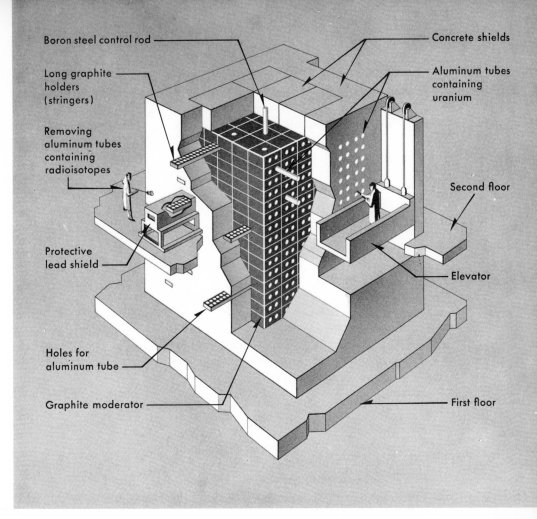

Boron steel control rod

Concrete shields

Long graphite holders (stringers)

Aluminum tubes containing uranium

Removing aluminum tubes containing radioisotopes

Second floor

Protective lead shield

Elevator

Holes for aluminum tube

Graphite moderator

First floor

Fig. 20.2 A cutaway drawing showing the main features of a nuclear reactor. The method for preparing radioisotopes is shown, as well as the inserting of tubes containing uranium for producing the chain reaction, leading to manufacture of plutonium.

nucleus. This kind of transmutation, which occurs in the hydrogen bomb, is of interest more for the energy that is obtained than for the nuclides formed. A thermonuclear explosion does, however, produce an extraordinarily high intensity of neutron radiation for a fraction of a second. This causes many new isotopes to be produced as by-products of the explosion.

20.4 Plutonium and the Actinides

For all practical purposes, the natural element of highest atomic number is uranium, the transuranium elements (of atomic number 93 or higher) must be made synthetically. At the time of this writing, 11 transuranium elements have been synthesized; their preparation is one of the most spectacular achievements in all science.

The first transuranium element to be prepared was synthesized by E. M. McMillan and P. H. Abelson in 1940. They bombarded uranium with neutrons to obtain uranium-239 by a neutron capture (n,γ) reaction:

$$^{238}_{92}U + ^{1}_{0}n \rightarrow ^{239}_{92}U + \text{gamma rays}$$

The uranium-239 then disintegrated by beta emission, with a half-life of 23.5 min, to produce an element of atomic number 93. The element was named neptunium:

$$^{239}_{92}U \rightarrow ^{239}_{93}Np + e^{-}$$

Elements of still higher atomic number have been synthesized chiefly by G. T. Seaborg and his associates. By far the greatest interest has centered on element 94, named plutonium. This element is produced in substantial quantities as a nuclear explosive for atomic bombs and as a power source for nuclear reactors. The production of plutonium in the uranium nuclear reactor will be described in some detail. The sequence of reactions involved are those already given for neptunium-239 plus a further beta disintegration of the neptunium, with a half-life of 2.3 days, to yield plutonium-239:

$$^{239}_{93}Np \rightarrow ^{239}_{94}Pu + e^{-}$$

Although the plutonium-239 may be made to undergo the nuclear fission reaction, yet its normal spontaneous alpha ray activity has a half-life of 24,000 yr.

When natural uranium containing only 0.7 percent uranium-235 is placed in a graphite-moderated reactor, as described in the preceding section, the spontaneous fission of the $^{235}_{92}U$ liberates enough neutrons to sustain a chain reaction, provided the size and arrangement of the reactor and its fuel elements are appropriate. The neutrons given off during fission have such a high energy that they cannot be captured by the more abundant uranium-238 to produce $^{239}_{92}U$ as required first for the production of plutonium. Another way of stating this is: While the fission cross-section of $^{235}_{92}U$ may be low for fast neutrons, the capture cross-section of $^{238}_{92}U$ for fast neutrons is very low. (The fission cross-section of $^{238}_{92}U$ is very low for all neutrons, but the capture cross-section of $^{238}_{92}U$ for slow neutrons is high.) For this reason, a nuclear reactor must contain a moderator such as graphite if any plutonium is to be obtained.

After natural uranium has been in the reactor for some time, at an appropriate neutron flux level, it will be found that the sequence of reactions given above, leading from $^{238}_{92}U$ through $^{239}_{92}U$ to $^{239}_{93}Np$ to $^{239}_{94}Pu$, has taken place and that the uranium metal sample, if analyzed, contains a small proportion of plutonium. The uranium plus plutonium and accumulated fission-product impurities may then be removed from the reactor and treated chemically to concentrate and purify the plutonium. Methods for this purification procedure will be described in Chapter 21.

Plutonium, which is itself synthetic, may serve as a target for the production of elements of still higher atomic number. Thus, intense slow-neutron bombardment of plutonium-239 yields successively plutonium isotopes of higher mass number. Some of these isotopes decay by beta emission to form elements of higher atomic number. Plutonium-239 bombarded with slow neutrons may, for instance, yield plutonium-241, which decays to form americium-241. Americium-241, in turn, may be bombarded to form americium-244, which decays to curium-244. In this manner it has been possible to extend the Periodic Table through, at least, element 103 (lawrencium). Furthermore, neutrons are not the only possible bombardment particles that may be used for this purpose. Plutonium itself was first made by bombarding uranium-238 with high-energy deuterons, the isotope obtained being $^{238}_{94}Pu$. High-energy alpha particles (helium ions) have been used to produce elements of atomic number over 100. Element 103 has been made by bombarding the artificial element 98 with high-energy boron nuclei. At the time of this writing, the transuranium elements that have been synthesized are those of atomic numbers 93 to 103. Most of them have been prepared as several isotopes. The names of these elements, and their symbols are given in Table 20.2

TABLE **20.2**   TRANSURANIUM ELEMENTS

Atomic number	Element	Symbol
93	neptunium	Np
94	plutonium	Pu
95	americium	Am
96	curium	Cm
97	berkelium	Bk
98	californium	Cf
99	einsteinium	Es
100	fermium	Fm
101	mendelevium	Md
102	*	*
103	lawrencium	Lw

* A prior claim for the synthesis of element 102 has not been confirmed. If confirmation is obtained, the name adopted will doubtless be nobelium, No. Otherwise, a new name may be suggested for this element, two isotopes of which are known.

Some of the transuranium elements have been prepared in quantities so small that only a relatively few atoms were involved, and these had such a short half-life that not very much could be learned about their properties. But the chemical and physical properties of other transuranium elements are better known than are those of several naturally occurring elements.

All the transuranium elements are radioactive, many of them decaying by alpha emission, but some isotopes decay by beta emission or other mechanisms. Some of the isotopes also undergo the nuclear fission reaction, the fission cross-section for plutonium-239 being somewhat larger than that of uranium-235. Up through californium the half-life of the most nearly stable isotope is measured in years. Consequently, it is in principle possible to accumulate fairly substantial quantities of these elements, but those elements of atomic number higher than 100 have the half-lives of all their isotopes measured in days, minutes, or seconds. Practical difficulties associated with such short half-lives may make it impossible to extend the Periodic Table much further.

In Sec. 16.5 it was pointed out that the elements lanthanum through lutetium, and the elements actinium through lawrencium, have the unique structural feature that electrons are built into a sublevel, namely, the 4f level for the lanthanides and the 5f level for the actinides. This feature causes the lanthanides to exhibit certain characteristic properties, and the same is true of the actinides. Thus, all the lanthanides show an oxidation state of 3+, forming ions of which La^{3+} is an example, although a few other oxidation states are also known. Similarly, all the actinides show an oxidation state of 3+, although here, too, other oxidation states are known. In general, the concept of a "transition series within a transition series" is not quite so applicable to the actinides as to the lanthanides, but there is little doubt concerning the view that 5f electrons may be present in these elements.

The actinides are all metals, and their activity is such that vigorous reduction conditions are essential to obtain the metal from typical compounds, as already described for uranium (Sec. 18.4).

20.5   Elements 43, 61, 85, and 87

Prior to about 1937 there were blanks in the Periodic Table corresponding to elements of atomic number 43, 61, 85, and 87. These blanks are now all filled with artificially prepared elements. The methods used in these syntheses will be described briefly, although none of these four elements has achieved an importance in any way comparable to that of some of the transuranium elements.

Element 43, named technetium, may be made by neutron irradiation of molybdenum-98. The (n,γ) reaction yields molybdenum-99, which undergoes beta decay $(t_{1/2} = 67$ hr$)$ to yield technetium-99. This isotope is also one of the fission products of uranium. A large uranium reactor manufactures several grams of $^{99}_{43}$Tc per day. This has the longest half-life $(t_{1/2} = 2.1 \times 10^5$ yr$)$ of several known isotopes. It decays to ruthenium-99, which is stable. Technetium resembles manganese and rhenium in its chemical properties, as might be inferred from its position between these elements in Group VIIA of the Periodic Table.

Promethium, element 61, is another by-product of uranium fission. It may also be made by neutron irradiation of neodymium-146. This yields $^{147}_{60}$Nd, which undergoes beta decay $(t_{1/2} = 11$ days$)$ to $^{147}_{61}$Pm. The isotope of promethium, with the longest half-life, has $t_{1/2} = 18$ yr. The element closely resembles the other rare earths (the lanthanides) in its chemical properties.

Element 85, astatine, has been made by bombarding bismuth-209 with high-energy alpha particles. The reaction is

$$^{209}_{83}\text{Bi} + {}^4_2\text{He} \rightarrow {}^{211}_{85}\text{At} + 2{}^1_0\text{n}$$

This nuclide, $^{211}_{85}$At, undergoes K capture, with $t_{1/2} = 7.2$ hr. The longest half-life for any astatine isotope is only 8.3 hr for $^{211}_{85}$At. The element resembles iodine, as far as is known.

Francium, element 87, like plutonium, actually occurs in nature, but the quantities are insignificant and could never have been detected if the synthetic element had not first been prepared and studied. Francium is formed because (although its parent nuclide, actinium-227, decays mainly by beta-ray emission to form thorium-227) about 1 percent of the actinium-227 decays by alpha emission:

$$^{227}_{89}\text{Ac} \xrightarrow[\text{(1 \% only)}]{t_{1/2} = 22 \text{ min}} {}^{223}_{87}\text{Fr} + {}^4_2\text{He}$$

This, the longest lived of any francium isotope, has a half-life of only 22 min. Francium is obviously a difficult element to study. It appears to be a very active metal resembling cesium and the other alkali metals in Group IA of the Periodic Table.

20.6   *Some Useful Isotopes*

This section will be devoted to some specific isotopes which, for one reason or another, have received more than passing attention. All the isotopes to be mentioned are of elements that occur more or less abundantly in nature, but the particular isotopes to be discussed do not, with one or two exceptions, occur in nature; and they are all radioactive.

The isotope of hydrogen, of mass number 3, is called tritium.

Although it occurs in nature, the relative abundance is almost vanishingly small. Tritium was first synthesized in 1934 by a (d,p) reaction:

$$_1^2D + {}_1^2D \rightarrow {}_1^3T + {}_1^1H$$

Another possible deuteron bombardment reaction for the production of tritium is of beryllium-9:

$$_4^9Be + {}_1^2D \rightarrow 2{}_2^4He + {}_1^3T$$

But a more important method for tritium production is slow-neutron bombardment of lithium-6:

$$_3^6Li + {}_0^1n \rightarrow {}_2^4He + {}_1^3T$$

While the most spectacular use of tritium is for thermonuclear explosions, it is available commercially in small quantities for use as a tracer element and for other purposes.

Tritium is radioactive, being a beta emitter with a half-life of 12.3 yr. The use of tritium as a tracer may be illustrated as follows: Water is soluble in hydrocarbons such as heptane, C_7H_{16}, to an extraordinarily small degree, and the accurate determination of the solubility poses some experimental difficulties. But suppose that a sample of heptane is mixed with a sample of water that contains an appreciable fraction of tritium in the form of H—O—T, or possibly T_2O, molecules. After the excess water has been removed, it is possible to measure the apparent beta-ray radioactivity of the heptane, this radioactivity being due to the trace of tritium-rich water that has gone into solution. The extreme sensitivity of radioactivity measurements (as by a Geiger counter) makes possible a fairly accurate estimate of how much tritium-rich water has gone into solution. In interpreting such data, it must be remembered that, because of the large difference in mass between tritium and protium, some moderate differences in properties between H—O—T, T_2O, and H_2O may be expected.

Use of tritium in the thermonuclear bomb is related to the nuclear fusion process previously described (Sec. 7.6). The fusion of deuterium and tritium to yield helium-4 plus neutrons is an extraordinarily exothermic reaction:

$$_1^2D + {}_1^3T \rightarrow {}_2^4He + {}_0^1n + energy$$

which becomes a self-sustaining chain reaction when it is detonated by the high temperature produced by a nuclear fission bomb.

The isotope carbon-14 is another nuclide that occurs in trace concentrations in nature, but which is produced commercially for tracer purposes. Carbon-14 is made by an (n,p) reaction on nitrogen-14:

$$_7^{14}N + {}_0^1n \rightarrow {}_6^{14}C + {}_1^1H$$

Minute amounts of this isotope, which decays by beta emission ($t_{1/2} = 5760$ yr) are sufficient for most tracer work. Use of this isotope has led to many improvements in the understanding of chemical reaction mechanisms. An illustration of its use is the technique of radiocarbon dating, developed by W. F. Libby. Air normally contains a very small, though measurable, concentration of carbon-14. This carbon-14 is present as carbon dioxide. When living organisms such as trees grow, they take in carbon dioxide, including traces of the radioactive carbon. This isotope then proceeds to disintegrate slowly, and after the tree dies, no further uptake or exchange of carbon with that in the air occurs. Hence it is possible, by measuring the radioactivity of the carbon in the wood, to estimate how many years have passed since the tree stopped growing. In this way, quite accurate dates have been found for ancient, and even for prehistoric, articles of wood going back 10,000 yr and more.

Two other isotopes of more than ordinary importance are cobalt-60, and strontium-90. Cobalt-60 may be made in a nuclear reactor by neutron irradiation of the stable cobalt-59, the reaction being one of simple neutron capture:

$$\ce{^{59}_{27}Co} + \ce{^1_0 n} \rightarrow \ce{^{60}_{27}Co}$$

Cobalt-60 decays by beta emission plus high-energy gamma rays:

$$\ce{^{60}_{27}Co} \rightarrow \ce{^{60}_{28}Ni} + e^- + \gamma$$

the half-life being 5.3 yr. This isotope is useful as a source of radiation for treating malignant disease, as a substitute for x-ray tubes in radiography, and for studying and treating all forms of matter under controlled gamma irradiation.

Strontium-90 is a good example of a useful isotope recovered from the fission products obtained from a uranium nuclear reactor. This isotope forms a fairly large fraction (about 6 percent) of the fission products, and consequently it must be purified under conditions of very high radioactivity. Strontium-90 is almost a pure beta-ray emitter, with only weak gamma rays. The half-life is 28 yr. Because of the availability of this isotope and its high energy output relatively uncomplicated by other reactions, it has become a useful source of energy for specialized situations such as space probes. It may, for instance, be used to heat one junction of a thermocouple (Sec. 1.6), arranged so as to generate electricity instead of for the more conventional measurement of temperature.

EXERCISES

1. Explain why, although many are known, less than a third of all nuclides occur in nature.

2. Predict the stability of the following (X stands for any element):

$$^{160}_{80}X, \ ^{42}_{21}X, \ ^{50}_{24}X, \ ^{166}_{73}X$$

3. Predict possible products, and write balanced equations for the following:
   (a) Proton bombardment of beryllium-9
   (b) Deuteron bombardment of oxygen-16
   (c) Neutron bombardment of aluminum-27
   (d) Neutron bombardment of argon-40
   (e) Helium ion bombardment of magnesium-28

4. A stable nuclide, molybdenum-95, is irradiated in several different experiments as follows:
   (a) Protons
   (b) Alpha particles
   (c) Deuterons
   (d) Neutrons
   Predict possible products.

5. What mechanism is proposed for the formation of, say, carbon-14 by neutron irradiation of nitrogen-14?

6. Describe the cyclotron.

7. Explain the following terms used in reference to a nuclear reactor: moderator, control rods, fuel, fission products, capture cross-section, shielding, reproduction factor.

8. Describe the production of plutonium.

9. If and when element 104 is synthesized, what electronic and chemical properties may it be expected to exhibit? Where will it go in the Periodic Table?

10. Account, on the basis of electron distribution, for the unique properties of the lanthanides and the actinides.

11. Suppose that a sample of tritium could be kept tightly sealed for 12.3 yr. How would the final gas pressure compare with the initial pressure, at the same temperature?

12. The actual masses in amu of the species involved in the nuclear fusion reaction of deuterium and tritium are as follows: $^2_1H = 2.01410$; $^3_1H = 3.0161$; $^4_2He = 4.00260$; $^1_0n = 1.00866$. Find the energy liberated per gram of helium formed.

13. The normal radioactivity of the carbon, due to the carbon-14 in the air, is conveniently expressed as 15.3 counts per minute (cpm) per gram of carbon on a Geiger counter. The half-life of ^{14}C is 5760 yr. Wood from an ancient Egyptian tomb was found to give 6.89 cpm/gram of C. Find the age of the wood.

14. The mass of the outer 10-mile layer of the earth's crust is estimated at about 2×10^{22} kg, and of this about 4 parts per million is uranium. The half-life of uranium-238 is 4.5×10^9 yr (which makes

up 99.3 percent of the whole). What weight of uranium is lost to the earth's crust every second? What volume (STP) of helium is gained by the earth every second by the disintegration of uranium-238?

15. If 0.10 gram of sodium metal is added to 10 grams of pure T_2O, what will be the molal concentration of the resulting NaOT solution?

16. Sometimes it is possible to use fairly heavy atoms as projectiles in nuclear bombardment. One of these is the $({}^{12}_{6}C, 6n)$ reaction, which occurs when uranium-238 is bombarded with carbon-12 ions. Write a completely balanced equation for the reaction.

17. Neptunium metal may be obtained by reducing NpF_3 with barium metal vapor at 1200° C. What minimum weight of barium should be used to react with 1 gram of NpF_3?

18. A certain nuclide is being produced at the rate of 1 gram/day. This nuclide is radioactive, with a half-life of 23.8 days. What weight of nuclide will be present at the steady state?

19. The human body contains about 0.35 percent of potassium, and of this potassium, 0.012 percent is the radioactive isotope ${}^{40}K$, which has a half-life of 1.3×10^9 yr. Find the number of disintegrations per second in the average human body weighing, say, 75 kg.

20. The solubility product of strontium fluoride is 2.8×10^{-9} at room temperature. Suppose that you have 100 ml of $0.0155M$ solution of ${}^{90}Sr^{2+}$ ions. What volume of $6M$ NaF must be added to lower the strontium-90 concentration to $3 \times 10^{-5}M$?

21. It was reported in the 1920's that element 61 had been discovered in nature. What circumstances place extreme doubt on any such claim?

22. Describe a method for making tritium.

23. Given that the oxidation potential of plutonium is

$$Pu \rightleftharpoons Pu^{3+} + 3e^- \qquad E_0 = +2.03 \text{ volts}$$

suggest a method for obtaining metallic plutonium from its compounds in which it has the 3+ oxidation state.

24. Judging from their relative positions in the Periodic Table, what methods would be appropriate for obtaining the free elements francium and astatine from their respective compounds?

25. Explosion of hydrogen bombs has a tendency to increase the concentration of carbon-14 in the atmosphere. What effect will this have on the apparent age of ancient samples studied by the radioactive carbon dating method?

21

Purification of
Chemical Elements
and Compounds

21.1   General Procedures

Few chemical elements are found in nature in a condition remotely approaching absolute purity. Most elements occur in chemical combination, and the combinations themselves are generally mixed with other elements and compounds. Nevertheless, a few elements do occur in a surprisingly pure condition. One of these is carbon (in diamond) and another is sulfur. Free sulfur of about 99.5 percent purity occurs in underground deposits from which it is obtained by the Frasch process. This consists of melting the sulfur underground with the aid of superheated water. Compressed air then forces the liquid sulfur to the surface, as shown in Fig. 21.1. For many purposes the sulfur does not require further purification.

Most sources of chemical elements are so impure that a preliminary procedure of beneficiation is required, as mentioned on page 16.2. There are many methods by which beneficiation may be achieved; two of these will be described in a little more detail. These two are magnetic concentration, and oil flotation.

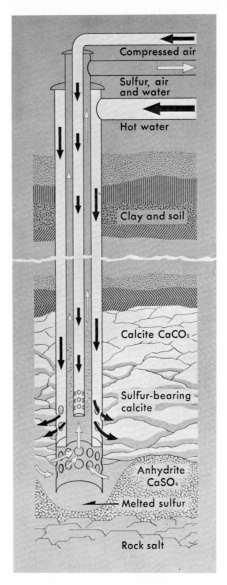

Compressed air

Sulfur, air
and water

Hot water

Clay and soil

*Fig. 21.1 Diagrammatic representation of
the Frasch process for obtaining sulfur.*

Calcite CaCO₃

Sulfur-bearing
calcite

Anhydrite
CaSO₄

Melted sulfur

Rock salt

An example of how magnetic concentration may be used is found
in the treatment of iron ore which is not rich enough in iron oxide for
direct reduction in the blast furnace. The ore may be roasted under reducing
conditions to convert the ferric oxide to the oxide known as magnetite,
Fe_3O_4.

$$6Fe_2O_3 + C \rightarrow 4Fe_3O_4 + CO_2$$

Moderate temperatures and comparatively little expenditure for coke are necessary to bring about this change. But when the ferric oxide has been converted to magnetite, it may very easily be concentrated by magnetic separators. The magnetite is strongly attracted to a magnet, while worthless residues such as silica and silicates are not so attracted. The magnetic separators cannot be used on ferric oxide before it is converted to magnetite because ferric oxide, as it occurs in nature, is only weakly attracted to a magnet.

Oil flotation, another widely used procedure in beneficiation, is a process in which crushed ore is thoroughly mixed with a froth of air bubbles in water to which a small amount of an oil has been added. The process depends on the fact that some mineral surfaces are more "wettable" than others by such an oil-water mixture. Those particles that are wetted by the liquid fall to the bottom of the vessel, while those not wetted cling to the air bubbles and are thus buoyed up to the top of the container, where they are easily removed, as shown in Fig. 21.2. In this way an efficient separation of valuable mineral from worthless gangue is easily and cheaply achieved. It should be emphasized that the process does not depend on the relative densities of valuable and worthless matter, but rather on how effectively each is wetted by the oil-froth mixture.

This chapter will be devoted to descriptions of procedures used

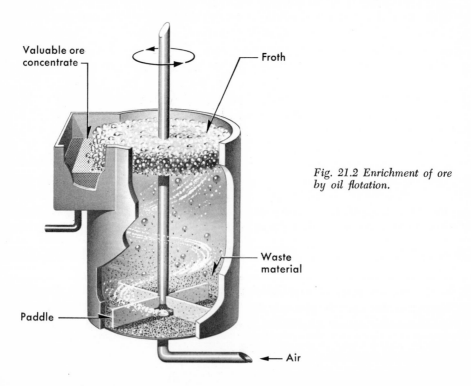

Fig. 21.2 Enrichment of ore by oil flotation.

in the further refining of metals and nonmetals and to purification procedures in general as they may be used both for elements and for chemical compounds. The refining, or purification, of a chemical substance means the removal of impurities down to some predetermined level. The plan of presentation will be to describe about six methods of major importance, and then to describe a few more methods that are especially adapted to the purification of one isotope from other isotopes of the same element. Illustrations of how the methods may be used will be taken chiefly from the metals and nonmetals described in the Chapters 18 and 19.

The term *purity* in relation to a chemical substance has a rather peculiar significance. Absolute purity exists only in the imagination. Water that is, for instance, perfectly safe and "pure" for drinking may contain appreciable concentrations of dissolved "impurities" such as calcium ion, chloride ion, and fluoride ion. But a minute trace of strontium-90 in water that is otherwise truly pure will render the water dangerously poisonous. The concentration of impurities in a substance must be considered in relation to the nature of the impurities and to the probable use of the substance. A trace of acetylene in air may be of no consequence in a blast furnace operation, but it may create a dangerously explosive condition in the manufacture of liquid air. Rather than striving for unattainable absolute purity, we should concern ourselves with reaching a condition that is best described as "pure enough" for the particular purpose at hand. It is with this criterion in mind that the several methods and principles will be described in the succeeding sections. Remember that germanium is purified by extraordinarily painstaking methods for use in electronic devices; no more than one atom in ten billion of this germanium is an impurity atom. Nevertheless, a simple calculation involving Avogadro's number tells us that in a gram of such ultrapure germanium, there must be about one trillion impurity atoms.

21.2 Distillation

The most widely used method for separating one liquid from another is *distillation*. This method is applicable when two or more liquids have different boiling points. The greater the difference between the boiling points, the more easily is the mixture separated. If the difference in boiling points is very great, the method is more frequently called *evaporation;* if the difference is small, use is made of fractional distillation.

An example of distillation used in the purification of a metal is found in the case of zinc and silver. As will be shown in Sec. 21.4, zinc is sometimes added to metallic lead (in which zinc is almost insoluble) for the purpose of removing traces of silver. The problem then arises of how to separate the silver from the zinc so that the zinc may be

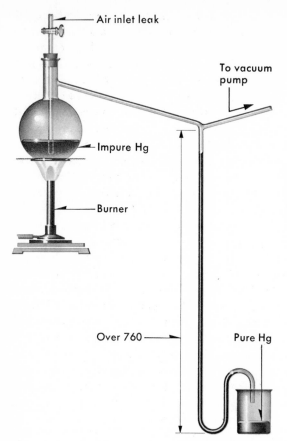

Air inlet leak

To vacuum pump

Impure Hg

Burner

Over 760

Pure Hg

Fig. 21.3 Preparation of pure mercury by distillation. The purpose of the air leak is to oxidize impurities which might otherwise distill over with the mercury.

used again and the silver may be marketed. The normal boiling point of silver is 1950° C; that of zinc, only 907° C. If the mixture of the two metals is strongly heated, the zinc will be converted to a vapor, which may be removed, while the silver remains as a liquid. In this way, a virtually quantitative separation of the two metals may be made. Another example is the purification of mercury from various other metals. The normal boiling point of mercury is only 356° C, and this may be lowered by lowering the pressure. All other metals have substantially higher boiling points; consequently, mercury may be purified by distillation; a typical still for this purpose is shown in Fig. 21.3.

It more often occurs that the boiling points of components in a mixture are too close together to permit efficient separation in the simple apparatus shown in Fig. 21.3, and then it becomes necessary to use *fractional distillation.* The process (Fig. 21.4) involves heating the liquid mixture and allowing the vapors to pass through a fractionating column. The column may be simply a glass or metal tube, or the tube may

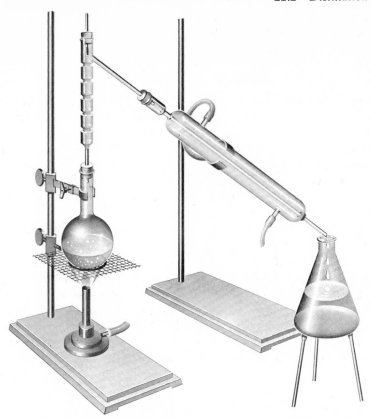

Fig. 21.4 Apparatus for fractional distillation. Industrial equipment is, of course, often quite large and complicated as compared with the simple laboratory set-up shown.

be packed with rods or gauze of glass, or ceramic, or metal. Part of the mixed vapor in the column is condensed to liquid and runs back into the heated chamber from which it is vaporized again. In this way, there is set up a countercurrent flow, and as the rising vapor passes over the descending film of liquid, the differences in vapor pressure of the several components in the mixture are used repeatedly to effect an efficient separation. Those components with the lowest boiling points (and highest vapor pressures) are found to concentrate at the top of the column, where they may be removed and condensed if it is so desired. Fractional distillation may be made highly efficient. It is, for instance, possible to separate heavy water (D_2O) from ordinary water in this way, although the difference in boiling points is only about 1.4 deg. A good example of a purification made in this way is that of bromine from chlorine.

    The example of fractional distillation chosen for detailed presentation in this section is the separation of air into its components, of which the most valuable by far, in terms of tonnage, is oxygen. The production of oxygen from air involves liquefaction of the air. The principle involved is the Joule-Thomson effect which is used in the liquefaction of most gases. The *Joule-Thomson* effect is observed when a gas under pressure is caused to expand by lowering the pressure. It will be found that the gas sample generally becomes cooler. This effect, which should not be confused with Charles' law relating the volume of a gas sample to the temperature, may also be observed in reverse. If the pressure on a gas sample is increased it will be generally found that the gas becomes warmer. The reason for these temperature changes is that when, for instance, the gas is compressed, work is done on the gas and some additional kinetic energy is given to the gas molecules. Conversely, when the gas expands, some kinetic energy is lost by the molecules.

Air is first freed of carbon dioxide, moisture, and undesirable impurities such as dust and potentially flammable gases. The air is then compressed to about 200 atm, and the heat generated by the Joule-Thomson effect is removed by letting the gas flow through pipes cooled by running water. The pressure on the air is now lowered; for instance, by permitting the gas to escape through a small orifice. In this process, the gas sample loses kinetic energy and becomes cooler. This cooler air now flows over pipes, bringing in more compressed air so that as *this* compressed air reaches the orifice, it has already been precooled. The decompressed air is led back to the compressor and in due course to the decompression chamber. This procedure continues until the gas undergoing decompression becomes cold enough to liquefy. The sequence of steps in this process is shown in Fig. 21.5.

The liquid air is then separated by fractional distillation into its several components. Oxygen boils at −183° C (SP) and nitrogen at −196° C. The nitrogen has the higher vapor pressure and therefore rises to the top of the distillation column. The various Group Zero gases may also be separated and purified in this way. If the gases obtained from air are desired as liquids, they may be kept in double-walled vessels called Dewar flasks. Ozone is similarly purified by distillation from molecular oxygen, its normal boiling point being −112° C, but the operation is hazardous.

It sometimes occurs that elements and compounds undergo direct conversion from solid to vapor by the process known as *sublimation*. Thus, iodine may be purified from many less volatile impurities by gentle heating to produce iodine vapor.

While fractional distillation ranks at the front of chemical engineering operations, it must not be thought that any mixture may be separated by this method, even though the boiling points are sufficiently different. Hydrogen chloride boils (SP) at −83.7° C and water, of course, at 100° C. But a solution of hydrogen chloride in water, namely, hydro-

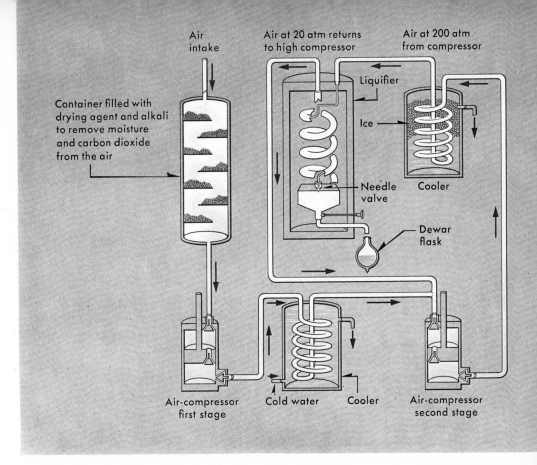

Air
intake

Air at 20 atm returns
to high compressor

Air at 200 atm
from compressor

Liquifier

Container filled with
drying agent and alkali
to remove moisture
and carbon dioxide
from the air

Ice

Needle
valve

Cooler

Dewar
flask

Air-compressor
first stage

Cold water

Cooler

Air-compressor
second stage

Fig. 21.5 Production of liquid air. Various minor modifications are in use, but they all depend on the Joule-Thomson effect.

chloric acid, shows the following effect: If the solution is rich in hydrogen chloride (if the acid is of high molarity) the gas HCl will distill preferentially, the solution becoming less concentrated. If the solution is dilute, the water will distill preferentially, the solution becoming more concentrated. When the concentration of hydrogen chloride reaches about 20 percent (at 760 mm pressure), the solution distills with concentration unchanged. Such a solution is called a *constant-boiling mixture.* This behavior is fairly common, and such mixtures which resist purification by distillation are called *azeotropes.* Sometimes the azeotrope may be purified by changing the pressure or by the addition of a third component.

21.3 Crystallization

Cooling a liquid below its melting point invariably produces a metastable condition, which generally results in crystallization. Most substances may also crystallize directly from the vapor, under appropriate

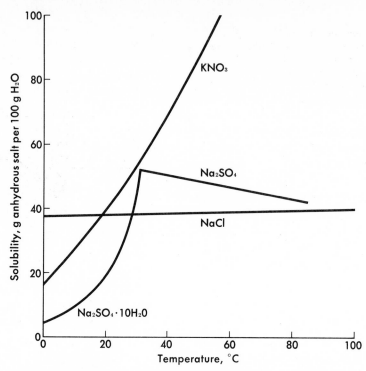

Fig. 21.6 *Solubility as a function of temperature for* NaCl, KNO₃, Na₂SO₄, *and* Na₂SO₄·10H₂O.

conditions. But the term *crystallization* as applied to purification procedures generally, though not always, means the formation of a solid phase from a solution. This is, next to distillation, probably the most widely used method of separation and purification employed in chemistry.

Crystallization from solution implies that the solution must, at least momentarily, have become supersaturated. Supersaturation may be brought about by removing some of the solvent, or by changing (generally lowering) the temperature, or sometimes by the judicious addition of another component. Removal of solvent is generally achieved by evaporation. Most of the principles involved in purification by crystallization are illustrated by reference to sodium chloride. Sodium chloride is one of the most widely used raw materials in chemical industry, and it is, of course, important in the diet of humans and animals.

Figure 21.6 shows the solubility as a function of temperature for sodium chloride, potassium nitrate, and two forms of sodium sulfate. Let us take a rather artificial case in which it is desired to obtain high-purity sodium chloride from a solution containing nearly saturated KNO₃ and

NaCl at 60° C. The solubility of KNO_3 at 60° C is 109.6 grams/100 grams H_2O, while at 10° C it is only 20.9 grams/100 grams H_2O. By cooling the solution to 10° C, it is possible to crystallize $109.6 - 20.9 = 88.7$ grams of KNO_3 for every 100 grams of H_2O treated. This means that 81 percent of the original KNO_3 has been removed from solution. Meanwhile, the solubility of sodium chloride is not greatly changed by a change of temperature. The solubility is 37.3 grams NaCl/100 grams H_2O at 60° C, and 35.8 grams/100 grams at 10° C. Only 1.5 grams of NaCl will have crystallized per 100 grams of H_2O treated, leaving 96 percent of the NaCl still in solution.

If now the liquid at 10° C is poured off the crystals, most of the KNO_3 will remain in the crystals and most of the NaCl will still be in solution. Now evaporate away about four-fifths of the water; for instance, by heating it in air. Then about 80 percent of the NaCl will crystallize in nearly pure form from the hot solution while all the remaining KNO_3 will stay in solution.

21.4 Solvent Extraction

If it should be desired to separate a mixture of sugar and sand into its pure components, a simple procedure would be to add sufficient water to dissolve all the sugar, leaving the sand undissolved. The sugar solution could be decanted through some filter paper and then evaporated. In this way a quantitative separation and purification of the two components would have been achieved. This is a very simple illustration of a useful procedure known as *solvent extraction* which, in many different forms, is used in the purification of elements and compounds.

This account will be restricted to so-called liquid-liquid extraction. Iodine dissolves in water to give a brown solution. Let us say that this solution also contains dissolved salts such as sodium iodide and that it is desired to obtain the iodine free from such salts. It so happens that chloroform is an excellent solvent for iodine but not for salts like sodium iodide. It also is true that chloroform is almost insoluble in water, and water is almost insoluble in chloroform. If chloroform is added to the water containing dissolved iodine, it will be found that a considerable fraction of the iodine will dissolve in the chloroform, giving it a purple color. But none of the sodium iodide will dissolve in the chloroform. The chloroform layer, which is at the bottom because of its higher density, may be removed from the water solution with the aid of a separatory funnel (Fig. 21.7). If now a second quantity of chloroform is added to the water solution, and the mixture is shaken, a further fraction of the iodine

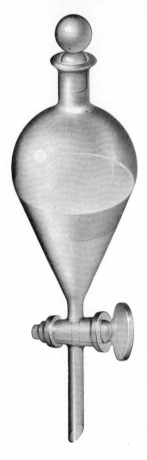

Fig. 21.7 Separatory funnel.

will be removed from the water. By repeated extraction the concentration of a substance in solution may in this way be made negligibly small.

The use of liquid-liquid extraction depends on having a solute that is soluble in two solvents, and these solvents must be immiscible, that is, not appreciably soluble in each other. Under ideal conditions, the concentration of a solute in two mutually immiscible solvents at equilibrium is given by

$$\frac{C_1}{C_2} = K_D$$

where C_1 and C_2 are the concentrations of solute in solvents number 1 and 2, respectively. The quotient K_D is called the *distribution constant*, and the equation given is one form of the *Nernst distribution law*. The equation holds best for dilute solutions and for those in which the molecules of solute are the same in each solvent. Sometimes the process is called *partition*.

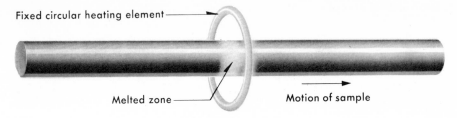

Fixed circular heating element

Melted zone

Motion of sample

Fig. 21.8 Zone refining.

Another example of liquid-liquid extraction is the Parkes process for purifying metallic lead from silver. To the molten impure lead there is added a small amount of zinc metal, which is only very slightly soluble in lead. Silver dissolves readily in the zinc, probably in the form of inter-metallic compounds. The liquid layer of zinc-silver alloy is then readily removed from the surface of the purified lead.

Solvent extraction has many other applications. One of these is in the purification of plutonium from uranium and fission products. Here the problem is complicated by the dangerously high radioactivity and also by the unique problem of avoiding a concentration of plutonium sufficiently high to undergo a nuclear fission explosion.

One other process, somewhat related to both crystallization and to solvent extraction, is *zone refining*. This process is used to obtain metals and semiconductor materials of very high purity. Zone refining consists of applying heat to melt a narrow zone of the metal, which is first prepared in the form of a cylindrical rod. The rod is then moved slowly so that the liquid zone travels, in effect, from one end of the cylinder to the other. As the metal melts, most impurities become dis-solved in the liquid zone. But as the metal recrystallizes, in passing beyond the source of heat, most of the impurities tend to stay in solution in the liquid phase. The impurities thus tend to concentrate in the narrow liquid zone. When it reaches the end of the rod, the zone and the impurities it contains are easily removed and discarded. The method, which is shown diagrammatically in Fig. 21.8, may also be used to purify organic com-pounds. Impurities are commonly lowered to less than 1 part in 10^9 in this way.

21.5 *Chemical Refining*

All the purification methods described above may be classed as physical methods, because no chemical change occurs during the process. The methods to be described in this and the succeeding two sections are chemical methods in that chemical valence bonds are formed and broken as purification proceeds. This section will be concerned with examples of relatively simple chemical reactions that make possible efficient separation of an element from unwanted impurities.

Let us say that a sample of copper metal contains a percent or two of silver and that it is desired to remove the silver. A possible procedure is to add some reagent that will precipitate the silver from solution but leave the copper unchanged. To achieve this purpose, it will first be necessary to dissolve the impure copper sample, and this may be done with concentrated nitric acid.

$$Cu + 4HNO_3 \rightarrow Cu(NO_3)_2 + 2NO_2 + 2H_2O$$
$$Ag + 2HNO_3 \rightarrow AgNO_3 + NO_2 + H_2O$$

The resultant solution now contains Cu^{2+} ions and Ag^+ ions. This solution may be diluted with water and then treated with dilute hydrochloric acid. The solubility of silver chloride is very low (it has a low solubility product, Sec. 14.6), whereas the solubility of cupric chloride is over 700 grams/liter of water. Under the circumstances, virtually all the silver precipitates as silver chloride, but all the copper remains in solution:

$$Ag^+ + Cl^- \rightarrow AgCl$$

The precipitate of silver chloride is now simply filtered from the solution. It is, of course, true that the copper is now present as Cu^{2+} ions and that, if the metal is required, it will be necessary to go through some reduction procedure such as electrolysis. But the particular purposes in mind for the purified copper may, or may not, require that it be in the form of metal.

A process closely related to chemical precipitation, and one that is particularly suited for the purification of an element present in very low concentration, is known as *coprecipitation*. It will be illustrated with reference to plutonium. This element, as described in the preceding chapter, is prepared artificially by slow neutron bombardment of uranium-238. When the nuclear reaction has proceeded for sufficient time, the remaining uranium, together with the plutonium and the accumulated fission products are dissolved in acid. It so happens that plutonium trifluoride, PuF_3, has a low solubility and that it may readily be precipitated from a solution containing Pu^{3+} ions by the addition of hydrofluoric acid. But for this precipitation to occur, it is necessary, of course, that the solubility product of PuF_3 should be exceeded, and this is generally impossible because the Pu^{3+} ion concentration is too low.

Under these circumstances it is still possible to precipitate PuF_3 if there is first added a moderate concentration of the rare earth lanthanum in the form of La^{3+} ions. The compound LaF_3 also has a very low solubility, and it is so nearly like PuF_3 in ionic radius and in crystal form

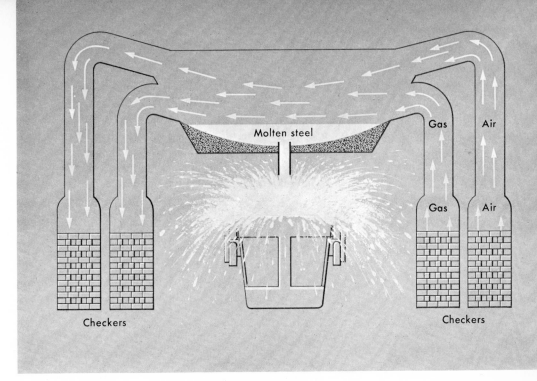

Fig. 21.9 Open-hearth furnace.

that the PuF_3 precipitates (or rather, coprecipitates) with the LaF_3. The LaF_3 is said to "carry" the PuF_3. The coprecipitate of LaF_3 plus a trace of PuF_3 may now be filtered, and through appropriate oxidation and reduction procedures the plutonium is separated from the lanthanum and progressively concentrated until it can be precipitated in the normal manner without the aid of a carrier. This procedure of coprecipitation is widely used in radiochemistry for study of specific radioactive nuclides.

Another process to be described here is the removal of nearly all impurities from iron. Iron, that is nearly free from impurities such as oxygen, sulfur, phosphorus, and silicon, but which contains small definite percentages of carbon, is known as steel. The chemical reactions involved in steel making are: first, the pig iron is purified until it consists of little but pure iron; and second, proper amounts of carbon are added.

The open-hearth process (Fig. 21.9) consists of a furnace in which pig iron is heated. Heat is directed over the iron until impurities are oxidized, or combined, in such a way that they may be removed as gases or as a scum on the surface of the liquid iron. A typical reaction is the removal of sulfur impurity by direct combination with oxygen to form sulfur dioxide, but oxygen may also, if necessary, be added in the form of hematite or of rusty iron. Carbon impurity will, of course, react with iron oxide to form iron plus gaseous carbon monoxide or dioxide. Oxygen itself is an undesirable impurity and may be removed by the addition of measured amounts of an active metal such as magnesium, titanium, or aluminum. Metals added for this purpose are called *scavengers*. The exact procedure necessary in the purification of iron depends on the particular kinds of impurities present. The composition of the furnace lining generally has to be selected to react with unwanted impurities. For instance, a basic furnace lining containing, say, magnesium oxide reacts with and removes a nonmetal such as phosphorus by forming a magnesium phosphate.

When the iron has reached the desired stage of purity, measured amounts of carbon are added to form steel. Other elements such as tungsten or chromium may be added to form alloy steels.

The last example of chemical refining is a unique process used for nickel. If nickel metal is heated to about 60° C in an atmosphere of carbon monoxide, it forms the gaseous compound nickel tetracarbonyl, $Ni(CO)_4$:

$$Ni + 4CO \rightleftharpoons Ni(CO)_4$$

Nickel is by no means the only metal that forms a carbonyl, but it is the only one that forms a volatile carbonyl under the conditions described. If a stream of carbon monoxide is allowed to flow over the impure nickel metal at 60° C, all the nickel will be removed as a gas, and all impurities will remain unchanged. The gaseous nickel carbonyl is readily decomposed to pure metal plus carbon monoxide by heating it to 200° C. The carbon monoxide may be circulated and used again. The process was invented by L. Mond, after whom it is named.

21.6   Electrolytic Refining

Certain metals are commonly purified by electrolysis. The principles involved will be illustrated by reference to copper.

If a solution of copper sulfate is electrolyzed with the use of platinum electrodes, copper will plate on the cathode, and oxygen will be liberated at the anode. The reason that copper, rather than hydrogen, is deposited at the cathode is that the copper oxidation potential is lower than that of hydrogen (Sec. 15.3).

If now the anode is made of copper rather than of such an inactive metal as platinum, then copper metal will be oxidized to cupric ions and go into solution from the surface of the anode. The competing processes here are essentially:

$$2H_2O \rightleftharpoons O_2 + 4H^+ + e^- \qquad E_0 = -1.23 \text{ volts}$$

and

$$Cu \rightleftharpoons Cu^{2+} + 2e^- \qquad E_0 = -0.34 \text{ volt}$$

The second of these processes, having the higher oxidation potential, occurs more readily.

In the electrolytic purification of copper, impure "blister" copper is cast into slabs for use as anodes. Thin sheets of pure copper are used as cathodes. The electrolyte is copper sulfate acidified with sulfuric acid. Copper dissolves from the anode in the form of cupric ions and copper deposits on the cathode as metal. The electrolyte gains and loses Cu^{2+} ions at about the same rate, and hence it does not change appreciably in copper concentration. Impurities in the blister copper anode may be either higher or lower than copper in the electromotive series. If they are more active than copper, they will go into solution in the form of ions. Zinc serves as an example of an impurity more active than copper, but at the cathode, the zinc ions are reduced less readily than the copper ions. Hence the zinc remains in solution while the pure copper is deposited. From time to time, the electrolyte may be removed for recovery (or discard) of the accumulated zinc.

Elements less active than copper do not undergo oxidation at the anode in the presence of copper. The reason for this is that they cannot compete with the copper in the loss of electrons. As the anode is dissolved away, less active impurities, of which silver is an example, simply fall to

Fig. 21.10 Electrolytic purification of copper. The impure anode dissolves away and the cathode is built up. Impurities either fall to the bottom of the tank (for example, Ag) or are left in solution (for example, Zn^{2+}).

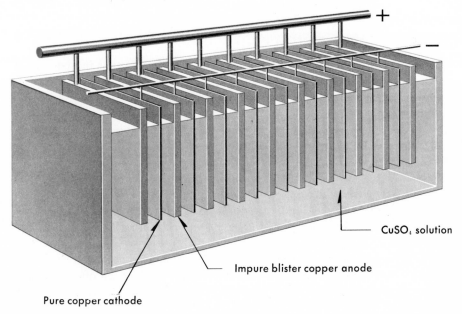

CuSO₄ solution

Impure blister copper anode

Pure copper cathode

the bottom of the cell (Fig. 21.10) as a sludge. The sludge is recovered from time to time for the valuable elements it may contain. The pure "electrolytic" copper is obtained at the cathode.

21.7   Ion Exchange

One of the most versatile purification methods ever developed is called *ion exchange*. It will be recalled that graphite has a structural arrangement (Sec. 19.6) in which the atoms are arranged in sheets of little hexagons. Let us suppose that one sheet is partially separated from others and that some of the bonds between carbon atoms are broken and replaced by bonds between carbon and some other group, of which the sulfonic acid group, —SO_3H, is one example. The resulting structure might then be approximately as follows:

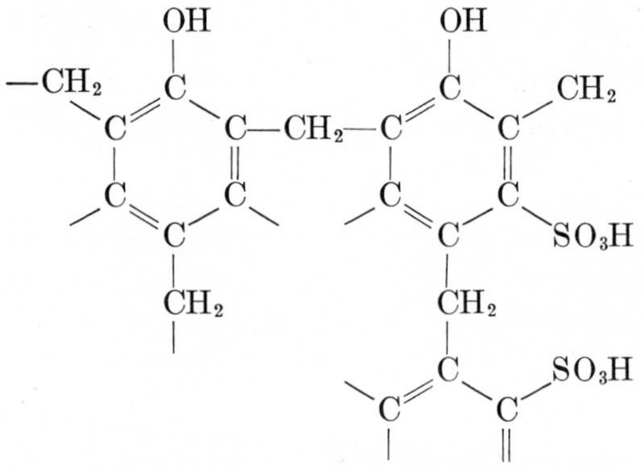

The structure shown may extend more or less indefinitely in space, and such a structure is called an *ion exchange resin*. The particular resin of which a small fragment is shown above is called a phenolsulfonic acid cation-exchange resin.

The hydrogen atoms that form part of the sulfonic acid groups behave as do the hydrogens in other Brönsted acids: They may readily ionize, and they may be replaced by other positive ions to form salts. If, for instance, we let R—SO_3H stand for the resin, then R—SO_3Na will be the salt formed when the acid hydrogen is replaced by sodium ions. This process of exchange of one cation for another occurs readily when the resin (which is generally available as a granular solid) is brought in contact with a water solution containing other positive ions.

The removal of dissolved electrolytes from water by ion exchange is a good example of how the process works. Hard water often contains Ca^{2+}. These and other cations are often objectionable because they lower the effectiveness of soap as a cleanser and tend to precipitate as calcium carbonate when the hard water is heated. If such hard water is allowed to flow over a cation-exchange resin in which the cation already present is sodium ion, then the exchange reaction that takes place is

$$2RSO_3Na + Ca^{2+} \rightleftharpoons (RSO_3)_2Ca + 2Na^+$$

(In the preceding formulas, the letter R stands for all the resin except the functional group.) The calcium ions are thus held on the resin and the sodium ions dissolve in the water where they are (generally) not objectionable. The hard water is then said to have been "softened." It is, of course, necessary to remove the accumulated calcium and other undesirable ions from time to time. This may be done by allowing concentrated sodium chloride solution to flow over the resin.

It is possible to construct resins that exchange negative rather than positive ions. These are known as anion-exchange resins, and they contain, for example, the quaternary ammonium group, $-N(CH_3)_3OH$, trimethyl ammonium hydroxide. The action with the resin in contact with a solution containing, say, chloride ion, is

$$RN(CH_3)_3OH + Cl^- \rightleftharpoons RN(CH_3)_3Cl + OH^-$$

With the use of a cation-exchange resin plus an anion exchange resin, it is possible to remove both positive and negative ion impurities from water containing dissolved salts. The water is allowed to flow over a cation-exchange resin in which the positive ion is H^+; that is, the resin is in the acid form, and assuming that the dissolved salt is sodium chloride, the reaction taking place is

$$RSO_3H + Na^+ + Cl^- \rightleftharpoons RSO_3Na + H^+ + Cl^-$$

Then the water is allowed to flow over an anion-exchange resin in the base (OH^-) form. The reaction is

$$RN(CH_3)_3OH + H^+ + Cl^- \rightleftharpoons RN(CH_3)_3Cl + H_2O$$

It will be noted that the hydroxide group liberated by the anion-exchanger reacts with the hydrogen ion liberated by the cation-exchanger and forms pure water. This procedure effectively removes virtually all ionic impurities, and the electrical conductivity of such "deionized" water is as low or lower than that of the best distilled water.

There are many other applications of ion exchange in chemistry. One such application described here is the separation and purification of the actinides. The method is also applicable to the lanthanides and, in fact, to many other elements. If one has, for instance, a mixture of elements such as plutonium, americium, and curium, they may be separated from each other by the following procedure: A small volume of solution con-

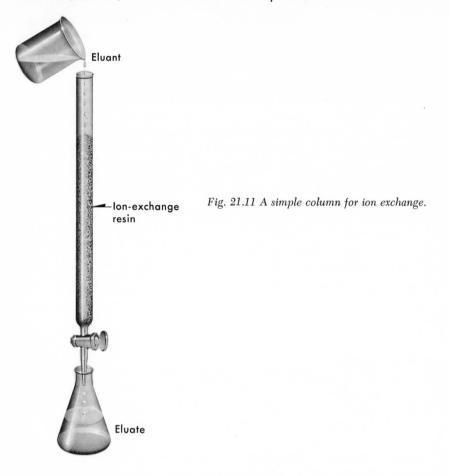

Eluant

Ion-exchange
resin

Fig. 21.11 A simple column for ion exchange.

Eluate

taining the elements in dilute hydrochloric acid is allowed to flow over a cation-exchange resin. The simple form of apparatus is shown in Fig. 21.11. All the actinide ions are exchanged and held by the resin. Now a solution of some reagent that will form complex ions with the actinide ions is added. Ammonium citrate is suitable for this purpose, the general form of the complexes being M(citrate)$_2$. The citrate solution washes the actinides from the resin, which exchanges them for ammonium ions. The process is called *elution*, and a separation is achieved because the actinide ions of higher atomic number are eluted before those of lower atomic number. Consequently, as the citrate solution is allowed to flow very slowly over the resin, the first drops eluted contain the curium ion, later drops contain the americium, and finally the plutonium appears. The fantastic ability of this method to separate ions is seen in the first identification of element 101, mendelevium, in which a sample containing only 17 atoms of this element was studied.

21.8 *Methods Especially Applicable to Isotopes*

It is becoming increasingly true that purification procedures are needed for the individual isotopes of chemical elements. It has already been described how, for instance, uranium-235 and deuterium have unique properties that make it necessary to isolate these nuclides from the natural mixtures of isotopes in which they occur. A few methods for the separation of specific isotopes have already been mentioned briefly. These methods will now be reviewed, and others will be described. The methods to be presented in this section are diffusion, gas chromatography, exchange reactions, and mass spectrometry, with briefer reference to one or two other procedures.

Diffusion as a method for separating the components of a gas mixture has already been described (Sec. 1.8). It will be recalled that the rate of diffusion of a gas varies inversely as the square root of the density. Inasmuch as the density of a gas varies directly as the molecular weight, it follows that hydrogen chloride, for example, which contains chlorine-37 atoms, will diffuse more slowly than a sample containing only chlorine-35 atoms. A separation of the molecules H—^{37}Cl from H—^{35}Cl is therefore possible.

The most spectacular use of diffusion in the purification of isotopes is that of uranium-235 from uranium-238 as it occurs in natural uranium. This separation is possible because uranium forms a gaseous compound, uranium hexafluoride, UF_6. The molecular weight of $^{235}UF_6$ is then slightly less than that of $^{238}UF_6$, and a separation is possible, although the experimental difficulties are formidable. To achieve a separation when the difference in gas densities is so small, it is necessary to permit the gases to diffuse through a membrane. To solve the problem of large-scale uranium-235 production, it is necessary to use literally acres of membranes and to repeat the diffusion step thousands of times.

Rather distantly related to diffusion is the method of *gas chromatography*. It will be recalled that vapor molecules are adsorbed on the surfaces of solids (Sec. 10.5) and that this adsorption is in many cases similar to a condensation such as of a vapor to a liquid. The tenacity with which a molecule is adsorbed to a surface is often, though not always, related to the boiling point of the vapor substance.

If a mixture of a higher boiling and a lower boiling gas (such as, for instance, propane and nitrogen) is allowed to flow through a tube loosely packed with granular aluminum oxide as adsorbent, it will be found that the nitrogen moves ahead of the propane, and if the tube is long enough, a complete separation of these two gases is effected.

Gas chromatography is useful in some rather difficult purifications such as that of pure HD from a mixture of H_2, HD, and D_2. It is also possible to separate pure *para*-hydrogen from a mixture of *ortho*- and

H₂O (I)
HDO (I)   → H₂ (g)

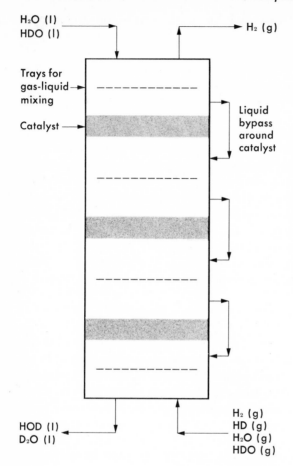

Trays for
gas-liquid →
mixing

Catalyst →

Liquid
bypass
around
catalyst

HOD (I)
D₂O (I)

H₂ (g)
HD (g)
H₂O (g)
HDO (g)

Fig. 21.12 *Countercurrent catalytic exchange process for enriching deuterium. The principle is shown diagrammatically—many such stages being actually required. Normal water (containing a little deuterium) is admitted at the top; normal H₂ gas plus water vapor is introduced at the bottom. At the top H₂ almost stripped of deuterium escapes; at the bottom water enriched in deuterium flows out.*

para-hydrogen. In addition to its rather limited range of applicability in isotope work, gas chromatography is widely used in the separation and analysis of many gas mixtures. A closely related form of chromatography is also widely applied to liquid mixtures.

Exchange reactions are used principally in the purification of deuterium. They have other applications in the study of chemical reaction mechanisms. The nature of exchange has already been described (Sec. 17.6). It will be recalled that if a mixture of H_2 and D_2 is held over a catalyst until equilibrium has been reached, the ratios of the three possible species, H_2, HD, and D_2, will be found to be not quite that corresponding to a random distribution of these three molecules. In other words, the equilibrium constant for the reaction

$$H_2 + D_2 \rightleftharpoons 2HD$$

is only about 3.3 at room temperature, although it approaches 4.0 at higher temperatures. This means that the product $[H_2] \times [D_2]$ at equilibrium at room temperature is slightly greater than $[HD]^2$.

Now consider an exchange reaction between HD and H_2O:

$$HD + H_2O(l) \rightleftharpoons H_2 + HOD(l)$$

This reaction between gaseous HD and liquid H_2O takes place in the presence of a catalyst, and the equilibrium is such that slightly more deuterium concentrates in the liquid phase, as HOD, than in the gas phase, as HD. This slight enrichment may be used to separate the isotopes: The enriched liquid water will react with fresh gas in a countercurrent arrangement (Fig. 21.12) in which the gas moves in one direction, and the liquid in the other, in successive stages until the pure D_2O on the one hand and virtually pure H_2 on the other are obtained.

Heavy water, D_2O, is actually produced by the Spevak exchange method, in which the reaction is between liquid water and hydrogen sulfide:

$$HOD(l) + H_2S(g) \rightleftharpoons H_2O(l) + HSD(g)$$

At a temperature of about 100° C, the deuterium is enriched in the gas phase; that is, the reaction as written to the right is favored. But at 25° C, the reverse is true, and deuterium tends to concentrate in the liquid phase. Continued cycles yield water containing about 2 percent D_2O (mostly as HOD), and this is concentrated by fractional distillation and electrolysis to virtually pure D_2O.

The concentration and purification of D_2O by electrolysis is a unique procedure. If water is electrolyzed, the products at cathode and anode, respectively, are hydrogen and oxygen. If the water contains some deuterium, as is the case for normal water, it will be found that the lighter isotope, $_1^1H$, is liberated somewhat more readily that the heavier, $_1^2D$. If the electrolysis is prolonged, the heavier isotope tends to concentrate in the remaining liquid electrolyte. Ultimately, pure D_2O may be obtained in this way, although if the starting material is ordinary tap water, it requires a long and tedious electrolysis before all the light $_1^1H$ has been eliminated.

The last method to be mentioned in connection with isotope purification is *mass spectrometry*. It will be recalled (Sec. 2.6) that in the mass spectrometer, the ions of various masses are separated by the magnetic field through which they travel. The amounts of matter separated in this way by the mass spectrometer are extremely small, but during World War II great installations were built and these are capable of separating substantial quantities of matter. The original installation was made to obtain uranium-235, but the method is now used to separate various isotopes, especially of the elements of higher atomic numbers.

EXERCISES

1. What is the significance of the word "purity" as used in reference to a chemical substance?

2. For distillation to be successful in the separation of components, it is necessary that the vapor phase composition be different from that of the liquid phase. Krypton boils at 120° K, xenon at 166° K, and no azeotropes are formed. Is the vapor phase during distillation of these two substances richer or poorer in xenon than the liquid phase?

3. What is an azeotrope?

4. If distillation of a mixture is continued until all the components have been vaporized, what, if anything, has been achieved in terms of purification?

5. Describe how liquid air is made.

6. For hydrogen, the Joule-Thomson effect is such that compression results in a *cooling* effect, but this effect changes sign at −80° C, which is called the Joule-Thomson inversion temperature. Suggest a procedure for obtaining liquid hydrogen.

7. The following solubilities are available, in grams of solute per 100 grams of water at the temperatures indicated:

	0° C	20° C	40° C	60° C	80° C	100° C
KCl	27.6	34.0	40.0	45.5	51.1	56.7
KClO$_3$	3.3	7.4	14.0	24.5	38.5	57

Plot the solubilities and describe how to separate potassium chloride and potassium chlorate from a solution containing 1 mole of each in 1 liter of water. State residual impurity in each.

8. At 25° C, a water solution of iodine contains 0.0516 gram of I$_2$ per liter. This is in equilibrium with carbon tetrachloride, which is found to contain 4.412 grams of I$_2$ per liter. Find the distribution constant.

9. To 100 ml of water containing 0.300 gram of dissolved iodine at 25° C, there is added 100 ml of carbon tetrachloride. The mixture is stirred until equilibrium is reached. What weight of I$_2$ will remain in the water?

10. Describe the purification of nitrogen by zone refining.

11. Design methods for the purification of the following:

    (a) F$_2$ containing traces of HF
    (b) H$_2$ containing a trace of O$_2$
    (c) O$_2$ containing a trace of H$_2$
    (d) Cu containing a trace of Ni

(e) Ni containing a trace of Cu

(f) K containing a little Na

(g) Phosphorus from nitrogen impurity

(h) He from D_2 impurity

(i) Carbon impurity from silicon

(j) $_2^3$He from HD

12. A solution contains 3.0 grams/liter of Pb^{2+} and 1.0 gram/liter of Cu^{2+}. To 100 ml of this solution, how much $12M$ HCl must be added to lower the Pb^{2+} ion concentration so that the total weight of lead remaining in solution is less than 0.01 percent of the total weight of copper?

13. What is coprecipitation?

14. There seems to be an anomaly that the object in a blast furnace is to *reduce* the iron to metal; yet, large quantities of oxygen are used. What is the explanation?

15. What current of electricity is necessary to produce 200 tons of electrolytic copper per day, with 90 percent current efficiency?

16. In the electrolytic purification of copper it appears that the anode process is approximately the reverse of the cathode process. If this is the case, then why does the purification require the expenditure of electric energy?

17. Equipment for making deionized water gradually becomes ineffective, owing to saturation of the cation- and anion-exchangers with impurities. Describe how to restore them to efficiency.

18. List methods available for isotope separation, determine which state of matter (solid, liquid, dissolved, or gas) is required, and indicate any general limitations.

19. Suggest a method for separating H_2 and HD by diffusion so that the end products are H_2 and D_2.

20. Compare the diffusion rates of H_2, HD, and D_2.

21. Gas chromatography is widely used for the analysis of vapor mixtures. It is sometimes referred to as the "poorman's mass spectrograph." Compare the two methods.

22. What is the chief objection to preparing D_2O by electrolysis of tap water?

23. A sample of radiolead, ^{209}Pb, has a half-life of 21.5 hr, and this gives 5200 counts/min. It is desired to coprecipitate this radiolead as $PbCl_2$ by adding ordinary lead in the form of $Pb(NO_3)_2$ until $[Pb^{2+}] = 0.35M$, and then adding hydrochloric acid until $[H^+] = 1.0M$. How many counts per minute will remain in the solution after the $PbCl_2$ has been filtered off?

24. Assuming that compounds may be classified into those that are essentially ionic and those that are essentially covalent, list puri-

fication methods applicable to each category (for example, gas chromatography could not be used for a substance that cannot be obtained in the form of a gas).

25. List purification methods applicable to substances that may be obtained only as (a) solids, (b) solids or liquids, (c) solids, liquids, or gases.

22

Hydrides

22.1   Binary Compounds of Hydrogen

This chapter will be devoted to compounds containing hydrogen plus one other element. Such substances are called *binary* compounds, provided two, and only two, elements are present. It is *not* necessary in a binary compound that the ratio of atoms present should be 1:1. For instance, H_2O is a binary compound, as are NH_3 and HCl, but $LiAlH_4$ is a ternary compound.

Some authors restrict the term *hydride* to those compounds in which hydrogen is the more electronegative. According to this rule, LiH is properly called lithium hydride, but HCl is hydrogen chloride. In this chapter we shall adhere to a growing practice of using the word "hydride" rather loosely for any binary compound containing hydrogen, and for a few compounds containing more than two elements.

A preliminary survey of hydrogen and its compounds has already been given in Chapter 17. It is probably correct to say that all elements combine with hydrogen to form compounds, with the exception of the Group Zero elements, and even these may form transitory ion complexes (Sec. 16.6). Table 22.1 is an outline periodic table showing examples of hydrides. It should be understood that the table is in no sense complete, although no very important hydride has been omitted.

TABLE 22.1 EXAMPLES OF BINARY COMPOUNDS OF HYDROGEN

	Saltlike		Interstitial									Molecular				
	LiH	BeH$_2$										B$_2$H$_6$ B$_4$H$_{10}$ etc.	CH$_4$ C$_2$H$_6$ etc.	NH$_3$ N$_2$H$_4$ NH$_3$	H$_2$O H$_2$O$_2$	HF
	NaH	MgH$_2$										(AlH$_3$)$_\infty$	SiH$_4$ etc.	PH$_3$ P$_2$H$_4$	H$_2$S etc.	HCl
	KH	CaH$_2$	TiH$_x$	VH$_x$	CrH CrH$_2$		FeH$_2$ FeH$_x$	CoH$_2$	HiH$_2$	CuH	ZnH$_2$		GeH$_4$ etc.	AsH$_3$	H$_2$Se	HBr
								PdH$_x$					SnH$_4$	SbH$_3$	H$_2$Te	HI
								PtH$_x$								

* Saltlike hydrides are at the left (for example, LiH), interstitial in the center (for example, TiH$_x$), and molecular at the right (for example, NH$_3$). The table is not intended to be complete.

There are three classifications of binary hydrides. These are:

1. *Saltlike hydrides*, of which LiH is an example
2. *Interstitial hydrides*, of which TiH_x is an example
3. *Molecular hydrides*, of which HCl is an example

The three kinds of hydrides are differentiated in Table 22.1, and one may see that the saltlike hydrides are formed for the most part by the strongly electropositive metals, the interstitial hydrides by the transition metals, and the molecular hydrides by the nonmetals. As frequently occurs, it is sometimes difficult to define a sharp boundary between one classification and another.

In the remainder of this chapter, the several types of hydrides will be described. The compounds selected for detailed presentation are those that are of major importance to science or industry, or those whose preparation or properties illustrate some important principle. It is particularly to be noted that nearly all the binary compounds of hydrogen may be prepared by direct synthesis; that is, by bringing the two elements together. Sometimes, as is the case for hydrogen and fluorine, the reaction goes immediately to completion with explosive violence. But sometimes, as in the case for hydrogen and nitrogen, there is an activation energy to be overcome, and the equilibrium may be so unfavorable that full use must be made of the opportunities presented by Le Châtelier's principle to obtain a satisfactory yield.

22.2   Saltlike Hydrides

Treatment of the alkali (Group IA) metals or of the alkaline earth (Group IIA) metals with hydrogen at moderately elevated temperature yields compounds known as saltlike hydrides. Examples of these, as formed by lithium, sodium, and calcium, are

$$2Li + H_2 \rightarrow 2LiH$$
$$2Na + H_2 \rightarrow 2NaH$$
$$Ca + H_2 \rightarrow CaH_2$$

These compounds have similarities in structure and properties to the true salts, such as sodium chloride. With the possible exception of europium hydride, EuH_2, and ytterbium hydride, YbH_2, in the lanthanide group, the saltlike hydrides are not formed by the transition metals, and they are not formed by the nonmetals. All the true saltlike hydrides are white or silvery crystalline solids that decompose to hydrogen and metal at elevated temperatures. They all have a higher density than the metal from which they are formed, and some of them ignite spontaneously in air. Proof that the hydrogen in these compounds is the negative ion is found in the experimental observation that electrolysis of liquid lithium hydride (mp 680° C) or of calcium hydride dissolved in fused potassium chloride yields hydrogen at the positive electrode.

X-ray diffraction, aided by diffraction studies in which neutrons rather than x-rays are used, show that hydrides such as NaH have the same crystal structure as sodium chloride (Sec. 4.5), the hydride, H^-, ion taking the place of the chloride ion, although the latter is larger (1.81 Å radius for Cl^- as compared with 1.54 Å for H^-).

It has already been pointed out that the hydride ion is a strong reducing agent. It may also be regarded as a very strong Lewis base (Sec. 13.4). The reaction of hydride ion with a proton may, in the Lewis sense, be regarded as a neutralization of a base H^- by an acid H^+. Thus, any saltlike hydride will vigorously react with water or with ammonia to yield molecular hydrogen on the one hand, plus either hydroxide ion OH^- or amide ion NH_2^- on the other hand, as the case may be:

$$H^- + H_2O \rightarrow H_2 + OH^-$$
$$H^- + NH_3 \rightarrow H_2 + NH_2^-$$

The hydride ion is seen from the above reactions to be a stronger base than either hydroxide ion or amide ion.

22.3   Interstitial Hydrides

The transition metals, including the $3d$, $4d$, $5d$, $4f$, and $5f$ series, react with hydrogen to form hydrides called *interstitials*. With few exceptions the method of preparation is that of direct synthesis, although sometimes elevated pressure is used. The substances so formed generally resemble the metals from which they are made, and the density of the hydride is, in contrast to that of the saltlike hydrides, *less* than that of the original metal. Sometimes, though not always, the metal atoms retain their original arrangement in the unit cell. The interstitial hydrides also exhibit variable compositions. For instance, titanium metal may progressively combine with hydrogen. A definite crystal structure resembling that of calcium fluoride is found over the composition range $TiH_{1.50}$ to $TiH_{1.97}$.

In view of the variable compositions generally found, it may be wondered if the interstitial hydrides may be considered as true chemical compounds. The answer to this question can be only that there is definite evidence of chemical bond formation in these substances. When palladium is exposed to hydrogen, there is a loss of the paramagnetism associated with unpaired electrons in the metal, and it is difficult to see how this could occur without electron pairing (that is, without bond formation).

The name "interstitial" arose when it was thought that the hydrogen in these substances merely occupied holes (interstices) between the layers of metal atoms; this view is no longer held.

Among interstitial hydrides of interest, in addition to those of titanium and palladium mentioned before, uranium hydride has received considerable attention. This may reach the composition UH_3. The formation of an iron interstitial hydride, FeH_x, is thought to be related to the phenomenon of hydrogen embrittlement, which sometimes causes disastrous failure of steel equipment.

22.4 Molecular Hydrides, Preparation

The molecular hydrides such as water, ammonia, and hydrogen chloride rank among the most important of all chemical compounds. Most such compounds may be prepared by direct synthesis or by displacement. (The term *displacement* is used here in a different sense than in Sec. 15.4.) Hydrolysis and other methods are also used in some cases. Table 22.2 shows the compounds to be considered, either in detail or more briefly, and the preparative methods applicable.

The hydrogen halides, with the exception of hydrogen fluoride, are commonly prepared by direct synthesis. For hydrogen chloride, the hydrogen may be said to burn in an atmosphere of chlorine:

$$H_2 + Cl_2 \rightleftharpoons 2HCl$$

For hydrogen bromide, hydrogen iodide, and ammonia, a catalyst is necessary. Other hydrides that may be prepared by direct synthesis include hydrogen fluoride, water, and methane, but the synthesis of water and methane is rarely necessary, and a more convenient method is available for hydrogen fluoride.

TABLE 22.2 IMPORTANT MOLECULAR HYDRIDES AND THEIR PREPARATIVE METHODS

Direct synthesis	Displacement	Hydrolysis	Other
NH_3	HF	NH_3	H_2O
HF	HCl	PH_3	B_2H_6
HCl	HBr	HCl	SiH_4
HBr	HI	HBr	N_2H_4
H_2O	H_2S	HI	
	H_2O	CH_4	
	HN_3		

A review and amplified description of the important Haber process for the synthesis of ammonia will now be given. The principles involved in this synthesis have already been presented in Sec. 11.3. If nitrogen and hydrogen are heated together, a reversible reaction takes place, yielding a small percentage of ammonia:

$$N_2 + 3H_2 \rightleftharpoons 2NH_3 + 21.9 \text{ kcal}$$

The reaction at ordinary temperatures is so slow as to be useless. The reaction is exothermic, and hence, according to Le Châtelier's principle, an increase of temperature will decrease the equilibrium yield of ammonia. Increase of pressure will, however, increase the yield of ammonia, and use of a catalyst will increase the speed of reaction without the unfavorable consequences of raising the temperature. The Haber process consists of passing a mixture of hydrogen and nitrogen over a catalyst, which generally consists of iron to which small amounts of aluminum oxide and of potassium compounds have been added as promoters. The gases are held at several hundred atmospheres of pressure. The equilibrium mixture of nitrogen, hydrogen, and ammonia is removed from the catalyst chamber, the ammonia is taken out of the gas mixture (as, for instance, by cooling it or by dissolving the ammonia in water), and the remaining gases are recirculated over the catalyst after the addition of more nitrogen and hydrogen. A diagram of the process is shown in Fig. 22.1.

The second preparative method to be considered for molecular hydrides is displacement. The term *displacement* was used previously to mean a reaction such as the reduction of cupric ion by metallic zinc to yield metallic copper. In the present usage, displacement means the liberation of a hydride by use of an acid that either is a stronger acid than the hydride under consideration or has a much higher boiling point. The chief examples selected will be hydrogen sulfide and hydrogen chloride. If a metal sulfide such as ferrous sulfide or calcium sulfide is treated with dilute hydrochloric acid, the reaction yields hydrogen sulfide plus a solution of the metal chloride:

$$FeS + 2HCl \rightleftharpoons H_2S + Fe^{2+} + 2Cl^-$$

The reaction runs smoothly, virtually to completion. The reason for this is not solely that hydrogen sulfide is a gas, since hydrogen chloride is also a gas. The reasons the reaction goes to completion are that hydrogen sulfide forms a very weak acid and that it is not very soluble in water. The displacement reaction is therefore that of a weak acid by a strong acid. This may best be written as

$$FeS + H^+ \rightarrow Fe^{2+} + H_2S$$

The preparation of hydrogen chloride by displacement is similar to

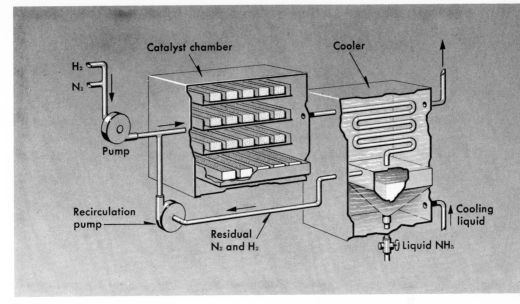

Fig. 22.1 Flow diagram for the Haber synthesis of ammonia.

that of hydrogen sulfide except that, since hydrogen chloride forms a strong acid in water, and since it is very soluble in water, it is necessary to use a high-boiling acid to displace the hydrochloric acid. Sulfuric acid has a high boiling point and is suitable for this reaction:

$$NaCl + H_2SO_4(conc) \rightleftharpoons NaHSO_4 + HCl$$

It has the added advantage that hydrogen chloride is not very soluble in concentrated sulfuric acid. In the presence of excess sodium chloride and with a higher temperature, the reaction is

$$2NaCl + H_2SO_4(conc) \rightleftharpoons Na_2SO_4 + 2HCl$$

The explosive hydride hydrazoic acid, HN_3, may be prepared similarly by heating sodium azide (prepared by heating nitrous oxide, N_2O, with sodamide, $NaNH_2$) with sulfuric acid:

$$NaN_3 + H_2SO_4 \rightarrow HN_3 + NaHSO_4$$

The preparation of hydrazoic acid is very hazardous.

Displacement reactions of these kinds may be used similarly for the preparation of hydrogen fluoride:

$$CaF_2 + H_2SO_4 \rightarrow CaSO_4 + 2HF$$

When we consider hydrogen bromide and hydrogen iodide, a difficulty arises because these compounds are increasingly effective reducing agents, and concentrated sulfuric acid is an oxidizing agent. This difficulty may be surmounted by using a high-boiling acid that is not an oxidizing agent. Phosphoric acid serves this purpose:

$$2NaBr + H_3PO_4 \rightarrow 2HBr + Na_2HPO_4$$

The equation for hydrogen iodide is similar. It will be noted that hydrogen bromide and hydrogen iodide are stronger acids than phosphoric, but they are volatile and phosphoric acid is not.

Similar displacement reactions may be used to obtain hydrides of silicon:

$$Mg_2Si + 4HCl \rightarrow SiH_4 + 2MgCl_2$$

The product is actually a mixture of silicon hydrides of the general formula Si_nH_{2n+2}. It must also be pointed out that the two "hydrides" of oxygen, namely, water and hydrogen peroxide, may be prepared by analogous reactions:

$$CaO + H_2SO_4 \rightarrow H_2O + CaSO_4$$
$$BaO_2 + 2HCl \rightarrow H_2O_2 + BaCl_2$$

These are not, of course, practical methods for the preparation of either compound.

Reactions of hydrolysis bear some relationship to those discussed above. If, for example, magnesium nitride (prepared by heating magnesium in nitrogen) is treated with water, a reaction of hydrolysis goes virtually to completion, yielding ammonia and magnesium hydroxide:

$$Mg_3N_2 + 6H_2O \rightarrow 2NH_3 + 3Mg(OH)_2$$

Certain other compounds of nitrogen yield ammonia by hydrolysis. One of these is calcium cyanamide, $CaCN_2$ (made by heating calcium carbide in nitrogen.) The equation for this reaction is

$$CaCN_2 + 3H_2O \rightarrow 2NH_3 + CaCO_3$$

Hydrolytic reactions similar to that of magnesium nitride occur for many other compounds. Examples are

$$Ca_3P_2 + 6H_2O \rightarrow 2PH_3 + 3Ca(OH)_2$$
$$Al_4C_3 + 12H_2O \rightarrow 3CH_4 + 4Al(OH)_3$$

The hydrogen halides may also be prepared by hydrolysis of the appropriate halides. For instance, phosphorus trichloride plus water yields hydrogen chloride plus phosphorous acid:

$$PCl_3 + 3H_2O \rightarrow 3HCl + H_3PO_3$$

It will be noted that in this case, the hydrolysis results in the formation of two acids. Similar reactions occur for phosphorus tribromide and phosphorus triiodide, but these two reactants may conveniently be made *in situ* by allowing bromine to drop onto a mixture of red phosphorus and water, on the one hand, and of water to drop onto a mixture of red phosphorus and iodine, on the other:

$$2P + 3I_2 + 6H_2O \rightarrow 6HI + 2H_3PO_3$$

For the remaining molecular hydrides to be mentioned, it is most convenient to use special methods. For instance, the neutralization of a Brönsted acid by a Brönsted base always yields water as one product, but this is implicit in the Brönsted definitions. The simple hydrides of boron and of silicon may be prepared best by the action of the appropriate halide on lithium aluminum hydride, $LiAlH_4$ (prepared by adding lithium hydride to aluminum chloride in ether solution). The reaction for the hydride diborane, B_2H_6, is

$$3LiAlH_4 + 4BF_3 \rightarrow 2B_2H_6 + 3LiF + 3AlF_3$$

A similar reaction occurs with lithium borohydride, $LiBH_4$. Silane, SiH_4, may be prepared as follows:

$$LiAlH_4 + SiCl_4 \rightarrow SiH_4 + LiCl + AlCl_3$$

The method illustrated here is of fairly general applicability.

The compound hydrazine, N_2H_4, must be regarded as a special case. It may be prepared by the reaction of sodium hypochlorite on ammonia:

$$2NH_3 + NaOCl \rightarrow N_2H_4 + NaCl + H_2O$$

22.5 Molecular Hydrides, Physical Properties and Structure

With the exception of water and hydrazoic acid, all the common molecular hydrides are gases at room temperature, and these two are easily vaporized at moderately elevated temperatures. In view of this, the gas density may be found readily from the molecular weight, and vice versa, for all cases except hydrogen fluoride, in which there are some complexities, to be described below. All these hydrides are colorless. Most have strong characteristic odors that are frequently unbearably sharp or nauseating. Nearly all are poisonous, and most are lethal in the extreme. Several physical properties of these compounds are shown in Table 22.3.

Examination of Table 22.3 shows that ammonia, water, and hydrogen fluoride have boiling points that are notably higher than the corresponding hydrides of the elements immediately below nitrogen, oxygen, and fluorine, respectively, in the Periodic Table. Thus the boiling point of

TABLE 22.3   PHYSICAL PROPERTIES OF SOME MOLECULAR HYDRIDES

Name	Formula	Mp, °C	Bp, °C	Dipole moment, debyes
Diborane	B_2H_6	−165	−92	0
Methane	CH_4	−183	−162	0
Silane	SiH_4	−185	−112	0
Ammonia	NH_3	−78	−33	1.47
Hydrazine	N_2H_4	2	113	0
Hydrazoic acid	HN_3	−80	37	0.85?
Phosphine	PH_3	132	−87	0.55
Arsine	AsH_3	−116	−62	0.16
Water	H_2O	0	100	1.85(g)
Hydrogen sulfide	H_2S	−83	−62	0.92
Hydrogen fluoride	HF*	−92	19	1.91
Hydrogen chloride	HCl	−112	−85	1.03
Hydrogen bromide	HBr	−88	−67	0.80
Hydrogen iodide	HI	−51	−35	0.42

* See text concerning the molecular weight of hydrogen fluoride.

ammonia is 54 degrees higher than that of phosphine; water boils 162 degrees higher than hydrogen sulfide, and hydrogen fluoride boils 104 degrees higher than hydrogen chloride. The reason for these abnormal boiling points for the hydrides of nitrogen, oxygen, and fluorine is related to a unique kind of interatomic attraction. A hydrogen atom, even though already bonded, as in water, is able to take part in another, weaker bond toward an electron pair that is not otherwise utilized in bond formation. For water this means that a hydrogen atom of one molecule forms such a bond with the oxygen of another molecule:

$$\ddot{:}\text{O}-\text{H}--------:\overset{\overset{\textstyle H}{|}}{\text{O}}-\text{H}$$
$$|$$
$$H$$

The bond shown as (------------) is primarily electrostatic in origin. It is called a *hydrogen bond*, and although its strength is only a small fraction of a normal covalent bond, it is sufficient to make more difficult the separation of water molecules, which occurs in the phase transition from liquid to gas. This process of evaporation consequently requires a higher temperature (a greater energy input) than is the case for a substance such as hydrogen sulfide in which hydrogen bonding is less important. Hydrogen bonding often contributes to properties such as boiling point, hardness, and mechanical strength. In hydrogen fluoride, hydrogen bonding is so strong that it persists in the vapor state, giving rise to molecules such as H—F ------------H—F, and even longer chains. For this reason, measurements of vapor density on hydrogen fluoride lead to apparent molecular weights two or more times the expected value, 20, for the simple molecule HF.

Table 19.1 gave the distances between centers of several homopolar molecules, and the covalent radius of hydrogen was stated in Sec. 17.5 to be about 0.28 Å. We may therefore calculate the length of the bond in a few hydrides. Our choice will be of molecules reasonably free from complications, such as multiple bonds, and especially of situations such as encountered in diborane. The hydrogen halides will serve this purpose. Taking, for instance, one-half the distance between chlorine atoms in Cl_2, as obtained from electron diffraction studies, we find the covalent radius of chlorine atoms in combinations to be 1.0 Å. Adding to this the covalent radius of hydrogen in compounds, we obtain 1.28 Å for the calculated interatomic distance in HCl. The length found from spectroscopic studies in 1.26 Å. The slight difference found may be related to the partially ionic character of the bond in HCl. Similar results are found with many other compounds, the deviations generally being explainable in terms of electrovalent effects or sometimes by hydrogen bonding.

In Sec. 8.6 it was stated that a chemical bond that includes both covalent and electrovalent character simultaneously is called a *polar* bond. We shall examine this situation more thoroughly. In molecular chlorine the two atoms are bonded by covalence and, since the atoms are the same, the electron pair bond is shared equally by the two atoms. The same is true of molecular hydrogen. Such bonds are often said to be *homopolar*. But hydrogen chloride is an example of a molecule in which the one atom is able, because of its larger nuclear charge, to attract the electron pair more closely than is the other atom. The electrons are drawn a little more closely to the chlorine than they are to the hydrogen. Another way of stating this is to say that the *average* center of positive electricity does not exactly coincide with that of negative electricity in this molecule, although the centers do coincide in both molecular chlorine and in molecular hydrogen. The bond between atoms such as hydrogen and chlorine is often called a *heteropolar bond,* and the molecule itself is said to be *polar*. While the bonding in molecular hydrides is essentially covalent, it always has some ionic character.

It is possible to determine the polarity of a chemical bond. This is done with the aid of a dielectric constant measurement, as mentioned in Sec. 13.1. The details of this determination need not concern us; it will suffice to say that under the influence of an electric charge, as shown in Fig. 22.2, polar molecules tend to become oriented. This tendency leads to an increased dielectric constant, which is, however, diminished as the temperature is raised and molecular collisions tend to

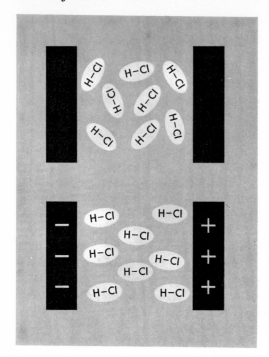

Fig. 22.2 *Upper, random orientation of hydrogen chloride molecules before application of electric charge to the plates. Lower, directed orientation of molecules after application of charge to plates. A substance showing this effect is said to be "polar." Owing to thermal agitation the actual number of molecules oriented at any one instant may be quite small.*

orient the molecules at random. These effects do not occur for nonpolar molecules such as molecular chlorine. The polarity of a molecule may be expressed as the dipole moment. The *dipole moment* is the product of the charge times the distance between the *average* centers of positive and negative electricity. If ζ is the charge and d is the distance between *average* charges, then the dipole moment, μ, is given by

$$\mu = \zeta d$$

The electronic charge, expressed in electrostatic units, is about 5×10^{-10} esu, and many molecules are about 10^{-8} cm long. Dipole moments are expressed in debye units, named after the developer of this branch of science, P. Debye. One debye unit is 10^{-18} esu cm.

The dipole moment of hydrogen chloride is 1.03 debyes, and this indicates a small but definite charge separation. Hydrogen chloride is definitely a polar molecule. Hydrogen bromide and hydrogen iodide have smaller dipole moments, and this must mean that, other things being equal, larger atoms have less attraction for electrons than do the smaller ones; they have lower electronegativities (Sec. 8.6), and the bonds they form tend to be more nearly true covalent bonds.

A bond between two different atoms has, invariably, some polarity; but this does not mean that a molecule containing such bonds is necessarily polar. For example, both methane and silane have zero dipole moment, although the C—H bond and the Si—H bond must certainly be heteropolar. The reason the molecules CH_4 and SiH_4 have zero moments is that the hydrogen atoms are arranged symmetrically around the central atom as if at the corners of a tetrahedron, shown in Fig. 22.3. The moment associated with each bond is just compensated by those of the other three bonds. By contrast, both water and ammonia show dipole moments. This eliminates the linear arrangement H—O—H for water, and it eliminates the symmetrical arrangement of the three hydrogens in a plane around the nitrogen of ammonia. Structures that are consistent with the dipole moments are angular for water and pyramidal for ammonia as shown below:

$$\text{H}-\overset{\cdot\cdot}{\underset{|}{\text{O}}}\text{:} \qquad \text{H}\diagdown\overset{\cdot\cdot}{\underset{|}{\text{N}}}\diagup\text{H}$$
$$\text{H} \qquad\qquad \text{H}$$

In addition to the complications related to polarity in many covalent hydrides, there is a further complication, shown by diborane and a few related compounds. Examination of the electron distribution in diborane shows that each of the 2 boron atoms supplies 3 valency electrons, and each of the 6 hydrogen atoms supplies 1. This gives 12 valency electrons, but examination of possible arrengements shows that a reasonable expectation would require 6 B—H bonds and 1 B—B bond. This would require 14 valency electrons, but only 12 are available.

Compounds such as diborane are called *electron-deficient* compounds. The current view concerning their structure is that two of the

Fig. 22.3 *Three ways of representing the methane molecule. The model at the left shows the arrangement of the four hydrogens symmetrically about the carbon atom, as at the corners of a tetrahedron. The model in the center shows a more appropriate relation between the sizes of the atoms and the distances between them. The reason that the methane molecule has zero dipole moment is due to the symmetrical arrangement of the hydrogens about the carbon.*

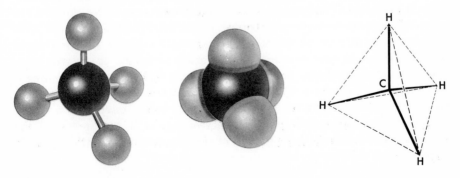

hydrogen atoms act to form "bridges" between the boron atoms. A representation widely accepted is as follows:

$$\begin{array}{ccccc}
H & & H & & H \\
 & \diagdown & & \diagdown & \\
 & B & & B & \\
 & \diagup & & \diagup & \\
H & & H & & H
\end{array}$$

It is to be noted that the molecule borine, BH_3, is unknown.

22.6 *Molecular Hydrides, Chemical Properties*

The molecular hydrides show many varied chemical properties. Some, such as hydrogen fluoride, are so active that they attack glass; some, such as methane, are so comparatively inactive that the class of compounds to which methane belongs is called paraffins (from the Latin, meaning "slight affinity"). Some, such as hydrogen chloride, react with water to form strong acids; some such as ammonia, react with water to form weak bases. But in spite of this diversity, we shall find certain broad generalizations in the kinds of reactions that the covalent hydrides undergo. For instance, they all undergo dissociation to the elements although, in a few cases, this dissociation is not reversible. They also all undergo reactions of oxidation. And, with a few exceptions they have the ability to add more hydrogen, although the manner in which this is done leads to quite diverse results. Our attention in this section will be concentrated on these three classes of chemical reactions.

It was pointed out earlier that almost all binary compounds of hydrogen may be prepared by direct synthesis from the elements, although this method is not always the most convenient. The reaction of dissociation is, of course, merely the reverse of synthesis. The conditions under which most molecular hydrides dissociate to the elements will be reviewed because this gives some idea concerning the stability of the molecule and the strengths of the chemical bonds involved. In this connection one should distinguish between rate of decomposition and the equilibrium involved. A hydride such as diborane is actually unstable at room temperature, but it may be heated fairly strongly without suffering rapid decomposition. As the temperature is raised, diborane is in part converted to other hydrides such as tetraborane, C_4H_{10}. But it requires a temperature approaching 700° C before decomposition is rapid and complete. By contrast, ammonia at room temperature is essentially a stable compound, but at a few hundred degrees, under 1 atm pressure, the equilibrium is so far in the direction of decomposition that little ammonia is present.

Methane is an unusually stable compound. Above about 900° C, it decomposes to carbon and hydrogen:

$$CH_4 \rightarrow C + 2H_2$$

but the controlled thermal decomposition of higher hydrocarbons of the general formula C_nH_{2n+2} yields molecules of lower molecular weight by the process known as "cracking." This is a process of major importance in the production of motor fuels from petroleum. Carried further, the process yields carbon black, which is also an important article of commerce. The hydrides of silicon, of which silane is the simplest, are less stable than their carbon analogs. All decompose above 500° C. This is a general rule that the hydrides become less stable as one goes down any group in the Periodic Table. Thus, phosphine is less stable than ammonia, and arsine, AsH_3, is still less so. Hydrogen iodide is much less stable to decomposition than is hydrogen fluoride.

Both water and hydrogen fluoride are examples of very stable binary compounds of hydrogen, but hydrogen iodide is easily decomposed at room temperature. It will be recalled (Sec. 17.4) that the energy of the H—H bond is 103 kcal/mole. For purposes of comparison it will be most convenient if the corresponding single bond energies are listed for the several molecular hydrides discussed. This is done in Table 22.4.

It must be recognized that the energy given is that necessary to separate, say, H from Cl in the compound HCl. If there are two or more hydrogen atoms in the molecule (as, for instance, in water), then the bond energy given is the average energy required to remove one hydrogen and then the other. Furthermore, it will be clear that dissociation of hydrogen bromide, for example, does not yield atoms of hydrogen and of bromine (except at extremely high temperatures). Hence the total energy for the reaction

$$2HBr \rightarrow H_2 + Br_2$$

TABLE **22.4** SINGLE-BOND ENERGIES FOR SOME COVALENT HYDRIDES

Bond	kcal/mole	Bond	kcal/mole
C—H	99	S—H	81
Si—H	70	H—F	135
N—H	93	H—Cl	103
P—H	76	H—Br	88
As—H	59	H—I	71
O—H	110		

is the energy required to break the two H—Br bonds, minus the energy recovered in the formation of the H—H and the Br—Br bonds. For hydrogen bromide the net energy would be $(2 \times 88) - 103 - 46 = 27$ kcal.

In spite of these complications, it will be found that single-bond energy values are very useful. We shall have reference to them again.

The second general type of reaction undergone by molecular hydrides is oxidation. All hydrides undergo oxidation, but the products may include the free element or they may include one or more oxides, depending on the experimental conditions. With one or two exceptions, we shall limit our discussion to the reactions with oxygen as oxidizing agent.

Water does not normally react with oxygen, although there is some evidence that, under special conditions, some oxidation to hydrogen peroxide may be possible. The reverse reaction,

$$2H_2O_2 \rightarrow 2H_2O + O_2$$

is rapid and complete under the influence of a catalyst. Water may, however, be oxidized by fluorine to yield oxygen and hydrogen fluoride:

$$2H_2O + 2F_2 \rightarrow O_2 + 4HF$$

Similar reactions yielding the free element are given by methane, ammonia, hydrogen sulfide, hydrogen chloride, hydrogen bromide, and hydrogen iodide:

$$CH_4(\text{excess}) + O_2 \rightarrow C + H_2O$$
$$4NH_3 + 3O_2 \rightarrow 2N_2 + 6H_2O$$
$$2H_2S(\text{excess}) + O_2 \rightarrow 2S + 2H_2O$$
$$4HCl + O_2 \rightarrow 2Cl_2 + 2H_2O \qquad \text{(same for HBr and HI)}$$

Of these reactions, the burning of hydrocarbons in restricted access to air has already been mentioned as a method for manufacturing carbon black. The formation of free chlorine by air oxidation of hydrogen chloride under the influence of cuprous chloride catalyst is the obsolete Deacon process for manufacturing chlorine. Hydrogen fluoride may also react to yield free fluorine by an analogous reaction, but only under the influence of electrolytic oxidation.

In the presence of an appropriate catalyst and excess oxygen, several of the reactions given will go on to yield an oxide. This is true of methane, which may yield carbon monoxide or dioxide;

$$2CH_4 + 3O_2 \rightarrow 2CO + 4H_2O$$
$$CH_4 + 2O_2 \rightarrow CO_2 + 2H_2O$$

the latter being the principal reaction in the burning of natural gas.

Similarly, ammonia in the presence of excess oxygen and a platinum catalyst will yield nitric oxide by the Ostwald process:

$$4NH_3 + 5O_2 \rightarrow 4NO + 6H_2O$$

this being a step in the manufacture of nitric acid. Hydrogen sulfide will similarly yield an oxide if burned in excess air:

$$2H_2S + 3O_2(\text{excess}) \rightarrow 2SO_2 + 2H_2O$$

Some elements are, however, so active that oxidation of their hydrides always yields an oxide. In this class fall diborane, silane, and phosphine:

$$B_2H_6 + 3O_2 \rightarrow B_2O_3 + 3H_2O$$
$$SiH_4 + 2O_2 \rightarrow SiO_2 + 2H_2O$$
$$2PH_3 + 3O_2 \rightarrow P_2O_3 + 3H_2O$$
$$2PH_3 + 4O_2(\text{excess}) \rightarrow P_2O_5 + 3H_2O$$

Phosphine often ignites spontaneously in air, possibly owing to the presence of impurities.

The third and last class of reaction to be considered in this section is the ability of molecular hydrides to combine with more hydrogen. This reaction (or better, this series of reactions) is responsible for many of the uniquely useful properties of these compounds. The reactions occur for all covalent hydrides except those of Group IV elements in the Periodic Table.[1]

Some of the molecular hydrides add more hydrogen by accepting a hydride ion H^-. Other covalent hydrides add hydrogen by accepting a proton H^+. Those that accept a hydride ion are compounds that have an unoccupied valence orbital (energy level). Those that accept a proton have an orbital that is occupied by an electron pair, but these electrons are not used in bond formation until the proton is accepted.

The processes involved will be described with reference to diborane and to ammonia. Diborane has the formula B_2H_6, but it often reacts chemically as if it were BH_3. An electron dot formula for BH_3

$$
\begin{array}{c}
H \\
\overset{\cdot\cdot}{B}:H \\
\overset{\cdot\cdot}{H}
\end{array}
$$

would show a vacant orbital capable of accepting two more electrons. If

---

[1] There are exceptions to this exception. For instance, ethylene, C_2H_4, adds hydrogen to become ethane, C_2H_6. But this is a rather different kind of phenomenon, and we shall not describe it in detail here.

diborane is passed into an ether solution of lithium hydride, the reaction that occurs yields lithium borohydride, $LiBH_4$:

$$2LiH + B_2H_6 \rightarrow 2LiBH_4$$

The borohydrides are saltlike substances. The crystal structure of solid sodium borohydride is face-centered cubic, and it consists of Na^+ ions and borohydride, BH_4^-, ions; $LiBH_4$ is approximately the same. The borohydride ion has the structure

$$\left[\begin{array}{c} H \\ H:\overset{..}{\underset{..}{B}}:H \\ H \end{array} \right]^-$$

and what has happened is that the two electrons in the hydride ion have occupied the vacant orbital in the (hypothetical) BH_3 molecule, forming a fourth boron-hydrogen bond:

$$BH_3 + H^- \rightarrow BH_4^-$$

This fourth group carries a negative charge because there is now one more negative electron than the combined positive charges on the five nuclei present.

The kind of reaction illustrated for boron hydride occurs for hydrides of other Group III elements; lithium aluminum hydride, $LiAlH_4$, being a well-known and useful compound. The type of reaction described here may be thought of as a neutralization of a Lewis acid (Sec. 13.4) by a Lewis base; the acid in this case being the hypothetical BH_3, or $\langle AlH_3 \rangle_\infty$, and the base being the H^- ion. Analogous reaction occurs for the Lewis acid BF_3 and the Lewis base F^-, with the formation of the tetrafluoroborate ion BF_4^-.

By contrast, the ammonia molecule has a "lone" pair of electrons,

$$\begin{array}{c} H \\ :\overset{..}{N}:H \\ H \end{array}$$

and as already indicated (Sec. 22.5), this and similar molecules are able to accept positive ions, of which H^+ is the simplest example;

$$NH_3 + H^+ \rightleftharpoons NH_4^+$$

with formation of the ammonium ion NH_4^+. This ion, in turn, is able to unite electrovalently with negative ions to form salts, of which ammonium chloride, NH_4Cl, is a familiar example. The ammonium ion has approximately the same radius as the potassium ion. It is therefore not surprising that ammonium salts bear considerable superficial resemblance to the corresponding salts of the alkali metals sodium, potassium, and rubidium.

A similar reaction occurs for the phosphorus hydride, phosphine, but whereas ammonium ion in its compounds is fairly stable, phosphonium ion, PH_4^+, is less so:

$$PH_3 + H^+ \rightarrow PH_4^+$$

Phosphonium iodide, PH_4I, is one of the few relatively simple phosphonium compounds known.

Reactions very similar to that of ammonia with protons occur for the covalent hydrides of Group VI and VII. The reactions for water, and for hydrogen fluoride,

$$H_2O + H^+ \rightleftharpoons H_3O^+ \quad \text{(hydronium)}$$
$$HF + H^+ \rightleftharpoons H_2F^+ \quad \text{(no name)}$$

have already been described in connection with the general properties of acids and solvents (Sec. 13.2). Hydrogen chloride and the other hydrogen halides enter into similar reactions, as does hydrogen sulfide, but the stability of the positive ion formed is less in these cases.

It will be noted that these reactions may be described as the neutralization of a Lewis base (for example, NH_3) by a Lewis acid H^+. Analogous reactions may occur between the covalent hydrides of Groups V, VI, and VII and positive ions other than that of hydrogen. For instance, ammonia unites to form a complex ion with silver ion:

$$2NH_3 + Ag^+ \rightarrow Ag(NH_3)_2^+$$

and this may, similarly, be regarded as the neutralization of a Lewis base by a Lewis acid. Water also similarly unites with many positive ions and with neutral molecules to form substances called *hydrates*, of which barium chloride hydrate, $BaCl_2 \cdot 2H_2O$, is a familiar example. While not all hydrate formations may be considered as neutralization, the process is often so interpreted.

It should now be clear why the simple hydrides of Group IV, such as methane and silane, do not enter into these reactions by which hydrogen is added (see, however, footnote on page 389). These hydride molecules have no vacant orbitals and no "lone pair" of electrons. They are therefore incapable of entering a reaction unless one or more of the hydrogen atoms already present is removed or exchanged.

The reader will probably have the following two questions in mind: First, why does ammonia in water give a basic reaction, and hydrogen fluoride an acid reaction? The answer is that we are speaking here of Brönsted acidity and basicity, in which water plays an essential part. Ammonia in water gives a basic reaction because ammonia is a stronger base than is water. Ammonia is therefore able to remove a proton from water, leaving the hydroxide ion in solution, although at a rather low equilibrium concentration:

$$NH_3 + H_2O \rightleftharpoons NH_4^+ + OH^-$$

Note that the ammonium ion is not a base in any sense; the ammonium ion is actually a weak Brönsted acid.

The case of hydrogen fluoride is a contrast to ammonia. Water is a stronger Brönsted base than is hydrogen fluoride. The water molecule is therefore able to take a proton from hydrogen fluoride, forming the strong acid H_3O^+, although only at moderate equilibrium concentration:

$$HF + H_2O \rightleftharpoons F^- + H_3O^+$$

The second question is this: Why is hydrofluoric (a dangerously corrosive substance able to dissolve glass) only a moderately weak acid, whereas hydrochloric is a strong acid? The answer to this question lies in the strength of the H—F bond, which (see Table 22.4) is considerably stronger than that for H—Cl. The fluorine holds the hydrogen more tightly, the reason for this being possibly related to the strong electronegative character of the fluorine as shown by the high dipole moment. Hydrogen bonding probably also contributes to the failure of this molecule to form a strong acid in water.

EXERCISES

1. Name the three classes of hydrides, give an example of each, and explain how these classes differ in terms of molecular structure.
2. Suggest methods for the preparation of the hydrides of potassium, magnesium, and europium. Give equations.
3. For a saltlike hydride in the sodium chloride crystal lattice structure, give the coordination numbers of (a) metal ions with respect to hydride ions and (b) hydride ions with respect to metal ions.
4. Write equations for the reaction of calcium hydride (a) burning in air and (b) with water.
5. Interstitial hydrides may often be made by making the metal the cathode in an electrolytic cell and literally electrolyzing hydrogen into the metal. Show, with a diagram, how this could be done. State a possible composition of the electrolyte.
6. Molecular hydrides are often called covalent hydrides. What is the basis for this?

7. Write equations for the preparation of HF, HI, H_2Te, AsH_3, GeH_4, and B_2H_6.

8. Describe the Haber process for the synthesis of ammonia, with particular reference to considerations of reaction velocity and equilibrium.

9. Concentrated sulfuric acid may be used for the displacement of HF. What reactions may be expected from attempts to prepare the following by a similar reaction: H_2O, H_2S, HCl, HI, NH_3?

10. Several hydrides, as of lead and antimony, may be made by reacting atomic hydrogen with the metal. Suggest an experimental arrangement for this kind of reaction.

11. Calcium sulfide dropped into water gives a strong smell of hydrogen sulfide. What kind of reaction is this, and why should it occur?

12. All the molecular hydrides have certain properties in common. Name them.

13. Why is the dipole moment of HI so much smaller than that of HF?

14. Hydrazine has a high dipole moment (1.83 debyes). Suggest a structure for the hydrazine molecule.

15. Methane has zero dipole moment, but the C—H bond could certainly not be homopolar. What is the explanation?

16. Diborane is diamagnetic. What possible electron structure is thereby eliminated from consideration?

17. Write equations for the preparation of: $LiBH_4$, $LiAlH_4$, $In(AlH_4)_3$.

18. Saltlike hydrides have a higher density, interstitials a lower density, than the metals from which they are made. Is it possible to say anything about the densities of the molecular hydrides?

19. Complete the following equations:

$HF + H^+ \rightarrow$

$PH_3 + H^+ \rightarrow$

$C_2H_6 + O_2(\text{excess}) \rightarrow$

$LiH + H^- \rightarrow$

$CH_4 + H^+ \rightarrow$

$NH_3 + H_2 \rightarrow$

$NH_3 + H^- \rightarrow$

$H_2Se + O_2(\text{excess}) \rightarrow$

$H_2Te + \text{heat} \rightarrow$

20. Select several hydrides that exhibit self-ionization (autoprotolysis) and write the equations.

21. Diborane reacts with cold water to yield boric acid, H_3BO_3, plus hydrogen. Write an equation for this reaction.

22. Find the heat associated with the reactions

$$2HCl \rightarrow H_2 + Cl_2$$

and

$$2HI \rightarrow H_2 + I_2$$

23. Point out any obvious relation between single-bond energies for the H—X bond in molecular hydrides and the electronegativity scale (Sec. 8.6).

24. Which would be the more efficient method of transporting hydrogen in liters of H_2 per gram of reagent (a) as LiH, and (b) as NH_3? Assume water is available.

25. A $0.001M$ solution of hydrazoic acid has a pH of 3.85. Calculate the ionization constant.

26. The dissociation of HI is a second-order reaction. Write an expression for the rate law for this reaction.

23

Metal Oxides and
Related Compounds

23.1 Oxides and Oxidation States

The oxides of the chemical elements include the most important of all chemical compounds. Oxides range in structure and valence type from the essentially ionic compounds of the more electropositive metals to the covalent, molecular oxides of the nonmetals. We shall find that the term *oxide*, like *hydride*, is loosely used in several different senses in chemistry. This chapter will be concerned with ionic oxides of the metals other than transition metals. This affords an opportunity to present several basic principles of compound formation and structure, and to do so without encountering the complexities (presented in Chapter 24) to be found when we examine the compounds of the more numerous transition metals.

All the relatively simple ionic oxides to be described here contain the oxide ion O^{2-}, and with almost no exceptions they do not contain any particulate molecule. The compounds to be described in detail are the oxides of magnesium, calcium, aluminum, and zinc, with briefer reference to the oxides of the alkali metals and to those of mercury, thallium, tin, lead, antimony, and bismuth.

It will be recalled (Table 6.3) that all the valence shells of the nontransition metals contain a number of electrons corresponding to the Periodic Table group in which the element is situated. Thus the alkali

TABLE 23.1 PRINCIPAL OXIDES OF THE METALS, OTHER THAN TRANSITION METALS. *

IA	IIA	IIIB	IVB	VB	VIB	VIIB	VIII	VIII	VIII	IB	IIB	IIIA	IVA	VA	VIA	VIIA	0
Li_2O	BeO																
Na_2O	MgO											Al_2O_3					
K_2O	CaO	Sc_2O_3									ZnO	Ga_2O_3					
Rb_2O	SrO	Y_2O_3									CdO	In_2O_3	SnO, SnO_2	Sb_2O_3			
Cs_2O	BaO	La_2O_3*									HgO	Tl_2O, Tl_2O_3	PbO, Pb_3O_4, PbO_2	Bi_2O_3			
Fr_2O	RaO	Ac_2O_3**															

* Many authorities consider scandium and the other Group IIIA elements to be transition metals. These, including the lanthanides (La_2O_3*) and the actinides (Ac_2O_3**) will be described in Chapter 24.

metals such as sodium and potassium are all characterized by one valence electron; the alkaline earth elements such as calcium are all characterized by two such electrons. For all these elements, the formation of an ion is simply a matter of losing *all* the valence electrons, as a consequence of which we find that the ions formed by all these elements are readily predictable, typical examples being Na^+, Ca^{2+}, Al^{3+}, and Sn^{4+}. Writing the formulas of the oxides of these metals is therefore a very simple matter. The oxides of the metals mentioned are Na_2O, CaO, Al_2O_3, and SnO_2. Most of the oxides known for the nontransition metals are shown in Table 23.1, and it will be noted that the only complexities occur toward the bottom of Groups IV and V. These complexities will be described in Sec. 23.3.

23.2   Introduction to Crystal Structure

All the oxides to be considered in this chapter are solids at room temperature, and some have very high melting points indeed. We shall therefore take the opportunity to review some principles of crystal structure (Sec. 4.5), and to present some examples of the arrangement of ions in relatively simple solids in which the valence forces are primarily electrovalent. Most of the oxides to be discussed fall into this class.

It will be recalled that x-ray diffraction studies yield the distance between successive planes of atoms in solids (Sec. 4.4), and that this circumstance makes it possible to learn the arrangement of atoms in many solids. In the cases of metals (Sec. 18.5) it is possible to assign numbers representing the radii of the atoms, and these are known as metallic radii.

The method of x-ray diffraction may be applied to any solid, regardless of the kind of valence bonds present. It has, for instance, already been shown (Sec. 4.5) that sodium chloride crystals consist of assemblies in which each chloride ion is surrounded by six sodium ions, and each sodium by six chlorides. It is a comparatively simple matter to determine by x-ray diffraction the distance between the centers of two adjacent ions of opposite charge, such as Na^+ and Cl^-. But here a difficulty is encountered. In setting up tables of metallic radii, or of covalent radii, it was sufficient to take half the interatomic distance. This was reasonable because the atoms in combination were the same. But in ionic solids the ions in combination are of opposite charge. The problem is to divide the interionic distance between positive and negative ions. It is obvious that even though, for example, Na^+ and F^- have the same number of electrons (they are isoelectronic), the positive ion will tend to draw in its remaining electrons, while the negative ion will permit them to expand.

A possible method to divide the interionic distance is to assume that the respective radii are inversely proportional to the nuclear charges. Thus,

$$\frac{R_{Na}}{R_F} = \frac{Z_F}{Z_{Na}}$$

where R is the radius and Z the atomic number. But this procedure is obviously not completely satisfactory because the inner electrons present in each ion tend to screen the outermost electrons from the positive charge on the nucleus. In view of this, the nuclear charge should be corrected by a "screening constant" S, so that a more acceptable division of the interionic distance would be to write

$$\frac{R_{Na}}{R_F} = \frac{(Z_F - S)}{(Z_{Na} - S)}$$

where S is the screening constant. Actually, this procedure is not quite so arbitrary as it may seem, and methods are available for estimating the screening constants. In the preceding case, $R_{Na}/R_F = 4.5/6.5$, and as the interionic distance in sodium fluoride is 2.31 Å, we have $R_{Na} + R_F = 2.31$ Å. We may then solve for R_{Na} as follows:

$$R_{Na} + \left(\frac{6.5}{4.5}\right) R_{Na} = 2.31 \text{ Å}$$
$$R_{Na} = 0.95 \text{ Å}$$

The radii determined in this way vary somewhat, depending on the particular compound and on the coordination; but tables of ionic radii are certainly useful. Table 23.2 gives *ionic radii* for many of the common elements.

Table 23.2 completes the presentation of the several kinds of atomic radii, namely, van der Waals, metallic, covalent, and ionic. Each has its uses. It will be noted that a positive ion is always smaller than the neutral atom of the same element. For instance, the metallic radius of lithium is 1.52 Å and the ionic radius of Li^+ is 0.68 Å. The radius of a negative ion is always larger than the covalent radius of the same atom. For instance, the ionic radius of Cl^- is 1.81 Å and the covalent radius of chlorine is 0.99 Å.

A typical arrangement of the ions in a metal oxide is shown by magnesium oxide, MgO. The structure of this compound is the same as that of sodium chloride and it is often said to have the "sodium chloride" structure. Each magnesium ion is surrounded by six oxide ions, and each oxide ion by six magnesiums. There is no individual molecule recognizable in this substance. The sodium chloride structure is also assumed by the following oxides: CaO, SrO, BaO, CdO, VO, TiO, NbO, FeO, CoO, NiO, and MnO. It is one of the commoner arrangements of ions in a crystal

TABLE 23.2   IONIC RADII*

Element	Ion	Radius, Å
Aluminum	Al^{3+}	0.45
Beryllium	Be^{2+}	0.30
Bismuth	Bi^{3+}	1.16
Bromine	Br^-	1.95
Calcium	Ca^{2+}	0.94
Cesium	Cs^+	1.67
Chlorine	Cl^-	1.81
Chromium	Cr^{3+}	0.55
Copper	Cu^{2+}	0.69
Fluorine	F^-	1.33
Hydrogen	H^-	1.54
Iodine	I^-	2.19
Lead	Pb^{2+}	1.17
Lithium	Li^+	0.68
Magnesium	Mg^{2+}	0.65
Manganese	Mn^{2+}	0.80
Mercury	Hg^{2+}	1.05
Nickel	Ni^{2+}	0.68
Oxygen	O^{2-}	1.45
Potassium	K^+	1.33
Rubidium	Rb^+	1.48
Sodium	Na^+	0.95
Tin	Sn^{4+}	0.74
Titanium	Ti^{4+}	0.64
Uranium	U^{4+}	0.89
Vanadium	V^{4+}	0.64
Zinc	Zn^{2+}	0.70

*This table gives some approximate ionic radii derived as described in the text. There is no such thing as a "true" ionic radius, but the data given will be helpful.

lattice. If, however, the ratio of the radii of positive and negative ions is very different from that in NaCl, or in MgO, it will be found that the sodium chloride structure is no longer possible, and another structure is assumed by the compound. This occurs in, for instance, beryllium oxide, in which (because of the small size of the Be^{2+} ion) the ratio R_{Be}/R_O is only $0.30/1.45 = 0.21$ instead of $0.65/1.45 = 0.45$, as it is in MgO. The reason why the *radius ratio* is important in determining the structure is mostly a matter of geometry. As shown in Fig. 23.1, the Mg^{2+} ion is large enough to permit six oxide ions to cluster around it, but the smaller Be^{2+} ion permits only four. The fact that NaCl and MgO have the same crystal structure shows that the radius ratio is more important in determining structure than is the actual charge on the ions, which is, of course, 1+ for Na^+ and 2+ for Mg^{2+}. But for this statement to be true, it is necessary that both positive and negative charges in a compound should be the same, even though of opposite sign.

If the charges on positive and negative ions are not the same, the structure may be quite different. This will be illustrated by α-Al_2O_3. (Aluminum oxide has several polymorphic forms; we shall consider only the *alpha* modification.) As the positive charge on an ion increases, the radius becomes much smaller. This is shown by the sequence Na^+, Mg^{2+}, Al^{3+}, in which the radii are 0.95, 0.65, and 0.45 Å, respectively. In Al_2O_3, not only are the Al^{3+} ions very small compared with the O^{2-} ions, but there are one and one-half times as many oxygens as there are aluminums. Under these circumstances, the oxide ions tend to dominate the structure. The oxide ions are arranged in a close-packed array (Sec. 4.5) and thus account for most of the space-filling. The aluminum ions fit into the little holes between groups of six oxide ions, as shown in Fig. 23.2.

Each Al^{3+} has six nearest O^{2-} neighbors, and each O^{2-} has four nearest Al^{3+} neighbors. The structure shown is called the corundum (another name for α-Al_2O_3) structure, and it is assumed by α-Fe_2O_3, Cr_2O_3, Ti_2O_3, V_2O_3, α-Ga_2O_3, Rh_2O_3, and many others. The coordination of the elements M and O in the M_2O_3 corundum structure is given as 6:4, and this is in contrast to 6:6 for NaCl and MgO, and 4:4 for BeO. It may be noted that the ratio of the coordination numbers could not be other than those given, provided the formulas for the compounds are themselves correct. It will also be noted that many oxides (and other inorganic compounds)

Fig. 23.1 *Diagrammatic representation in one plane only, showing how a larger central ion (left) can have more nearest neighbors than a smaller ion (right).*

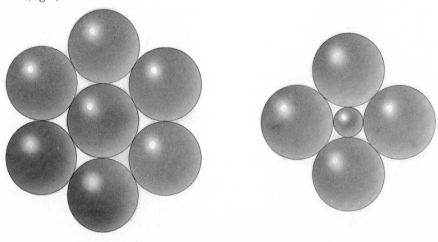

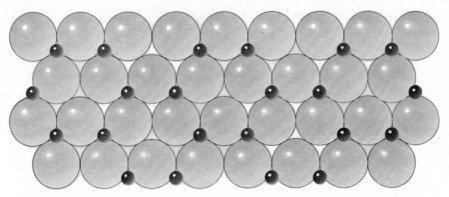

Fig. 23.2 One plane of the alpha-alumina structure, showing a close-packed layer of oxide ions with the smaller aluminum ions filling some but not all of the spaces between the oxides.

have the same crystal structure. Substances such as the pair NaCl and MgO, or substances such as the pair $\alpha\text{-}Al_2O_3$ and $\alpha\text{-}Fe_2O_3$ are said to be *isomorphous* (the word means literally "same shape").

In summary, we may say that the two factors of chief importance in determining the structure of an ionic solid are (1) the *radius ratio* and (2) the *charge ratio*. The absolute values of the radii and the charges are not important in establishing the structure of ionic solids. There are, however, many complications in relation to crystal structure. We shall return to some of these in Chapter 24.

23.3   *Metal Oxides, Preparation and Properties*

Direct synthesis is the most generally useful method for the preparation of metal oxides, and at least one oxide of all but the most noble metals, such as gold and platinum, may be made in this way. Other useful methods include thermal decomposition of the hydroxides or of oxy-salts such as the nitrates or carbonates. Each of these methods will be illustrated by at least one example. In a few cases it is necessary to resort to more complicated reactions in order to obtain specific oxides when two or more are possible, but the preparation of pure, single-phase oxides of exact stoichiometry (true to the formula) is often difficult. Notoriously difficult are FeO and MnO_2. In this section we shall survey the preparation and properties of nine or ten oxides, leaving those of the transition metals to Chapter 24.

We shall start with magnesium oxide, as an important article of commerce and as a relatively uncomplicated case. Magnesium oxide may be made by burning magnesium in oxygen; if air is used, the product is contaminated by magnesium nitride, Mg_3N_2. The union of magnesium with oxygen is highly exothermic, and it is accompanied by a blinding white light:

$$2Mg + O_2 \rightarrow 2MgO + 287 \text{ kcal}$$

Magnesium metal will burn in steam, the products being the oxide plus hydrogen:

$$Mg + H_2O \rightarrow MgO + H_2$$

Magnesium oxide, often called *magnesia*, is also obtained by strong heating of magnesium hydroxide:

$$Mg(OH)_2 \rightarrow MgO + H_2O$$

Magnesia is a white solid, frequently prepared as a soft powder. It has a very high melting point ($2800°$ C). It is used as a refractory and in cements, toothpastes, and toilet preparations.

Calcium oxide may be prepared by burning calcium metal in oxygen, or in air, similar to the preparation of magnesia. More frequently, it is obtained by heating the natural mineral calcium carbonate, $CaCO_3$, which is familiar under the name "limestone":

$$CaCO_3 \rightleftharpoons CaO + CO_2$$

This reaction, which is carried out in furnaces called *lime kilns,* is reversible, and to effect more or less complete conversion of the carbonate to oxide, it is necessary to keep the partial pressure of carbon dioxide low. This may be done by blowing air through the kiln, as shown in Fig. 23.3. The calcium oxide, called *lime* or *quicklime,* is used in making mortar and plaster, as a refractory, and in chemical operations.

Aluminum oxide, or alumina, Al_2O_3, may also be prepared by direct synthesis, the reaction being violently exothermic:

$$4Al + 3O_2 \rightarrow 2Al_2O_3 + 798 \text{ kcal}$$

For use in the preparation of metallic aluminum by the Hall-Héroult electrolytic process, alumina is obtained by heating one or more of the hydroxides or oxide hydrates. The following reaction is an example:

$$2Al(OH)_3 \rightarrow Al_2O_3 + 3H_2O$$

This substance is also a white solid, with a melting point of $2015°$ C. Well-crystallized alumina is the gem stone sapphire.

Sodium oxide, Na_2O, is not a very important compound, and this is true also of the oxides of the other alkali metals. Direct combustion of sodium in air or in oxygen yields mostly sodium peroxide, Na_2O_2, but the

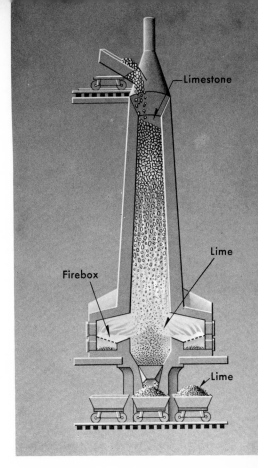

Fig. 23.3 Lime-kiln.

true oxide may be obtained by heating sodium metal under conditions such that there is always present an excess of metal:

$$4Na(\text{excess}) + O_2 \rightarrow 2Na_2O + 200 \text{ kcal}$$

It may be wondered why magnesium and calcium metals burn in oxygen to yield the oxides, whereas sodium and several other alkali metals burn to yield chiefly the peroxides. The peroxide is also formed in part by burning barium metal, so that the charge assumed by the positive ion is not the controlling factor. The reason for peroxide formation in some cases is related to the heat of combustion. It will be recalled that the strength of the oxygen-oxygen bond in O_2 is unusually high. Rupture of this bond does not occur to any great extent during the combustion of sodium unless excess metal (a strong reducing agent) is also present to reduce the peroxide, —O—O—, linkage to two oxide ions, $2O^{2-}$. Magnesium, calcium, and aluminum burn with a substantially higher liberation of heat per mole of oxygen used than do the alkali metals or barium.

We turn now to the oxide of a metal (namely, zinc), which lies just after the end of a transition series (the $3d$) and which, partly because of this position, exhibits some unique properties. Zinc oxide is a white solid (yellow at higher temperatures), which is readily formed by the combustion of zinc metal in oxygen or air; but the reaction is not so strongly exothermic as is the case for the metals discussed before in this section. Zinc oxide may also be made more readily by ignition of the nitrate or other oxy-salt:

$$2Zn(NO_3)_2 \rightarrow 2ZnO + 4NO_2 + O_2$$

If zinc oxide is strongly heated, it undergoes sublimation without decomposition. It is used in making white-walled automobile tires, in medicine, and elsewhere. But this compound has another property that makes it of more than ordinary interest. If zinc oxide, which is normally a poor conductor of electricity, is first heated in vacuum or in hydrogen, the electrical conductivity becomes markedly greater, even when the oxide has been returned to room temperature. But the conductivity decreases again if the oxide is reheated in oxygen. Furthermore, the electrical conductivity is of an unusual type. All metals conduct electricity, and it is found that their conductivity *decreases* with increasing temperature. For zinc oxide that has first been heated in vacuum, it is found that the electrical conductivity *increases* with increasing temperature. A substance of which this is true is said to be a *semiconductor*.

There are many known semiconductors, and some of them have important uses in electronic devices such as transistors. The reason for the existence of semiconductivity may be different in different substances. For zinc oxide, the reason seems to be that during heat treatment in vacuum, or in hydrogen, a very small proportion of the oxygen present as oxide ions is removed, either as gaseous O_2 or as H_2O, as the case may be. But removal of oxide ions, even in trace proportions, means that there will be an excess of positive ion charge in the solid. This is corrected by the reduction of a corresponding number of Zn^{2+} ions to Zn^+, or even to Zn^0. The solid conducts electricity by the movement of electrons in this case, but other semiconducting solids may have different conduction mechanisms. A solid that does not have the accurate stoichiometric balance implied by the formula ZnO, but which might better be represented by a formula such as $ZnO_{0.998}$, is called a *defect solid*. There are various kinds of defect solids; the kind illustrated by zinc oxide is called a *nonstoichiometric* solid. Such solids are frequently found, especially among transition element compounds.

In passing, we shall mention mercuric oxide, HgO, which has an important place in the history of chemistry. This red substance is formed by moderate heating of mercury in air or oxygen. The reaction is slow and reversible. It is quite different from the violently exothermic reactions mentioned before.

All the elements described thus far in this chapter form only one true ionic oxide, although several form other compounds with oxygen, and several (in addition to zinc) form defect solids. But now at the bottom of Groups III and IV in the Periodic Table we encounter elements that form two or more well-characterized oxides. These elements are thallium, tin, and lead. We shall describe the tin and lead oxides in some detail.

Stannic oxide or tin dioxide is a white solid that occurs in nature as the mineral cassiterite. At elevated temperatures, tin burns in excess air or oxygen, forming the dioxide by direct synthesis:

$$Sn + O_2 \rightarrow SnO_2$$

This compound is also formed by dissolving tin metal in concentrated nitric acid, followed by ignition to drive off excess water. The overall equation for this reaction is

$$Sn + 4HNO_3 \rightarrow SnO_2 + 4NO_2 + 2H_2O$$

Stannic oxide may exist in three different crystalline modifications. It is a moderately effective oxidizing agent.

Tin may also form a monoxide, SnO, a black solid generally called stannous oxide. This may be made by first dissolving tin in a nonoxidizing acid such as hydrochloric. Owing to the position of tin in the electromotive series, the tin dissolves, liberating hydrogen:

$$Sn + 2H^+ \rightarrow Sn^{2+} + H_2$$

If now a base is added to the solution, there is formed a precipitate that may contain a variable proportion of water and which is best written $SnO \cdot xH_2O$. This, on heating, yields the black monoxide, SnO, which is a moderately effective reducing agent.

The oxides of lead are somewhat more complicated than are those of tin. If metallic lead is heated in air, it forms the monoxide PbO, which is a yellow or buff-colored solid often called litharge. It is an important article of commerce, widely used in storage batteries, insecticide manufacture, and paints. If litharge is heated in air to about 450° C, it accepts more oxygen and becomes a red solid, Pb_3O_4, known as red lead:

$$6PbO + O_2 \rightarrow 2Pb_3O_4$$

This is the familiar pigment used in the paints on bridges and ship hulls because it is effective in preventing corrosion. Red lead is the first example we have encountered of an oxide in which the metal ions have two different oxidation states, namely, Pb^{2+} and Pb^{4+}. Red lead is not a mixture of PbO and PbO_2; because of its definite composition and crystal structure, it must be considered a true chemical compound.

Lead dioxide, PbO_2, may be prepared by the oxidation of divalent lead with chlorine or sodium hypochlorite in alkaline (basic) solution. For instance, the oxidation of lead monoxide may be represented as follows:

$$PbO + Cl_2 + 2NaOH \rightarrow PbO_2 + 2NaCl + H_2O$$

Lead dioxide is a brown solid, useful as a strong oxidizing agent. As do many compounds rich in oxygen, it decomposes, liberating part of its oxygen when heated:

$$2PbO_2 \rightarrow 2PbO + O_2$$

It will be recalled that lead dioxide is the substance formed on the anode of the lead storage battery during charging.

Various reasons have been advanced to explain the ability of tin and lead (and thallium) to exhibit two different oxidation states, with the result that two different series of compounds (for example, the stannous and the stannic) are formed. We shall encounter in Chapter 24 many examples of such behavior, but the reason for this is that transition metals use the d electrons, or their orbitals, in compound formation. It is virtually certain that d electrons are not involved in the elements considered in this chapter. Inasmuch as no generally acceptable explanation has been offered, we shall be forced to dismiss this phenomenon as a group of unexplained experimental facts.

It remains to mention the oxides of antimony and bismuth. Both elements yield the sesquioxides, Sb_2O_3 and Bi_2O_3, respectively, if they are heated in oxygen. These are white solids. Strong oxidizing agents yield substances, or mixtures, sometimes referred to as Sb_2O_5 and Bi_2O_5, but if these oxides exist, they are not well characterized.

The chemical properties of the metal oxides with which we shall be principally concerned are: the ease of reduction to lower oxide or to metal, as the case may be; reactions with oxides of nonmetals; and the specific reactions of the metal oxides with water. The first property has already been discussed in Chapter 18, in which it was shown that oxides, such as MgO and Al_2O_3, with high heats of formation are very difficult to reduce, whereas those with low heats of formation, such as HgO, will dissociate, liberating the free metal on moderate heat treatment. The reactions of metal oxides with nonmetal oxides will be treated in Chapter 28; and the reactions of metal oxides with water will be discussed in the following section.

23.4   *Hydroxides, Bases, and Amphoterism*

In Chapter 16 it was stated that some, but not all, metal oxides react with water to form bases. It will be recalled (Sec. 13.4) that a base affects indicators in a manner opposite to that of acids, and that bases are able to neutralize acids. This topic will now be amplified.

If sodium oxide, as an example, is placed in water, a vigorous exothermic reaction takes place and the resulting solution is found to be strongly basic. The overall reaction may be written as

$$Na_2O + H_2O \rightarrow 2NaOH$$

and this is supported by the fact that evaporation of the excess water yields pure sodium hydroxide. But the preceding equation does not give a complete picture of the reaction that is essentially the neutralization of a Brönsted (or Lewis) base by a proton. The base is the oxide ion, O^{2-}, which reacts vigorously with water, with the equilibrium going virtually to completion as follows:

$$O^{2-} + H_2O \rightarrow 2OH^-$$

A result of this reaction is that nearly all soluble metal oxides give strongly basic solutions in water. Examples of oxides that react in this way include Li_2O, Na_2O, K_2O, Rb_2O, Cs_2O, CaO, SrO, BaO, RaO, and Tl_2O.

Some metal oxides are not very soluble in water, and when this occurs, it is obvious that the concentration of hydroxide ions cannot rise very high. This is especially true when the hydroxide of the metal is itself insoluble. An example of an oxide that is only slightly soluble in water is magnesia. Crystalline magnesia gives only a slight basic reaction in water, although finely powdered magnesia reacts somewhat more, and when suspended in water, is often used in medicine to neutralize excess gastric acid. In connection with this use, it is called "milk of magnesia."

But some metal oxides present still further complications. Alumina is so nearly insoluble in water that for crystalline α-Al_2O_3, no reaction is perceptible. It is, however, possible to prepare hydroxides of the elements by methods other than merely placing the oxide in water. One may, for instance, prepare aluminum hydroxide by the addition of a strong base such as sodium hydroxide to a solution of, say, $Al_2(SO_4)_3$ containing Al^{3+} ions:

$$Al^{3+} + 3OH^- \rightleftharpoons Al(OH)_3$$

The product is a gelatinous white precipitate that gives no appreciable reaction with water. But if to this aluminum hydroxide there is added some strong acid such as hydrochloric, the acid will be neutralized and the aluminum hydroxide precipitate will disappear. This reaction is a true neutralization, and it suggests that aluminum hydroxide, though insoluble in water, is nevertheless a base:

$$Al(OH)_3 + 3H^+ \rightleftharpoons Al^{3+} + 3H_2O$$

If this were the only reaction of aluminum hydroxide, we might characterize it as a base that owes its weakness to its low solubility in water, but the situation is more complicated. If to aluminum hydroxide there is added a strong base such as sodium hydroxide, it will be found that the base is neutralized and that the aluminum hydroxide precipitate disappears. This reaction is also a true neutralization, and it suggests that aluminum hydroxide is an acid:

$$Al(OH)_3 + OH^- \rightleftharpoons Al(OH)_4^-$$

A hydroxide capable of thus acting either as a base or an acid is said to be *amphoteric*. Many hydroxides fall in this category.

The ability of a hydroxide to act amphoterically appears to be related to the kind of bond formed between the metal and oxygen. A small, highly charged metal ion forms a bond to oxygen with more covalent character and more strength than does a large metal ion of lower charge. Thus barium hydroxide is essentially an ionic compound, the bond between Ba^{2+} or OH^- being electrovalent. But the corresponding bonds in beryllium hydroxide have a substantial covalent character. Similarly, KOH is essentially ionic and $Zn(OH)_2$ is much less so. Let E be any element that forms a hydroxide EOH; then in the presence of water this compound may react in either of two ways:

$$E\!-\!O\!-\!H + H_2O \rightarrow EO^- + H_3O^+ \qquad \text{(acidic reaction)}$$

or

$$E\!-\!O\!-\!H + H_2O \rightarrow EOH_2^+ + OH^- \qquad \text{(basic reaction)}$$

Thus, to take an extreme case, the hydroxide of chlorine, ClOH (hypochlorous acid), gives an acidic reaction because the Cl—O bond is largely covalent, but the hydroxide of thallium, TlOH, gives a basic reaction because the Tl—O bond is essentially ionic. In general the larger, positive ions of low charge yield the electrovalent basic reaction; the smaller, highly charged ions give the more covalent acidic reactions. But this rule is complicated by the relative electronegativities of the elements in question, and of oxygen. The rule is also complicated by the presence of d electrons (or of unfilled d orbitals) among the transition elements. In spite of these complications, the rough rules given will be found useful. Zinc oxide yields an amphoteric reaction, but cadmium and mercury oxides are basic, the Cd^{2+} and Hg^{2+} ions being larger than Zn^{2+}. For the same reason, SnO and PbO tend to give amphoteric reactions, whereas SnO_2 and PbO_2, containing smaller, more highly charged metal atoms, show acidic reactions.

23.5   *Peroxides and Superoxides*

If sodium metal is burned in excess air or oxygen, it is in part converted to sodium peroxide, Na_2O_2. The formula for sodium peroxide is established by the relative proportions of sodium and oxygen present.

Furthermore, if sodium peroxide is added to cold water or to cold dilute acid, there is formed hydrogen peroxide, H_2O_2, which may be identified by its unique properties, to be described below. Peroxides contain pairs of oxygen atoms united by a single bond $[O—O]^{2-}$, and it will be recalled (Sec. 19.6) that the pair of oxygen atoms present in molecular oxygen is not dissociated into single atoms, or ions, unless the heat of formation of the compound is unusually high, as it is for CaO and Al_2O_3. Ionic peroxides are formed by all the alkali metals, although the preparation of lithium peroxide must be indirect. Barium peroxide, BaO_2, is formed readily by direct combustion. The reader may have some difficulty in deciding when a compound (such as BaO_2) is a peroxide and when one (such as PbO_2) is a dioxide. It is sometimes stated that all peroxides are good oxidizing agents, but PbO_2 is also a good oxidizing agent. The true test of a peroxide is the presence of the $[O—O]$ linkage, and in the absence of other evidence such as the formation of hydrogen peroxide on treatment of the compound with water, recourse must be made to x-ray diffraction studies. Just as there are many true oxides that are not ionic solids, so there are many peroxides that are covalent molecules. Peroxosulfuric acid is one of these, but all such compounds are characterized by the —O—O— linkage.

Ionic peroxides, if heated, especially under reduced pressure, will yield part of their oxygen,

$$2BaO_2 \rightleftharpoons 2BaO + O_2$$

becoming true oxides. The reaction shown for barium peroxide was at one time used in the production of oxygen.

The only other general reaction of peroxides that we shall consider here is that with water or dilute acid. It will be recalled that the oxide ion, O^{2-}, is a very strong base and that it reacts with water, or H^+, to yield hydroxide ion, which in turn reacts with H^+ to yield water. Similarly, the peroxide ion is a strong base, which reacts with water or dilute acid to form the hydroperoxide ion, $[O_2H]^-$:

$$O_2^{2-} + H_2O \rightarrow O_2H^- + OH^-$$
$$O_2^{2-} + H^+ \rightarrow O_2H^-$$

The hydroperoxide ion may also react with dilute acid to form hydrogen peroxide:

$$O_2H^- + H^+ \rightarrow H_2O_2$$

This is the basis for formation of hydrogen peroxide when any other peroxide is treated with dilute acid. At one time, hydrogen peroxide was made by treating BaO_2 with dilute sulfuric acid, but this method was later superseded by the hydrolysis of ammonium peroxodisulfate, $(NH_4)_2S_2O_8$.

At the time of writing, H_2O_2 is made chiefly through air oxidation of an organic compound.

The hydrogen peroxide may be purified, as required, by fractional distillation. This process is potentially hazardous. Although no longer considered so dangerous as formerly, it should be remembered that hydrogen peroxide in high concentration is poisonous and that, in contact with the skin, it can produce severe burns. Ordinary "drug store" hydrogen peroxide is a 3 percent solution containing a trace of inhibitor to retard decomposition into oxygen and water.

Hydrogen peroxide may act either as an oxidizing agent or as a reducing agent. It is able to do this because it may react by accepting electrons as follows:

$$H_2O_2 + 2e^- + 2H^+ \rightarrow 2H_2O$$

or it may yield electrons:

$$H_2O_2 \rightarrow 2H^+ + O_2 + 2e^-$$

In the first reaction the H_2O_2 is acting as an oxidizing agent, an example being the oxidation of sulfurous acid:

$$H_2SO_3 + H_2O_2 \rightarrow H_2SO_4 + H_2O$$

In the second reaction the H_2O_2 is acting as a reducing agent, an example being the reduction of silver oxide to metallic silver:

$$Ag_2O + H_2O_2 \rightarrow 2Ag + H_2O + O_2$$

True oxides and peroxides do not exhaust the list of possible metal-oxygen compounds. If sodium metal is burned in excess air or oxygen, a moderate fraction of the product consists of sodium superoxide, NaO_2. This compound, and the corresponding potassium superoxide KO_2, may be made in nearly pure form by reaction of the peroxides with oxygen, the sodium compound being formed under pressure. These compounds are characterized by the high proportion of oxygen present and by the reaction with water to yield hydrogen peroxide and oxygen:

$$2KO_2 + 2H_2O \rightarrow 2KOH + H_2O_2 + O_2$$

Even more convincing is the fact that KO_2 is paramagnetic because of the odd number of electrons present in the superoxide ion O_2^-. It might be thought, by analogy with oxides and peroxides, that superoxides would react with dilute acid to yield a compound HO_2, and there is some evidence that such a substance may exist as an unstable intermediate. A use of superoxides was mentioned in Sec. 19.3.

EXERCISES

1. Write formulas for the more important oxides of the metals other than transition metals.
2. What is the reason that it requires two atoms of sodium to unite with one of oxygen, whereas one atom of calcium unites with one of oxygen, and two of aluminum with three of oxygen?
3. How are ionic radii determined?
4. Name and compare the several kinds of atomic radii, and explain why they differ for a given element.
5. Are there any significant differences to be expected between the radii of isotopes of a given element?
6. Why is it not acceptable to determine ionic radii by halving the interionic distance in a compound?
7. How does the interionic distance in sodium fluoride compare with that in a selected isoelectronic compound?
8. If, in the sodium chloride structure, we ignore the chloride ions, is it possible to recognize any simple structure in the arrangement of sodium ions?
9. If, in many oxide structures, the oxygens are close-packed, how is there any room for the positive ions?
10. Draw diagrams for the sodium chloride and the corundum structures.
11. For isomorphism to occur, is it necessary that the ions in the two or more substances be the same size?
12. List three general methods for the preparation of metal oxides, with an example of each.
13. Write equations for methods that would be worth trying for the preparation of K_2O, SrO, CdO, Ga_2O_3, Tl_2O_3, and Tl_2O.
14. Why does burning sodium in air yield principally sodium peroxide, whereas burning magnesium in air yields magnesium oxide contaminated with magnesium nitride?
15. How does semiconductivity differ from metallic conductivity?
16. Magnesium oxide may exhibit semiconductivity at elevated temperatures, but this is very small and generally attributed to trace impurities. By contrast, semiconducting zinc oxide is very easy to prepare. Suggest a reason for this difference.
17. List those metals that do not belong to a transition series and yet which show two or more oxidation states (in addition to the free metal).
18. Write equations for the preparation of tin and lead in each of their oxidation states, starting with the metal in each case.
19. Why does Na_2O form a strong base in water and MgO a much weaker base?

20. Explain with the use of ionic equations how $Al(OH)_3$ is able to dissolve either in strong acid or in strong base.

21. What determines whether a hydroxide will react as an acid, a base, or amphoterically?

22. A compound has the formula MO_2. How may it be determined if this is (a) an oxide, (b) a peroxide, or (c) a superoxide?

23. Compare the reactions with water of O^{2-}, O_2^{2-}, and O_2^-.

24. Show by equations (and examples) how hydrogen peroxide may react either as an oxidizing or a reducing agent.

25. If PbO_2 contains neither peroxide ions nor superoxide ions, to what may we attribute its strong oxidizing ability?

24

Transition Metal Oxides and Related Compounds

24.1 Preliminary Survey and Preparation Methods

A glance at Table 24.1, which lists only some of the more important and better characterized oxides of the transition elements, gives some hint of the complexities into which we now venture. To the uniquely developed ability of these elements to form compounds in many different oxidation states we must add that, here, the defect state is more the rule than the exception. The oxides of these elements are also able to combine with each other to form new, more complex oxides. In many such cases it becomes difficult to establish the structural relationships between one atom and another or between one series of compounds and another. The transition elements show, in addition, many unusual properties of color, magnetism, catalytic activity, and ability to form so-called coordination compounds, of which potassium ferricyanide, $K_3Fe(CN)_6$, is a relatively simple example. Most of these complexities are related to the presence of partly filled d orbitals in these elements.

Most of the metal oxides presented in Chapter 23 were simple geometrical aggregates of metal ions and oxide ions, held together essentially by electrovalence. A survey of transition metal oxides shows that some of these are likewise relatively simple ionic structures, and we shall continue to refer to these as ionic oxides. But among the transition

TABLE 24.1 SOME OXIDES OF THE TRANSITION ELEMENTS[1]

Sc_2O_3	TiO Ti_2O_3 TiO_2	VO V_2O_3 VO_2 V_2O_5	CrO Cr_2O_3 CrO_2 CrO_3	MnO Mn_2O_3 Mn_3O_4 MnO_2 Mn_2O_7	FeO Fe_3O_4 Fe_2O_3	CoO Co_3O_4 Co_2O_3	NiO NiO_2	Cu_2O CuO
Y_2O_3	ZrO_2	NbO_2 Nb_2O_5	MoO_2 MoO_3	TcO_2 Tc_2O_7	RuO_2 RuO_4	Rh_2O_3	PdO	Ag_2O AgO
La_2O_3*	HfO_2	TaO_2 Ta_2O_5	WO_2 WO_3	ReO_2 ReO_3 Re_2O_7	OsO_2 OsO_4	IrO_2	PtO PtO_2	Au_2O_3
Ac_2O_3**								

[1] The lanthanides, La_2O_3,* and actinides, Ac_2O_3,** are discussed in Sec. 24.6.

metal oxides there are many cases in which two or more different metal atoms are present. One example of this is $MnFe_2O_4$ which is manganese iron spinel and which is sometimes written $MnOFe_2O_3$. Another example is sodium chromate, which is always written Na_2CrO_4. If, as in $MnFe_2O_4$, there is no important contribution of covalency between metal atoms and oxygen, the structure is called a *complex ionic oxide*. But if there is evidence of discrete, essentially covalent, ion formation, such as the chromate CrO_4^{2-} ion in Na_2CrO_4, then the compound is called an *oxy-salt*. Oxy-salts will be discussed in Chapter 28. If the reader finds these distinctions somewhat confusing, it is to be hoped that clarification will come as we present several more examples. This terminology of metal oxides as ionic, complex, or oxy-salt is that advocated by leading authorities in the field. All transition metal oxides are solids with the exception of Mn_2O_7, which is a liquid. Ruthenium tetroxide, RuO_4, and osmium tetroxide, OsO_4, are somewhat volatile at room temperature.

Preparation of transition metal oxides is, as are those of other metal oxides, most conveniently achieved either by direct synthesis or by ignition of a hydroxide or of an oxy-salt. Oxy-salts that are appropriate include the nitrates, carbonates, and oxalates, the object being to choose a salt such that all by-products are gases and so may be driven off. But the large number of oxides formed by most transition metals makes it difficult to obtain any specific oxide in a condition approaching reasonable purity. Our plan will be to prepare each of the several oxides of one element, namely, manganese. Then, with the oxides of manganese as examples, we shall proceed to discuss oxides of other elements.

The oxide of manganese containing the lowest proportion of oxygen is MnO, known as manganous oxide or manganese (mon)oxide. It occurs in nature as the mineral manganosite. Very strong heating of this oxide alone or in the presence of hydrogen does not reduce it to the metal. Consequently, any other oxide of manganese may be converted to MnO by heating it in flowing hydrogen. A simple example is

$$MnO_2 + H_2 \rightarrow MnO + H_2O$$

Alternatively, MnO may be prepared by thermal decomposition of an appropriate oxy-salt. The MnO is readily oxidized by oxygen or by any oxidizing agent. Consequently, thermal decomposition of the nitrate, $Mn(NO_3)_2$, will yield a higher oxide because of the strong oxidizing action of the decomposing nitrate ion. Thermal decomposition of manganous carbonate is satisfactory, provided air is excluded. A solution of manganous nitrate (which is readily available) may be treated with ammonium carbonate. This precipitates manganous carbonate:

$$Mn^{2+} + (NH_4)_2CO_3 \rightarrow MnCO_3 + 2NH_4^+$$

The precipitate is filtered, washed free of ammonium ions and nitrate ions, and then decomposed to MnO by heating it at 500° C under vacuum:

$$MnCO_3 \rightarrow MnO + CO_2$$

All other oxides of manganese, with the exception of Mn_2O_7, represent an intermediate oxidation state or states. They must be prepared therefore, under rather specific conditions if a relatively pure compound is to be obtained. It so happens that Mn_2O_3, manganese sesquioxide, is stable up to about 600° C. If, therefore, an oxy-salt such as the nitrate is heated in air, with the temperature slowly rising to 600° C, it will be found that virtually pure Mn_2O_3 results. A lower ignition temperature may result in a product having too much oxygen; a higher temperature, in one having not enough oxygen. The selection of the proper ignition temperature in a case such as this can be determined only by trial and error:

$$2Mn(NO_3)_2 \rightarrow Mn_2O_3 + 4NO_2 + \tfrac{1}{2}O_2$$

Trimanganese tetroxide, Mn_3O_4, is similar to Mn_2O_3 in that it has an upper stability limit, which in this case is about 1100° C. This compound occurs in nature as the mineral hausmannite. If almost any oxy-salt of manganese is heated in air to about 1000° C, the result is virtually pure Mn_3O_4:

$$3Mn(NO_3)_2 \rightarrow Mn_3O_4 + 6NO + 4O_2$$

It will be noted that the proportion of oxygen in Mn_3O_4 is less than that in Mn_2O_3 The Mn_3O_4 is typical of complex ionic oxides, the manganese being present in two different oxidation states.

When we come to manganese dioxide, MnO_2, which occurs in nature as the mineral pyrolusite, we find the thermal stability diminishing. Manganese dioxide begins to lose oxygen if it is heated over about 200° C; yet, in view of the fairly high oxidation state, it is generally necessary to prepare the compound under oxidizing conditions. This may be done by heating the nitrate at a slowly rising temperature up to 200° C:

$$Mn(NO_3)_2 \rightarrow MnO_2 + 2NO_2$$

It will be clear that many alternative preparations are available for the preparation of all these oxides. It would, for instance, be possible to prepare Mn_2O_3 by heating MnO_2 to 600° C. Direct synthesis from the metal and oxygen is also possible, but careful attention must be paid to experimental conditions if a relatively pure compound is to be obtained.

The highest oxide of manganese, Mn_2O_7, must be regarded as a special case. It is obtained as a dangerously explosive liquid when powdered potassium permanganate is added to concentrated sulfuric acid and the mixture is cooled to −10° C.

The examples given above show that the conversion of a metal to an oxide or mixture of oxides is a simple matter. But the preparation of a reasonably pure sample of any specific transition metal oxide calls for certain specified conditions. These conditions are determined by what higher or lower oxidation states may be produced and by the stability of the desired compound. Thus vanadium pentoxide, V_2O_5, ferric oxide (iron sesquioxide), $Fe_2O_3(\alpha)$, and osmium tetroxide, OsO_4, may be made by heating the metal in oxygen. In each of these cases the metal is in its highest normal oxidation state (although 6+ iron is known), and the compounds themselves are reasonably stable against heat. Other oxides in the same category include cupric oxide, CuO, zirconium dioxide (zirconia, ZrO_2), and molybdenum trioxide, MoO_3.

The following oxides may be made by heating the metal in oxygen under controlled conditions, as indicated: chromium sesquioxide, Cr_2O_3, must be heated in hydrogen to remove CrO_2 and CrO_3; vanadium sesquioxide is similar in this respect; magnetite, Fe_3O_4, may be made in a manner similar to Mn_3O_4; ferrous oxide, FeO, is a special case to be described in the next section.

Ignition of an oxy-salt is appropriate for many oxides. Vanadium pentoxide may be made by heating ammonium vanadate, NH_4VO_3, in excess air, as follows:[1]

$$4NH_4VO_3 + 3O_2 \rightarrow 2V_2O_5 + 8H_2O + 2N_2$$

Similarly, NiO, CoO, and CuO may all be obtained by heating the appropriate nitrate. But chromium trioxide is, like Mn_2O_7, a special case. It may be obtained as a red powder by adding concentrated sulfuric acid to a solution of sodium chromate:

$$Na_2CrO_4 + H_2SO_4(conc) \rightarrow CrO_3 + H_2O + Na_2SO_4$$

One other special method is that for titanium dioxide, which is an important article of commerce. After the removal of other elements from the mineral ilmenite, $FeTiO_3$, the titanium is prepared in the form of titanyl sulfate, $TiOSO_4$, which, on hydrolysis, yields TiO_2. Alternatively, titania may be made by passing the vapor of titanium tetrachloride, $TiCl_4$, through a flame in the presence of excess oxygen.

24.2 Structural Relationships

The principles used for determining ionic radii, described in Chapter 23, apply also to the transition elements. This is true even though the bonds formed by transition elements tend to be somewhat more covalent than in

---

[1] The reader may be confused as to whether heating an ammonium salt or a nitrate yields nitrogen, nitric oxide, or nitrogen dioxide. This depends on the temperature (high temperature favors NO), and the presence of reducing conditions (favors N_2), or of oxidizing conditions (favors NO_2).

TABLE 24.2   IONIC RADII (Å) FOR SOME TRANSITION
METAL IONS*

	Sc^{3+}, 0.83		
	Ti^{3+}, 0.95	Ti^{4+}, 0.64	
	V^{3+}, 0.69	V^{4+}, 0.64	V^{5+}, 0.40
	Cr^{3+}, 0.55		
Mn^{2+}, 0.80	Mn^{3+}, 0.66		
Fe^{2+}, 0.75	Fe^{3+}, 0.53		
Co^{2+}, 0.78			
Ni^{2+}, 0.68			
Cu^{2+}, 0.69			

* The limitations on these data were discussed in Chapter 23.

the case for the more strongly electropositive metals. Table 24.2 gives ionic radii for various transition metal ions in various oxidation states. It will be noted that the rule of decreasing radius with increasing positive charge is always obeyed, and that all positive ions have radii smaller than that of oxide ion (1.45 Å). It will also be noted that, in general, the radii for ions of equivalent charge tend to decrease as the atomic number increases. For instance, the radius of scandium (3+) is 0.83 Å, that of iron (3+) is 0.53 Å. This progressive change is erratic in the $3d$ transition series, but it is very clearly shown in the $4f$ series, namely, the lanthanides. For that reason the effect is known as the *lanthanide contraction*. We shall have more to say about this later.

A large number of the transition metal ions have radii that differ only slightly from each other, and recalling that crystal structure depends primarily on radius ratio and charge ratio (Sec. 23.2), it may be surmised that numerous examples of isomorphism would be found among the compounds of these elements. One might, for instance, look for isomorphism in the series of oxides MnO, FeO, CoO, NiO, and CuO. Furthermore, the radius of each of these ions is close to that of Mg^{2+} (0.65 Å), so that one might expect all these oxides to assume the rock salt structure characteristic of MgO (and of NaCl). Actually, all but one of these oxides is isomorphous, and to the list we might have added the less familiar VO, TiO, and NbO. The exception is CuO, which (possibly because of a somewhat different kind of bonding) has a more complicated structure. Other examples of isomorphism are shown by the sequence Ti_2O_3, V_2O_3, Cr_2O_3, and α-Fe_2O_3, all of which crystallize in the corundum (α-Al_2O_3) structure. Another example is the sequence TiO_2, CrO_2, MnO_2, OsO_2, TcO_2, all of which crystallize in the rutile (TiO_2) structure, or very close to it. The rutile structure, shown in Fig. 24.1, is also adopted by SnO_2.

Transition metal ions form complex oxides, of which the mineral magnetite, Fe_3O_4, is a familiar example. The structure of this and related

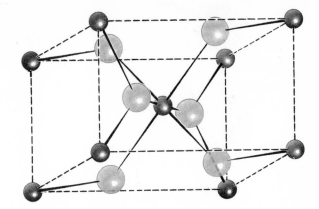

Fig. 24.1 Rutile (TiO_2) crystal structure.

compounds is related to that of corundum, but it involves some further complexities, which will be described in the following discussion.

It will be recalled that the corundum structure is based on a close-packed array of oxide ions, with an appropriate number of the smaller M^{3+} ions distributed in the spaces between groups of six oxygens. If one assembles a model of close-packed spheres, as of golf balls, it will be found that after the first and second layers have been put down, there arises an option as to how the third layer is to be placed. Either each sphere in the *third* layer may be directly over a sphere in the *first* layer or directly over a hole in the *first* layer. This option is illustrated in Fig. 24.2. One may refer to the first arrangement as the *ABABAB* arrangement where *A* and *B* stand for layers. But in the second arrangement, the third layer is not identical with the first; hence the arrangement may

Fig. 24.2 Layers of equal diameter spheres arranged to show the cubic (ABC) packing arrangement, and also the hexagonal (ABA) arrangement.

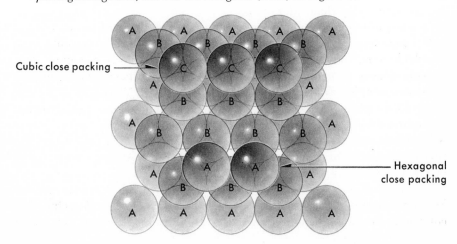

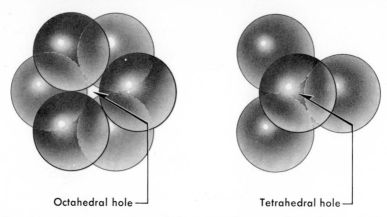

Octahedral hole ⏤   Tetrahedral hole ⏤

*Fig. 24.3 Arrangement of equal diameter spheres to show (left) an octa-
hedral hole between six spheres, and (right) a tetrahedral hole between four
spheres.*

be called *ABCABC*. If one continues to build these two structures according to the plan started, it will be found that the symmetry of *AB* is
hexagonal, while that of *ABC* is cubic. For that reason, the two are referred
to respectively as *hexagonal close-packed* (hcp) or as *cubic close-packed*
(ccp). Cubic close-packed is identical with face-centered cubic (Sec.
4.5). The corundum structure is hexagonal close-packed as far as the
oxide ions are concerned.

Now let us concentrate on the small holes between the groups of
oxide ions. Reference to Fig. 24.3 will show that between the oxide
ions in the corundum (and also in the ccp) structure, there are two kinds
of holes. One of these kinds of holes is formed by four oxygens in a group.
This is called a *tetrahedral hole* because the "hole" has four sides. The
other is formed by six oxygens in a group. This is called an *octahedral
hole* because it has eight sides.

In corundum the aluminum ions occupy two-thirds of the octahedral
holes, but none of the tetrahedral. It is clear that structures could exist
in which some of or all the tetrahedral holes could be occupied. This
actually occurs in many complex oxides, of which the mineral *spinel* is
a good example. This has the formula $MgAl_2O_4$. The oxide ions are
arranged in cubic close-packing, the magnesium ions are in tetrahedral
holes, and the aluminum ions are in the octahedral holes. This structure
is common and is known as the "spinel" structure. The Mg^{2+} may be
replaced by Fe^{2+}, Ni^{2+}, and other (2+) ions, and the Al^{3+} may be replaced
by certain other (3+) ions.

It so happens, however, that in certain complex oxides, all the
M^{2+} ions go into octahedral holes, with half of the M^{3+} ions in octahedral
holes and the other half in tetrahedral holes. Such structures, of which

Fe_3O_4 is one, still have the oxygens arranged in cubic close-packing. They are called *inverse spinels*.

This section will be concluded with a survey of the oxides of iron. These are sufficiently varied as to serve, in themselves, as an introduction to structural inorganic chemistry. The oxide having the lowest atomic proportion of oxygen is ferrous oxide, FeO. This compound is unstable at room temperature, but the rate of decomposition is immeasurably slow until the temperature reaches several hundred degrees, when the following reaction occurs:

$$4FeO \rightleftharpoons Fe + Fe_3O_4$$

Above 570° C, it is possible to obtain a stable composition approaching FeO, but this is always deficient in iron, although at 1000° C it may approach FeO very closely (actually about $Fe_{0.946}O$). Nearly stoichiometric FeO may thus be prepared by heating Fe_2O_3 or Fe_3O_4 in a mixture of hydrogen and steam at 1000° C and then suddenly cooling (quenching) the product, called wüstite, so that the disproportionation reaction (shown above) to form Fe and Fe_3O_4 does not have time to occur. The purpose of the steam is to prevent reduction of the oxide to metallic iron. In this way, ferrous oxide may be prepared, but it is a typical defect solid, always deficient in iron. The reason that ferrous oxide is a nonstoichiometric defect solid is that a small proportion of the Fe^{2+} ions has been replaced by two thirds their number of Fe^{3+} ions.

In ferrous oxide the oxide ions are arranged in cubic close-packed array. If this structure is exposed to oxygen at moderately elevated temperatures, more of the iron becomes Fe^{3+} ions, and oxygen builds onto the structure as additional oxide ions. The Fe^{3+} ions diffuse into the new positions thus made available until, in due course, the composition becomes Fe_3O_4. Here the oxide ions are still cubic close-packed, but the iron ions have the distribution described above for the inverse spinel.

TABLE **24.3** RELATIONSHIPS AND PROPERTIES OF THE OXIDES OF IRON

Common name	Formula	Color	Ferro-magnetic	Structure	O^{2-} ion lattice
Ferrous oxide	FeO	black	no	"NaCl"	ccp
Magnetite	Fe_3O_4	black	yes	inverse spinel	ccp
Gamma ferric oxide	γ-Fe_2O_3	red	yes	defect spinel*	ccp
Alpha ferric oxide, or hematite	α-Fe_2O_3	red	no	corundum*	hcp

* The two forms of ferric oxide constitute an excellent example of structural dimorphism.

If further oxidation is now permitted, the same process continues until all the iron is present as Fe^{3+} ions; hence the formula is Fe_2O_3. But this is not the familiar ferric oxide that has the corundum structure. This is a spinel with the usual cubic close-packed oxide ion lattice, but one in which the M^{2+} ions are missing. The oxide is called *gamma* ferric oxide. If gamma ferric oxide is strongly heated, it undergoes a transition to the familiar alpha ferric oxide. This transition involves a change of the oxide ion lattice from cubic close-packed to hexagonal close-packed. The series of changes is summarized in Table 24.3.

24.3   Physical Properties

The general properties that distinguish the transition metals were mentioned in Sec. 16.5, and those properties were attributed to the presence of partially filled d orbitals. Some of these physical properties, insofar as they apply to oxides, will be discussed more fully in this section. These properties are color, magnetism, and isomorphous replacement. We shall include copper in this discussion because, while copper, silver, and gold do not, as metals, have unpaired d electrons, they may have them in certain oxidation states. This makes these elements closely resemble some of the true transition metals.

Most of the oxides discussed in the preceding two sections are strongly colored. The nonstoichiometric solids are generally black; Cr_2O_3 is green; Fe_2O_3, red-brown; and so forth. Some of these compounds are so stable, and the colors so strong and permanent, that they are used as pigments. Ferric oxide is, for instance, used in rouge and in various red paints. The reason why so many transition oxides are strongly colored, and this applies to most of the compounds of these elements, is that electronic transitions are particularly easy in a partially filled d orbital. The colors arise when electrons are excited from one energy level to a higher by absorption of specific wavelengths of light. Whenever the d orbital is completely emptied of electrons, as in Sc^{3+} or Ti^{4+}, we find that the compound (such as Sc_2O_3 or TiO_2) is colorless (or white, if finely powdered). The same is true of ions such as Zn^{2+}, in which the d orbital is completely filled, as in ZnO.

The magnetic properties of transition elements and their compounds are also related to the partial filling of the d orbital. It will be recalled that a substance containing one or more unpaired electrons is invariably attracted to a magnetic field and is said to be *paramagnetic*. Other substances are weakly repelled by a magnetic field and are said to be *diamagnetic*.

Now let us consider the Fe^{3+} ion. According to Table 6.3, atoms of iron in the free (vapor) state have six 3d *electrons* and two 4s electrons.

When the atom is oxidized to Fe^{3+}, it loses one $3d$ electron and both $4s$ electrons, thus leaving five electrons in the $3d$ orbital. The total capacity of any d orbital is ten electrons. We have, therefore, several possibilities of electron distribution, one of which may be represented as

and another:

the direction of the arrows representing the direction of electron spin. It is found experimentally that, almost always, the second arrangement is adopted (this is known as Hund's rule), and that in any partially filled d or f orbital the number of unpaired electron spins tends to be a maximum. For instance, Sc^{3+} as in Sc_2O_3 is diamagnetic, as is Ti^{4+} in TiO_2. But Cr^{3+} has three unpaired electrons, Fe^{3+} has five, and Ni^{2+} has two. The magnetization agrees with these predictions, and in fact is the strongest argument in favor of the view presented.

In oxides and other compounds in which the transition ions are concentrated close to each other, there may arise several complications. The commonest of these is that the electron spins tend to oppose each other to a degree, and the substance (below a certain temperature, called the *Néel point*) loses much of its paramagnetism. Such a substance is said to be *antiferromagnetic*. But in a few substances, of which Fe_3O_4 and γ-Fe_2O_3 are notable examples, the opposite effect occurs. In such substances the electron spins tend to operate cooperatively and (below a certain temperature, called the *Curie point*) the substance becomes very strongly attracted to a magnet. Such substances are said to be *ferromagnetic*, although some authors prefer to reserve the word "ferromagnetic" for substances such as metallic iron, cobalt, and nickel, and use *ferrimagnetic* for Fe_3O_4 and γ-Fe_2O_3.

This section will be concluded by reference to *isomorphous replacement*. It was pointed out in Sec. 24.1 that the ions of a transition series show only slight changes in ionic radii in going from one end of the series to the other. This means that, for any given compound, it is probably possible to find some foreign ion that can fit into the crystal lattice just as well as a normal ion. For instance, the compound iron titanate is actually a complex oxide containing Fe^{2+}, Ti^{4+}, and O^{2-} in the proportions indicated by the formula $FeTiO_3$ (This is the mineral ilmenite.) Now the Mg^{2+} ion is not very different in radius from the Fe^{2+} ion, and it is therefore possible for Mg^{2+} to replace Fe^{2+} in this compound, in fact going all the way from $FeTiO_3$ to $MgTiO_3$.

The partially replaced substance (or solid solution) may be written $(Fe_x, Mg_{1-x})TiO_3$, where x stands for the fraction of a gram-atom of Fe in a mole of the substance. It is obvious that the sum of gram-atoms of Fe^{2+} and Mg^{2+} in a mole must equal 1, as for instance, in the composition $(Fe_{0.75}, Mg_{0.25})TiO_3$. Many examples of this phenomenon are known and many useful materials may be prepared in this way. The effect is known as *isomorphous replacement* because no important change of crystal lattice structure occurs.

24.4   Chemical Properties

The chemical properties of the transition metal oxides with which we shall be chiefly concerned are as follows:

1. Reactions of decomposition on ignition
2. Reactions of oxidation and reduction
3. Reactions as catalysts
4. Reactions with water, with acids, and with bases

The first three of these classes of reactions will be discussed in this section, but reactions 4 are so closely related to the hydroxides and the oxy-acids that they will be deferred to Sec. 24.5. It will suffice for the moment to say that most transition metal oxides are almost insoluble in water, but that a few in which the metal has a high oxidation state (as in V_2O_5, CrO_3, and Mn_2O_7) dissolve in water to form acids. The more strongly acid-forming of these oxides will also react directly with base-forming oxides to form oxy-salts. These will be described in Chapter 28.

In Chapter 23 it was stated that some metal oxides, of which HgO is a good example, may be readily decomposed to metal and oxygen by moderate heat treatment. This is also true of some transition metal oxides such as Ag_2O, Au_2O_3, and several oxides of the platinum group of elements. But, in general, the transition metal oxides may yield part of their oxygen, but not all, and some such as zirconia, ZrO_2, are so stable and have such a high melting point (2700° C) that they are used as refractories. We shall content ourselves by describing a few examples of familiar partial decomposition reactions.

If a transition oxide is one of two or more possible oxides of the same metal, then ignition of the higher oxide generally produces a lower one. Thus, strong heating of V_2O_5, CrO_3, MnO_2, Mn_2O_7 (explosive), and Fe_2O_3 will yield, respectively, VO_2, Cr_2O_3, Mn_3O_4 or Mn_2O_3, and Fe_3O_4, plus, of course, oxygen. But the lower oxides such as V_2O_3, CrO, MnO, FeO, and CoO resist further decomposition until extremely high temperatures have been reached.

Those oxides with a high proportion of oxygen are oxidizing agents, and oxides such as CrO_3 and Mn_2O_7 are among the strongest oxidizing agents known. By contrast, those oxides with a low proportion of oxygen, such as CrO, MnO, and FeO, are reducing agents. It will, however, be recalled that oxidizing and reducing ability is relative. Ferrous oxide will reduce mild oxidizing agents, but is itself easily reduced by hydrogen at moderately elevated temperatures. Cupric oxide has moderate oxidizing ability but no reducing ability. It is obvious that transition metal oxides may often act as oxidizing or reducing agents, but how effective they may be depends not only on what reactant is to be oxidized or reduced but also on what other oxidation states are possible for the metal itself. Consideration of Table 24.1 will provide clues to the oxidizing or reducing abilities of most of the oxides listed. The oxide AgO would correctly be predicted to have strong oxidizing power, but TiO would have virtually none.

The last chemical property to be considered in this section is catalysis. It is probably correct to say that every transition metal oxide known has been tested for catalytic activity, and many such oxides have large-scale industrial uses. We shall mention a few such oxides as examples. Vanadium pentoxide is used in the manufacture of sulfuric acid; it catalyzes the oxidation of sulfur dioxide to sulfur trioxide, which in turn may be united with water to form sulfuric acid. Chromium sesquioxide, Cr_2O_3, is used in the manufacture of toluene from other hydrocarbons and in various dehydrogenation reactions. Manganese dioxide is familiar as a catalyst for the decomposition of potassium chlorate; the oxide MnO is more important in industry. Iron oxide is used in the synthesis of hydrocarbons, as is cobalt oxide; nickel oxide is used in making plastics; copper oxide is used in catalytic oxidations, as is silver oxide. This list could be extended throughout virtually all of the 3*d*, 4*d*, and 5*d* series, and in part through the 4*f* and 5*f* series.

It may be wondered why there is such a concentration of catalytic activity among the transition elements and their compounds. A current view is that unpaired electrons, or unfilled orbitals, are responsible for these properties, as they are for the color, the magnetic properties, and for many chemical properties. Certainly, the participation by electron pairing or unpairing during catalytic activity has been amply demonstrated, but just how catalysis functions has not been established, even for the simplest of chemical reactions.

24.5   *Hydroxides and Oxy-acids of the Transition Metals*

Hydroxides of the transition metals are, without exception, virtually insoluble in water. Examples of solubility products for a few of these compounds are given in Table 14.3. The hydroxides may therefore be prepared by precipitation by adding a base to the water solution containing the metal ion. If, for instance, the formation of chromic hydroxide, $Cr(OH)_3$, is desired, the procedure is to add hydroxide ions to a solution of Cr^{3+} ions until precipitation is complete:

$$Cr^{3+} + 3OH^- \rightarrow Cr(OH)_3$$

In this way, it is possible to form hydroxides of most of the transition elements, the following being examples: $Sc(OH)_3$, $Cr(OH)_2$, $Mn(OH)_2$, $Fe(OH)_2$, $Co(OH)_2$, $Ni(OH)_2$, and $Cu(OH)_2$. With care, these gelatinous precipitates may be dehydrated to form the pure compound, but all will go over to an oxide if heated too strongly, as shown for cupric hydroxide:

$$Cu(OH)_2 \rightarrow CuO + H_2O$$

Several complications may arise in the formation of a transition metal hydroxide. One of these is that the hydroxide formed may be oxidized by air if the metal ion is in a low oxidation state, such as Cr^{2+} or Fe^{2+}. This occurs for $Cr(OH)_2$ and $Fe(OH)_2$, which are impossible to maintain unless oxygen is excluded. Another complication is that most of these hydroxides appear to dissolve in excess strong base. Thus, if excess sodium hydroxide is added to a suspension of $Cr(OH)_3$, the solution becomes clear. But such systems show the Tyndall effect and are properly considered to be colloids. Still another complication may occur if the base used for precipitation is ammonium hydroxide. Several of the transition metal ions form complex ions with ammonia, $Cu(NH_3)_4^{2+}$ being one of these. If ammonium hydroxide is added to a solution containing Cu^{2+} ions, the first reaction is to form a precipitate of pale blue, gelatinous $Cu(OH)_2$. But with excess ammonium hydroxide, the precipitate dissolves, leaving a rich blue solution containing the complex ion. This phenomenon, which is also shown by Co^{2+} and Ni^{2+}, will be described more fully in Chapter 29. A final complication to be mentioned is that some hydroxides are not very well characterized as chemical compounds. So-called ferric hydroxide, $Fe(OH)_3$, appears actually to be a hydrated form of ferric oxide, better written as $Fe_2O_3 \cdot xH_2O$.

The various hydroxides are all weak bases (with the exception of a very few compounds such as $HMnO_4$, which in a sense may be regarded as hydroxides but which are always called acids). All the hydroxides show the effect mentioned in Sec. 23.4, namely, that other things being the same, a smaller positive ion tends to form a weaker base and hence a stronger acid. Thus $Cr(OH)_2$ is a somewhat stronger base than is $Cr(OH)_3$ because the Cr^{3+} ion is the smaller. If, then, the oxidation state becomes very high, as may occur (especially for vanadium, chromium, and manganese), it will be found that the hydroxy compounds so formed are acids. Vanadic, chromic, and permanganic acids are all known. Of these, the last two will be described here.

Strong oxidation of almost any chromium compound in basic solution yields the yellow chromate ion, CrO_4^{2-}, in which the chromium has an oxidation state of 6+:

$$2Cr_2O_3 + 8NaOH + 3O_2 \rightarrow 4Na_2CrO_4 + 4H_2O$$

If this solution is acidified, it will be found that the solution turns orange, owing to formation of the dichromate ion, $Cr_2O_7^{2-}$, as follows:

$$2CrO_4^{2-} + 2H^+ \rightleftharpoons Cr_2O_7^{2-} + H_2O$$

Therefore the acid formed by chromium in its highest (6+) oxidation state is $H_2Cr_2O_7$, which is called dichromic acid. (It exists only in solution.) There is no substance of the formula H_2CrO_4, but if a positive ion such as Pb^{2+}, which forms an insoluble chromate, is added to dichromic acid solution, the preceding equilibrium reaction will be shifted as the yellow lead chromate, $PbCrO_4$, precipitates:

$$Cr_2O_7^{2-} + Pb^{2+} + H_2O \rightarrow 2PbCrO_4 + 2H^+$$

Dichromic acid is a simple example of an effect that we shall encounter again, later. This is the formation of a *poly-acid*. In this particular case, only two oxy-ions unite to form the di-acid, but vanadium, molybdenum, tungsten, phosphorus, and other elements in their higher oxidation states often show this tendency to form poly-acids or poly-salts. In some cases the simple acids of two or more *different* elements may thus unite to form *heteropoly-acids*. The tendency to poly-acid formation is so strong for vanadium and molybdenum that the simple vanadic or molybdic acids and their salts are rarely if ever found.

Dichromic acid is a powerful and useful oxidizing agent, as are solutions of chromates and dichromates. A typical reaction is the oxidation of hydrogen sulfide:

$$Cr_2O_7^{2-} + 6H_2S + 2H^+ \rightarrow 6S + 2Cr^{3+} + 7H_2O$$

The behavior of manganese is somewhat similar to that of chromium. If any lower oxide of manganese, such as MnO_2, is heated with a strong oxidizing agent in the presence of a strong base, the manganese is oxidized to the green manganate (6+) oxidation state:

$$2MnO_2 + O_2 + 4KOH \rightarrow 2K_2MnO_4 + 2H_2O$$

There is no acid corresponding to this state of oxidation, but if the mixture in solution is now acidified by an acid even as weak as carbonic, H_2CO_3, a reaction of disproportionation occurs. A *disproportionation* reaction is one by which an element in an intermediate oxidation state is converted to a mixture of a higher and a lower state. In the case of the manganate ion the disproportionation yields the purple permanganate, MnO_4^-, ion in which the manganese has a 7+ oxidation state, plus MnO_2:

$$3MnO_4^{2-} + 4H^+ \rightarrow 2MnO_4^- + MnO_2 + 2H_2O$$

The free permanganic acid exists only in solution, but potassium permanganate is well known and widely used as an oxidizing agent. An example of an oxidizing reaction in which permanganate takes part is the following:

$$5Fe^{2+} + MnO_4^- + 8H^+ \rightarrow 5Fe^{3+} + Mn^{2+} + 4H_2O$$

In such a reaction, which is often used in quantitative analysis, the purple permanganate acts as its own indicator during titration.

Dichromic acid and permanganic acid may, of course, act as acids in neutralizing bases. But their reactions are much complicated by the fact that they are also strong oxidizing agents. The reader may wonder what happens if the basic manganous hydroxide, $Mn(OH)_2$, is treated with permanganic acid. The result would certainly be a neutralization, but there would also be oxidation and reduction, yielding some intermediate stage or mixture of stages. The first product of the neutralization might be thought to be manganous permanganate, $Mn(MnO_4)_2$, but if this is actually formed, it quickly decomposes in a manner such as the following:

$$3Mn(OH)_2 + 2HMnO_4 \rightarrow 5MnO_2 + 4H_2O$$

24.6   *Oxides and Hydroxides of the Lanthanides and Actinides*

It was previously stated in Sec. 16.5 that the lanthanides and the actinides are characterized by progressive filling of the $4f$ and the $5f$ energy levels, respectively. This gives rise to some unique properties in these elements. The f levels are similar to the d levels in that electrons in these levels tend to remain unpaired until, because of their numbers, they can no longer do so. There are seven available sublevels in both the $4f$ and the $5f$ levels; consequently, a total of 14 electrons may be placed in each of these levels. This is the reason that there are 14 lanthanide elements and 14 actinide elements.

A consequence of the tendency for electrons to remain unpaired is that a maximum of seven unpaired electrons may be found in the gadolinium ion Gd^{3+}. It is found, therefore, that the lanthanides exhibit some properties similar to those of the d series of transition elements. These properties are color, paramagnetism, and lanthanide contraction. But the f series differ from the d series in that the f electrons are shielded by the electrons in still higher levels. One of the consequences of this is that the lanthanides show a much diminished tendency toward variable oxidation states and a diminished tendency to form complex ions. The actinides also show these effects, but because the difference in energy between $5f$ and $6d$ levels is less than that between $4f$ and $5d$, the actinides show a somewhat greater variability in oxidation states and somewhat more tendency to complex ion formation.

TABLE 24.4   OXIDATION STATES AND OXIDES OF THE LANTHANIDES

Element	Oxidation states	Oxides
Lanthanum	3+	La_2O_3
Cerium	3+, 4+	Ce_2O_3, CeO_2
Praseodymium	3+, 4+	Pr_2O_3, PrO_2, Pr_6O_{11}
Neodymium	3+	Nd_2O_3
Promethium	3+	Pm_2O_3
Samarium	2+, 3+	SmO, Sm_2O_3
Europium	2+, 3+	EuO, Eu_2O_3
Gadolinium	3+	Gd_2O_3
Terbium	3+, 4+	Tb_2O_3, TbO_2, Tb_4O_7
Dysprosium	3+	Dy_2O_3
Holmium	3+	Ho_2O_3
Erbium	3+	Er_2O_3
Thulium	3+	Tu_2O_3
Ytterbium	2+, 3+	Yb_2O_3
Lutetium	3+	Lu_2O_3

TABLE 24.5   OXIDATION STATES OF THE ACTINIDES

Element	Oxidation states*
Actinium	3+
Thorium	(2+), (3+), 4+
Protactinium	(3+), 4+, (5+)
Uranium	3+, 4+, (5+), (6+)
Neptunium	3+, 4+, (5+), (6+)
Plutonium	3+, 4+, (5+), (6+)
Americium	3+, (4+), (5+), (6+)
Curium	3+, (4+)
Berkelium	3+, 4+
Californium	3+
Einsteinium	3+
Fermium	3+
Mendelevium	3+

* The parentheses indicate less important states. Some examples of oxides are Ac_2O_3, ThO_2, UO_2, U_3O_8, NpO_2, and PuO_2. The elements that can assume the 6+ oxidation states form ions such as UO_2^{2+}, called uranyl ion, and PuO_2^{2+}, called plutonyl.

Table 24.4 shows the known oxidation states for all the lanthanides and the formulas for all oxides. It will be noted that a few complex oxides are known. Table 24.5 gives some related information for the actinides. The oxides of all these elements may be prepared by methods that, by now, should be familiar. These are direct synthesis, or ignition of the hydroxide or oxy-salt. Most of the oxides are refractory, some having very high melting points indeed. The melting point of thoria, ThO_2, is 3050° C. The hydroxides, particularly of the 3+ oxidation state, are made by direct precipitation by addition of OH^- ions to a solution containing the 3+ ion. In view of the lanthanide contraction, the hydroxides become slightly weaker bases as we go from the beginning of a series to the end. Although both $La(OH)_3$ and $Lu(OH)_3$ are almost insoluble compounds, the former has a definitely higher solubility product; that is, it is a stronger base.

EXERCISES

1. Name the properties and the structural basis that distinguish transition metals from other metals.
2. Classify the following as probably being ionic oxides, complex oxides, or oxy-salts: Sc_2O_3, Mn_3O_4, FeO, $KMnO_4$, and $BaFeO_4$.
3. Complete the following statement: "All metal oxides are solids at room temperature except . . . .
4. Direct synthesis of metal oxides from the elements is quite satisfactory for metals such as Mg, Ca, Al, and others. What complication arises for the transition metals?
5. Suggest preparative procedures for the following: Y_2O_3, ZrO_2, CoO, CuO, WO_3, TcO_2.
6. What is the lanthanide contraction, and why is it so called?
7. How can it happen that α-Fe_2O_3 is isomorphous with α-Al_2O_3?
8. Are there any transition metal oxides that are based on a cubic close-packed array of oxide ions?
9. An ion in an octahedral hole has six nearest neighbors. How then can it be called an octahedral hole?
10. What is a spinel?
11. Gamma ferric oxide is used in magnetic recording tape. Is this compound on ionic oxide, a complex oxide, or an oxy-salt?
12. What general properties distinguish the transition metal oxides from other metal oxides, and to what are these properties attributable?
13. Estimate the magnetization in terms of unpaired electron spins for each of the following ions: Cu^{2+}, Mn^{2+}, and Cm^{3+}.

14. Manganous oxide, MnO, is antiferromagnetic; chromium dioxide, CrO_2, is ferromagnetic. To what may the difference be attributed?

15. Certain spinels containing iron may be regarded as examples of isomorphous replacement in which, for instance, Mg^{2+} takes the place of Fe^{2+} in Fe_3O_4. A certain spinel of this type contains 15.1 percent Fe^{2+}, 4.5 percent Mg^{2+}, 51.0 percent Fe^{3+}, and 29.3 percent O. Find a formula for this substance.

16. In another spinel, some of the Fe^{3+} in Fe_3O_4 was replaced by Al^{3+}. The composition was total iron, 65.9 percent; aluminum, 4.9 percent; and the balance, oxygen. Find a formula for this substance.

17. Write equations showing expected products when each of the following is moderately strongly heated: PtO_2, MnO_2, HfO_2, and PbO_2.

18. Write equations showing expected products when hydrogen is passed over the following oxides at moderately elevated temperature: Cu_2O, Mn_3O_4, FeO, Sc_2O_3, MoO_3, Co_2O_3, and Au_2O_3.

19. On the basis of current thinking about heterogeneous catalysis, which of the following might be expected to be of major interest in catalysis: MoO_2, CoO, CaO, La_2O_3?

20. Suggest methods for preparing the following compounds: $Mn(OH)_3$, $Co(OH)_2$, and $Pr(OH)_3$.

21. To a solution containing Fe^{2+} ions there is added OH^- ions in the presence of air. A white precipitate appears, but this soon turns brown. Explain these changes.

22. Which forms the weaker base, $Nd(OH)_3$ or $Er(OH)_3$? Explain

23. Write an equation for the oxidation of Cr_2O_3 with Cl_2 in basic solution.

24. Is it possible to form an oxy-salt even though no corresponding oxy-acid is known?

25. Several of the actinides exhibit the oxidation state of 6+, but none of the lanthanides do. Suggest a reason.

25

Oxides and Oxy-acids
of the Nonmetals

25.1 Introduction to Nonmetal Oxides

Table 25.1 shows all the important oxides of the nonmetals. Only three of these compounds (CO_2, SiO_2, and As_2O_3) occur in appreciable concentrations in nature; consequently, we shall not be concerned with mineralogical names except for silicon dioxide, or silica, one of the several known polymorphs of which is called quartz. All the oxides shown may be named in the manner of P_2O_5, namely, diphosphorus pentoxide. The acids derived from many of these oxides will be described in Sec. 25.7.

In general, the preparative method of most use for these compounds is direct synthesis from the elements. But for all, except boron, two or more oxides are known. The situation is therefore reminiscent of that encountered with the transition metal oxides, namely, that if the experimental conditions are not carefully controlled, it is probable that the product will be a mixture of oxides. If, for instance, phosphorus is burned in air, the result will be a mixture of P_2O_3 and P_2O_5. This difficulty may be overcome by the use of one or the other reactant in excess. In the case mentioned, excess phosphorus yields P_2O_3 and excess oxygen, P_2O_5. For some of the oxides shown in Table 25.1, it is necessary to use special methods, which will be described in due course. It will be found that analogies to the transition metal oxides became increasingly apparent for the highest oxidation states. Thus, Mn_2O_7 and Cl_2O_7 are

TABLE 25.1 IMPORTANT OXIDES OF THE NONMETALS

$\langle B_2O_3 \rangle_\infty$	CO CO$_2$ C$_3$O$_2$	N$_2$O NO N$_2$O$_3$ NO$_2$ N$_2$O$_5$		OF$_2$
	$\langle SiO_2 \rangle_\infty$ SiO	P$_2$O$_3$ P$_2$O$_5$ $\langle PO_2 \rangle_\infty$	SO$_2$ SO$_3$	Cl$_2$O ClO$_2$ Cl$_2$O$_6$ Cl$_2$O$_7$
		As$_2$O$_3$	SeO$_2$ SeO$_3$	Br$_2$O BrO$_2$ BrO$_3$
			TeO$_2$ TeO$_3$	I$_2$O$_5$

both oily liquids, powerful oxidizing agents, dangerously explosive, and both react with water to yield an oxy-acid. But in the lowest oxidation states, these analogies disappear: NO bears no relation to MnO.

It was shown in Chapter 24 that the transition metal oxides exhibit a notable range of properties, and this is also true of the nonmetal oxides. But many transition metal oxides could be considered as true ionic oxides. There are no ionic oxides of the nonmetals. It is probably correct to say that the bonding between the atoms in nonmetal oxides is, without exception, essentially covalent. It is found, therefore, that molecular compounds are the rule, most are volatile, many are normally gases, none conducts electricity appreciably, and the defect state is virtually, if not quite, absent.

But in spite of the predominance of covalency and the numerous and varied kinds of particulate molecules to be found among these compounds, it will also be found that the structures may range all the way from simple molecules such as carbon dioxide to infinite three-dimensional lattices such as silicon dioxide. The nonmetal oxides are scarcely less complex than the metal oxides, but they are complex in different ways. There appear to be no nonmetal peroxides or superoxides, although oxy-acid peroxides are fairly common. In the succeeding sections about a dozen compounds have been selected for detailed discussion. Our criterion for selection has, as usual, been the overall importance of the compound to science or industry, or the convenient illustration of some principle.

25.2   *Oxides of Carbon*

The oxides of carbon of chief importance are the monoxide, CO, and the dioxide, CO_2. Carbon monoxide may be prepared by direct synthesis, provided the carbon is present in excess:

$$2C(\text{excess}) + O_2 \rightarrow 2CO$$

This reaction may proceed in two steps, the carbon first being oxidized to the dioxide, which is then reduced by contact with fresh carbon:

$$CO_2 + C \rightarrow 2CO$$

Nearly pure carbon monoxide may be prepared in relatively small quantities by the dehydration of formic acid, HCO_2H. Concentrated sulfuric acid may be used for this purpose, as may phosphorus pentoxide. In each case, a molecule of formic acid yields a molecule of water to the dehydrating agent:

$$HCO_2H + H_2SO_4 \rightarrow CO + H_3OHSO_4$$

Carbon monoxide is a colorless gas, generally described as odorless. The gas is extremely poisonous, and because of this and because its lack of odor and color give no warning of its presence, it causes many deaths. Carbon monoxide boils at $-190°$ C, and the gas is almost insoluble in water. The molecule is isoelectronic (has the same number of electrons) as the molecule of nitrogen. For this reason, a number of the physical properties of the two substances are similar, but this is not true of the chemical properties.

Carbon monoxide is stable up to very high temperatures, although it finally disproportionates to carbon and carbon dioxide:

$$2CO \rightarrow C + CO_2$$

The gas burns in air with a blue flame, yielding carbon dioxide. Reference has already been made to the use of carbon monoxide as a reducing agent (Sec. 18.3) in the production of iron and other metals from their oxides, and also in the reduction of water (Sec. 17.2) by the water-gas shift reaction to yield hydrogen and carbon dioxide.

Carbon monoxide also reacts with some metals, such as nickel and iron, to form carbonyls. Nickel carbonyl has already been mentioned (Sec. 21.5). These interesting compounds will be described in Chapter 29. Carbon monoxide reacts with certain nonmetals such as chlorine, bromine, and sulfur:

$$CO + Cl_2 \rightarrow COCl_2$$
$$CO + S \rightarrow COS$$

The compound $COCl_2$ is called carbonyl chloride or phosgene (it was used in World War I as a chemical warfare agent). The compound COS is carbon oxysulfide. Carbon monoxide does not dissolve in water to form an acid; it cannot be considered, therefore, an acid anhydride in the sense that P_2O_5 dissolves in water to form phosphoric acid. The reaction of carbon monoxide with hydrogen over a catalyst is used for the industrial production of methanol, CH_3OH.

Carbon dioxide is one of the most important of all chemical compounds. It occurs in the atmosphere, where it averages 0.03 percent by volume. In certain locations, high concentrations of carbon dioxide emerge from the earth. Preparation of carbon dioxide may be achieved by several methods, of which direct synthesis in excess oxygen is one:

$$C + O_2(\text{excess}) \rightarrow CO_2$$

Combustion of carbon monoxide is, of course, also a possible method, as is the combustion in excess air of almost any organic compound such as methane, CH_4, ethanol, C_2H_5OH, or sucrose $C_{12}H_{22}O_{11}$.

Carbon dioxide may also be prepared by thermal decomposition of certain carbonates. The preparation of calcium oxide by this method, which yields carbon dioxide as a by-product, has already been described in Sec. 23.3. Carbonates will also yield carbon dioxide if treated with a strong acid. Calcium carbonate will, for instance, react with acid to yield carbon dioxide as follows:

$$CaCO_3 + 2H^+ \rightarrow Ca^{2+} + H_2O + CO_2$$

This reaction is possible because of the very low stability of carbonic acid, H_2CO_3, and the moderately low solubility of carbon dioxide in water, except under pressure. Still another preparation of carbon dioxide is the fermentation of organic matter under the influence of an enzyme (an organic catalyst):

$$C_6H_{12}O_6 \rightarrow 2C_2H_5OH + 2CO_2$$
$$\text{glucose} \qquad\quad \text{ethanol}$$

The exhalation of carbon dioxide in the breath of humans and animals is a result of catalyzed oxidation processes in the organism.

Carbon dioxide is a gas under normal temperature and pressure, but it may be obtained as a solid known as "dry-ice" at $-78.5°$ C and 1 atm, or it may be obtained as a liquid below the critical temperature $31°$ C, provided the pressure is sufficiently high. A phase diagram for carbon dioxide is shown in Fig. 25.1. It will be noted that the molecular weight of carbon dioxide is such (44) that the density of the gas is considerably higher than that of nitrogen or oxygen. Carbon dioxide gas will flow into depressions in somewhat the same manner as water. The gas is colorless and almost odorless. It is not poisonous in the sense that carbon monoxide is poisonous, although high concentrations are dangerous. The molecule is linear,

$$\overset{..}{O} = C = \overset{..}{\underset{..}{O}}$$

the representation shown being, of course, only an oversimplified attempt at what must actually be a complicated resonance structure.

Carbon dioxide does not generally support combustion. This property, together with its high gas density, accounts for its wide use in fire extinguishers. But a few active metals, of which magnesium is one, will burn in carbon dioxide:

$$2Mg + CO_2 \rightarrow 2MgO + C$$

Apart from reactions such as this, the CO_2 molecule may be said to have no oxidizing ability, and it has no reducing ability whatever. The chemical properties of carbon dioxide of most interest are those related to its action as an acid anhydride to form an oxy-acid. These properties will be described in Sec. 25.7.

It may be wondered if silicon, the element directly below carbon in the Periodic Table, also forms oxides analogous to CO and CO_2. The answer is yes, indeed, but SiO_2 is so different from CO_2 that it will

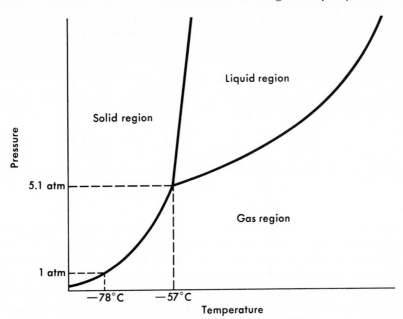

Fig. 25.1 Phase diagram for carbon dioxide.

be described in Sec. 25.6. If silicon dioxide is strongly heated with silicon, a reaction occurs which is thought to be as follows:

$$Si + SiO_2 \rightleftharpoons 2SiO$$

Silicon monoxide is a gas, with the formula shown, but it apparently decomposes by disproportionation as it is cooled to room temperature.

25.3 *Oxides of Nitrogen and Phosphorus*

Nitrogen forms the oxides shown in Table 25.2. It will be noted that every oxidation state from $1+$ to $5+$ is represented in these compounds, and if it is recalled that nitrogen also forms ammonia, hydrazine, and hydroxylamine (NH_2OH), it will be obvious that nitrogen exhibits the complete range of oxidation states from $3-$ to $5+$, a total range of eight units.

From the list of nitrogen oxides we shall choose N_2O and NO_2 for detailed discussion. Nitrous oxide is variously known as dinitrogen (mon) oxide, or as "laughing gas." This substance is one of the few oxides that cannot be prepared by direct synthesis. A preparation method often used is thermal decomposition of ammonium nitrate:

$$NH_4NO_3 \rightarrow N_2O + 2H_2O$$

TABLE 25.2   OXIDES OF NITROGEN

Name	Formula	Color	Mp, °C	Bp, °C
Nitrous oxide	N_2O	none	-102.4	-88.5
Nitric oxide	NO	dark blue	-163.6	-151.8
Dinitrogen trioxide	N_2O_3	light blue	-102.0	$3.5*$
Nitrogen dioxide	NO_2	brown	. . .	. . .
Dinitrogen tetroxide	N_2O_4	none	-9.3	$21.3*$
Dinitrogen pentoxide	N_2O_5	none	$30*$	$47*$

* Decomposes.

It will be noted that in ammonium nitrate, one nitrogen atom has the oxidation state 3—; the other, 5+. Nitrous oxide is a fairly stable compound with a slight, not unpleasant, odor. Breathing it produces anesthesia, sometimes to the accompaniment of hysterical laughter. In the molecule, the two nitrogens are joined to each other N—N—O. Nitrous oxide supports combustion; the reason for this is that above about 600° C, it decomposes into oxygen and nitrogen:

$$2N_2O \rightarrow 2N_2 + O_2$$

The molecule is isoelectronic with carbon dioxide, but this does not result in N_2O being an acid anhydride, even though there is an acid (hyponitrous, $H_2N_2O_2$) in which the nitrogen has the same oxidation state as in N_2O. Nitrous oxide is used in prepared "whipped cream" dispensers and in surgical anesthesia.

The properties of nitrogen dioxide, NO_2, are quite different from those of N_2O. Nitrogen dioxide may be obtained by synthesis from the elements, but only in two steps, one of which involves the preparation of nitric oxide. Nitrogen and oxygen do not react at room temperature, a fact that should be obvious from their coexistence as elements in the atmosphere. But at elevated temperatures, the equilibrium for the reaction

$$N_2 + O_2 \rightleftharpoons 2NO$$

shifts toward the right, and at 3000° C the equilibrium gas mixture contains several percent of NO. If this mixture is cooled to room temperature, the equilibrium will shift back to the left. But if the gas mixture at equilibrium at 3000° C or higher is cooled rapidly, the rate of decomposition of NO will be lowered to such a degree that a considerable yield may be obtained. At room temperature, NO may be kept indefinitely, even though it cannot be considered to be a stable compound. If, now, NO is exposed to oxygen at or near room temperature, a reaction will quickly occur to yield the brown gas nitrogen dioxide, NO_2:

$$2NO + O_2 \rightarrow 2NO_2$$

This sequence of reactions was at one time part of an important method for producing nitric acid from air and water. At the present time, NO_2 is prepared on a large scale by the catalytic oxidation of ammonia over platinum to produce NO, followed as in the preceding reaction by addition of more oxygen to form NO_2:

$$4NH_3 + 5O_2 \rightarrow 4NO + 6H_2O$$

Another method for the preparation of NO_2 is to reduce concentrated nitric acid by metallic copper:

$$Cu + 4HNO_3(conc) \rightarrow Cu(NO_3)_2 + 2NO_2 + 2H_2O$$

Less concentrated nitric acid, or a metal more active than copper, will yield reduction products such as NO in which the nitrogen has a lower oxidation state.

Although nitrogen dioxide at moderately elevated temperatures is a gas with the formula NO_2, it undergoes *dimerization* (doubling up) as the temperature is lowered:

$$2NO_2 \rightleftharpoons N_2O_4 + heat$$

The *monomer* (single unit) is brown; the *dimer* (double unit) is colorless. At the boiling point, $21.3°$ C, the mixture contains about 1 percent of the monomer; at $100°$ C, the gas contains about 90 percent monomer. The dimerization reaction and its reverse, the dissociation reaction, occur readily at all ordinary temperatures. It is therefore impossible to obtain pure N_2O_4 at elevated temperatures, and difficult to maintain appreciable concentration of NO_2 at lower temperatures. Nitric oxide also exhibits this phenomenon, but the dimerization to form N_2O_2 does not occur appreciably unless the temperature is very low. Both nitric oxide and nitrogen dioxide molecules possess an odd number of electrons. They are, therefore, paramagnetic, but this property is lost and the oxides become diamagnetic as dimerization occurs.

The molecule of NO_2 has the structure

the angle between the two oxygens being 132 degrees. The structure of the dimer is thought to be as follows:

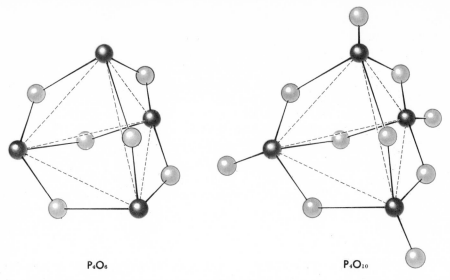

P_4O_6 P_4O_{10}

Fig. 25.2 Arrangement of atoms in the molecules of P_4O_6 and of P_4O_{10}. The basic tetrahedral arrangement of the four phosphorus atoms is the same as in elementary phosphorus, P_4, as shown in Fig. 19.6.

It will be clear that in these representations, no attempt is made to show electron distribution.

If nitrogen dioxide is strongly heated, it decomposes to nitric oxide and oxygen. The compound is a strong oxidizing agent, and it is used both for oxidizing organic compounds and for nitrations (that is, converting elements and compounds to nitrates). Nitrogen dioxide is a dangerous poison. Its reactions with water leading to the formation of oxy-acids will be described below.

The oxides N_2O_3 and N_2O_5 are respectively the anhydrides of nitrous and nitric acids. The N_2O_3 may be made from NO and N_2O_4, the latter by dehydration of HNO_3 with P_2O_5. They have few uses.

The three oxides of phosphorus are P_4O_6, $\langle PO_2 \rangle_\infty$, and P_4O_{10}, although they are more often than not referred to simply as P_2O_3, PO_2, and P_2O_5. The last is the most important and it is the only one that we shall describe in detail.

Phosphorus pentoxide, P_4O_{10}, is produced when phosphorus burns in excess oxygen:

$$P_4 + 5O_2 \rightarrow P_4O_{10}$$

This is the only important method of preparation. The oxide is a white solid which sublimes at 360° C. The molecular weight of the vapor corresponds to the formula P_4O_{10}. These molecules are also present as P_4O_{10} in the solid. It was pointed out in Sec. 19.6 that yellow phosphorus forms molecules having the formula P_4 and that the four atoms are arranged as at the corners of a tetrahedron. Formation of the pentoxide does not alter the geometrical arrangement of the phosphorus atoms, but places an oxygen atom nearly between each pair of phosphorus atoms, plus an oxygen attached to a phosphorus at each of the four corners of the tetrahedron. This arrangement is shown in Fig. 25.2. The pentoxide also has at least two other allotropic (polymorphic) modifications of greater complexity. We shall not be concerned with these, except to mention that they form infinite lattices $\langle P_2O_5 \rangle_\infty$.

Phosphorus pentoxide has no reducing properties and no important oxidizing properties. It is useful for the extraordinary way in which it takes up water. It is one of the most powerful drying agents known, and as such, is able to remove water from concentrated sulfuric acid, which is itself a good drying agent. The products of reaction between P_2O_5 and water are oxy-acids, which will be described in Sec. 25.7.

25.4   Oxides of Sulfur

Of the several known and possible oxides of sulfur, only two will be described. These are the dioxide, SO_2, and the trioxide, SO_3. Sulfur dioxide is easily prepared by direct synthesis, the burning of sulfur in air to form the choking, poisonous gas SO_2 having been known since prehistoric times:

$$S + O_2 \rightarrow SO_2$$

Sulfur dioxide may similarly be obtained by roasting in air any of the common metal sulfides that, as for PbS, form important ores. Normally these reactions do not yield the higher oxide except under conditions to be described below. Sulfur dioxide may also be produced by treating a sulfite, or bisulfite, with a strong acid, provided the strong acid is not also a strong oxidizing agent. Thus, dilute sulfuric acid reacts with sodium sulfite, Na_2SO_3, or with sodium bisulfite, $NaHSO_3$:

$$Na_2SO_3 + 2H_2SO_4 \rightarrow SO_2 + H_2O + 2NaHSO_4$$

This reaction, which resembles the analogous preparation of carbon dioxide from carbonates, goes virtually to completion because the intermediate product sulfurous acid, H_2SO_3, is a weak acid and one that readily decomposes to sulfur dioxide and water. The solubility of sulfur dioxide in water under 1 atm pressure is moderate.

Sulfur dioxide is a gas. The boiling point at 1 atm is $-10°$ C. The molecule is angular, and this is consistent with the fairly high dipole moment (1.6 debyes). The arrangement of electrons in this molecule is a good example of how two (or more) resonance structures taken

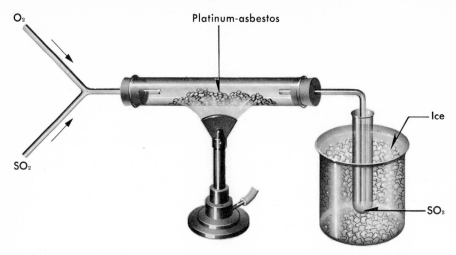

Fig. 25.3 *Laboratory demonstration of the contact process for making sulfur trioxide,* $2SO_2 + O_2 \rightleftarrows 2SO_3$.

together give a better representation of the molecule than either one structure taken alone. The resonance structures often given for the molecule are

and

The bond length is the same for both sulfur-oxygen bonds.

Sulfur dioxide is a colorless gas, the powerful and offensive odor of which was referred to above. It may act either as an oxidizing agent, as when it reacts with hydrogen sulfide in the presence of a trace of water,

$$2H_2S + SO_2 \rightarrow 3S + 2H_2O$$

or it may act as a reducing agent, as in the reduction of permanganate ion in acid solution,

$$2MnO_4^- + 5SO_2 + 2H_2O \rightarrow 2Mn^{2+} + 5SO_4^{2-} + 4H^+$$

Sulfur dioxide is used chiefly in the manufacture of sulfuric acid and as a bleaching agent.

Sulfur trioxide is made by catalytic oxidation of the dioxide:

$$2SO_2 + O_2 \rightarrow 2SO_3 + \text{heat}$$

Catalysts used include vanadium pentoxide or platinum in the heterogeneous "contact" process, or nitric oxide in the homogeneous "lead chamber" process. Illustrations of equipment for the contact process both on a laboratory scale and on a large scale as used for sulfuric acid manufacture are shown in Figs. 25.3 and 25.4. If sulfur is burned in air, the product contains a little SO_3 because the nitrogen present is oxidized in trace amounts sufficient to catalyze some oxidation to the higher oxide.

Sulfur trioxide is generally obtained as a white solid. Above about 45° C, it may be obtained as a vapor consisting of SO_3 molecules. But at room temperature there are several polymorphic forms. One of these, with a melting point of 16.8° C, resembles ice. It consists of $(SO_3)_3$ groups. Another form has long chains; here again there is no implication concerning electron distribution:

$$
\begin{array}{ccccccc}
 & O & & O & & O & \\
 & | & & | & & | & \\
-S & -O- & S & -O- & S & - \\
 & | & & | & & | & \\
 & O & & O & & O &
\end{array}
$$

A third form has similar chains, but these appear to have cross-links from chain to chain. The icelike form may be obtained as a liquid. It appears to be a mixture of monomer and trimer, SO_3 and $(SO_3)_3$.

Fig. 25.4 Industrial production of sulfuric acid by the contact process, at the left, sulphur is burned in air to form sulfur dioxide, which is then thoroughly purified in a dust catcher, two scrubbers, and an arsenic purifier. The mixture of sulfur dioxide and air is then passed over the catalyst, where heat from the exothermic reaction $2SO_2 + O_2 \rightarrow 2SO_3$ is used to warm incoming gases. Finally the sulfuric acid is absorbed in concentrated sulfuric acid.

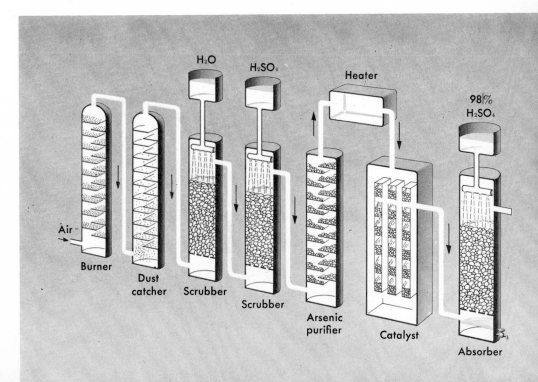

Sulfur trioxide is a powerful, and rather hazardous, oxidizing agent. It has many uses in chemical industry. The chief of these is in the manufacture of sulfuric acid. The reactions of both SO_2 and SO_3 with water will be described in Sec. 25.7.

25.5   *Oxides of the Halogens*

There are at least a dozen known compounds of oxygen with the halogens, and all halogens form binary compounds with oxygen. The compounds selected for discussion are oxygen difluoride, OF_2; chlorine dioxide, ClO_2; and (di)iodine pentoxide, I_2O_5. Most of the oxides of the halogens are explosive, all are hazardous, and all are poisonous. There are no generally applicable methods for the preparation of these compounds; each must be regarded as a special case.

Oxygen difluoride (so-called because fluorine is the more electronegative element) may be prepared by passing fluorine rapidly through dilute sodium hydroxide solution:

$$F_2 + 2OH^- \rightarrow 2F^- + F_2O + H_2O$$

This substance is a colorless gas (bp $-145°$ C). The angle between the fluorides in the F—O—F molecule is 103 degrees. Compared to most oxides of the halogens, it is relatively unreactive, although when mixed with hydrogen and ignited it produces a violent explosion, as it also does with steam. Oxygen difluoride reacts with bases yielding free oxygen:

$$OF_2 + 2OH^- \rightarrow O_2 + 2F^- + H_2O$$

It does not form an acid in water.

Chlorine dioxide (so-called because the oxygen is the more electronegative element) may be made by treating silver chlorate with chlorine:

$$2AgClO_3 + Cl_2 \rightarrow 2AgCl + 2ClO_2 + O_2$$

Commercially, ClO_2 is made by reacting sodium chlorate with sulfur dioxide in sulfuric acid solution. Chlorine dioxide is a yellowish gas (bp $11°$ C). The structure of the molecule is O—Cl—O, with the angle between the oxygens at 117 degrees. It will be noted that ClO_2 has an odd number of electrons and hence is paramagnetic. It has no tendency to dimerize as does NO_2. The gas is extraordinarily reactive and liable to explode, but if the partial pressure of ClO_2 is kept less than about 50 mm, it is safe to handle mixtures of the gas in air. Chlorine dioxide is a powerful oxidizing agent, and it has uses as an oxidizer and bleaching agent, especially in the paper industry. In water the gas is soluble. In the dark these solutions are stable, but in light the ClO_2 disproportionates to form hydrochloric and chloric acids. Therefore, chlorine dioxide is in one sense an acid anhydride, but the acids formed do not have the chlorine in the same oxidation state as it is in ClO_2 $(4+)$.

Iodine pentoxide is a white solid made by dehydrating iodic acid, HIO_3, in a stream of dry air at about 200° C:

$$2HIO_3 \rightleftharpoons I_2O_5 + H_2O$$

The structure of the molecule is not known. Iodine pentoxide is stable up to about 300° C, above which it decomposes into iodine and oxygen. It is a useful oxidizing agent. The oxide is a true acid anhydride, uniting with water to form iodic acid by the reverse of the preceding reaction.

25.6   Polymeric Oxides of Silicon and Boron

With one or two exceptions, all the oxides previously described in this chapter form particulate molecules of low to moderate molecular weight. Determination of the molecular weight by standard procedures such as vapor density offers no special difficulty. An exception was sulfur trioxide, and this in only one of its several polymorphic forms. We shall now describe two oxides that give no evidence of forming discrete molecules except at temperatures far above everyday experience. These oxides are silicon dioxide, SiO_2, and boron sesquioxide, B_2O_3. They are themselves important compounds, and their molecular structures are representative of those found in many substances.

Both SiO_2 and B_2O_3 may be prepared by direct synthesis from the elements, but this method is not often used. Both boron and silicon readily form oxy-salts, and from these it is a simple matter to obtain the corresponding oxy-acids H_4SiO_4 and H_3BO_3. These, on ignition, yield the oxides by elimination of water. Further details concerning the oxy-acids will be given in Sec. 25.7.

Silicon dioxide occurs widely distributed in nature as the mineral quartz. White sand is silicon dioxide in various degrees of purity. Quartz itself exists in two modifications, and other polymorphic forms known as tridymite and cristobalite also occur. The name "silica" is applied to all forms of silicon dioxide. Silica consists of silicon atoms surrounded by four oxygen atoms, each of which is attached to two silicons. This arrangement (shown in Fig. 25.5) extends indefinitely in space. All the silicon-oxygen bond distances appear to be the same, and the bonds themselves are thought to be covalent, with a considerable degree of ionic character. The differences among the several polymorphs of silica are due to some twisting of the relationship between the SiO_4 tetrahedra. Silica has no identifiable group of atoms that may be considered to be a discrete molecule. This is the reason why such substances are designated in this book by formulas in the form of $\langle SiO_2 \rangle_\infty$ whenever any possible

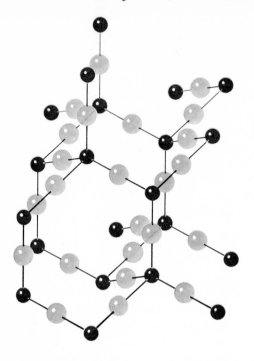

Fig. 25.5 Structure of silica $\langle SiO_2 \rangle_\infty$. Each silicon atom is surrounded by four tetrahedrally arranged oxygen atoms, and each oxygen is combined with two silicons. This arrangement extends indefinitely in three dimensions in space.

ambiguity may occur concerning the presence or absence of particulate molecules.

Silica is a hard, colorless solid melting at 1710° C. It has a strong tendency to form a "glassy" solid rather than a crystal. Silica is transparent to ultraviolet light, in contrast to ordinary glass, and it has a notably small coefficient of thermal expansion. Red-hot silica may be plunged into water without shattering. Although silica may be made by the dehydration of silicic acid, it is virtually insoluble in water and in many other reagents. It is attacked by hydrogen fluoride, with the formation of the gas silicon tetrafluoride:

$$SiO_2 + 4HF \rightarrow SiF_4 + 2H_2O$$

It is also attacked by strong alkalis, with the formation of silicates:

$$SiO_2 + 4NaOH \rightarrow Na_4SiO_4 + 2H_2O$$

Common acids do not react with silica.

If silicic acid is dehydrated in such a way as to leave a few percent of water in the product being formed, the result is a hard, translucent material of very high specific surface. This is known as "silica gel." It is used as a dehydrating agent and as a support for catalysts such as platinum or vanadium pentoxide. Mixed with about 10 percent alumina, silica gel is used as a "cracking" catalyst in the petroleum industry.

Boron oxide is another substance that forms a polymeric solid. This substance is difficult to obtain in the form of well-developed crystals, and there is still some uncertainty concerning its structure. But in the crystallized oxide, there appear to be infinite arrays in three dimensions of boron atoms linked to four oxygen atoms, by essentially covalent bonding. Each of the oxygens is, in turn, linked to two boron atoms. There is some probability that not all the boron-oxygen bond lengths are the same, but this need not concern us. The important feature of the structure for our purposes is that here again there is no atom or group of atoms that can be singled out as forming a discrete molecule. In all three dimensions the bonding of boron to oxygen to boron extends to infinity, that is to say, to the geometrical edge or surface of the crystal sample. This is true also of the more readily prepared "glassy" form of B_2O_3 in which, however, each boron appears to be attached to three rather than to four oxygens. Be that as it may, it is clear that one cannot properly refer to a "molecule" of B_2O_3 because, in the solid, such discrete molecules do not exist.

It may be wondered why B_2O_3 is so different from Al_2O_3, which is considered as an ionic solid. The reason is that the aluminum in its oxide has a radius 2.5 times larger than that of boron. This difference is responsible for most of the contrast in properties between boron and aluminum and the other elements in Group III of the Periodic Table.

Boron oxide is a white solid melting at 450° C. It dissolves readily in water to form the weak boric acid H_3BO_3. Other nonmetal oxides that exhibit varying degrees of polymerization include phosphorus dioxide, PO_2; one form of arsenic sesquioxide, As_2O_3; and one form of P_2O_5. But among the oxy-salts to be described in Chapter 28, such structures are common.

25.7   *Oxy-acids*

Most, but not all, oxides of nonmetals react with water to form acids. Of the oxides listed in Table 25.1, those that are *not* acid anhydrides (those that do not react with water to form acids) are CO, N_2O, NO, OF_2, SiO, and PO_2. Silicon dioxide is so unreactive that it should probably be added to this list. The acids so formed by the remaining oxides all contain oxygen, and they all contain one or more oxygen-hydrogen groups, X—O—H, arranged in such a manner that one or more protons may be given up, thus giving the compound its acid character. Such acids are called *oxy-acids* in contrast to the binary acids formed by several molecular hydrides of the nonmetals (Sec. 22.6). Hypochlorous acid, HClO (better written as Cl—O—H), is a good example of an oxy-acid (although a weak one); hydrochloric, HCl, is a good example of a binary acid. It

TABLE 25.3 SOME OF THE MORE IMPORTANT OXY-ACIDS OF THE NONMETALS

III	IV	V	VI	VII
HBO_2 H_3BO_3	H_2CO_3	$H_2N_2O_2$ HNO_2 HNO_3		
	H_4SiO_4	H_3PO_2 H_3PO_3 HPO_3 $H_4P_2O_7$ H_3PO_4	H_2SO_3 H_2SO_4 $H_2S_2O_7$	$HClO$ $HClO_2$ $HClO_3$ $HClO_4$
		H_3AsO_4	H_2SeO_3 H_2SeO_4	$HBrO$ $HBrO_3$
				HIO HIO_3 H_5IO_6

will be recalled that some metals, of which manganese is one, form oxy-acids if the oxidation state of the metal is sufficiently high. In this connection it must be mentioned again that acidity is a property that depends both on the acid and on the solvent. Nitric acid is a strong acid in water:

$$HNO_3 + H_2O \rightarrow H_3O^+ + NO_3^-$$

but in liquid hydrogen fluoride, HNO_3 behaves as a base.

$$HNO_3 + HF \rightarrow H_2NO_3^+ + F^-$$

Table 25.3 gives the more important oxy-acids of the nonmetals. Peroxy-acids are not listed in the table, but are mentioned later in this section. Our plan will be to describe some general preparation methods and properties of oxy-acids and then to select five of the most important acids for more detailed discussion. The five are perchloric, sulfuric, nitric, phosphoric, and carbonic; briefer reference will be made to some acids related to those named.

Most of the acids listed in Table 25.3 may be prepared by dissolving the appropriate acid anhydride in water. Thus orthoboric acid, H_3BO_3, results from the reaction of B_2O_3 with water. (If the temperature is raised, a molecule of water is eliminated and metaboric acid, HBO_2, results.) Similarly, P_2O_5 in water yields several phosphoric acids; SeO_3 yields selenic acid, H_2SeO_4; and so forth. But this convenient method is not invariably applicable. It has already been pointed out that silicon dioxide is so unreactive that it is impossible to make silicic acid directly through trying to dissolve the oxide in water. Sometimes if there is available an oxy-salt containing the negative ion of the acid, then this may be put through a cation exchange resin in the acid form (Sec. 21.7) to yield the desired acid. For instance, hypophosphoric acid, $H_4P_2O_6$, may be obtained in solution by pouring a solution of sodium dihydrogen hypophosphate, $Na_2H_2P_2O_6$, through such an ion exchanger:

$$2R\!-\!H + Na_2H_2P_2O_6 \rightarrow 2R\!-\!Na + H_4P_2O_6$$

(The sodium salt may be obtained by treating red phosphorus with sodium hypochlorite, $NaOCl$, solution.) Hypophosphorous acid, H_3PO_2 may be made by adding dilute sulfuric acid to a solution of barium hypophosphite, $Ba(H_2PO_2)_2$:

$$Ba(H_2PO_2)_2 + H_2SO_4 \rightarrow 2H_3PO_2 + BaSO_4$$

The barium sulfate precipitates, leaving the desired acid in solution. The $Ba(H_2PO_2)_2$ is made by adding white phosphorus to hot $Ba(OH)_2$ solution. In still other cases, oxidation or reduction in solution is necessary. This will be illustrated for perchloric acid, to be discussed in detail later in this section. Even when a reactive oxide is available, it may not react with water to yield the expected acid. If, for instance, chlorine dioxide is treated with a base, it does not yield an oxy-anion in which chlorine has the oxidation state of 4+, but rather it disproportionates to yield a mixture of chlorite and chlorate ions in which the chlorine has respectively the oxidation states 3+ and 5+:

$$2ClO_2 + 2OH^- \rightarrow ClO_2^- + ClO_3^- + H_2O$$

If this mixture is acidified with dilute sulfuric acid, the products will include both chlorous acid, $HClO_2$, and chloric acid, $HClO_3$. Chlorine dioxide may therefore be considered an acid anhydride only in a sense considerably more complicated than is the case for, say, B_2O_3 or SO_3. This situation occurs also for nitrogen dioxide, as will be described below.

Our choice for the first oxy-acid to be presented in detail is perchloric. This choice is dictated by the relatively simple structure and properties of this acid, although, unfortunately, its preparation is not so simple. The acid is an important article of commerce.

It will be recalled that if chlorine is allowed to react with water, it forms a mixture of hydrochloric and hypochlorous acids:

$$Cl_2 + H_2O \rightleftharpoons HCl + HClO$$

If this reaction is carried out in the presence of a base, the products are, of course, a chloride and a hypochlorite:

$$Cl_2 + 2OH^- \rightarrow Cl^- + ClO^- + H_2O$$

But if the reaction mixture is hot, the products are a chloride and a chlorate:

$$3Cl_2 + 6OH^- \rightarrow 5Cl^- + ClO_3^- + 3H_2O$$

Consequently, if a hot solution of sodium chloride is electrolyzed, and if the chlorine normally liberated at the anode is allowed to mix with the sodium hydroxide formed (with hydrogen) at the cathode, it will be found that sodium chlorate, $NaClO_3$, accumulates in the electrolyte.

If sodium or potassium chlorate is gently heated, it will be converted partly into perchlorate:

$$4KClO_3 \rightarrow 3KClO_4 + KCl$$

Industrially, sodium perchlorate is made by electrolysis of sodium chlorate solution. The reaction is often said to be represented by the following equation, although it is probably more complicated:

$$NaClO_3 + H_2O \xrightarrow{\text{electrolysis}} NaClO_4 + H_2$$

Of the several methods for producing perchloric acid, one is to treat the sodium perchlorate solution with hydrogen chloride under conditions such that sodium chloride crystallizes:

$$NaClO_4 + HCl \rightarrow HClO_4 + NaCl$$

The perchloric acid may be concentrated by fractional distillation.

Pure perchloric acid is a colorless oily liquid that is likely to detonate if heated in the presence of a trace of reducing agent such as any combustible carbon compound. The concentrated acid is a strong oxidizing agent, but when diluted with water, the reaction with a metal such as zinc yields merely hydrogen, with no reduction of the perchlorate ion. Perchloric is a strong, useful acid. The ion ClO_4^- is tetrahedral in structure and has only very slight tendency to enter into complex formation with positive ions. It will be noted that this acid has only one replaceable hydrogen atom per molecule. The structure of the acid may be crudely represented as follows:

$$\begin{array}{ccc} O & & O \\ & \diagdown\!\!\diagup & \\ & Cl & \\ & \diagup\!\!\diagdown & \\ O & & OH \end{array}$$

Nitric acid, in its preparation and properties, bears considerable resemblance to perchloric. Nitric acid may be prepared by heating sodium nitrate with sulfuric acid:

$$NaNO_3 + H_2SO_4 \rightarrow HNO_3 + Na_2SO_4$$

but on an industrial scale, the acid is made by reaction of nitrogen dioxide with water. This, the *Ostwald process,* involves the preparation of nitric oxide by catalyzed air oxidation of ammonia, followed by exposure of the NO to more air, to cause further oxidation to NO_2 (or N_2O_4). Nitrogen dioxide reacts with water to yield nitric acid and nitric oxide. (The latter may be recirculated for further oxidation.)

$$3NO_2 + H_2O \rightleftharpoons 2HNO_3 + NO$$

The pure HNO_3 is a colorless liquid, but often yellow or brown, owing to partial decomposition yielding NO_2. The concentrated acid is a strong oxidizing agent, able to "dissolve" all but a few metals with the liberation of reduction products that may include NO_2, NO, or even NH_4^+. Nitric acid is a strong acid, and as does perchloric, it yields only one hydrogen per molecule. Unlike many acids it rarely reacts with metals to liberate hydrogen. Magnesium plus dilute nitric appears to be the only metal that reacts to liberate hydrogen rather than some reduction product of the nitrate ion. The structure of nitric acid may be represented as follows:

$$\begin{array}{ccc} & O & \\ & \| & \\ & N & \\ & \diagup\!\!\diagdown & \\ O & & OH \end{array}$$

If sodium nitrate is heated moderately, it loses oxygen to become sodium nitrite:

$$2NaNO_3 \rightarrow NaNO_2 + O_2$$

If now the $NaNO_2$ is treated with dilute sulfuric acid, the solution will be found to contain nitrous acid, formed by displacement:

$$NaNO_2 + H_2SO_4 \rightarrow HNO_2 + NaHSO_4$$

Nitrous acid is a weak acid, known only in solution. As are all nitrites, it is a mild reducing agent.

As we turn now to sulfuric acid, we encounter some complications due to the presence of two replaceable hydrogen ions. The acid is made by reacting the anhydride SO_3 with water or, more conveniently with concentrated H_2SO_4 to form persulfuric acid, $H_2S_2O_7$, which is then diluted with water to form H_2SO_4. The sulfur trioxide is made by oxidation of SO_2, as described in Sec. 25.4. The pure acid is a colorless, oily liquid of surprisingly high density (1.8 grams/ml). It is a good oxidizing agent and a powerful dehydrating agent. A drop of water added to concentrated sulfuric acid acts with dangerous violence. An example of the oxidizing action of sulfuric acid is the reaction with free sulfur:

$$S + 2H_2SO_4 \rightarrow 3SO_2 + 2H_2O$$

An example of the dehydrating action may be observed by adding concentrated sulfuric acid to a strong sugar solution. Sugar does not actually contain water, but the formula, $C_{12}H_{22}O_{11}$, shows that the hydrogen and oxygen are present in the same proportion as in water. The action of concentrated sulfuric acid on sugar is to yield a black char of carbon.

Sulfuric is a moderately strong acid. It undergoes dissociation in two steps:

$$H_2SO_4 \rightleftharpoons H^+ + HSO_4^-$$

and

$$HSO_4 \rightleftharpoons H^+ + SO_4^{2-}$$

The bisulfate (hydrogen sulfate) ion, HSO_4^-, is itself an acid, although a rather weak one. It is possible, therefore, to displace one or two atoms of hydrogen from a molecule of sulfuric acid, and this gives rise to two series of salts: the bisulfates, containing HSO_4^-; and the sulfates, containing SO_4^{2-}. These salts will be described in Chapter 28.

Sulfuric acid is one of the most widely used of all industrial chemicals. The structure of the molecule may be represented as

$$\begin{array}{ccc} O & & OH \\ & \diagdown S \diagup & \\ O & & OH \end{array}$$

Sulfurous acid, H_2SO_3, is formed by dissolving the anhydride SO_2 in water. It is a weak acid, known only in solution. Sulfurous acid is a useful reducing agent.

Proceeding now to phosphoric acid, we encounter still more complexities. This acid may be made by heating a phosphate rock with concentrated sulfuric acid:

$$Ca_3(PO_4)_2 + 3H_2SO_4 \rightarrow 3CaSO_4 + 2H_3PO_4$$

It may also be made by reacting phosphorus pentoxide with water. The products obtained in these reactions are complex. In moderately dilute solution the acid, which is rather weak, seems definitely to be made up of H_3PO_4 molecules. There are three replaceable hydrogens:

$$H_3PO_4 \rightleftharpoons H^+ + H_2PO_4^-$$
$$H_2PO_4^- \rightleftharpoons H^+ + HPO_4^{2-}$$
$$HPO_4^{2-} \rightleftharpoons H^+ + PO_4^{3-}$$

The ionization constants are as shown in Sec. 14.1. There are therefore three separate series of salts possible from this one acid.

In more concentrated solution there is some tendency for the molecules to combine with each other and to split off molecules of water. This process leads to the formation of chains and rings of condensed molecules. In view of this, it is necessary to have names for the various compounds formed. The acid H_3PO_4 is called *orthophosphoric*. Partial removal of water from orthophosphoric acid yields pyrophosphoric, $H_4P_2O_7$, in which all four hydrogens are replaceable. Still further dehydration yields metaphosphoric acid, HPO_3, which, however, always polymerizes to molecules containing four, six, and even more HPO_3 units. It will be seen from this that the oxy-acids of phosphorus can be almost impossibly complicated, and we have not even mentioned the series of acids called the phosphorous series in which phosphorus has the $3+$ oxidation state. There is, however, one aspect of phosphorus chemistry that makes it a little less complex. The phosphoric acids have negligible oxidizing properties and no reducing properties; the phosphorous acids are merely mild reducing agents. Table 25.4 gives a summary of formulas and names of the more important oxy-acids and oxy-ions of phosphorus.

The final, normal oxy-acid to be considered in this section is the familiar carbonic acid, H_2CO_3, the essential ingredient in all carbonated beverages. Carbon dioxide dissolves readily in water; under elevated pressure the quantity of CO_2 that will dissolve is very large. If the pressure is released, the bubbles of CO_2 appear and rise to the surface. It has already been pointed out (Sec. 14.1) that carbonic acid is a very weak acid, but this weakness is at least in part due to the fact that a large fraction of the CO_2 is simply dissolved as such in the water. There is some evidence that the "true" carbonic acid is present only in solu-

TABLE 25.4   OXY-ACIDS AND IONS OF PHOSPHORUS

Acid formula	Acid name	Ions formed and general name
H_3PO_2	hypophosphorous	$H_2PO_2^-$, hypophosphite
HPO_2	metaphosphorous	PO_2^-, metaphosphite
$H_4P_2O_5$	pyrophosphorous	$H_3P_2O_5^-$, $H_2P_2O_5^{2-}$; pyrophosphites
H_3PO_3	orthophosphorous	$H_2PO_3^-$, HPO_3^{2-}; orthophosphites
$H_4P_2O_6$	hypophosphoric	$H_3P_2O_6^-$, $H_2P_2O_6^{2-}$, $HP_2O_6^{3-}$, $P_2O_6^{4-}$; hypophosphates
HPO_3	metaphosphoric	PO_3^-, metaphosphate
$H_4P_2O_7$	pyrophosphoric	$H_3P_2O_7^-$, $H_2P_2O_7^{2-}$, $HP_2O_7^{3-}$, $P_2O_7^{4-}$; pyrophosphates
H_3PO_4	orthophosphoric	$H_2PO_4^-$, HPO_4^{2-}, PO_4^{3-}; orthophosphates

tion and only at rather small concentration. Carbonic acid is thought to have the structure

$$O=C\begin{array}{c}\nearrow OH \\ \searrow OH\end{array}$$

There are two replaceable hydrogens, leading to the formation of bicarbonates containing the HCO_3^- ion and of carbonates containing the CO_3^{2-} ion. Carbonic acid is not an oxidizing acid.

This section will be concluded with a brief mention of the peroxy acids, of which peroxysulfuric is one. These acids have one or more of the —OH groups in certain oxy-acids replaced by the —OOH group. Peroxysulfuric acid has the structure

$$\begin{array}{c}O\\ \diagdown\end{array}S\begin{array}{c}OH\\ \diagdown\\ OOH\end{array}$$

Such acids react in water to form the normal acid plus hydrogen peroxide:

$$H_2SO_5 + H_2O \rightleftharpoons H_2SO_4 + H_2O_2$$

EXERCISES

1. Most nonmetal oxides are volatile; few metal oxides are volatile except at extremely high temperatures. What is the reason for this difference?

2. Select those nonmetal oxides that cannot easily be prepared by direct synthesis and determine if they have any feature in common that may give a clue as to why special methods of preparation are necessary.

3. A sample of carbon monoxide has been prepared and contains some carbon dioxide as impurity. How could the CO be purified?

4. At approximately what pressure may carbon dioxide be kept as a liquid at room temperature?

5. What structural feature in the atom of nitrogen might account for its ability to show oxidation states from 3— to 5+?

6. Name several other elements that show a range of eight units in oxidation state. Give formulas of representative compounds in each state.

7. Nitrous oxide supports combustion better than air. Why should this be true?

8. Prepare a list of "odd" molecules or ions, substances in which there is one unpaired electron, exclusive of transition metal compounds.

9. Write a balanced equation for the reduction of dichromate ion with sulfur dioxide.

10. The gaseous oxides CO_2 and SO_2 are readily prepared by treating carbonates and sulfites respectively with concentrated sulfuric acid. Do analogous reactions occur if formates, nitrites, and chlorates are treated with concentrated H_2SO_4?

11. It is often stated that a nonmetal is an element of which the oxide dissolves in water to form an acid. Of what nonmetals and what oxides is this statement not true?

12. Is it correct to say that all preparation methods for nonmetal oxides involve oxidation or reduction?

13. In the basic hydrolysis of oxygen difluoride, what element is oxidized and what reduced? Name one analogous reaction.

14. Write equations for the preparation of those oxides that may be obtained by dehydration of the corresponding oxy-acid.

15. If SiO_2 consists of an infinite three-dimensional lattice of SiO_4 tetrahedra, how could crystalline B_2O_3 contain BO_4 tetrahedra when the atomic proportion of oxygen present is less than in SiO_2?

16. A sample of silica gel may have a surface area of 1000 m^2/gram. Find the area per gram of a sheet of silicon plus oxygen atoms, only one atom layer thick. The Si—O bond length is 1.6 Å.

17. Sodium chloride is, in a sense, an infinite three-dimensional lattice, as is any metal. But these differ sharply in structure and properties from the kind of infinite lattice exhibited by SiO_2 and B_2O_3. What are these differences?

18. In what ways does an oxy-acid differ from a binary acid (such as HCl)?

19. Of the five oxy-acids of major importance, namely, perchloric, sulfuric, nitric, phosphoric, and carbonic, describe in detail (with equations) the preparation of each one that is not manufactured by the simple process of adding water to the anhydride.

20. Having at hand an appropriate oxy-salt, illustrate at least four methods that may be tried to obtain the corresponding oxy-acid.

21. Nitrogen is directly above phosphorus in the Periodic Table. Suggest a reason why nitrogen forms only the *meta* acid and not the *ortho,* as does phosphorus.

22. Orthophosphorous acid may yield one or two hydrogens by ionization, but not all three. Consider possible structures for H_3PO_3 that might lead to this difference between H_3PO_3 and H_3PO_4.

23. Write an equation, using structural formulas, for the hydrolysis of peroxy(*ortho*)phosphoric acid.

24. Suppose that someone discovered a catalyst that would greatly speed up the union of nitrogen and oxygen to form nitric oxide. Would there not be serious danger that all the oxygen in the air would be used up?

25. Orthophosphorous acid, H_3PO_3, is peculiar, as mentioned above, in that only two of the three hydrogens may be replaced. If a solution of this acid is exposed to air, it absorbs oxygen and slowly changes to orthophosphoric acid.
    (a) Does the normality of the solution change?
    (b) Does the molarity change?

26. The pH of a $0.01M$ boric acid solution is about 5.6. How does the hydrogen ion concentration in this solution compare with that in pure water?

27. The tetraborate ion, $B_4O_7^{2-}$, reacts with acidified water to precipitate boric acid. What weight of borax, $Na_2B_4O_7 \cdot 10H_2O$, is required to thus react with 35.3 ml of $0.050M$ H_2SO_4?

26

Binary Salts

26.1   Classification of Binary Compounds

Binary compounds may be formed by two metals, as described briefly in Sec. 8.6. The product in this case is called an *intermetallic compound*. Binary compounds may also be formed by two nonmetals, although there is no general name for such substances, of which carbon disulfide is an example. A possible, though awkward, name is "internonmetal"; internonmetals will be described in Chapter 27. A third class of binary compounds consists of a metal in combination with a nonmetal. Such compounds are often called salts. The term *salt* is used in several senses in chemistry. Not infrequently, a salt is defined as a substance formed by the neutralization of an acid by a base. It is true that neutralization yields salts, but some true salts are known (sodium dithionite, $Na_2S_2O_4$, is one) for which no corresponding acid exists. Sometimes salts are defined as compounds (not necessarily binary) in which the valence forces are essentially ionic. For the purposes of this chapter we shall define a salt as a compound formed between a metal and a nonmetal. In doing so, we recognize that difficulties of classification are inevitable and that all the metal oxides already described may be salts according to this definition. The oxy-salts, which are certainly true salts, will be described in Chapter 28.

Table 26.1 gives the formula for many important binary salts, so defined, for representative elements. With the exception of a few, such as

457

TABLE **26.1**   Some important binary salts

	B	C	N	F	Si	P	S	Cl	As	Br	I
Na		Na_2C_2	Na_3N NaN_3	NaF		Na_3P	Na_2S	NaCl		NaBr	NaI
Be		Be_2C	Be_3N_2	BeF_2				$BeCl_2$		$BeBr_2$	BeI_2
Mg			Mg_3N_2	MgF_2	Mg_2Si		MgS	$MgCl_2$		$MgBr_2$	MgI_2
Ca	CaB_6	CaC_2	Ca_3N_2 $Ca(N_3)_2$	CaF_2	$CaSi_2$	Ca_3P_2	CaS	$CaCl_2$	Ca_3As_2	$CaBr_2$	CaI_2
Cr	CrB	Cr_3C_2	CrN	CrF_2 CrF_3	Cr_3Si_2	CrP	CrS Cr_2S_3	$CrCl_2$ $CrCl_3$	CrAs	$CrBr_2$ $CrBr_3$	CrI_2
Mn	MnB	Mn_3C		MnF_2 MnF_3	Mn_2Si	MnP	MnS	$MnCl_2$ $MnCl_3$	MnAs	$MnBr_2$	MnI_2
Fe	FeB	Fe_3C	Fe_2N Fe_4N	FeF_2 FeF_3	FeSi	FeP	FeS	$FeCl_2$ $FeCl_3$	FeAs	$FeBr_2$ $FeBr_3$	FeI_2
Ni	NiB	Ni_3C		NiF_2		Ni_2P	NiS	$NiCl_2$	NiAs	$NiBr_2$	NiI_2
Pt				PtF_2 PtF_4			PtS	$PtCl_2$	$PtAs_2$	$PtBr_2$ $PtBr_4$	PtI_2 PtI_4
Cu	Cu_3B_2	Cu_2C_2	Cu_3N	CuF CuF_2	Cu_4Si	Cu_3P	Cu_2S CuS	CuCl $CuCl_2$	Cu_3As	CuBr $CuBr_2$	CuI
Ag		Ag_2C_2	AgN_3	AgF			Ag_2S	AgCl		AgBr	AgI
Zn			Zn_3N_2	ZnF_2		Zn_3P_2	ZnS	$ZnCl_2$	Zn_3As_2	$ZnBr_2$	ZnI_2
Hg			$Hg_2(N_3)_2$ Hg_3N_2	Hg_2F_2 HgF_2			Hg_2S HgS	Hg_2Cl_2 $HgCl_2$		Hg_2Br_2 $HgBr_2$	Hg_2I_2 HgI_2
Al	AlB_2	Al_4C_3	AlN	AlF_3			Al_2S_3	$AlCl_3$		$AlBr_3$	AlI_3
In				InF_3			InS	$InCl_3$	InAs	$InBr_3$	InI_3
Sn				SnF_2 SnF_4		SnP	SnS SnS_2	$SnCl_2$ $SnCl_4$		$SnBr_2$ $SnBr_4$	SnI_2 SnI_4
Pb			$Pb(N_3)_2$	PbF_2			PbS	$PbCl_2$ $PbCl_4$		$PbBr_2$	PbI PbI_2
Sb				SbF_3 SbF_5			Sb_2S_3 Sb_2S_5	$SbCl_3$ $SbCl_5$		$SbBr_3$	SbI_3 SbI_5
U	UB_2	UC_2	U_3N_4	UF_4 UF_6			U_2S_3 US_2	UCl_3		UBr_3 UBr_4	UI_4

$SnCl_4$, they are all solids at room temperature. Many of them show astonishing complexities of structure, changing the arrangement of atoms and even of valence types as the temperature and pressure are changed. In naming these compounds, the reader will find it most convenient to name all according to the simple plan of using prefixes to indicate the number of atoms present in the empirical formula. Thus, $CrCl_2$ is chromium dichloride; Ca_3As_2 is tricalcium diarsenide; Al_4C_3 is tetraluminum tricarbide. In a few cases such as $Pb(N_3)_2$, lead diazide, it is necessary to use a special name for the ions present. Many elements are, of course, known in two or more oxidation states. Names such as ferric chloride, $FeCl_3$, and ferrous chloride, $FeCl_2$, are often encountered.

The preparation of binary salts may be achieved by a variety of methods of which direct synthesis is applicable in a substantial number of cases. If two or more oxidation states are possible, it may be necessary to use one or the other reactant in excess to ensure that the desired product is obtained. Other methods of general applicability include treating the metal or its oxide with the appropriate molecular hydride. In view of the fact that many salts are insoluble in water, it is often possible to precipitate the desired compound by mixing the two ions in solution. All these and other special methods will be illustrated in the succeeding sections.

Table 26.1 shows most of the more important binary salts of the elements. The succeeding sections consist of a selection of these binary salts, classified as fluorides, chlorides, sulfides, and so forth. For each nonmetal at least one, and generally several, salts are presented. Selection of particular salts has been based on importance to science, or industry, or on convenience in illustrating some principle. For each compound there is given one or more preparation methods, plus some information concerning the physical properties, structure, and chemical properties.

26.2 *Fluorides*

The fluorides to be described are NaF, CaF_2, MnF_2, MnF_3, SnF_2, SnF_4, and UF_6.

Sodium fluoride, NaF, is not a compound of major importance, but it will be described here because it offers the opportunity of comparison between fluorides and oxides. It often occurs that a salt may be prepared by neutralization of an acid with a base. Thus, sodium chloride may be obtained by neutralizing hydrochloric acid with sodium hydroxide. It is true that sodium chloride is soluble in water and that preparation of the pure, dry salt involves evaporation of the water, but this offers no difficulty. It will, however, be recalled that sodium oxide could not possibly be prepared by neutralizing sodium hydroxide. The reason for this, described in Sec. 23.4, is that the oxide ion is a very strong Brönsted base, reacting with water to form hydroxide ions. One might say that sodium oxide added to water suffers hydrolysis to virtual completion.

The fluoride ion is also a Brönsted base, though not so strong a one as oxide ion. If sodium fluoride is added to water, the following equilibrium is set up:

$$F^- + H_2O \rightleftharpoons HF + OH^-$$

If sodium hydroxide is neutralized with hydrofluoric acid, it will be found that the reaction is a typical neutralization of a strong base by a (moderately) weak acid, as described in Sec. 14.4. If now an attempt is made to evaporate the water from the sodium fluoride, which is soluble in water, it will be found that hydrogen fluoride gas is liberated and that the product finally obtained is a mixture of NaF and NaOH. It so happens, however, that the solubility of NaF is considerably less than that of NaCl, being 40 grams/liter as compared with about 350 grams/liter for NaCl. By careful adjustment of the pH and the other concentrations, it is possible to precipitate and dry NaF, with only a moderate hydrolysis to NaOH taking place. This is the commercial process for making NaF, but it does not yield a pure compound, as is the case for NaCl prepared by an analogous method. Similar considerations apply to the fluorides of the other alkali metals. The rule illustrated here is a general one, namely, that a soluble salt formed from a weak acid and a strong base cannot readily be obtained pure by neutralization and evaporation. The same difficulty is encountered in the preparation of a salt from a weak base and a strong acid, although there are some exceptions, ammonium chloride being one.

Calcium (di)fluoride, CaF_2, offers a contrast to NaF. It will be recalled that in spite of the strong Brönsted base activity of the oxide ion, CaO forms a weaker base in water than does Na_2O, and Al_2O_3 scarcely reacts with water. Similarly, CaF_2 is virtually insoluble in water. It may be prepared very simply by adding fluoride ion, as in HF solution, to calcium ion, as in $Ca(OH)_2$ solution. The reaction goes virtually to completion, and the water may be removed without appreciable hydrolysis occurring. The same is true of several other insoluble fluorides such as SrF_2, BaF_2, PbF_2, LaF_3, and PuF_3. It may be surprising to learn that both AgF and TlF are quite soluble in water. Aluminum fluoride is, as expected, insoluble in water, but for other reasons it is not readily prepared by precipitation from water solution.

Manganous fluoride, MnF_2, may be prepared by a method of fairly general applicability. This is the treatment of the corresponding chloride, $MnCl_2$, with anhydrous HF:

$$MnCl_2 + 2HF \rightarrow MnF_2 + 2HCl$$

It will be noted that the HF has no important oxidizing or reducing action, so that the manganese remains in the same oxidation state. If manganese trifluoride, MnF_3, is desired, it is necessary either to start with $MnCl_3$ or to oxidize MnF_2 with excess F_2:

$$2MnF_2 + F_2 \rightarrow 2MnF_3$$

This reaction, which is representative of many, is possible here because manganese does not form a fluoride containing a higher proportion of fluorine than that present in MnF_3. Both MnF_2 and MnF_3 are red solids. Fluorides such as these have applications in catalysis.

Stannous fluoride, SnF_2, may be obtained as a hydrate by dissolving metallic tin in hydrofluoric acid. A "dry" method is to heat tin tetrafluoride with metallic tin:

$$SnF_4 + Sn \rightarrow 2SnF_2$$

This is a method of fairly general applicability for obtaining a salt in which the metal is in a low oxidation state. The method is obviously applicable only when a higher state is available. Tin tetrafluoride may be prepared by treating tin with excess fluorine. Our interest in these compounds is that they are both "saltlike." This property would be expected in the difluoride, but that it occurs also in the tetrafluoride is surprising and a contrast to uranium hexafluoride, to be described next.

Uranium hexafluoride, UF_6, is representative of the molecular fluorides. It is not a "saltlike" compound, and it is included here for convenience. The hexafluoride is one of several fluorides formed by uranium. Of these, only UF_3 is a truly ionic, "saltlike" compound. The hexafluoride may be obtained by treating metallic uranium with excess fluorine in the presence of some chlorine, or by treating one of the lower fluorides with fluorine. It forms molecules of the formula UF_6, and it is the only readily obtained gaseous compound of uranium. The fluoride atoms are arranged around the uranium as at the corners of an octahedron, as shown:

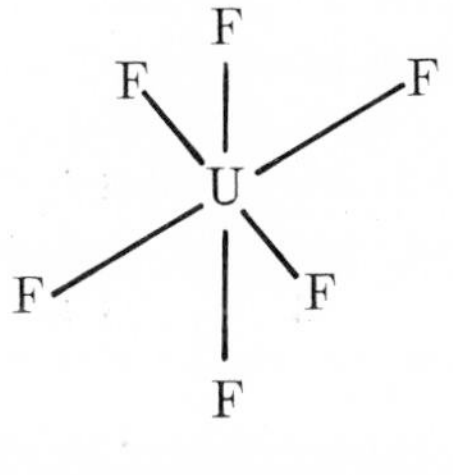

This compound forms colorless crystals with a vapor pressure of about 120 mm at 25° C and reaching 760 mm at 56° C. It is stable except for hydrolysis in water. The uses of UF_6 in connection with the separation of uranium isotopes have already been described (Sec. 21.8).

26.3 Chlorides

The chlorides constitute one of the most important classes of metallic salts. Those chlorides to be considered include $NaCl$, $MgCl_2$, $BeCl_2$, $AlCl_3$, $FeCl_3$, $AgCl$, Hg_2Cl_2, $HgCl_2$, and $SnCl_4$.

Sodium chloride, $NaCl$, is an invaluable industrial raw material. It occurs abundantly in the earth's crust, as the crystalline solid, in salt brines, or in the oceans. Its occurrence, its preparation through neutralization or direct synthesis, its purification, and its properties have all been described repeatedly in previous chapters, as have many of its uses.

Magnesium chloride, $MgCl_2$, is a contrast to NaCl. The solubility of $MgCl_2$ in water is high, and it is the salt of a weak base and a strong acid. If an attempt is made to evaporate the water from dissolved $MgCl_2$, it will be found that hydrolysis may take place, the final product being a mixture containing MgO. This hydrolysis may, if it is so desired, be prevented by carrying out the dehydration in a stream of dry HCl. The product is a white solid, used in the electrolytic production of magnesium metal.

Beryllium chloride, $BeCl_2$, is of interest to us principally because it is a "borderline" compound between the true ionic chlorides such as NaCl and the true molecular chlorides such as CCl_4. Beryllium chloride may be prepared by a fairly general procedure, which consists of passing CCl_4 over BeO at 800° C:

$$BeO + CCl_4 \rightarrow BeCl_2 + COCl_2$$

(The by-product $COCl_2$ is the very poisonous carbonyl chloride, or phosgene.) The $BeCl_2$ is a white solid at room temperature. It melts at 405° C, and the vapor contains linear Cl—Be—Cl molecules. These are known to be linear from the zero dipole moment. As the temperature is lowered, some polymerization occurs to a structure which may be represented thus:

This is a structure consisting of infinitely long chains. (A similar structure occurs for $PdCl_2$.) As might be expected, the $BeCl_2$ readily hydrolyzes in water. The electrical conductivity of the fused salt is much lower than that of fused NaCl, but higher than that of CCl_4, thus again showing the intermediate character of the compound.

Aluminum chloride, $AlCl_3$, might be expected, because of the position of aluminum in the Periodic Table, to have some properties reminiscent of $BeCl_2$, and this is the case. The preparation of $AlCl_3$ is possible by direct synthesis from the metal and chlorine, or of metal plus hydrogen chloride gas. Another method is to pass chlorine at about 900° C over a mixture of Al_2O_3 and powdered carbon. The carbon at this temperature tends to reduce the aluminum, which is converted by the Cl_2 to $AlCl_3$. Sublimation of the $AlCl_3$ from the reaction mixture serves to displace the equilibrium in the desired direction. The $AlCl_3$ is a white solid that appears to have a continuous lattice represented approximately as follows:

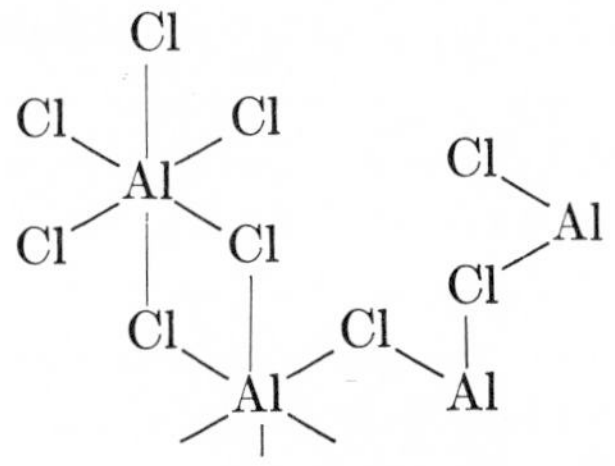

$$
\begin{array}{c}
\text{Cl} \\
| \\
\text{Cl} \quad \text{Cl} \\
\diagdown | \diagup \\
\text{Al} \\
\diagup | \diagdown \\
\text{Cl} \quad \text{Cl} \\
\end{array}
$$

The bonds between Al and Cl are at least partially covalent. But, as a liquid (mp 193° C, under pressure), the compound consists of Al_2Cl_6 molecules:

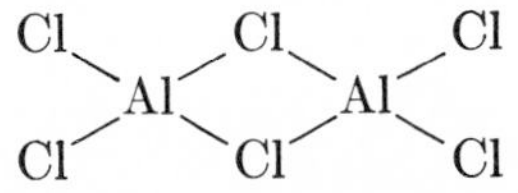

These dimeric molecules persist in the vapor up to about 400° C, above which monomeric $AlCl_3$ molecules appear. It will be noted that in the change from solid to liquid, the coordination of the Al atom changes from octahedral to tetrahedral. Similar changes of structure are fairly common among the halides of the metals; other examples are $CrCl_3$, $FeCl_3$, $AlBr_3$, AlI_3, $AuCl_3$, $CuCl$, and SnF_4. Aluminum chloride reacts violently with water, undergoing hydrolysis to HCl and $Al(OH)_3$. The compound is used in catalysis.

Ferric chloride, $FeCl_3$, is very similar to $AlCl_3$. It cannot be prepared in water because it undergoes extensive hydrolysis. Direct synthesis may be used, but excess chlorine is essential, otherwise, the more ionic salt of iron in the 2+ oxidation state (namely, ferrous chloride, $FeCl_2$) will be formed.

Silver chloride, AgCl, is most readily prepared by precipitation by adding Cl^- to a solution containing Ag^+. The salt is virtually insoluble, a property that is shared with the other silver halides except the fluoride, and also with $PbCl_2$ (soluble in hot water), TlCl, and Hg_2Cl_2. Silver chloride and certain other silver salts undergo partial decomposition to the free metal if they are exposed to light. Thus, white AgCl left in sunlight for a few moments turns dark. This photochemical reaction is the basis for the use of silver compounds in photography.

Mercuric chloride, $HgCl_2$, is a compound in which mercury has the higher of its two oxidation states, 1+ and 2+. Mercuric chloride may be prepared by treating mercury metal with excess chlorine. The product is a white solid, soluble in water, but the solution conducts electricity poorly. The reason for this is that this "salt" exists principally as $HgCl_2$

molecules rather than as Hg^{2+} and Cl^- ions, and this is true both in the solid and in solution. In view of this structural situation, it might be thought that $HgCl_2$ would be appreciably volatile, and this is the case, the normal boiling point being only 303° C. Further evidence concerning the "molecular" nature of $HgCl_2$ is found in its appreciable solubility in nonionizing solvents such as benzene. Mercuric chloride is a very dangerous poison. An old name for it is "corrosive sublimate."

Mercury in its lower oxidation state forms no oxide, but it forms mercurous chloride, Hg_2Cl_2, a peculiar substance. It may be prepared by the action of chlorine on excess mercury metal. This procedure results in contamination of the product with some $HgCl_2$, but this is readily removed because $HgCl_2$ is soluble in water and Hg_2Cl_2 is not. Alternatively, Hg_2Cl_2 may be precipitated from a water solution of Hg_2^{2+} ions to which Cl^- is added. (The Hg_2^{2+} solution may be prepared by allowing $Hg(NO_3)_2$ solution to stand in contact with mercury metal.) The product of precipitation is a white solid, formerly known as "calomel." The unique feature in this compound and in other mercurous compounds is the presence of the dimeric ion Hg_2^{2+}. This ion appears to have a covalent $[Hg:Hg]^{2+}$ structure, but the Hg—Hg bond distance is different in different compounds. The few salts of mercurous mercury that are soluble in water appear to be good conductors of electricity, although they suffer hydrolysis. Mercurous chloride was formerly used in medicine as a cathartic.

It will have been noted that the chlorides described have ranged in structure from the almost purely ionic, as in NaCl, to the borderline such as $BeCl_2$, and even to the partially molecular as in $HgCl_2$. Tin tetrachloride (stannic chloride), $SnCl_4$, is an example of an unequivocal molecular compound, similar in some respect to UF_6, and in contrast to SnF_4. The $SnCl_4$ is readily obtained by direct synthesis in excess chlorine. The product is a colorless liquid (mp $-36°$ C, bp 114 degrees). Tin tetrachloride is a stable compound that does, however, hydrolyze strongly in water, yielding SnO_2 and HCl. Similar properties are shown by $GeCl_4$, $PbCl_4$, $TiCl_4$, and several other halides. It will be noted that there is a parallelism between the oxides—which range from almost purely ionic (as in BaO) to molecular (as in Mn_2O_7)—and the halides, which range from ionic NaCl to molecular $SnCl_4$ and UF_6. The reason is the same in both cases, namely, that small size and high formal charge on the metal atom favor covalence; large size and low charge favor electrovalence.

26.4   Bromides and Iodides

The only bromides and iodides we need consider are $CaBr_2$, AgBr, NaI, and AgI. Calcium bromide is a typical ionic solid resembling the corresponding chloride. It may be made by neutralizing $Ca(OH)_2$ with HBr. The product is a colorless solid, soluble in water. Silver bromide is much like AgCl and it may be prepared in a similar manner—namely, by precipitation from a solution of Ag^+ to which Br^- is added. Silver bromide undergoes a photochemical decomposition like that of AgCl. The color of AgBr is ivory, and the solubility is even less than that of AgCl.

Sodium iodide, NaI, is a white solid soluble in water, and is much like NaCl. It is mentioned here because of the reaction of iodide ion with free, molecular iodine. If to a solution of NaI or of any other soluble iodide in water, there is added some I_2, it will be found that the solution turns brown and that the I_2 has united with the iodide ion to form a triiodide ion:

$$I_2 + I^- \rightleftharpoons I_3^-$$

Triiodides may be formed with many metal ions, in addition to Na^+; but iodine is not the only halogen that shows this property. Silver iodide is a yellow solid that has an extremely low solubility in water. Otherwise, it closely resembles AgBr. One other aspect of iodide ion chemistry must be mentioned. The iodide ion is fairly good reducing agent. This is a property not shared by Br^- or by Cl^-. If an attempt is made to prepare an iodide of a positive ion which itself is fairly readily reduced, then it will be found that a reaction of oxidation and reduction takes place spontaneously. If, for instance, iodide ion is added to ferric ion in the hope of obtaining ferric iodide, FeI_3, it will be found that the iron reduces to Fe^{2+} and the I^- oxidizes to I_2:

$$2Fe^{3+} + 2I^- \rightarrow 2Fe^{2+} + I_2$$

Ferrous iodide, FeI_2, is a stable compound, but FeI_3 is not. Similar considerations apply to CuI_2, which becomes $CuI + I_2$.

26.5 Sulfides

Many sulfides occur in nature as minerals, some such as PbS (galena) and HgS (cinnabar) as important ores. The valence bonding in metallic sulfides tends to be more covalent than is the case for the corresponding oxides (although there are not so many volatile metal sulfides as there are oxides). In spite of this change of bond type, we consider all metal sulfides as salts. While direct synthesis is the commonest method of preparation for these compounds, many sulfides may be obtained by precipitation or by neutralization of the metal hydroxide by hydrogen sulfide. The sulfides that will be described in some detail are Na_2S, Al_2S_3, NiS, CuS, and ZnS.

Sodium sulfide, Na_2S, may be prepared by direct synthesis, but excess sulfur yields compounds (called polysulfides) of the general formula Na_2S_x, where x has any value from 2 to 5. A commercial preparation used for many years involves reduction of sodium sulfate, Na_2SO_4, with carbon (or alternatively, with hydrogen). Attempted preparation of Na_2S from water solution encounters the same difficulty as preparation of Na_2O in the presence of water, namely, that hydrolysis is so strong that no pure compound may be obtained. If, however, a water solution of NaOH is saturated with H_2S, it is possible to obtain a hydrated salt of the formula $NaHS \cdot 3H_2O$. This may be considered as either a sulfur analog of NaOH itself or, alternatively, as a salt of H_2S in which only one of the two hydrogens has been replaced. Sodium sulfide is a white ionic solid, often obtained as the hydrate $Na_2S \cdot 9H_2O$. The salt is strongly hydrolyzed in water, the solution smelling of H_2S. The compound is used in the leather industry and elsewhere.

Aluminum sulfide, Al_2S_3, may be prepared by direct synthesis. The reaction between powdered aluminum and sulfur takes place with considerable violence and may even become explosive. The compound cannot be prepared from water solution. When added to water, Al_2S_3 undergoes virtually complete hydrolysis to $Al(OH)_3$ and H_2S. The compound is a yellow solid with few uses.

Nickel sulfide, NiS, is an example of a transition metal sulfide, of which two have been selected for presentation. The compound occurs in nature as the mineral millerite, or it may be prepared by direct synthesis. Our chief interest in NiS and in CuS is the preparation by precipitation from aqueous solution. There is no question that NiS may be considered as a salt of a weak base, $Ni(OH)_2$, and a weak acid, H_2S, but the solubility of NiS is so low that no appreciable hydrolysis takes place. If a source of S^{2-} ions is added to a solution containing Ni^{2+} ions, a precipitate at once appears. This may be dried, and if protected from oxygen during the drying process, substantially pure NiS is obtained. The interesting feature of this reaction (and one that was discussed briefly in Sec. 14.7) is that the solubility product of NiS is such that a fairly high concentration of S^{2-} is required if precipitation of the Ni^{2+} as NiS is to be substantially complete. Hydrogen sulfide dissolved in water provides a scarcely high enough S^{2-} ion concentration for this purpose. In acid solution the ionization of H_2S is diminished by the common-ion effect, and under these circumstances, no precipitate of NiS may be obtained. But if the solution is made basic, as by adding some NH_4OH, the S^{2-} ion concentration is increased to such a degree that virtually quantitative precipitation of NiS occurs. The sequence of reactions involved here forms an excellent example of simultaneous equilibria. Other sulfides that cannot be precipitated in appreciably acid solution include MnS, ZnS, FeS, and CoS. Nickel sulfide is a black solid. Its only important use is as an ore of the metal.

Cupric sulfide, CuS, occurs in nature as the mineral covellite. It may be prepared by heating copper with excess sulfur. Insufficient sulfur results in formation of cuprous sulfide, Cu_2S, which also occurs in nature as the mineral and ore chalcocite. But once again our chief interest is in the precipitation of CuS from aqueous solution. Cupric sulfide, as is NiS, is virtually insoluble in water, but the solubility product of CuS is considerably smaller than that of NiS. Even in an acidic solution of H_2S, the S^{2-} ion concentration is sufficiently high to ensure practically complete precipitation of CuS from any solution containing Cu^{2+} ions. Cupric ions may therefore be separated quantitatively from Ni^{2+} ions in solution by adding a small quantity of a strong acid such as HCl and then saturating the solution with H_2S. The precipitate of CuS is removed by filtration. Then, if so desired, the solution is made alkaline with NH_4OH and saturated again with H_2S to precipitate all the nickel as NiS. Other metal ions that behave like Cu^{2+} in this respect include Pb^{2+}, Hg^{2+}, Cd^{2+}, As^{3+}, Sb^{3+}, and Bi^{3+}. Cupric sulfide is a black solid, the chief use of which is as an ore of the metal.

Zinc sulfide, ZnS, also occurs in nature as the minerals wurtzite and sphalerite. It too may be made by direct synthesis or by precipitation from an aqueous solution. Zinc sulfide is like NiS in that, although it is virtually insoluble in water, it cannot be precipitated by H_2S from a strongly acid solution. The compound is a white solid used in pigments. If traces of certain impurities such as copper are present, the zinc sulfide acquires the property of fluorescence and is used in x-ray screens and television tubes.

It must be noted that although free sulfur is an oxidizing agent in many reactions, yet the sulfide ion is a moderately strong reducing agent. It has already been described (Sec. 18.2) how the sulfide ion is able to reduce copper oxide to form metallic copper. This reducing action of the sulfide ion makes it difficult or impossible to prepare metal sulfides if the metal ion is one than can be readily reduced. Thus Fe_2S_3 is very difficult to prepare; MnS_2 has not yet been prepared.

26.6   Carbides and Nitrides

As we go to nonmetals of lower electronegativity, we find that they unite with metals to form compounds of increasingly diverse nature. Carbon is one of the most versatile of elements; we shall use the term *binary carbide* for those compounds in which carbon is united to an element of lower electronegativity. These may be saltlike compounds, and this section will be limited to such substances. But carbon, as does hydrogen, forms not only saltlike binary compounds but also interstitial carbides and covalent carbides. The interstitials will be treated in Sec. 26.7 and the covalent inorganic carbides in Chapter 27.

Carbides may in general be prepared by direct synthesis at high temperature. It is often feasible to use the metal oxide rather than the metal because at elevated temperatures most metal oxides are reduced by carbon, and sometimes vapors of hydrocarbons such as ethylene, C_2H_4, may be substituted for the carbon. In a few cases, certain carbides may be precipitated by passing acetylene, C_2H_2, into a water solution containing the metal ion.

True saltlike carbides are formed by the most electropositive metals. Examples are Be_2C, CaC_2, and Al_4C_3. These form colorless transparent crystals, and they are hydrolyzed to complete decomposition by water. Some carbides contain simple C^{4-} ions; others contain C_2^{2-} ions. The compounds Be_2C and Al_4C_3 are examples of the first type; on hydrolysis they yield methane, CH_4, as one product:

$$Al_4C_3 + 12H_2O \rightarrow 4Al(OH)_3 + 3CH_4$$

But calcium carbide, CaC_2, contains the C_2^{2-} ion and yields acetylene on hydrolysis:

$$CaC_2 + 2H_2O \rightarrow Ca(OH)_2 + C_2H_2$$

Silicon is another element that forms saltlike binary compounds. These are called silicides, of which Ca_2Si is an example.

Binary compounds are also formed by nitrogen, and these fall into saltlike, interstitial, and covalent classifications. The ionic nitrides are formed by Mg, Ca, Zn, Li, Th, and other electropositive elements. These salts may be prepared by direct synthesis or by heating the corresponding amides; for example,

$$3Ba(NH_2)_2 \rightarrow Ba_3N_2 + 4NH_3$$

The formulas of the ionic nitrides may be written with the usual oxidation state of the metal and the assumption that the nitrogen is present as the nitride N^{3-} ion. All ionic nitrides hydrolyze to yield ammonia, as is the case for Mg_3N_2:

$$Mg_3N_2 + 6H_2O \rightarrow 3Mg(OH)_2 + 2NH_3$$

Nitrogen forms another series of binary compounds with metals. These are the azides. The more electropositive metals form solid saltlike azides, of which NaN_3 is an example. These contain the linear N—N—N ion. Hydrazoic acid, HN_3, and many metal azides are dangerously explosive, but NaN_3 decomposes smoothly when heated to 300° C:

$$2NaN_3 \rightarrow 2Na + 3N_2$$

Lead azide, $Pb(N_3)_2$, finds use as a detonator. The ability to form binary salts is also found to a degree in the nonmetals boron, phosphorus, and arsenic, but with increasing complexities of structure and valency. We shall not be greatly concerned with these substances.

26.7 *Interstitials*

The elements boron, carbon, nitrogen, oxygen, silicon, phosphorus, arsenic, and sulfur, among others, all form interstitial binary compounds. We shall limit our discussion to a few examples. Interstitials formed by hydrogen have already been mentioned (Sec. 22.3).

The name "interstitial" was originally applied to these substances, as it was to hydrogen interstitials, because it was thought that the nonmetal entered interstices between atoms of the metal. Interstitials have properties reminiscent of the metals from which they are formed, namely, opacity, electrical conductivity, and metallic luster. The density of an interstitial is generally somewhat lower than that of the metal from which it is formed, but the interstitials are often very hard and have melting points much higher than the metals. There is also usually a fairly wide range of composition over which the same crystal structure occurs.

Interstitials may be prepared by direct synthesis or by heating the metal in the presence of some gaseous compound of the nonmetal. Examples of such gaseous compounds are CH_4, NH_3, and H_2S. The element chromium unites with boron in several different proportions, and all have some of the properties of interstitials. For instance, the composition CrB contains zigzig chains of boron atoms. The chain of borons are infinite in length. Other interstitial borides contain double chains of boron atoms, and AlB_2 has layers of borons with layers of aluminum atoms between them.

True interstitials of nitrogen are formed by the transition metals. Some of these, such as VN, have unusual and useful properties. Vanadium nitride is very hard and melts above 2500° C. Other compounds, some of which are quite difficult to classify as interstitials, salts, or otherwise, are notable for their electronic properties. Thus, indium arsenide, InAs (and InSb), are used in the detection and measurement of magnetic fields.

The interstitial carbides of iron are of particular interest in metallurgy and catalysis. There are at least two carbides of iron, Fe_3C and Fe_2C, the latter being dimorphous. The compound Fe_3C, called cementite, is found in the blast furnace, where it plays a part in the production of pig iron. Like iron itself, cementite is ferromagnetic. Similar kinds of carbides are formed by most of the transition metals.

1. What is a salt?
2. The compounds $SnCl_4$ and UF_4, together with a few others, are shown for convenience in Table 26.1. But these compounds do not show many of the properties of the true salts. What are these properties?
3. Name the following: Zn_3P_2, UB_2, InF_3, CuI, Sb_2S_5, KN_3, Be_3N_2.
4. Suggest, with equations and a few essential details, how to prepare each of the following: Ni_3C, $Pb(N_3)_2$, Mg_3N_2, ZnF_2, MnS, $SnCl_4$, $CaCl_2$, Hg_2Br_2, FeI_3.
5. Fluorine is the most electronegative of all elements and therefore might be expected to form the most nearly ionic compounds. Yet UF_6 is a molecular compound. Is there any contradiction here?
6. Cesium fluoride is often said to be an extreme example of an ionic compound. How would one prepare such a compound?
7. How is it possible to prepare pure $NaCl$ from a water solution, but not pure NaF? Pure CaF_2, but not pure NaF?
8. The chlorides, bromides, and iodides of the metals have much in common. Is this true of the fluorides?
9. It is often said that UF_6 is a gas. Is this correct?
10. Compare the electrical conductivity of the following as fused salts: $LiCl$, $BeCl_2$, $CaCl_2$, and $SnCl_4$.
11. Some binary compounds of metal plus nonmetal vaporize without any major change of molecular structure; others do not. Classify the following as to structure in the vapor as compared with structure in the solids: $NaCl$, $AlCl_3$, $FeCl_3$, $CuCl$, $SnCl_4$.
12. May it be said that all soluble salts form electrically conducting solutions in water?
13. The following iodides have not been prepared: FeI_3, CuI_2, and TlI_3. Is there any special reason for this?
14. Is it correct to say that no salt of a weak acid, or of a weak base, or of both, may be prepared pure from a water solution? Illustrate your answer with specific examples.
15. What is the chemical evidence that the carbide ion in aluminum carbide is different from that in calcium carbide?
16. Do the metal azides fall into the category of saltlike, interstitial, or covalent compounds of nitrogen?
17. Summarize the principal differences between saltlike and interstitial compounds of the same nonmetal.
18. Write equations showing the principal products, ions or otherwise, when each of the following is placed in contact with water: KCl, $ZnCl_2$, $PbBr_2$, $GaCl_3$, Rb_2S, Ca_3P_2, AlN, NaN_3.

19. Write equations showing the principal products formed when each of the following is treated with concentrated sulfuric acid: $AgCl$, KI, CuS, and MgF_2.

20. Neglecting hydrolysis, find the volume of saturated Ag_2S solution, which, on the average, would contain only one Ag^+ ion.

21. The solubility product for thallium sulfide, Tl_2S, is about 1×10^{-22}. Find the lowest pH at which Tl_2S will precipitate from a solution containing $1 \times 10^{-4}M$ Tl^+. The solution is saturated with H_2S.

22. If an acidified solution containing Fe^{3+} is saturated with H_2S, there is obtained a cloudiness due to free sulfur, but no precipitate of iron sulfide. Explain (a) why the sulfur forms, and (b) why no iron sulfide forms.

23. It is proposed to convert silver iodide to silver sulfide by shaking the AgI in water that contains $5M$ HCl and is saturated with H_2S. Show by appropriate calculations if this is possible.

24. A solution is made up containing 10 grams of sodium acetate, NaAc, and 5 ml of $6M$ acetic acid dissolved in 100 ml of solution. To this is added 50 mg of Mn^{2+} in the form of $Mn(NO_3)_2$. The solution is now saturated with H_2S. Find the number of milligrams of Mn^{2+} that will remain in the solution. For MnS, $K_{sp} = 7 \times 10^{-16}$.

25. A binary salt solution, NaA, is prepared at a concentration of $0.01M$ in water. The hydroxide ion concentration is then found to be $1 \times 10^{-5}M$. Find the ionization constant for the (obviously) weak acid HA.

27

Other Binary Compounds

Binary compounds involving metals only have already been mentioned (Sec. 18.5), and binary compounds involving a metal and a nonmetal were the topic of Chapter 26. The only binary compounds remaining to be described are those between two nonmetals. For want of a better name, we shall be forced to refer to such compounds as "other binary compounds."

The compounds to be considered in this chapter are shown in Table 27.1. The arrangement in the table is one of more or less increasing electronegativity from left to right and from bottom to top for the elements listed at top and side, respectively. Many of the pairs of elements form two or more binary compounds, and where this is the case, the more important compounds are all shown. For the sake of completeness the homoatomic substances such as molecular chlorine, Cl_2, and diamond, $\langle C \rangle_\infty$, are also shown. These elements have already been described in Chapter 18, as have the oxides of the nonmetals in Chapter 25; but these oxides are also binary compounds and they are included in Table 27.1. The hydrides of the nonmetals, which were described in Chapter 22, are not shown in the table. The reason for this omission is that the unique position of hydrogen in the Periodic Table makes it impossible to classify as metal or nonmetal.

Preparation methods for the compounds shown in Table 27.1 are in general those of direct synthesis from the elements. When two or more

TABLE 27.1 SOME BINARY COMPOUNDS OF THE NONMETALS

	B	Si	C	As	P	N	Se	S	O	I	Br	Cl	F
F	BF_3	SiF_4	CF_4	AsF_3 AsF_5	PF_3 PF_5	NF_3	SeF_4 SeF_6	SF_6 etc	OF_2	IF_5 IF_7	BrF_3 BrF_5	ClF ClF_3	F_2
Cl	BCl_3	$SiCl_4$	CCl_4	$AsCl_3$ $AsCl_5$	PCl_3 PCl_5	NCl_3 ClN_3	Se_2Cl_2 $SeCl_4$	S_2Cl_2 SCl_2 SCl_4	Cl_2O ClO_2 etc.	ICl ICl_3	$BrCl$	Cl_2	
Br	BBr_3	$SiBr_4$ etc.	CBr_4	$AsBr_3$	PBr_3 PBr_5	BrN_3	Se_2Br_2 Se_2Br_4	S_2Br_2	Br_2O BrO_2	IBr	Br_2		
I	BI_3	SiI_4	CI_4	AsI_3 AsI_5	PI_3	IN_3	...	...	I_2O_5	I_2			
O	$\langle B_2O_3\rangle_\infty$	$\langle SiO_2\rangle_\infty$	CO CO_2	As_2O_3	P_2O_3 P_2O_5	N_2O NO NO_2 etc.	SeO_2 SeO_3	SO_2 SO_3	O_2 O_3				
S	$\langle B_2S_3\rangle_\infty$	$\langle SiS_3\rangle_\infty$	CS_2	As_2S_3 As_2S_5	P_4S_3	S_4N_4 S_4N_2	$SeS?$ SeS_2	S_8					
Se	$\langle B_2Se\rangle_\infty$	...	...	As_2Se_3	P_4Se_3	Se_4N_4	Se_8						
N	$\langle BN\rangle_\infty$	$\langle Si_3N_2\rangle_\infty$	C_2N_2	...	P_3N_5	N_2							
P	$\langle BP\rangle_\infty$	...	...	AsP	P_4								
As	...	...	...	As_4									
C	$\langle B_4C\rangle_\infty$	$\langle SiC\rangle_\infty$	$\langle C\rangle_\infty$										
Si	$\langle B_3Si\rangle_\infty$	$\langle Si\rangle_\infty$											
B	$\langle B\rangle_\infty$												

compounds are possible for the same pair of elements, as is the case for PCl_3 and PCl_5, due regard must be paid to the relative proportions of the reacting elements. In a few cases it is necessary to use special methods, and these will in due course be described. The properties of the compounds show a great diversity. Some like SCl_2 are molecular, some like BN form infinite polymeric lattices resembling diamond in structure. These latter are designated by the special method adopted for this book, namely, $\langle BN\rangle_\infty$. But complexities do not end here; some binary compounds, such as CS_2, are dimorphous, forming particulate molecules in one form and infinite lattices in another.

Advantage will be taken of the opportunity presented in this chapter to outline some current theories concerning chemical valence.

27.2 *Interhalogens*

The first group of binary compounds, formed by two nonmetals, to be described is that in which two different halogens are involved. Such compounds are, quite appropriately, called *interhalogens*.

If some chlorine were to be prepared entirely from the isotope chlorine-35 and if this were to be mixed with some chlorine-37, it would be expected that under appropriate conditions of temperature and pressure, an exchange reaction would take place as follows:

$$^{35}Cl_2 + {}^{37}Cl_2 \rightleftharpoons 2({}^{35}Cl{}^{37}Cl)$$

Similarly, if chlorine is mixed with bromine under appropriate experimental conditions, the following reaction takes place:

$$Cl_2 + Br_2 \rightleftharpoons 2BrCl$$

The compound BrCl is an interhalogen. It is called bromine chloride, following the usual plan of placing the more electronegative element second in the name. The electron dot formula for bromine chloride is

$$:\overset{..}{\underset{..}{Br}}\!-\!\overset{..}{\underset{..}{Cl}}:$$

The bond between the halogen atoms is essentially covalent.

A considerable number of interhalogens is known, but none contains more than two different halogen atoms. A general formula for these compounds is XX'_n, where X is the less electronegative atom of the two. The subscript n may equal 1, 3, 5, 7; hence compounds are known with formulas such as ClF, ClF_3, BrF_3, IF_5 and IBr. Almost all the interhalogens may be prepared by direct synthesis. For instance, bromine vapor diluted with nitrogen reacts with fluorine, in suitable proportions, to yield BrF_3. Iodine monochloride, ICl, is obtained by mixing the elements in a 1:1 atomic ratio, and cooling the mixture.

The interhalogens such as BrF and ICl have properties similar to those of the true halogen molecules. Some of them are gases, some liquids, and some solids. Unlike the true halogens, the interhalogens have appreciable dipole moments, as might be expected from the appreciable difference in electronegativity between any two different halogen atoms. Bromine trifluoride appears to have an unusually high electrical conductivity for a pure compound. This is thought to be due to self-ionization as follows:

$$2BrF_3 \rightleftharpoons BrF_2^+ + BrF_4^-$$

It will be recalled that most of the halogens undergo reactions of hydrolysis in basic solution to yield, as in the case of chlorine, a chloride and a hypochlorite:

$$Cl_2 + 2OH^- \rightarrow Cl^- + OCl^- + H_2O$$

Several of the interhalogens react similarly, an example being the basic hydrolysis of iodine monochloride:

$$ICl + 2OH^- \rightarrow Cl^- + OI^- + H_2O$$

In such a reaction, the less electronegative of the two halogen atoms forms the hypohalite ion. Bromine trifluoride is useful as a fluorinating agent. It is possible to prepare compounds such as potassium hexa-fluorovanadate, KVF_6, by treating a mixture of KCl and VCl_3 with BrF_3. Iodine monochloride has applications in analytical chemistry.

27.3 Pseudohalogens

There are some diverse groups of atoms that show properties similar to those of the halogens. Some of these are binary compounds; some are more complex. These compounds are called *pseudohalogens* ("false" halo-gens). This discussion will be limited to a single example, namely, cyanogen, $(CN)_2$. Advantage will also be taken to review the chemical properties of the halogens, even though most of these properties have already been presented.

Cyanogen may be prepared by heating silver cyanide, AgCN:

$$2AgCN \rightarrow 2Ag + (CN)_2$$

Sodium cyanide may be prepared by heating sodamide with carbon:

$$NaNH_2 + C \rightarrow H_2 + NaCN$$

or by heating sodium carbonate with carbon in the presence of nitrogen:

$$Na_2CO_3 + 4C + N_2 \rightarrow 3CO + 2NaCN$$

Silver cyanide may be obtained by dissolving NaCN in water and then adding Ag^+ in the form of silver nitrate to precipitate AgCN. The decomposition of AgCN to yield $(CN)_2$ may be thought of as an oxidation of the CN^- ion by Ag^+. Other oxidizing agents such as Cu^{2+} or Pb^{4+} will serve this purpose so that, even in its preparation, cyanogen bears a resemblance to the true halogens, which are almost invariably prepared by oxidation of a halide ion. Cyanogen is a colorless, poisonous gas in which the atoms are arranged in the following order, N—C—C—N.

The properties of the halogens with which we shall compare those of the pseudohalogen cyanogen are as follows:

1. The halogens are all volatile compounds in which the molecule is formed from two identical units, as in $Cl + Cl \rightarrow Cl_2$. This is true also of cyanogen, which may be considered as being formed from CN units; thus: $CN + CN \rightarrow (CN)_2$.

2. The halogens undergo basic hydrolysis to yield halide and hypo-halite ions. For Cl_2 the reaction is

$$Cl_2 + 2OH^- \rightleftharpoons Cl^- + OCl^- + H_2O$$

Similarly, cyanogen undergoes basic hydrolysis yielding cyanide and cyanate ions:

$$(CN)_2 + 2OH^- \rightleftharpoons CN^- + OCN^- + H_2O$$

3. The halogens form interhalogens:

$$Cl_2 + I_2 \rightleftharpoons 2ICl$$

Cyanogen forms a pseudohalogen-halogen with fluorine:

$$(CN)_2 + F_2 \rightleftharpoons 2CNF$$

and other similar compounds such as CNCl and CNBr are known. Furthermore, true inter-pseudohalogens are formed between two pseudohalogens. An example is CN(SCN) and another is CN(N$_3$). (The azide ion, N$_3^-$, is sufficiently like the halide ions to be considered a pseudohalide, although no neutral pseudohalogen of the formula (N$_3$)$_2$ is known.)

4. The halogens may be reduced to form halide ions, and these in turn form a wide variety of salts of which NaCl is one. Similarly, cyanogen may form cyanide, CN$^-$, ions, which unite with many metal ions to form salts such as NaCN. And just as AgCl and certain other metal halides are insoluble in water, so AgCN is insoluble in water.

5. Some halogens may be displaced by others as, for example,

$$2I^- + Br_2 \rightarrow I_2 + 2Br^-$$

Similarly, the pseudohalogen thiocyanogen, (SCN)$_2$, may be displaced from silver thiocyanate by bromine:

$$2SCN^- + Br_2 \rightarrow (SCN)_2 + 2Br^-$$

6. The halide ions all unite with hydrogen ion to form the volatile hydrogen halides, of which HCl is one. Similarly, the cyanide ion unites with H$^+$ to form hydrogen cyanide, a poisonous gas. There is, however, a difference in that all hydrogen halides except HF are strong acids in water. All hydrogen pseudohalides are weak acids in water.

7. The halide ion enter into complex ion formation, an example being FeF$_6^{3-}$. Similarly, CN$^-$ enters into complexes of which Fe(CN)$_6^{3-}$ is one.

8. The pseudohalide ions are, in at least more than one case, oxidizable to yield the free pseudohalogen as described above for CN$^-$.

All the above and other properties establish the soundness of the view that these substances may indeed be considered as pseudohalogens.

TABLE 27.2   PSEUDOHALOGENS AND PSEUDOHALIDES

Pseudohalogen	Pseudohalide ion
Cyanogen $(CN)_2$	cyanide CN^-
	cyanate OCN^-
Thiocyanogen $(SCN)_2$	thiocyanate SCN^-
Selenocyanogen $(SeCN)_2$	selenocyanate $SeCN^-$
	tellurocyanate $TeCN^-$
	azide N_3^-
Azidocarbondisulfide $(SeSN_3)_2$	

Only four pseudohalogens are known as the free compound. These are $(CN)_2$, $(SCN)_2$, $(SeCN)_2$, and $(SCSN_3)_2$. Several others are known as the pseudohalide ion. Example of these are OCN^-, $TeCN^-$, and N_3^-. Table 27.2 gives the names and formulas of several of these compounds and ions.

In spite of their interesting properties, the pseudohalogens cannot be said to have many uses. But cyanogen itself burns in oxygen to produce a flame temperature of over $4500°$ C and may therefore find applications in high temperature research.

27.4 *Volatile Halides*

All the nonmetals combine with nearly all the halogens, and some of the compounds so formed are of considerable importance. This discussion will be concerned principally with the following: BF_3, CCl_4, $SiCl_4$, PCl_3, PCl_5, NF_3, NCl_3, SF_6, S_2Cl_2 and SCl_2. While it is true that most, if not all, of these substances may be formed by direct synthesis under appropriate conditions, yet in several cases other methods are much more convenient. Many of the nonmetal halides are gases at room temperature and nearly all are volatile.

Boron unites with each of the halogens to form compounds of the type BX_3. Of these, the trifluoride is the most important. It may be made by treating B_2O_3 with HF, the latter being conveniently prepared *in situ*:

$$B_2O_3 + 3CaF_2 + 3H_2SO_4 \rightarrow 2BF_3 + 3CaSO_4 + 3H_2O$$

The BF_3 is a pungent, colorless gas boiling at $-101°$ C, in sharp contrast to the ionic, crystalline AlF_3. Boron trifluoride is a fairly stable compound, although it undergoes reaction with water, forming either hydrates or fluoroboric acid, HBF_4. But the principal interest in BF_3 is its unusual strength as a Lewis acid. Reference to this property has already been made (Sec. 13.4) and it will suffice here to recall that the reaction represented in this way:

$$
\begin{array}{cccc}
& \text{F} & & \text{F} \\
& | & & | \\
\text{F}-\text{B} & + \ :\text{X} \rightarrow & \text{F}-\text{B}-\text{X} \\
& | & & | \\
& \text{F} & & \text{F}
\end{array}
$$

where :X is any Lewis base, takes place with considerable vigor. Examples of Lewis bases that react as above are F^- to form BF_4^-, and NH_3 to form $F_3B:NH_3$. Because of this potent "acid" reaction, BF_3 finds many uses as a catalyst or in the formation of intermediates, especially in organic chemistry. In contrast to BF_3, carbon tetrafluoride, CF_4, is an unusually unreactive gas.

Silicon tetrafluoride, SiF_4, is formed by the reaction of hydrogen fluoride or hydrofluoric acid on silica:

$$SiO_2 + 4HF \rightarrow SiF_4 + 2H_2O$$

This compound is also a gas. Like CF_4, it does not possess the Lewis acidity shown by BF_3. It does, however, undergo hydrolysis to yield fluorosilicic acid, H_2SiF_6, the lead salt of which, $PbSiF_6$, is used in the electrolytic purification of lead.

Carbon tetrachloride, CCl_4, is a familiar solvent. It is made by passing chlorine into carbon disulfide in the presence of iodine as a catalyst:

$$CS_2 + 3Cl_2 \rightarrow S_2Cl_2 + CCl_4$$

Carbon tetrachloride is a colorless liquid (bp 76° C) with a not too unpleasant odor. It is a relatively unreactive substance and it is used in some types of fire extinguishers, although less so than formerly. No reaction with water occurs under normal circumstances. As are most chlorinated hydrocarbons, it is a potentially dangerous poison. Carbon tetrachloride readily dissolves grease and is used for that purpose.

Silicon tetrachloride, $SiCl_4$, may be prepared by direct synthesis; a more convenient method is to heat silica with carbon and chlorine at high temperature:

$$SiO_2 + 2C + 2Cl_2 \rightarrow SiCl_4 + 2CO$$

The $SiCl_4$ is a colorless liquid (bp 57.5° C) that fumes strongly in damp air, owing to hydrolysis. Our chief interest in this substance is to explore the reason why BF_3, SiF_4, and especially $SiCl_4$, undergo hydrolysis while the corresponding halides of carbon are relatively unreactive. The reason for this in the case of BF_3 has already been stated, namely, that the strong Lewis acidity related to the vacant orbital readily accommodates other reactive atoms or ions. But CF_4 cannot exhibit this kind of activity because all valency electrons and all available orbitals are already engaged in forming bonds to the four fluorine atoms. There is no position on the CF_4 (or CCl_4) molecule where a water molecule could become attached to initiate the first step in hydrolysis.

In the corresponding silicon halides the situation is different. Not only is the silicon atom larger and thus able to surround itself with more atoms, but the $3d$ orbital, though normally empty in silicon, is capable of being utilized to form bonds with extra atoms. That such an effect is possible is clear from the existence of ions such as SiF_6^{2-} in which the silicon atom is bonded to six fluorines. A water molecule has, therefore, little difficulty in attaching itself to a SiF_4 or $SiCl_4$ molecule. Once this step has been achieved, the further reaction to liberate HF (or to form H_2SiF_4) or HCl, as the case may be, is easily completed.

Turning now to nitrogen, we find only four known binary halides. These are N_2F_2, N_2F_4, NF_3, and NCl_3. Nitrogen trifluoride may be prepared by the electrolysis of ammonium fluoride dissolved in anhydrous HF. In the presence of a copper catalyst, ammonia will react with excess fluorine to yield NF_3. This is a surprisingly stable gas (bp $-129°$ C). It is unreactive with water, and heating does not affect it unless a reducing metal is present. The fluoride N_2F_2 may have some applications as a high-energy fuel component.

Nitrogen trichloride, NCl_3, may be formed as a pale yellow oil (bp $\sim 71°$ C) if chlorine is passed into a solution of NH_4Cl in water. The NCl_3 is an exceedingly dangerous explosive substance. It undergoes complete hydrolysis to form ammonia and hypochlorite:

$$NCl_3 + 3OH^- \rightarrow NH_3 + 3OCl^-$$

Now that we have finished explaining why BF_3 is hydrolyzed and CF_4 is not, we have the more difficult problem of explaining why NCl_3 is so reactive and NF_3 is not. There is no generally accepted explanation for this effect, but it may be pointed out that fluorine is considerably more electronegative (which means more electron-attracting) than is chlorine. It seems possible that the unshared electrons present in NH_3, and which are responsible for the Lewis base character of NH_3, are somehow forced into different orbitals in NF_3 and that they are then not able to contribute to the chemical reactivity of the molecule. But in NCl_3 this influence on the electrons is much diminished, and they are able to exhibit their normal reactivity. Another possible reason for the failure of NF_3 to undergo hydrolysis is the absence of any fluorine ion (such as OF^-) corresponding to OCl^-.

It is often stated that nitrogen forms an iodide, NI_3. Certainly, a substance often called nitrogen triiodide is an astonishingly sensitive explosive, the tread of a fly being more than enough to set it off. But this substance is actually an ammoniate of nitrogen triiodide, the formula being $NI_3 \cdot NH_3$. No compound of the simple formula NI_3 is known.

Sulfur forms a considerable number of halides. Sulfur hexafluoride, SF_6, is a colorless gas that may be obtained by direct synthesis from the elements. It is one of the most inert of all compounds known, this property being doubtless related to the way in which the fluorines surround and protect the sulfur atom from attack by other atoms. The structure is an octahedral arrangement of the fluorines around the sulfur. Other sulfur halides of interest include S_2Cl_2 and SCl_2. The former is made by reaction of sulfur with a limited amount of chlorine; the latter, by treating S_2Cl_2 with more Cl_2. These compounds are orange and red liquids, respectively; the odor of S_2Cl_2 is especially revolting. Both are reactive compounds; S_2Cl_2 is used in the rubber industry.

Our discussion of phosphorus halides will be limited to PCl_3 and PCl_5. These are made by treating phosphorus with limited or excess of chlorine, respectively. Both compounds are solids and both hydrolyze strongly in water; PCl_3 yields HCl plus H_3PO_3 and PCl_5 yields HCl plus H_3PO_4, although with a restricted amount of water it is possible to obtain $POCl_3$.

27.5   Volatile Sulfides

Only one important compound needs be presented under this heading. This is carbon disulfide, CS_2. Carbon disulfide may be prepared by direct synthesis, sulfur vapor being passed over red-hot carbon:

$$C + S_2 \rightarrow CS_2$$

The product is a volatile colorless liquid (bp 46° C). Commercial carbon disulfide often has a nauseating odor, but this is due to impurities, the pure compound having only a slight and not unpleasant odor.

The structure of the CS_2 molecule is similar to that of CO_2, and in fact it is possible to replace one of the oxygens in CO_2 with sulfur to form carbon oxysulfide, COS, as already mentioned in Sec. 25.2. Carbon disulfide is highly flammable in air. It burns to form CO_2 and SO_2. It does not dissolve or react with water, but it is a good solvent for sulfur. The principal uses are in the manufacture of rayon and of carbon tetrachloride. Recently it has been found that at very high pressures, CS_2 may be converted into a stable, black polymer $\langle CS_2 \rangle_\infty$.

Another compound that will be mentioned is silicon disulfide, SiS_2. This is normally a polymeric substance, and it will be described more fully in Sec. 27.6. At high temperatures it is volatile and appears to form SiS_2 molecules.

The last compound to be mentioned in this section is tetranitrogen tetrasulfide, N_4S_4. This compound may scarcely be considered as volatile;

it explodes when heated. It is made by the reaction of dry NH_3 with S_2Cl_2 in ether solution:

$$6S_2Cl_2 + 16NH_3 \rightarrow N_4S_4 + 12NH_4Cl + S_8$$

The molecule appears to be a puckered ring:

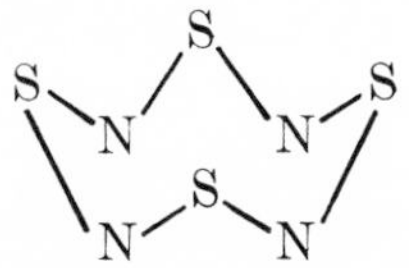

This resembles the puckered ring structure for the molecule S_8. It must, however, be pointed out that there is probably some bonding directly between sulfur atoms in N_4S_4. The compound has unusual chemical properties, and it is a parent substance for other sulfur-nitrogen compounds.

27.6 *Continuous Lattice Compounds*

In previous chapters there have been presented several substances that are not ionic but which show no evidence of forming particulate molecules in the sense that CO_2 forms molecules. Boron sesquioxide is one such substance, and silicon dioxide is another, in which the bonding between atoms is essentially covalent; arrays of atoms so bonded extend indefinitely throughout the solid example. Carbon in the form of diamond is a prime example of such an infinite lattice in three dimensions, but two-dimensional infinite lattices are also known, as are one-dimensional lattices. This section will be devoted to some additional examples of infinite lattice substances. The examples selected are boron nitride, silicon carbide, and silicon disulfide.

Boron nitride may be prepared by direct combustion of boron in nitrogen or by heating boron in ammonia:

$$2B + N_2 \rightarrow 2BN$$
$$2B + 2NH_3 \rightarrow 2BN + 3H_2$$

It may also be prepared by strong ignition of various compounds, of which the "salt" $F_3B:NH_3$ is one. The product is a white solid. The melting point appears to be in excess of 3000° C.

Chief interest in boron nitride lies in its structure. There are two known polymorphs, one of which resembles the structure of graphite. This form consists of sheets formed from six-membered hexagons of alternate boron and nitrogen atoms.

The distance B—N in any hexagon is 1.45 Å, which is consistent with the view that the bonds are covalent. But the distance between layers is 3.34 Å, suggesting that the bonding in this dimension is more nearly of the van der Waals type. This form of BN is a slippery substance, similar in this respect to graphite. This further supports the view of the structure being an infinite covalent lattice, but only in two dimensions, thus forming vast parallel sheets loosely held together. This form of boron nitride is sometimes referred to as "white graphite."

This analogy to carbon suggests that boron nitride might assume another crystal structure analogous to diamond. This is actually the case; at 70,000 atm pressure and 3000° C the graphite form of boron nitride may be converted to a structure like diamond in which each boron is surrounded by four nitrogens, and each nitrogen is surrounded by four borons.

This form of boron nitride is hard enough to scratch diamond, and it may be the hardest substance known. It is a true three-dimensional infinite lattice. It will be noted that B—N is isoelectronic with C—C. This feature is apparently responsible, at least in part, for the similarity in physical properties. Several other binary compounds, such as AlP, exhibit similar phenomena, but none to the degree shown by BN. The chemical properties of BN are perhaps of less interest. It is stable in air, but slowly hydrolyzes in contact with water.

The binary compound silicon carbide is familiar under the trade name Carborundum. While it could doubtless be synthesized from the elements, it is manufactured by the reaction of carbon with silica at high temperature:

$$SiO_2 + C \rightarrow SiC + 2CO$$

Silicon carbide is generally obtained as a black solid, but pure crystals are colorless. It has a melting point well in excess of 2000° C. The hardness approaches that of diamond. The crystal structure of silicon carbide is astonishing for the number of polymorphic forms shown, but all contain a three-dimensional infinite lattice consisting of silicons covalently bonded to four carbons and carbons to four silicons. Some of the polymorphic forms closely resemble the atomic arrangement in diamond. The compound is used as an abrasive and as a refractory. Chemically, it is rather inert.

The last continuous lattice compound to be described in this section is silicon disulfide. This compound may be prepared by the reaction of aluminum sulfide with silica at high temperature:

$$2Al_2S_3 + 3SiO_2 \rightarrow 2Al_2O_3 + 3SiS_2$$

As mentioned in the preceding section, the product is somewhat volatile at 1100° C and it appears as white needles in cooler parts of the furnace. Our chief interest in this compound is that it is an example of a one-dimensional infinite lattice. The atoms are arranged in long threadlike structures as follows:

The representation of this structure fails to indicate that the sulfur atoms are arranged tetrahedrally (rather than in a plane) about the silicons. The bonds between silicon and sulfur are essentially covalent, but those between the threadlike chains are apparently van der Waals. The compound is readily hydrolyzed in water.

27.7 *Some Valence Concepts*

Modern valence theory is so complicated that any attempt at simplification to the level of elementary chemistry carries with it a virtual certainty of planting serious misconceptions in the reader's mind. In recognition of this calculated risk, we shall proceed with caution and limit this discussion to some few examples that are reasonably free from complexities.

It was stated in Sec. 6.1 that the electron is a shadowy concept and that one of its properties is that its velocity and its position in space cannot be simultaneously determined accurately. This is a statement in words of the *Heisenberg uncertainty principle.* It is possible, however, to determine the energy of an electron in an atom, and this leads to the formulation of energy levels, or orbitals, as listed in Sec. 6.4. It will be recalled that

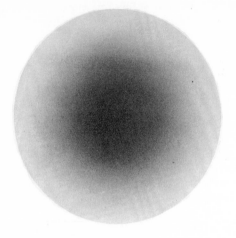

Fig. 27.1 Attempted spherical representation of an electron in a 1s orbital.

the orbitals are designated by the *s*, *p*, *d*, *f* system, in which the maximum possible number of electrons is 2, 6, 10, and 14, respectively. This limitation holds regardless of whether the electrons are 1*s*, 2*s*, 2*p*, 3*d*, or 4*f*, as the case may be. But the position in space of electrons in an atom can be stated only in terms of a mathematical probability that a given electron, be it *s*, *p*, *d*, or *f*, will be found in a certain geometrical position relative to the nucleus and to other electrons that may be present.

The probability of an *s* electron being present at any given distance from a nucleus is shown in Fig. 6.7, and this shows that the negative charge of the electron tends to concentrate at a certain distance from the nucleus. But this kind of representation fails to show that the charge distribution is three-dimensional and that it is spherical for any *s* electron, as show in Fig. 27.1. But Fig. 27.1 in turn carries the erroneous suggestion that the electron density is uniformly distributed within a sphere. Actually, the electron is concentrated near the surface of the sphere. If one could slice the sphere in two and adjust the thickness and density of the skin thus revealed to correspond with the probability distribution out from the nucleus, as shown in Fig. 6.7, then one would have a reasonably satisfactory representation of an *s* electron.

All other diagrammatic representations of electrons shown in this section must be interpreted in the manner indicated in the preceding paragraph. With this in mind, we shall attempt to represent the probability distribution for a *p* electron. With *p* electrons, we encounter the complication that the electron distributions are sausage-shaped and also that the three pairs of electrons present as a maximum in the three orbitals show maxima at right angles to each other. This effect will be shown best by a diagram in which the long axes of the probability distributions are arranged along coordinates *x*, *y*, and *z*, as shown in Fig. 27.2. The three possible *p* orbitals are then, for convenience, designated as p_x, p_y, and p_z. Each of these may contain two electrons, and they project both forward and backward (corresponding to the two electrons present) for each of the three orbitals, all of which are at right angles to each other. What happens when we reach *d* orbitals will be hinted at in Chapter 29, but for further details the reader must consult a more advanced text.

The only atoms that have nothing more than an *s* orbital are hydrogen and helium. All other atoms have both *s* and *p*; most atoms have *s*, *p*, and *d*; some have these plus *f* orbitals. Whenever an atom has two or more kinds of orbitals, these orbitals *overlap* each other. For our purposes, the chief interest in the overlap concept is when it occurs as two atoms approach each other. It is obvious that overlap between the orbitals of two (or more) atoms could occur between *s* orbitals, between *p* orbitals, or between *s* and *p* orbitals. Still other combinations will suggest themselves. The importance of this, for our present purposes, is that chemical (covalent) bonding may occur if orbitals of two or more atoms overlap and if electrons are available to occupy these orbitals.

One popular theory of chemical bonding treats valence as being derived from the several *atomic orbitals* present in the combining atoms. Another theory considers that the electrons in compounds are in new orbitals that have no independent existence prior to formation of the compound, but which are formed as the bond is formed. This is called the *molecular orbital* theory. We shall not attempt to describe either of these theories, but we shall discuss very briefly a few compounds in an attempt to show in a general way how the atoms involved are held together. The compounds to be described are all familiar binary compounds already presented, but they are not necessarily diatomic (two atoms only) molecules. A general formula for these substances is AB_n, where *n* may have any value from 1 to 4. The substances all form particulate molecules. The class AB is represented by H_2; AB_2 by H_2O; AB_3 by NH_3; and AB_4 by CH_4.

The hydrogen atom has only an *s* orbital, and this is spherical. Overlap of two *s* orbitals, as may occur when two hydrogen atoms come close together, is considered (according to the molecular orbital theory) to

Fig. 27.2 Attempted representation of the electron probability distribution for p electrons, separated in p_x, p_y, and p_z suborbitals.

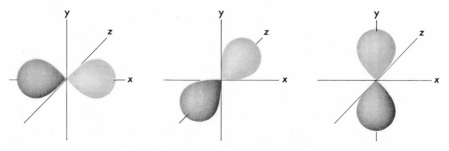

produce a cylindrical orbital extending over both nuclei. Orbitals of this kind are called σ (sigma) molecular orbitals, and the bonding so produced is called σ bonding. In favorable cases it is possible to calculate the strength of the bond.

The use of p orbitals in bond formation is complicated by their directional properties, p_x, p_y, and p_z, projecting at right angles to each other. However, combination of p and s orbitals are common.

In the water molecule the angle between the two hydrogens is 105 degrees. If bonding were solely a matter of overlap between s orbitals on the hydrogen atoms and p on the oxygen, it might be thought that the bond angle would be 90 degrees, in agreement with the normal bond angle between p orbitals. There has been considerable discussion about this matter, and a current view is that both s and p orbitals on the oxygen are combined by a process called *hybridization*. The hybrid orbital so produced is called sp^3, and the expected angle in this case is the tetrahedral angle, 109° 28′. Many other kinds of hybridizations have been invoked to explain the multitude of unique properties shown by various molecules.

In compounds such as CH_4 and CF_4, it is almost certain that sp^3 hybridization does occur. The bond angle in these compounds is exactly the tetrahedral angle.

Two further complications will be mentioned. It will be recalled that each p orbital projects in two directions. The signs of these are different. Now, if each of two atoms has (say) a p_z orbital available, they may form a bonding molecular orbital, but they will also form an antibonding orbital. Bonding and nonbonding molecular orbitals are also possible between p and s orbitals. Furthermore, if (say) p_z forms a *p σ-molecular orbital*, with the s orbital of another atom, then p_x and p_y may stick out more or less at right angles to the bonding p σ, and they in turn may form bonding and antibonding orbitals with some other atom. Bonds formed in this fashion are called π (pi) bonds.

EXERCISES

1. Compounds formed between a metal and a nonmetal are generally ionic substances; those between two metals are metallic. What kind of valence predominates in binary compounds formed between two nonmetals?

2. Is it correct to say that compounds formed between two nonmetals always occur as particulate molecules?

3. As far as valence forces are concerned, are the hydrides of the elements more like the compounds formed between metal and nonmetal or like those between nonmetal and nonmetal?

4. Direct synthesis from the elements is appropriate for all but a few of the compounds listed in Table 27.1. What are the exceptions?

5. Consider the general formula for interhalogens, XX_n'. Is there any obvious reason why the element that *may* be present in the greater proportion is always the more electronegative of the two?

6. A diatomic interhalogen always exhibits a small, though measurable, dipole moment, but the homopolar molecules do not. Why should this be true?

7. Bromine trifluoride is not the only compound that shows some analogy with water in its electric conductivity. Name a few more such substances.

8. Illustrate the hydrolysis of an interhalogen and suggest a reason why the less electronegative element should be the one to form the hypohalite ion.

9. List at least six properties of halogens and the corresponding properties of any pseudohalogen. Use equations.

10. Iodine forms polyhalide ions by reaction with iodide ion, as follows:

$$I_2 + I^- \rightleftharpoons I_3^-$$

(This is present in tincture of iodine, which contains I_2 dissolved in alcohol-water solution to which KI has been added.) Show how selenocyanogen could form a poly-pseudohalide ion.

11. Both BCl_3 and BBr_3 are rapidly and completely hydrolyzed by water, the products being H_3BO_3 and HCl or HBr, as the case may be. Does this mean that BCl_3 and BBr_3 are stronger or weaker Lewis acids than BF_3?

12. Consider the fluorides BF_3, CF_4, NF_3, OF_2, SF_4. Write reactions that may be expected when each is exposed to (a) F_2 and (b) F^-.

13. The sulfur chloride S_2Cl_2 is a by-product in the preparation of CCl_4. How could they be separated?

14. Certain fluorides such as CF_4, NF_3, and SF_6 are remarkably inert chemically. Other fluorides such as BF_3, SiF_4, OF_2, and SF_4 are highly reactive. What is the reason (or reasons) for this difference?

15. Using correct nomenclature for binary compounds (putting the less electronegative element first), we find that there are many volatile fluorides and chlorides but few volatile sulfides. Is there any obvious reason why this should be true?

16. In Table 27.1 the continuous lattice compounds seem to be concentrated in the lower left section. What explanation may be offered?

17. Give examples, with structures, for one-, two-, and three-dimensional continuous lattice compounds.

18. In silicon disulfide, are all the sulfur atoms in the same plane?

19. Explain briefly in general terms the following: Heisenberg uncertainty principle, orbital overlap, molecular orbital theory, orbital hybridization, σ bond, p σ-bond, π bond.

20. Indicate the electron probability distribution in space for an s orbital; for a p orbital.

21. What is the experimental evidence that the atoms in a water molecule do not lie in a straight line, H—O—H?

22. Is there any reason why xenon tetrafluoride could not have been discussed in this chapter rather than in Chapter 16?

23. The basic laws of chemical combination are the laws of conservation of mass, definite proportions, and multiple proportions. What is the status of these laws in modern chemistry?

24. Many substances have the same molecular structure in the solid as in the vapor, but many have a different structure. Is there any general principle that might aid in predicting to which class a given compound belongs?

25. Nonmetal vapors are common. Occasionally one hears the expression, "metallic gas." Is this conceivable?

28

Oxy-salts

28.1 General Properties of Oxy-salts

A table in the Appendix gives solubility information about a considerable number of salts, including oxy-salts. As outlined in Sec. 24.1, an oxy-salt is a salt in which it is possible to show by experimental procedures that some structural unit is present, that this unit carries a negative ionic charge, and that it consists of oxygen plus some other element in essentially covalent bonding. These oxy-ions may unite by electrovalence with various positive ions to form oxy-salts, many of which are substances of prime importance. This section will be devoted to some general properties of oxy-salts. The criterion for selection in this chapter will be that employed in previous chapters, namely, the substance taken up for discussion must be of importance to science or industry, it must exhibit some unusually interesting property, or it must conveniently illustrate some useful principle.

There are numerous methods by which oxy-salts may be prepared. Methods of general applicability will be outlined in this section and described with more examples in the succeeding two sections. An oxy-salt may, in general, be prepared by the reaction of an acid-forming oxide with a base-forming oxide. In many but not all cases, this means that the oxide of a nonmetal will react with the oxide of a metal to form an oxy-salt. A familiar example is to expose calcium oxide to carbon dioxide, to form the oxy-salt calcium carbonate:

$$CaO + CO_2 \rightarrow CaCO_3$$

This kind of reaction is suitable for almost any metal oxide, but it will yield an oxy-salt only for those nonmetal oxides that may be considered as acid anhydrides. Sometimes the reaction of a metal oxide with a nonmetal oxide is vigorous at or below room temperature. For other systems, it may be necessary to employ high temperatures.

An even more familiar preparation method for oxy-salts is to bring together, generally in aqueous solution, the positive ion, such as Ba^{2+}, and the negative oxy-ion, such as SO_4^{2-}. To do this, it is necessary to select compounds containing the two ions, and several possibilities present themselves. A simple, direct method is to neutralize the hydroxide containing the positive ion with the acid containing the negative ion. Thus, to form $BaSO_4$, one may mix in solution the base $Ba(OH)_2$ with the acid H_2SO_4:

$$Ba(OH)_2 + H_2SO_4 \rightarrow BaSO_4 + 2H_2O$$

This method has the advantage that the only by-product is water. If the salt is insoluble in water, it may be filtered and dried. If it is soluble in water, the water may be evaporated, provided hydrolysis does not decompose the salt.

A variant of the neutralization procedure for obtaining a salt is to add the appropriate acid to another salt of the cation. For instance, one might dissolve $Ba(NO_3)_2$ in water and then add H_2SO_4 to it. The $BaSO_4$ will precipitate as before. But these procedures for obtaining an oxy-salt depend on the availability of an appropriate oxy-acid. There are oxy-salts for which no corresponding oxy-acid is known, one of these being sodium manganate, Na_2MnO_4. For such salts it is necessary to use indirect preparation methods. Some of these will be described below.

Still other methods for bringing together the two ions of a salt include the reaction of a base with another salt. For example, $Ba(OH)_2$ will react with Na_2SO_4 in solution to yield a precipitate of $BaSO_4$, or alternatively, two appropriate salts may be mixed in solution. A solution of $Ba(NO_3)_2$ will yield a precipitate of $BaSO_4$ if it is mixed with a solution of Na_2SO_4. In such a case another salt, $NaNO_3$, may be formed in solution, but this is soluble in water and it may be removed by filtration. It may also be noted that should the desired product have been $NaNO_3$, it could have been obtained, after filtration, by evaporating the water, the $BaSO_4$ in this case being discarded.

Other preparative procedures may involve oxidation and reduction. Examples of these will be presented in due course. It may be noted that the positive ion in a salt need not be a metal. Ammonium, NH_4^+, and many other positive ions may form salts.

All oxy-salts are solids at room temperature. The properties with which we shall be chiefly concerned are the same as those described for binary salts, namely, thermal stability, solubility, hydrolytic behavior, and oxidation or reduction. The great variety and the usefulness of oxy-salts are due not only to the many different oxy-anions that are available, but also to the even greater variety of positive ions that may combine with the anions to form salts. It must also be pointed out that just as silicon dioxide and other substances form infinite structural lattices, so may certain oxy-ions form infinite lattices in one, two, or three dimensions. This will, in fact, form a convenient method for the classification of oxy-salts, and we shall divide them into the group that contains discrete anions and the group that contains infinite anions.

28.2 *Oxy-salts of Carbon*

We shall start with the bicarbonates and carbonates, all of which contain discrete HCO_3^- or CO_3^{2-} ions, respectively. It has already been pointed out that carbonic is a very weak acid and that the bicarbonate ion is even weaker. Although a solution of carbon dioxide in water appears to exist primarily as such, yet it also contains a small concentration of H_2CO_3 molecules, and these undergo dissociation according to the following two processes:

$$H_2CO_3 \rightleftharpoons H^+ + HCO_3^-$$

and

$$HCO_3^- \rightleftharpoons H^+ + CO_3^{2-}$$

The relative concentration of the three species is determined by the pH of the solution. A high pH (>11) results in a high relative concentration of CO_3^{2-} ions. A low pH (<6) favors CO_2 in water, and an intermediate pH in the neighborhood of 8 favors a higher relative concentration of HCO_3^-.

The addition of a positive ion such as Na^+, which may form a bicarbonate of low solubility, tends to lower the pH of the solution in accordance with the following reaction:

$$Na^+ + CO_2 + H_2O \rightarrow NaHCO_3 + H^+$$

This in turn diminishes the concentration of HCO_3^- and brings the reaction to a halt. To assure complete, or nearly complete, precipitation of $NaHCO_3$, it is necessary to add a weak base to react with the H^+ ions produced as shown in the preceding reaction. This is the basis of the Solvay process for the preparation of sodium bicarbonate.

In this process, CO_2, (derived principally from $CaCO_3$) is dissolved in water together with NH_3 and $NaCl$. The reaction that occurs is

$$Na^+ + CO_2 + NH_3 + H_2O \rightarrow NaHCO_3 + NH_4^+$$

The function of the NH_3 is to react with the water to keep the solution slightly basic; otherwise, the concentration of HCO_3^- would never become high enough to ensure the precipitation of $NaHCO_3$. It is obvious that for this method to succeed, close attention must be paid to concentrations.

The product is a white solid, properly called sodium hydrogen carbonate but generally known as baking soda or simply as "bicarbonate." If heated, it loses H_2O and CO_2 to form sodium carbonate:

$$2NaHCO_3 \rightarrow Na_2CO_3 + H_2O + CO_2$$

In water it forms a nearly neutral solution, but it reacts vigorously with all acids, liberating CO_2. This reaction is the basis of the use of $NaHCO_3$ in baking powder, the acid used being one such as tartaric. A similar reaction occurs when baking soda is used to combat gastric acidity, the acid in the stomach being hydrochloric. There are many positive ions that form soluble bicarbonates but insoluble carbonates. One of these is Ca^{2+}. This leads to a number of interesting reactions, which will be described below.

Sodium carbonate is made as indicated above, namely, by heating the bicarbonate. It is commonly known as washing soda or "soda-ash." The carbonate is also a white solid. Strong heating liberates some CO_2, but complete decomposition to the oxide requires a high temperature. Treatment with acid yields CO_2 readily and completely. The carbonate dissolves in water as a typical salt of a strong base and a weak acid and yields a basic solution. Sodium carbonate is widely used in chemical industry and in the home.

A few other carbonates, including those of the alkali metals and ammonium, are soluble in water, but most metal carbonates are insoluble. Examples of well-known insoluble carbonates are $MgCO_3$, $CaCO_3$, and $FeCO_3$. Magnesium, and calcium carbonates, either alone or in mixed carbonates, are important rock minerals that form a substantial fraction of the earth's crust. Heating liberates CO_2 from these compounds, as already described, and even though insoluble in water, they all dissolve in nitric acid, with the liberation of CO_2. The equilibrium relationships involving $CaCO_3$ in contact with water and CO_2 are based on the following reaction, which is essentially the neutralization of the weak acid CO_2 by the rather strong base CO_3^{2-}:

$$CaCO_3 + CO_2 + H_2O \rightleftharpoons Ca^{2+} + 2HCO_3^-$$

If Ca^{2+} ions are present in water to which CO_2 is added, a precipitate of $CaCO_3$ will form. But if $CaCO_3$ is treated with a higher concentration of CO_2 in water, then the $CaCO_3$ will dissolve, with the formation of Ca^{2+} ions and HCO_3^- ions, as indicated in the equation. This is the reason that the exhaled breath, blown into limewater, dilute $Ca(OH)_2$, will cause a cloudy, white precipitate of $CaCO_3$ (a frequently used test for CO_2). But if the exhaled breath or other CO_2 source continues to be blown into the limewater, the white cloudy precipitate of $CaCO_3$ will disappear. Similarly, water containing dissolved CO_2 under pressure as it sometimes occurs underground will dissolve $CaCO_3$, thus forming underground passages and caves. But if the solution of $Ca(HCO_3)_2$ thus formed comes into a space where the CO_2 may escape, thus lowering the CO_2 concentration in the water, then $CaCO_3$ will reprecipitate. This is the mechanism by which stalactites and stalagmites are formed in caves. The same mechanism controls the formation of scale in pipes and water vessels carrying hard water.

While bicarbonates and carbonates are the principal classes of inorganic oxy-salts of carbon, it must not be overlooked that all organic acids form oxy-salts. The formates, acetates, and oxalates are the simplest examples of these. Their sodium salts are respectively $NaHCO_2$, $NaCH_3CO_2$, and $Na_2C_2O_4$.

28.3   Oxy-salts of Nitrogen and of Phosphorus

The salts of nitric acid are simpler than those of carbon in that only one replaceable hydrogen is present in the acid. But there are other complexities related to the ready reducibility of the nitrate ion. Sodium nitrate occurs in nature as an ore in Chile. This and nitric acid constitute the only important sources of industrial nitrates, although bacterial action produces nitrates in soil. Metal nitrates are readily prepared by neutralization of the appropriate hydroxide by nitric acid. For all but the most noble metals, such as gold and platinum, the metal itself may dissolve in concentrated nitric acid, this being possible because of the very strong oxidizing action of this acid. If, as an example, silver is dissolved in concentrated HNO_3, the reaction proceeds as follows:

$$Ag + 2HNO_3(conc) \rightarrow Ag^+ + NO_3^- + NO_2 + H_2O$$

It so happens that all nitrates are soluble in water. To obtain a salt such as silver nitrate from solution, it is therefore necessary to evaporate the water. This may be done readily for the nitrate of a strong base, as occurs for $NaNO_3$, but for many nitrates, especially of the transition metals, some hydrolysis may occur. Furthermore, nitrates of the more active metals lose oxygen and become nitrites, and nitrates of the less active metals lose nitrogen dioxide and oxygen and become metal oxides or even a metal. The preparation of a pure dry metal nitrate may therefore require some care. Nevertheless, from acid solution, beautiful pure crystals of hydrated nitrates may be obtained. Ferric nitrate hydrate so prepared is a pale lavender color, although generally the product is colored brown by hydrolysis to hydrous ferric oxide. The nitrates of metals other than transition metals, and the nitrate of ammonium, are all colorless. But the nitrates of the transition metals often show a variety of colors, and they, like other compounds of these elements, often are paramagnetic. These properties are, of course, those of the positive ion rather than of the nitrate ion. The oxidizing property of the nitrate ion is often important. No better illustration of this is needed than old-fashioned gunpowder, which contains potassium nitrate as the oxidizing agent together with charcoal and sulfur as the substances to be oxidized. Another example is ammonium nitrate, which when heated (Sec. 25.3) undergoes internal oxidation and reduction to yield nitrous oxide and water.

It was mentioned before that if an alkali metal nitrate is gently heated, some oxygen is released, with formation of the nitrite:

$$2NaNO_3 \rightarrow 2NaNO_2 + O_2$$

Most nitrites are soluble compounds, distinguished chiefly by their useful reducing properties. Since nitrous acid is a weak acid, we find all nitrites to be more or less hydrolyzed in water.

The oxy-salts of phosphorus present most of the complexities found in carbonic acid plus those in the oxy-salts of nitrogen. Furthermore, many phosphorus oxy-salts undergo polymerization to form condensed anions, of which $P_2O_7^{4-}$ is only one simple example. In this discussion we shall be able to present only a very few of the almost innumerable classes of phosphorus oxy-salts known.

Natural phosphate minerals are all *ortho*-phosphates containing the discrete anion PO_4^{3-}. Thus, calcium phosphate, $Ca_3(PO_4)_2$, is an important rock-forming mineral. The unique properties of phosphates are mostly related to the particular phosphorus oxy-anion present. The *ortho*-phosphate, PO_4^{3-}, consists of four oxygen atoms coordinated tetrahedrally around one phosphorus which is in the 5+ oxidation state:

$$\left[\begin{array}{c} O \\ | \\ O-P-O \\ | \\ O \end{array} \right]^{3-}$$

This is a discrete ion, and its salts are readily prepared by reaction of P_2O_5 with an appropriate metal oxide or by neutralization of a suitable base with *ortho*-phosphoric acid. Inasmuch as *ortho*-phosphoric acid has three replaceable hydrogens, it is possible to have three series of *ortho*-phosphate salts. For the case of the sodium salts, these three are NaH_2PO_4, Na_2HPO_4, and Na_3PO_4, called respectively sodium dihydrogen *ortho*-phosphate, disodium hydrogen *ortho*-phosphate, and trisodium *ortho*-phosphate. These several salts may be prepared by adding the appropriate quantity of base (say, NaOH) to a given quantity of acid:

$$H_3PO_4 + NaOH \rightarrow NaH_2PO_4 + H_2O$$
$$NaH_2PO_4 + NaOH \rightarrow Na_2HPO_4 + H_2O$$
$$Na_2HPO_4 + NaOH \rightarrow Na_3PO_4 + H_2O$$

The sodium salts are all soluble, although most other metal phosphates are insoluble in water. It will be recalled that *ortho*-phosphoric is not a very strong acid. The $H_2PO_4^-$ ion is a weak Brönsted acid, and the HPO_4^{2-} ion is a very weak acid. Consequently, the several salts containing these anions undergo varying degrees of hydrolysis in water. The primary salt NaH_2PO_4 is only slightly hydrolyzed; the secondary salt Na_2HPO_4 gives a moderately strong basic hydrolysis, and the tertiary salt Na_3PO_4 gives a very strong basic reaction. These properties make the alkali metal *ortho*-phosphates of value as buffers. Other phosphates such as ammonium *ortho*-phosphate are useful as fertilizers, and calcium phosphates are found in bone and teeth.

When certain *ortho*-phosphates are heated, they may undergo condensation. This involves the elimination of some water and the formation of a polymeric anion that is not, however, necessarily infinite in length. One of these condensed phosphates is the pyrophosphate, which has the structure

$$\left[\begin{array}{c} \quad O \qquad O \\ \quad \| \qquad \| \\ O-P-O-P-O \\ \quad | \qquad | \\ \quad O \qquad O \end{array} \right]^{4-}$$

It will be noted that although the proportion of oxygen to phosphorus has diminished from that in the *ortho*-phosphate, yet the oxidation state of the phosphorus in the pyrophosphate is the same (5+), and the coordination with four oxygen atoms is the same. The pyrophosphate is an example of a linear polyphosphate, but cyclic polyphosphates are also known. One of these, formed by further heat treatment under appropriate conditions, has the structure

This cyclic polyphosphate is a tri-*meta*-phosphate. The cyclic tetra-*meta*-phosphates are useful articles of commerce. Condensed phosphates form soluble complexes with many metal ions. They are used, for example, as water softeners. It should be clear that the salts formed from these various anions may be almost infinite in their variety.

Phosphorus in its lower oxidation states forms oxy-salts scarcely less complex than those outlined above. Phosphorous acid is stronger than phosphoric, but only two of the three hydrogens in the *ortho*-phosphorous acid, H_3PO_3, are ionizable. Condensation also occurs for this series, the principal difference being that here one of the hydrogens present is attached directly to the phosphorus rather than through an oxygen. The accepted structure for the *ortho*-phosphite ion is

$$\left[\begin{array}{c} H \\ | \\ O\!-\!P\!-\!O \\ | \\ O \end{array} \right]^{2-}$$

Salts containing this ion are mild reducing agents, but the hypophosphites containing phosphorus in the 1+ oxidation state are capable of reducing ions such as Cu^{2+} to the metal, the hypophosphite itself being oxidized to *ortho*-phosphate. The accepted structure for the hypophosphite ion is

$$\left[\begin{array}{c} H \\ | \\ H\!-\!P\!-\!O \\ | \\ O \end{array} \right]^{-}$$

Arsenic forms oxy-salts somewhat related to those of phosphorus. *Ortho*-arsenates and arsenites are known. The former are useful oxidizing agents.

28.4   Oxy-salts of Sulfur

The sulfates, containing sulfur in the 6+ oxidation state constitute another major group of oxy-salts. A few sulfates occur in nature as minerals, one of these being the calcium salt in hydrated form (gypsum, $CaSO_4 \cdot 2H_2O$). But apart from the alkaline earth elements, most metals form soluble sulfates, and of course these are less likely to be found in nature. Sulfates of Ca^{2+}, Sr^{2+}, Ba^{2+}, Ra^{2+}, and Pb^{2+} are conveniently made by precipitation—sulfuric acid being added to a solution containing the appropriate cation. Other sulfates may be made by neutralizing a suitable base with H_2SO_4 and then evaporating the excess water. Hydrolysis is a major problem in only a few cases. As was true for salts of carbonic acid, there are two series of sulfuric acid salts, depending on whether one or two hydrogens in the acid have been replaced. The normal sulfates contain discrete SO_4^{2-} ions and the hydrogen sulfates, or bisulfates, contain HSO_4^- ions. Whether one or the other salt is obtained depends on the relative proportions of acid and base brought together. Of the sulfates of importance, a few will be mentioned. Sodium sulfate, Na_2SO_4, is used in glass and soap manufacture; barium sulfate, $BaSO_4$, is an insoluble salt of high density, used in x-ray radiography of the gastrointestinal tract and for treating oil wells. Calcium sulfate is used for making plaster of paris as follows: the dihydrate, $CaSO_4 \cdot 2H_2O$, is heated until three of every four molecules of water have been driven off, leaving the plaster of paris, which is a hemihydrate, $CaSO_4 \cdot \frac{1}{2}H_2O$ or $(CaSO_4)_2 \cdot H_2O$. This, on treatment with water, reforms the dihydrate, which sets to a hard solid:

$$CaSO_4 \cdot \tfrac{1}{2}H_2O + \tfrac{3}{2}H_2O \rightleftharpoons CaSO_4 \cdot 2H_2O$$

The uses of plaster of paris in building and in making plaster casts is well known. Aluminum sulfate, $Al_2(SO_4)_3$, is a salt of a strong acid and a weak base, and therefore it shows hydrolysis. The hydrolysis process yields a gelatinous precipitate of $Al(OH)_3$. This is used in the treatment of water supplies; the $Al(OH)_3$, as it forms, traps and removes suspended impurities. Sulfates of strong bases exhibit virtually no hydrolysis. Bisulfates show a moderate acid reaction. All sulfates and sulfites are colorless unless formed from a colored transition metal ion. Many sulfates (and this is true of other oxy-salts also) have a tendency to form double salts. For instance, potassium sulfate, K_2SO_4, will crystallize with aluminum sulfate, $Al_2(SO_4)_3$, together with water, and form a substance known as alum. There are many alums, some of which may be regarded as formed by isomorphous replacement of either the potassium or the aluminum, or both. Potassium-aluminum alum has the formula $KAl(SO_4)_2 \cdot 12H_2O$.

It may be wondered if the oxy-salts of sulfur form condensed anions in the same way that the polyphosphates are formed. The answer is that only one important example is known. If excess SO_3 is passed into concentrated H_2SO_4, there is formed pyrosulfuric acid, $H_2S_2O_7$. The salts of this acid may conveniently be made by heating an appropriate hydrogen sulfate salt, such as $NaHSO_4$:

$$2NaHSO_4 \rightarrow Na_2S_2O_7 + H_2O$$

The pyrosulfate ion in sodium pyrosulfate has the structure

$$\left[\begin{array}{c} O \quad\ O \\ \| \quad\ \| \\ O-S-O-S-O \\ \| \quad\ \| \\ O \quad\ O \end{array} \right]^{2-}$$

There are other salts, known as dithionates, in which two or more sulfur atoms are bonded directly together, with no intervening oxygen. The possibility also exists of replacing an oxygen in the sulfate ion by another sulfur atom. The salts so formed are called thiosulfates, of which sodium thiosulfate, $Na_2S_2O_3$, is the familiar "hypo" used in photography for "fixing" photographic negatives and positives. The thiosulfate ion has the structure

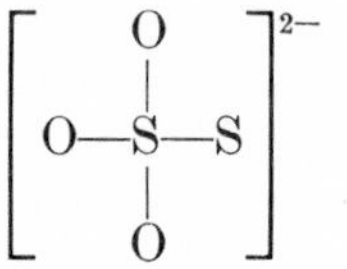

$$\begin{bmatrix} & O & \\ & \| & \\ O & -S-S \\ & \| & \\ & O & \end{bmatrix}^{2-}$$

(As in all these structures shown, no attempt has been made to indicate electron distribution.) Thiosulfates may be made by boiling sulfur with a solution of a sulfite; thus,

$$Na_2SO_3 + S \rightarrow Na_2S_2O_3$$

Proof that the two sulfur atoms are not equivalent to each other is obtained from the following tracer experiment: Normal Na_2SO_3 is boiled with radioactive sulfur (^{35}S). Then the product thiosulfate is treated with acid to cause decomposition to sulfur, SO_2, and water. It will be found that all the radioactive sulfur introduced is recovered as sulfur and that none of it appears in the SO_2. The sequence of reactions may be summarized as follows, with the use of S^* to indicate the "labeled" radioactive atoms:

$$SO_3^{2-} + S^* \rightarrow S^*SO_3^{2-}$$
$$S^*SO_3^{2-} + 2H^+ \rightarrow S^* + SO_2 + H_2O$$

The sulfites, containing sulfur in the 4+ oxidation series, are less important than the sulfates. They are readily formed by adding SO_2 to the appropriate solution of a base:

$$2NaOH + SO_2 \rightarrow Na_2SO_3 + H_2O$$

and

$$Na_2SO_3 + SO_2 + H_2O \rightarrow 2NaHSO_3$$

Two series, the sulfites and the hydrogen sulfites (bisulfites) are known. They are mild reducing agents, and because they are formed from a weak acid, they hydrolyze fairly strongly, smelling of SO_2. Sulfites are used in paper production.

28.5   Oxy-salts of the Halogens

With the exception of fluorine, all halogens form oxy-salts, although not all show the variety of oxidation states of which chlorine is capable. The more important oxy-salts of these elements are the hypochlorites, chlorites, chlorates, perchlorates, and the periodates. In general the sodium and calcium salts are the only ones we need consider. Most of the oxy-salts of the halogens appear to be soluble in water, although the NH_4^+, K^+ Rb^+ and Cs^+ salts of perchloric acid are only moderately soluble and some iodates are insoluble. The various salts differ greatly in their thermal stability, as will be pointed out below. All are colorless unless the positive ion is itself colored.

The reaction leading to formation of the hypohalite ions has already been described (Sec. 25.7) in connection with the oxy-acids. If Cl_2, Br_2, or I_2 is added to a base, a reaction of hydrolysis takes place, leading to the formation of hypohalite ion:

$$X_2 + 2OH^- \rightarrow X^- + XO^- + H_2O$$

This is the method used for preparing sodium hypochlorite, NaClO, or calcium hypochlorite, $Ca(ClO)_2$. But the hypohalite ions are all capable of disproportionation. The products are the halide, X^-, and the halate, XO_3^-:

$$3XO^- \rightarrow 2X^- + XO_3^-$$

For hypochlorite ion, this disproportionation does not take place readily unless the solution is heated. It has already been described how electrolysis of a hot NaCl solution yields sodium chlorate, $NaClO_3$, as the principal product. But unless the solution is hot, the chief product is the hypochlorite.

It will be noted that the chlorite ion ClO_2^- is not a product of the reactions given above. Chlorites may be prepared by the reaction of chlorine dioxide, ClO_2, with bases:

$$2ClO_2 + 2OH^- \rightarrow ClO_2^- + ClO_3^- + H_2O$$

Sodium and calcium hypochlorites and also the chlorites are articles of commerce, used in bleaching. Being salts of weak acids, they are subject to hydrolysis. But chlorates are salts of a strong acid and the chlorates of active metals do not readily hydrolyze. The chlorates are strong oxidizing agents, used as such and also for killing weeds.

It will be recalled that if $KClO_3$ is gently heated, it disproportionates to chloride and perchlorate. An industrial method for the preparation of perchlorates involves electrolytic oxidation of the chlorates.

In view of the reactions described above, it might be thought that hypobromites and hypoiodites could be prepared by analogous reactions.

But the disproportionation reaction, which takes place only at elevated temperatures for hypochlorite ion, takes place rapidly at room temperature for hypobromite and rapidly at all temperatures for hypoiodite. Salts of these ions are not known, but bromates and iodates are not too difficult to prepare.

Perbromates are not known, but periodates are fairly common and useful. The general method for preparing periodates is oxidation of iodine with chlorine in excess NaOH solution:

$$18\text{NaOH} + \text{I}_2 + 7\text{Cl}_2 \rightarrow 2\text{Na}_2\text{H}_3\text{IO}_6 + 14\text{NaCl} + 6\text{H}_2\text{O}$$

The reaction is complicated because, although the expected periodate (NaIO_4, called metaperiodate) is known, most periodates have other formulas. A few examples are $\text{Na}_4\text{I}_2\text{O}_9$, sodium dimesoperiodate; $\text{Pb}_3(\text{IO}_5)_2$, lead mesoperiodate; and Ag_5IO_6, silver paraperiodate. The periodates are strong oxidizing agents, able to oxidize Mn^{2+} to MnO_4^-.

The reader may wonder if pseudohalogens (Sec. 27.3) are able to form pseudo-oxy-salts. The answer is that cyanogen, a good example of a pseudohalogen, will undergo basic hydrolysis to form cyanide and cyanate:

$$(\text{CN})_2 + 2\text{OH}^- \rightarrow \text{CN}^- + \text{OCN}^- + \text{H}_2\text{O}$$

The cyanate ion, OCN^-, is itself a pseudohalide ion, but it may also be considered analogous to hypochlorite OCl^-. But pseudohalogen ions corresponding to chlorates and perchlorates are not known.

28.6   Chromates, Permanganates, and Related Compounds

It will be recalled (Sec. 24.5) that certain transition metals in high oxidation states form oxy-acids. To these may be added a few other metals that may not form oxy-acids but which do form oxy-salts. The properties of all these salts are so diverse that scarcely any general properties may be given, with the exception that they are all good oxidizing agents.

The preparation of both chromates and permanganates was described in (Sec. 24.5); these will be reviewed briefly. If chromium in a lower oxidation state is treated with a strong oxidizing agent, such as chlorine gas, in basic solution, the chromium will be oxidized to the 6+ chromate state. If the base is NaOH, it will be found possible to crystallize a yellow solid, sodium chromate, Na_2CrO_4. The chromates of the alkali metals and of ammonium are soluble in water and are not subject to appreciable hydrolysis, but most other chromates are insoluble. Some, such as PbCrO_4 and BaCrO_4, are useful as yellow pigments. Chromates are reasonably stable to heat treatment, and they bear some resemblances to sulfates.

If the chromate ion is acidified, it undergoes condensation to dichromate, $Cr_2O_7^{2-}$, and this ion also forms a series of salts. In this respect $Cr_2O_7^{2-}$ resembles $S_2O_7^{2-}$. But if Pb^{2+} or other cation that forms an insoluble chromate is added to a dichromate solution, the salt that precipitates is the chromate.

If manganese in a lower oxidation state is oxidized in basic solution, the product is a manganate containing MnO_4^{2-}. Although manganates are less well known than permanganates, the insoluble green barium manganate, $BaMnO_4$, is used as a pigment. If manganate ion is acidified, it disproportionates to purple permanganate, MnO_4^-, plus MnO_2. The only important permanganate is the potassium salt, $KMnO_4$, which is often used as an oxidizing agent.

A few other oxy-salts of transition metals are ammonium vanadate, NH_4VO_3; potassium perrhenate, $KReO_4$; barium ferrate, $BaFeO_4$; and calcium molybdate, $CaMoO_4$. More complicated salts are also formed by molybdenum and by tungsten. A few examples of these are the iso-molybdates, containing ions such as $Mo_8O_{26}^{4-}$, and the heteropolytungstates, containing ions such as $P_2W_{18}O_{62}^{6-}$.

28.7 *Continuous Anions*

Most of the earth's crust is composed of silica and silicates, and most inorganic building materials are silicates. There are some silicates that contain anions of finite dimensions, one example being magnesium *ortho*-silicate, Mg_2SiO_4, which occurs in nature as the mineral forsterite. This section will be devoted to those silicates that have infinite silicate ions in the same sense that the structure of diamond or of silica itself may be considered infinite. Continuous anions are not limited to silicates, but other examples such as the borates will not be described in detail here.

All silicates contain a silicon atom coordinated to four oxygen atoms arranged as at the corners of a tetrahedron. Therefore the simplest arrangement is as follows:

$$\begin{bmatrix} & O & \\ & | & \\ O & -Si- & O \\ & | & \\ & O & \end{bmatrix}^{4-}$$

This is the discrete anion that actually occurs in Mg_2SiO_4. It will be noted that the neutral grouping of atoms SiO_4 does not exist as an independent molecule, but that it may gain stability and occur as the SiO_4^{4-} ion, or it may gain stability and occur as a continuous three-dimensional lattice as it does in $\langle SiO_2 \rangle_\infty$.

The polysilicates may be considered as structures that are intermediate between the infinite silica structure and the discrete *ortho*-silicate ion structure. The simplest example of this is the ion formed by the sharing of one oxygen between two SiO_4 tetrahedra. The resulting structure is

$$\left[\begin{array}{c} \quad O \qquad O \\ \quad | \qquad\ | \\ O-Si-O-Si-O \\ \quad | \qquad\ | \\ \quad O \qquad O \end{array} \right]^{6-}$$

This ion is actually very rare, although it occurs in a scandium silicate, $Sc_2Si_2O_7$, which is found in nature as the mineral thortveitite.

If there are more than two SiO_4 tetrahedra involved, the resulting structure may be cyclic, as in $Si_3O_9^{6-}$, the structure of which, resembling tri-*meta*-phosphate, is

$$\left[\begin{array}{c} O \qquad\quad O \\ \ \diagdown \ {}_{Si} \diagup \\ O \qquad O \\ | \qquad\quad | \\ O-Si \qquad Si-O \\ | \diagdown_{O}\diagup | \\ O \qquad O \end{array} \right]^{6-}$$

This ion occurs in the mineral benitocite, $BaTiSi_3O_9$. In all such structures the positive ions are distributed, adjacent to the anion, in some regular geometric pattern not unlike the arrangement in the much simpler binary salts previously described.

All polysilicates, such as those illustrated above, have the feature in common that only one oxygen atom is shared between any two SiO_4 tetrahedra. A structure such as

$$\left[\begin{array}{c} O \qquad O \qquad O \\ \diagdown_{Si}\diagup \diagdown_{Si}\diagup \\ O \qquad O \qquad O \end{array} \right]^{4-}$$

in which two oxygens are shared between the same two SiO_4 tetrahedra, is never encountered. But even with this restriction it is clear that the process of sharing oxygens could continue indefinitely to form infinite anions. If only two oxygens in any tetrahedron are shared with adjacent tetrahedra, the resulting structure may be either a discrete cyclic ion as shown above, or it may be an infinite one-dimensional chain:

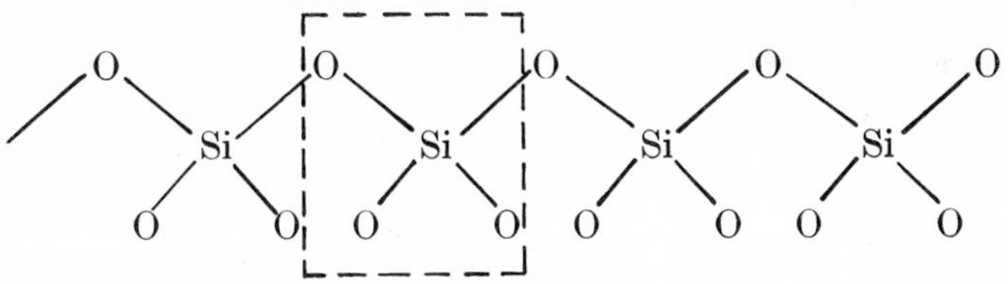

The repeating unit here is SiO_3 (indicated by dashes) and each unit carries a double negative charge, which may be indicated as $\langle SiO_3^{2-}\rangle_\infty$. This structure occurs in synthetic sodium *meta*-silicate, Na_2SiO_3 and in more complicated form in minerals such as asbestos.

In some silicates three oxygens are shared between SiO_4 tetrahedra. This leads to sheets (two-dimensional infinite anions) of a form that occurs in the minerals known as mica:

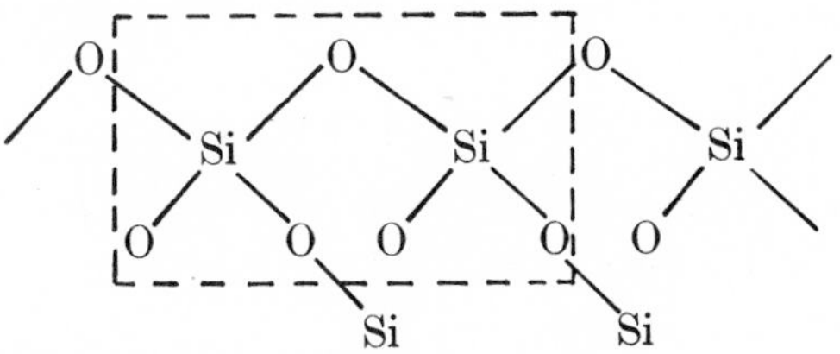

Here the repeating unit is Si_2O_5, with each unit carrying a double negative charge, so that the formula may be written $\langle Si_2O_5^{2-}\rangle_\infty$.

The final stage of sharing oxygens is achieved in silica itself, where all four oxygens in the SiO_4 tetrahedra are shared. No infinite anions of this kind are possible, but in aluminosilicates, where some of the silicons are replaced by aluminums, the anion is a three-dimensional, infinite "framework," of which $\langle AlSi_3O_8^-\rangle_\infty$ is an important example. This ion occurs in orthoclase, $KAlSi_3O_8$, and many such framework silicates make up important rock-forming minerals, of which the feldspars and the zeolites are only two examples.

The preparation of oxy-salts having continuous anions has not been described. It must suffice to say that strong heating of the appropriate mixtures of oxides will in general produce these substances, but the preparation and identification of pure samples is often difficult. Other elements that form continuous oxy-anions include boron, phosphorus, and germanium.

28.8 *The Vitreous State*

Many substances may be obtained in a vitreous, or "glassy," state in which matter exhibits some properties of both solids and liquids. Pure silica may, for instance, occur as a crystalline solid or as a glass. The vitreous state is by no means limited to silica and silicates, but silicates

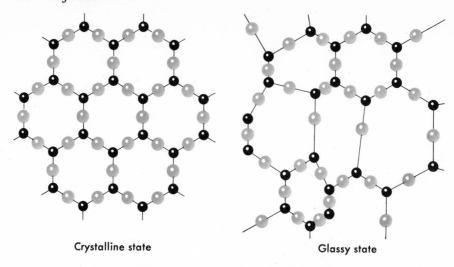

Crystalline state

Glassy state

Fig. 28.1 A glass differs from a crystal in the lack of long-range ordered arrangement in the former, although the immediate neighbors of each atom may be the same in each case. The illustrations are diagrammatic only—the third dimension being omitted for simplicity in drawing.

in the form of ordinary window glass are certainly more familiar. This discussion will be restricted to silicates in the vitreous state, but the opportunity will be taken to describe briefly certain other complex silicates that may or may not involve glasses. These other materials are ceramics, cement, and concrete.

Commercial glass is always a mixture rather than a pure chemical compound. The composition varies within wide limits, depending on the kind of glass desired and the formula used by the manufacturer. Silicon dioxide is a constituent of practically all glasses, and in window glass it amounts to be about 70 percent of the whole. The other constituents are alkali metal oxides and alkaline earths, such as sodium oxide, calcium oxide, and magnesium oxide. A typical analysis of glass is as follows: SiO_2, 70 percent; CaO, 10 percent; MgO, 2.5 percent; Na_2O (probably added in the form of Na_2CO_3), 15 percent; and other oxides such as Fe_2O_3 and Al_2O_3, 2.5 percent. These substances can scarcely be thought of as existing in the form of oxides in the glass. They are, rather, combined to form a mixture of, say, calcium silicate, magnesium silicate, and so forth. These several silicates are mutually dissolved in each other and in the excess of silicon dioxide. Common glass is therefore a complicated product, the composition and character of which have not been understood until recent years, although the manufacture of glass is one of the oldest of chemical industries.

X-ray diffraction studies show an essential difference between a glassy substance and the same substance in the crystalline state. In crystalline matter, the atoms are regularly arranged throughout the whole mass. In glasses, the atoms may be combined with each other in the same fashion as in crystals, but the arrangement of the atoms in space is much more nearly random. The regular rows and planes that characterize atomic arrangement in crystals are absent in glasses. An attempt to show this difference is given in Fig. 28.1.

Glasses resemble liquids with respect to the arrangement of atoms. A glass may be thought of as a liquid that has been subjected to a very great degree of supercooling so that the liquid can no longer flow freely. A glass might be defined as an amorphous (noncrystalline) substance, or a mixture of substances, that has been supercooled from the fused condition until it is, for all practical purposes, rigid. Glass that is very old, or which has been subjected to certain heat conditions, tends to crystallize or devitrify, which is what would be expected of a substance in the meta-stable, supercooled condition.

A large variety of glasses is made for special purposes. So-called lead glasses contain substantial amounts of lead added to the silicate mixture in the form of lead oxide. Such glass is as dense as cast iron. Pyrex glass contains B_2O_3, Al_2O_3, and K_2O in addition to Na_2O and SiO_2. It is widely used for laboratory glassware and for household utensils. Colored glass generally contains the oxide of a transition metal such as Cr_2O_3 (green), CoO (blue), but metallic gold as a colloid gives a red glass, as do selenium and cadmium sulfides.

Ceramics such as porcelain and pottery are related to glasses. The manufacture of these substances depends on the changes that occur in kaolin, or clay, when it is heated. Kaolin is a hydrated aluminosilicate, the formula for which may be crudely represented as $Al_2O_3 \cdot 2SiO_2 \cdot 2H_2O$. If this is strongly heated, it loses water and becomes a hard mixture of SiO_2 and $3Al_2O_3 \cdot 2SiO_2$. Ordinary fire bricks are made from impure kaolin mixed with Fe_2O_3, which gives them the red color. Pottery is made from purer grades of clay, and porcelain is made from the finest grades of clay, called China clay, mixed with feldspar and silica. The finished translucent product is not unlike a glass in being, in part, a solid solution. The glaze on pottery or on porcelain is essentially a glass surface put on by heating the ware after the surface has been coated with a mixture that will fuse to form a glass at a somewhat lower temperature than the body of the ceramic. The colors on ceramicware are generally transition metal oxides such as CoO.

Portland cement is a complex aluminosilicate mixture manufac-tured by heating limestone, or other source of CaO, together with clay and silica until a percentage composition is obtained of which the following is a typical example: CaO, 64.6; SiO_2, 21.8; Al_2O_3, 5.6; Fe_2O_3, 3.3; MgO, 2,9; other, 1.6. The clinker obtained after the heat treatment consists of several calcium silicates, some of them in the glassy state. Most Portland cement is used in the form of concrete, which consists of cement plus sand and gravel or crushed rock. These solid aggregates take no part in the setting process, but are simply enclosed and held in place by the paste of cement and water. The setting of cement is an action of hydration somewhat resembling that occurring with plaster of paris. Several reactions take place: The various calcium silicates in the clinker take up water to form hydrated calcium silicate and, in some cases, calcium hydroxide. These substances form the tough binder that holds the mass of concrete as a rocklike solid.

EXERCISES

1. There is a basic difference in structure between a complex oxide such as $MgAl_2O_4$ and an oxy-salt such as Mg_2SiO_4. What is this difference?

2. Suggest methods for preparation of the following (solubility in water is indicated): $Sr(ClO_4)_2$, sol; $Nd(NO_3)_3$, sol; $MnCO_3$, insol; $Na_2H_2P_2O_5$, sol; $Ca(OCl)_2$, sol; $Ba(MnO_4)_2$, insol; $PbCrO_4$, insol; $(NH_4)_2Cr_2O_7$, sol.

3. Using ionic equations, show each step in the crystallization of $NaHCO_3$ from a water solution to which $NaCl$, CO_2, and NH_3 have been added.

4. Why is washing soda highly objectionable in cooking?

5. A cave has some tendency to refill with stalactites and stalagmites. Show, using ionic equations, how a change in the partial pressure of CO_2 may account for this.

6. Does carbon monoxide bear a relation to sodium formate in the same sense that carbon dioxide is related to sodium carbonate?

7. Predict the colors of the following: $Mg(NO_3)_2$, $Ni(NO_3)_2$, $Cu(NO_3)_2$, $Zn(NO_3)_2$, K_2CrO_4, and $NaMnO_4$.

8. Which of the following would probably be paramagnetic? $Ca(NO_3)_2$, $Cr(NO_3)_2$, $Cu(NO_3)_2$, $Zn(NO_3)_2$, $Nd(NO_3)_2$, and $TlNO_3$.

9. Write equations for each of the following when heated moderately: KNO_3, $Hg(NO_3)_2$, $Cu(NO_3)_2$, $SrCO_3$, $MgSiO_4$, NaH_2PO_4, $KClO_3$, and $CaSO_4$.

10. How many different sodium salts are possible for *ortho*-phosphorous acid?

11. Show a structural formula for the cyclic tetra-*meta*-phosphate ion.

12. Draw structural formulas for some possible *meta*-phosphites.

13. Alums have been used in baking powders to provide the necessary acid reaction. How is this reaction possible?

14. Sulfur does not appear to form a cyclic condensed oxy-anion. If it did so, what would be the structure of the trimer?

15. What is the evidence that the structure of the thiosulfate ion is not, for instance, O—S—O—S—O?

16. Sulfites have some fairly close resemblances to the corresponding carbonates, and they have some sharp differences. What are these resemblances and differences?

17. (a) How does the degree of hydrolysis of the sodium oxy-halogen salts change from element to element? (b) How does the disproportionation of the hypohalites change from element to element?

18. List with names and formulas those oxy-halogen anions that are definitely known to form salts.

19. What is a heteropoly-oxy-salt?

20. The cyclic trimer ion $Si_3O_9^{6-}$ has a 6— charge, but the corresponding tri-*meta*-phosphate ion has a charge of only 3—. What is the reason for this difference?

21. Silicon is able to form discrete oxy-anions, threads, sheets, and frameworks. Illustrate all these with structural formulas and examples.

22. In what ways does a sample of matter in the vitreous (glassy) state differ from a crystalline solid?

23. Oxidation of thiosulfate ion to dithionate ion, $S_4O_6^{2-}$, by the use of iodine is a procedure often used in quantitative analysis. This is illustrated by the following problem:

   A preparation of the green potassium manganate is to be analyzed for purity. A sample weighing 0.300 gram was added to excess acidified aqueous potassium iodide solution. This liberated iodine according to the equation

$$K_2MnO_4 + 4I^- + 8H^+ \rightarrow 2I_2 + 2K^+ + Mn^{2+} + 4H_2O$$

The iodine was now titrated with standard 0.100M sodium thiosulfate, of which 40.8 ml was required. The equation is

$$2S_2O_3^{2-} + I_2 \rightarrow S_4O_6^{2-} + 2I^-$$

Report the percentage of pure K_2MnO_4 present in the potassium manganate sample. Assume that the impurity, if any, is inert toward iodide ion.

29

Complex Compounds

29.1 Volatile Compounds of the Metals

This chapter will be devoted to compounds that are generally referred to as "complex." This will include those generally called coordination compounds. All such compounds contain three or more different kinds of atoms, but we shall find that some are no more complex than those substances described in the preceding chapter. It will be found that complex compounds often present unique and obscure problems in valence and structure.

Our first topic will be those compounds of the metals that are truly molecular. With a few exceptions these compounds may be volatilized without decomposition. It will be recognized that a substantial group of such substances fall into the category of binary compounds of metal plus nonmetal. More than a few of these have already been described, examples being: $TiCl_4$, $SnCl_4$, UF_6, OsO_4, $AlCl_3$, and $FeCl_3$, and (at very high temperatures) even NaCl. It will be recalled that some of these compounds such as $TiCl_4$, $SnCl_4$, and UF_6 form particulate molecules even as solids, but that others such as $AlCl_3$ and $FeCl_3$ form continuous lattices in the solid and that both bond type and structure change as the solid is vaporized. All the compounds to be discussed in this section form particulate molecules in all states, and they are not restricted to the high oxidation states characteristic of, say, UF_6, or OsO_4.

The compounds to which we shall devote most of our attention in this section are the carbonyls. It will be recalled (Sec. 21.5) that nickel carbonyl may be used in the purification of nickel metal. The ability to form carbonyls of varying degrees of complexity is found among the transition metals and more especially in a certain area of the Periodic Table. Some important carbonyls are the following: $V(CO)_6$, $Cr(CO)_6$, $Fe(CO)_5$, $Fe_2(CO)_9$, $Fe_3(CO)_{12}$, $Co_2(CO)_8$, and $Ni(CO)_4$. The naming of these compounds follows the usual pattern, that is, vanadium hexacarbonyl, iron pentacarbonyl, dicobalt octacarbonyl, and so forth. Direct synthesis of the carbonyls from finely divided metal plus carbon monoxide is feasible only for $Ni(CO)_4$ and $Fe(CO)_5$, the latter at elevated temperature and pressure. These two carbonyls are articles of commerce. The compound $Fe_2(CO)_9$ may be obtained by irradiating a solution of $Fe(CO)_5$ with ultraviolet light:

$$2Fe(CO)_5 \rightarrow Fe_2(CO)_9 + CO$$

The carbonyl $Fe_3(CO)_{12}$ is made by heating $Fe_2(CO)_9$:

$$2Fe_2(CO)_9 \rightarrow Fe_3(CO)_{12} + Fe(CO)_5 + CO$$

Of the carbonyls mentioned above, only $Ni(CO)_4$ and $Fe(CO)_5$ are liquids at room temperature. All others are solids, but all may be vaporized at elevated temperature, with the possible exception of $Fe_2(CO)_9$. The colors range from colorless, $Cr(CO)_6$, $Ni(CO)_4$; through yellow-gold, $Mn_2(CO)_{10}$, $Fe_2(CO)_9$; and orange, $Co_2(CO)_8$; to greenish black and black, $Fe_3(CO)_{12}$ and $V(CO)_6$. All carbonyls are poisonous, and the more volatile ones such as $Ni(CO)_4$ are extremely dangerous. All burn in air to form the metal oxide plus carbon dioxide.

The structure and valence problems presented by the metal carbonyls are formidable. It will be clear that the normal concept of oxidation states is of little aid here because all the metal atoms involved appear to have an oxidation state of zero. It will, however, be noted that carbon monoxide has a lone pair of electrons which, presumably, may be used for bonding. If we take the total number of electrons in the metal atom plus the number of lone pair electrons contributed by the carbon monoxide, we obtain the same number of electrons as present in the next *succeeding* Group Zero element. Three examples should make this clear: In the iron atom there are 26 electrons, and each of the 5 carbon monoxide molecules present in $Fe(CO)_5$ brings in 2 electrons (the lone pair). This gives a total of 36 electrons, which is the number of electrons present in the krypton atom.

Similarly, nickel has 28 and adds 4×2 in $Ni(CO)_4$ for a total of 36. But cobalt normally has 27 electrons, and no formula involving only 1 cobalt atom would give 36 electrons. This is possibly related to the reason why cobalt does not form a simple carbonyl, but why it does form one in which 2 cobalt atoms are present.

One other complexity will be mentioned. The carbon monoxide in, say, $Ni(CO)_4$, is shown by electron diffraction and other studies to be attached to the nickel tetrahedrally as follows:

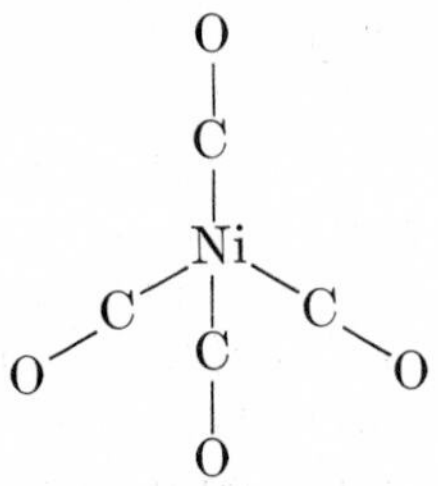

$$
\begin{array}{c}
O \\
| \\
C \\
| \\
Ni \\
C \quad | \quad C \\
C \\
| \\
O
\end{array}
$$

But in $Fe_2(CO)_9$ the bonding is of two different kinds, one being the Fe—C—O type and the other being related to two atoms as follows:[1]

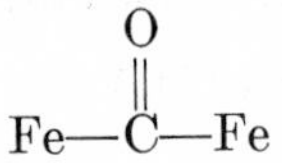

$$
\begin{array}{c}
O \\
\| \\
Fe-C-Fe
\end{array}
$$

The complete structure of $Fe_2(CO)_9$ is a kind of cage; thus;

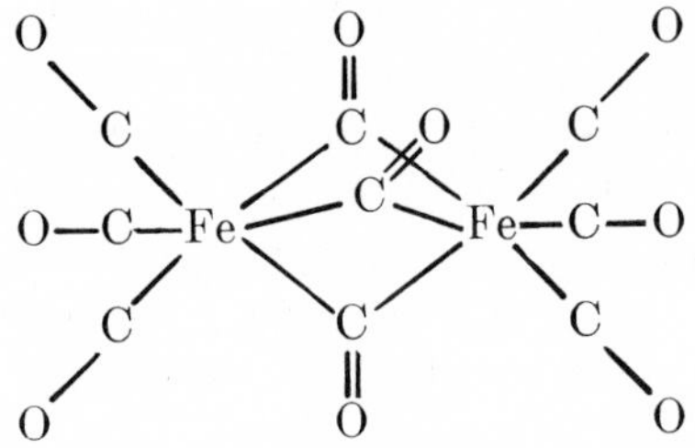

Still another difficulty is that carbon monoxide is an exceedingly weak Lewis base and could scarcely be expected to form the strong bonds in the carbonyls by a simple Lewis neutralization process.

It is clear that the elementary valence concepts presented in the early chapters of this book are inadequate as explanations of the metal carbonyls, and these carbonyls are only one of many groups of compounds in which valence anomalies present themselves. In Chapter 27 some remarks were made concerning two different classes of essentially covalent bonding, namely, σ (sigma) bonding and π (pi) bonding. A current view is that the weak metal-carbon σ bond in these carbonyls must be strengthened by a metal-carbon π bond.

---

[1] The bonding of metal atom to carbon monoxide cannot be represented in any simple fashion. The crude method shown above should not be taken literally, but the spatial relationships are almost certainly correct.

In conclusion it may be mentioned that there are several other kinds of volatile metal compounds. Examples of these are chromyl chloride, $CrOCl_2$; anhydrous copper nitrate, $Cu(NO_3)_2$; and various organo-metallics such as dimethyl magnesium, $(CH_3)_2Mg$; triethoxyaluminum, $Al(OC_2H_5)_3$; and especially a group of compounds related to cyclopentadienyl iron (or ferrocene), $(C_5H_5)_2Fe$.

29.2   *Coordination Complexes*

If to a solution containing Ag^+ ion there is added some CN^- ion, a white precipitate of AgCN will at once appear:

$$Ag^+ + CN^- \rightarrow AgCN$$

But if now some excess of CN^- is added, it will be found that the precipitate of AgCN disappears. The reason for this state of affairs is that the compound AgCN, which is certainly capable of an existence as such, is also capable of accepting more cyanide ions to form a complex ion, $Ag(CN)_2^-$. This is able, as are all negative ions, to form salts with positive ions. With Na^+, for instance, $Ag(CN)_2^-$ will form the salt $NaAg(CN)_2$, which happens to be a soluble salt dissociated in water to Na^+ and $Ag(CN)_2^-$ just as NaCl is dissociated into Na^+ and Cl^-.

Compounds such as $NaAg(CN)_2$ are generally called *coordination compounds*, and the unique part of the compound, which is in this case the $Ag(CN)_2^-$ ion, is a typical example of a complex ion. It will be recognized that many complex ions have already been presented; some authors would have included any ion containing two or more atoms under this name, but the term *coordination complex* is generally reserved for cases where the central atom is a metal. Thus MnO_4^-, $Cu(NH_3)_4^{2+}$, and $Fe(CN)_6^{3-}$ are all coordination complexes. It is by no means necessary that the complex should be a negative ion: $Cu(NH_3)_4^{2+}$ is positive and may form salts such as $Cu(NH_3)_4SO_4$; $Fe(CN)_6^{3-}$ is negative and may form salts such as $K_3Fe(CN)_6$; and $[Pt(NH_3)_2Cl_2]$ is a neutral molecule capable of independent existence. All these are considered coordination complexes.

It may be wondered how one can be sure that, for instance, the silver solution containing excess cyanide ion actually contains $Ag(CN)_2^-$ and no Ag^+. Many lines of evidence show this to be true, and in Sec. 29.4 we shall present some numerical exercises concerning this. For the present, it may suffice to say that if to a solution containing Ag^+ we add Cl^- ion, the precipitation of the Ag^+ as AgCl is prompt and virtually complete. But if we add Cl^- to a silver solution containing excess cyanide ion, no trace of precipitation occurs. It is obvious from this that in the presence of excess cyanide, the silver cannot possibly be present as Ag^+ ion.

Recognition of compounds such as those mentioned above as a distinct class of substance is due to A. Werner, who discovered the significance of the *number* as well as the *kind* of atoms, ions, or groups of atoms that could cluster around and combine with the central metal atom or ion. Werner introduced the term *coordination* to mean the bonding of a certain number (often four or six) groups to the central atom. This use is slightly different from the use we have made of the word "coordination" in earlier chapters, but not sufficiently so as to be confusing. The groups such as NH_3, CN^-, and so forth, which are coordinated to the central atom, are generally called *ligands*. The properties of coordination complexes will be described in later sections, but one property may be pointed out here. It will be recalled that for the metal carbonyls, it often occurs that the total number of electrons in the metal, plus those donated by the lone pairs of electrons in the carbon monoxide, is equal to the number of electrons in the next Group Zero gas. It is found in a large number of coordination complexes to be similarly true that all the electrons in the metal atom or ion plus two electrons from each of the ligands present gives the number of electrons in the succeeding Group Zero gas. Thus the complex ion $PtCl_6^{2-}$ obviously contains platinum in the 4+ oxidation state. The atomic number of platinum is 78, from which we subtract the 4 electrons lost, then add the 12 electrons brought in by the Cl^- ions, and have a total of 86 electrons. This is, of course, the atomic number of the Group Zero gas radon. The number so found is often called the *effective atomic number*, and it is a useful property to keep in mind. But there are sufficient exceptions to this rule to show that it is not a requirement for complex formation.

Metals that form coordination complexes are generally the transition metals, although examples are found among other metals and especially among these that occur just after the end of a transition series. All central atoms in complexes are characterized by a number of spatial positions which may be occupied by ligands. This number is known as the *coordination number*. Iron in the 2+ oxidation state generally has a coordination number of 6, which it exhibits in a large variety of complexes such as $Fe(NH_3)_6^{2+}$ and $Fe(CN)_6^{4-}$. Platinum in the 2+ oxidation state often shows a coordination number of 4, as in $PtCl_4^{2-}$. While 4 and 6 are the commonest coordination numbers shown by the metals, examples are known from 2 to 8.

The ligands that combine with these atoms are quite varied, although a large proportion of them has the common feature of an available pair of unshared electrons. In other words, most ligands are capable of acting as Lewis bases, but there is no requirement that the base action should be a strong one.

There do not appear to be many examples of positive ions acting as ligands ($N_2H_5^+$, hydrazinium, is one such). The reason for this is clear if we consider that metals all have an electropositive nature and would not, therefore, readily attract another positive group. But neutral molecules and negative ions as ligands are known in abundance. If the ligand is a neutral molecule, the charge on the complex will be simply that of the metal. If Fe^{3+} forms a complex with NH_3, the charge on the complex is $3+$, as in $Fe(NH_3)_6^{3+}$. But if the ligand is an ion, the charge on the complex is the algebraic sum of the charges on central atom and ligand; thus, in the ferricyanide ion formed from Fe^{3+} and $6CN^-$, the resultant charge is $3-$, as in $Fe(CN)_6^{3-}$.

Each ligand, whether neutral molecule or ion, may take one place in the coordination sphere or it may take more. Ligands that occupy two coordination spaces are said to be bidentate (two-toothed). Some ligands are even hexadentate. An example of a bidentate ligand is the carbonate ion, CO_3^{2-}, but a bidentate ligand need not carry a double negative charge, or any charge whatever.

Some examples of ligands, and the special names they are given when they so act, are given in Table 29.1.

The naming of coordination compounds is complicated and subject to elaborate rules. We shall content ourselves by stating some of the rules in abbreviated form and then by presenting a few examples of currently approved nomenclature. In writing the formulas for coordination compounds, it is the practice to enclose in square brackets everything within the coordination sphere. Thus, $[Cu(NH_3)_4]Cl_2$ means that there is a complex ion having the formula $Cu(NH_3)_4^{2+}$ and that this has formed a salt with

TABLE 29.1   SOME LIGANDS

Unidentate neutral molecules:	
CO	carbonyl
NH_3	ammine (*note spelling!*)
H_2O	aquo
NO	nitrosyl
Unidentate negative ions:	
F^-	fluoro
Cl^-	chloro
Br^-	bromo
OH^-	hydroxo
CN^-	cyano
NO_2^-	nitro
O^{2-}	oxo
Bidentate ligands:	
CO_3^{2-}	carbonato
$C_2O_4^{2-}$	oxalato
$H_2NCH_2CH_2NH_2$	ethylenediamine (*abbreviated* en)

Cl⁻ ions, two of which are, of course, required. The abbreviated naming rules are as follows:

1. If the compound is a salt the usual rule is followed of naming the cation first.

2. If the coordination complex is either a postive ion or a neutral molecule, the ligands are named first and then the central atom. The central atom is followed by a roman numeral or (0) in parentheses to show the oxidation state of the metal (in accordance with the Stock system of nomenclature).

3. If the coordination complex is a negative ion, the name of the metal atom is followed by -ate and then by the Stock system numeral.

The number of ligands of each kind in the complex is specified by prefixes. There are also rules for the order in which the ligands are to be named, but we shall not be concerned with this, although the rules are applied in the examples given in Table 29.2.

TABLE 29.2   Examples of coordination
COMPOUND NOMENCLATURE

$[Co(NH_3)_6]Cl_3$	hexa-amminecobalt (III) chloride
$[Co(NO_2)_3(NH_3)_3]$	trinitrotriamminecobalt (III)
$[Pt(NH_3)_6]Cl_4$	hexa-ammineplatinum (IV) chloride
$[CrCl_2(H_2O)_4]NO_3$	dichlorotetra-aquochromium (III) nitrate
$K_4[Ni(CN)_4]$	potassium tetracyanonickel (0)
$K_4[Fe(CN)_6]$	potassium hexacyanoferrate (II)
$K_3[Fe(CN)_6]$	potassium hexacyanoferrate (III)

Preparation methods for coordination compounds involve, in a large proportion of cases, nothing more than mixing the appropriate reagents, as given above for $NaAg(CN)_2$. If to a solution of platinum tetrachloride there is added potassium chloride, the complex compound $K_2[PtCl_6]$ is readily formed. If excess ammonia is added to a solution of $CuSO_4$, the complex ion $Cu(NH_3)_4^{2+}$ immediately betrays itself by its deep blue color.

29.3   Coordination Compounds, Properties and Structure

This section will be devoted to some general properties of coordination compounds. The complexes formed by platinum, in the 4+ oxidation state, with the ligands chloride ion and ammonia will be used as examples.

TABLE 29.3   COMPOSITION, CONDUCTIVITY IN WATER SOLUTION,
AND IONS ASSUMED TO BE PRESENT IN SOME PLATINUM (IV)
COMPLEX COMPOUNDS

Composition	Molar conductivity,* ohm^{-1}	Ions
(1) $Pt \cdot Cl_4 \cdot (NH_3)_6$	523	$[Pt(NH_3)_6]^{4+} + 4Cl^-$
(2) $Pt \cdot Cl_4 \cdot (NH_3)_5$	404	$[PtCl(NH_3)_5]^{3+} + 3Cl^-$
(3) $Pt \cdot Cl_4 \cdot (NH_3)_4$	229	$[PtCl_2(NH_3)_4]^{2+} + 2Cl^-$
(4) $Pt \cdot Cl_4 \cdot (NH_3)_3$	97	$[PtCl_3(NH_3)_3]^+ + Cl^-$
(5) $Pt \cdot Cl_4 \cdot (NH_3)_2$	0	none

* Strictly, the unit of conductivity is ohm^{-1}mole^{-1}cm^2.

In this oxidation state, the coordination number of platinum is almost always 6.

Platinum metal may be dissolved in aqua regia ($HCl + HNO_3$) to yield chloroplatinic acid, $H_2[PtCl_6]$, which may, if it is so desired, be crystallized from solution as a hydrate. Chloroplatinic acid may be neutralized with ammonium hydroxide to give the salt ammonium hexachloroplatinate(IV), $(NH_4)_2[PtCl_6]$. If now this salt is treated with excess ammonia, it is possible to isolate a compound of the composition corresponding to $Pt \cdot Cl_4 \cdot (NH_3)_6$. By similar procedures, the details of which need not concern us, it is possible to obtain at least five different compounds that contain different proportions of ammonia and chlorine. These five substances are listed in Table 29.3 together with the electrical conductivities of their solutions in water and also the ions presumed to be present on the basis of the conductivities and other evidence.

The progressive change of electrical conductivity is strong evidence that the total number of ions formed by 1 mole of each compound in solution is greatest for the hexa-ammine (compound 1 in Table 29.3) and least for the diammine (compound 5), which appears to be a molecular un-ionized compound of the formula $[PtCl_4(NH_3)_2]$. Further evidence that this view is correct is found by analyzing for Cl^- in each solution. The total chlorine in substances such as these may be found by decomposing the compound completely, as by heating it in concentrated H_2SO_4 and collecting the HCl given off. But that fraction of the chlorine present in solution as Cl^- ions may be found by adding Ag^+ to each of the solutions. This will precipitate all Cl^- as AgCl, which may be dried and weighed. When this is done, it is found that 1 mole of each compound, from the hexa-ammine to the diammine, yields progressively from 4 gram-ions of Cl^- to zero, as shown in Table 29.3. From these, and a wealth of other experiments, it is concluded that these compounds contain coordination complexes as shown. Atoms, groups of atoms, or ions within the coordination sphere exhibit properties different from those outside. The chlorine in

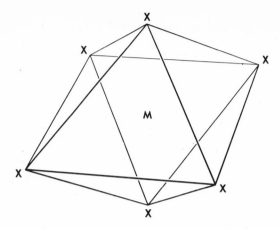

Fig. 29.1 Octahedral arrangement of six ligands (X) around
a central atom (M)

the sphere does not form AgCl; the ammonia does not smell of ammonia. Furthermore, if the view indicated is correct, it should be possible to form two more complex ions, namely: $[PtCl_5(NH_3)]^-$ and $[PtCl_6]^{2-}$. These ions should form salts with positive ions of metals such as potassium. The salts $K[PtCl_5(NH_3)]$ and $K_2[PtCl_6]$ are indeed known, and as would be expected, they show the molar conductivity in solution (108 and 256 ohm^{-1}, respectively) corresponding to the ions assumed to be present.

The next problem is to consider how the atoms in the coordination sphere are arranged, and it will be noted that every one of the seven compounds described has six ligands. This is true whether the ligands are all NH_3 as in the hexa-ammine ion or all chloride as in the chloroplatinate ion, or some combination as in the others. The simplest arrangement of six ligands around a central atom, and this is the arrangement supported by x-ray diffraction studies, is that the ligands should be arranged as at the corners of an octahedron. Figure 29.1 shows a regular octahedron with the positions of central atoms and six ligands all shown. A convenient and simple representation of an octahedral complex is

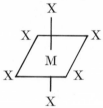

This has, however, the drawback that it seems to imply chemical bonds between the ligands themselves. The bonds in the cases discussed are between ligands and central atoms, and are perhaps more realistically represented as

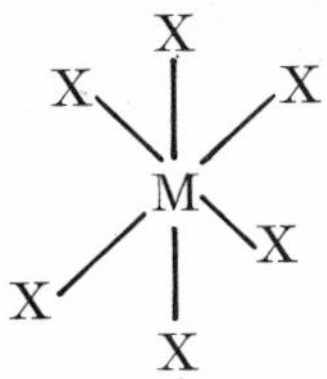

The six positions in the octahedral coordination sphere are thought to be all identical. If, then, we consider the pentammine (in which one chlorine only is coordinated to the platinum), it follows that one, and only one, such compound is possible.

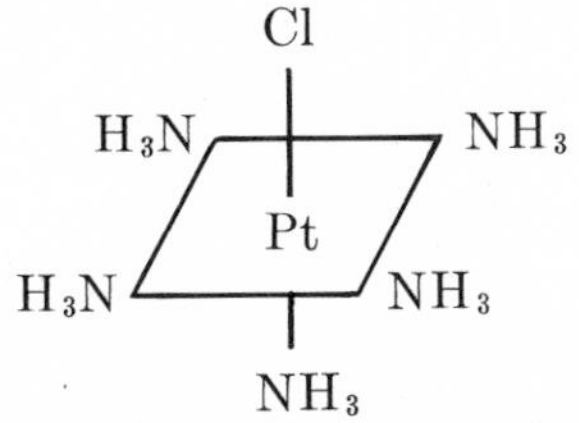

But, if two chlorines are present, as in the tetra-ammine, $[PtCl_2(NH_3)_4]^{2+}$, it is obvious that there are two possibilities. Either the two chlorines may be in positions adjacent to each other or they may be across from each other:

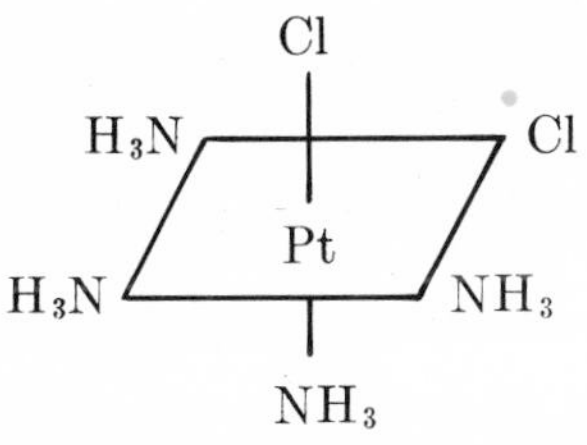

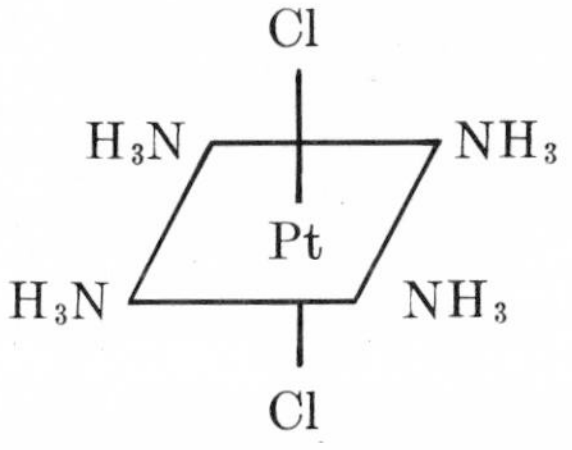

This is an example of a unique phenomenon, namely, *geometrical* (or *stereo-*) *isomerism*. There are actually two known series of salts of the ion $[PtCl_2(NH_3)_4]^{2+}$. They differ in color, solubility, and chemical reactivity.

In the preceding section, it was mentioned that some ligands may be attached to a central metal atom at two positions, that is, such bidentate ligands may occupy two positions in the coordination sphere. A polydentate ligand of a nature that permits attachment to a single metal at two or more sites is said to be a *chelate* ligand. (The word "chelate" is derived from the Greek, meaning a claw, as of a lobster.) The compound ethylenediamine is a good example of a chelate ligand. The structural formula for this compound is

$$
\begin{array}{ccccc}
\text{H} & \text{H} & \text{H} & \text{H} \\
| & | & | & | \\
:\!\text{N} & -\text{C} & -\text{C} & -\text{N}\!: \\
| & | & | & | \\
\text{H} & \text{H} & \text{H} & \text{H}
\end{array}
$$

Ethylenediamine happens to be a neutral molecule, but it has two functional positions provided by the lone pair of electrons on each of the two nitrogens.

Ethylenediamine is not a very long molecule, and it happens that it will react with a complex such as the dichlorotetra-ammineplatinum (IV) ion, shown above, to form ethylenediaminetetra-ammineplatinum (IV) ion. This is formed by replacing one chlorine for each of the two functional groups of the ethylenediamine. As ethylenediamine carries no charge, it follows also that the charge on the ion produced is larger than before the substitution took place. Writing "en" for ethylenediamine, we then have

$$[PtCl_2(NH_3)_4]^{2+} + en \rightarrow [Pten(NH_3)_4]^{4+} + 2Cl^-$$

Now our point is that this reaction is possible with the *cis*-isomer of the tetra-ammine but not with the *trans*-isomer. The reason for this is that the ethylenediamine can easily reach between two adjacent positions in the coordination sphere, but not between two positions that are opposite each other. A structural formula for the substitution product is, then,

$$
\begin{array}{c}
\text{H}_2\text{N}-\text{CH}_2 \\
\quad\quad\quad\quad\text{CH}_2 \\
\text{H}_3\text{N} \quad\quad\quad \text{NH}_2 \\
\text{Pt} \\
\text{H}_3\text{N} \quad\quad\quad \text{NH}_3 \\
\text{NH}_3
\end{array}
$$

Very many other examples of stereoisomerism and of chelate formation involving still other kinds of isomerism are known. But this example will serve to show the general nature of such compounds, which range in complexity from the comparatively simple FeF_6^{3-} ion to such extraordinarily complicated coordination complexes as hemoglobin, the red, oxygen-carrying compound in the blood of warm-blooded living organisms, including man.

29.4   Stability of Coordination Complexes

Coordination compounds undergo a wide variety of reactions. One of these reactions involves dissociation of the complex into the simpler

species of which it is made. Dissociation is merely the reverse of the reactions of formation described earlier. Another kind of reaction is the
replacement, or substitution, of one ligand for another. These two reactions
will be illustrated by two examples already encountered. The diammine-
silver complex ion, $Ag(NH_3)_2^+$, dissociates as follows:

$$Ag(NH_3)_2^+ \rightleftharpoons Ag^+ + 2NH_3$$

For this reaction, the equilibrium constant is

$$\frac{[Ag^+][NH_3]^2}{[Ag(NH_3)_2^+]} \approx 6 \times 10^{-8}$$

In other words, this complex has only a slight tendency to dissociate.
The complex is said to have a fairly high *stability,* and by this is meant
that the equilibrium lies far to the left, as written. Nothing is implied
concerning how fast equilibrium may be reached in this reaction. It so
happens that equilibrium is reached quickly.

Now let us consider the platinum complex ion $[PtCl_2(NH_3)_4]^{2+}$,
which was shown in the preceding section to react with ethylenediamine
to form $[Pten(NH_3)_4]^{4+}$. This reaction involves the replacement (or substitution) of two chlorines for the bidentate ethylenediamine. Ignoring the
question of where the equilibrium lies, we find that this reaction is
also a rapid one. The word "stability" is used in this branch of chemistry
to mean thermodynamic stability, namely, whether the equilibrium constant for the dissociation process is small or large, regardless of the speed
of attainment of equilibrium. To describe the rate at which equilibrium
may be reached, the term *lability* is used. Lability refers to the kinetic
process and not to the thermodynamic. The replacement of Cl^- by "en" in
the complex $[PtCl_2(NH_3)_4]^{2+}$ is said to be a labile process.

There is, however, a further complication. Most ions in water
solution are actually in the form of coordination complexes, the ligands in
this case being water molecules. Sometimes, as for hexa-aquochromium
(III) the number of water molecules so coordinated is definitely known; in
other cases it is indefinite. But in almost any case, the so-called dissociation
of a coordination complex actually involves merely the replacement of
one ligand for another. If, for instance, the dissociation of $[Cr(NH_3)_6]^{3+}$
in acidified water is to be considered, a correct representation of the
overall reaction is

$$[Cr(NH_3)_6]^{3+} + 6H_3O^+ \rightleftharpoons [Cr(H_2O)_6]^{3+} + 6NH_4^+$$

It so happens that this reaction has a surprisingly low lability (it is a
slow reaction). Some further remarks concerning lability will be made
in Sec. 29.5, but the reader should understand that stability and lability
as used here refer to the equilibrium concentration and to the rate of

TABLE **29.4**   DISSOCIATION CONSTANTS* FOR
SOME COMPLEX IONS AT $25°$ C

Dissociation reaction	K_d
$Ag(NH_3)_2^+ \rightleftharpoons Ag^+ + 2NH_3$	6×10^{-8}
$AgCl_2^- \rightleftharpoons Ag + 2Cl^-$	1×10^{-5}
$Ag(CN)_2^- \rightleftharpoons Ag^+ + 2CN^-$	2×10^{-19}
$Ag(S_2O_3)_2^{3-} \rightleftharpoons Ag^+ + 2S_2O_3^{2-}$	6×10^{-14}
$Cu(NH_3)_4^{2+} \rightleftharpoons Cu^{2+} + 4NH_3$	5×10^{-14}
$FeSCN^{2+} \rightleftharpoons Fe^{3+} + SCN^-$	1×10^{-3}

* Most of the values are approximate only. Different authors have reported widely different results.

attainment of equilibrium, respectively. These two terms may be applied to any reaction.

Table 29.4 gives dissociation constants for a few complex ions. Some authors call these "stability" constants (others call them "instability" constants). Use of these data for calculating ion concentrations will be illustrated by two examples.

PROBLEM: To 1 liter of $1.0M$ KCN solution there is added 0.10 mole $AgNO_3$. What is the concentration of Ag^+ ions?

SOLUTION: The equilibrium expression is

$$\frac{[Ag^+] \times [CN^-]^2}{[Ag(CN)_2^-]} = 2 \times 10^{-19}$$

The dissociation constant is extremely small. This must mean that nearly all the silver is in the form of the complex ion $Ag(CN)_2^-$. Hence the concentration of the complex ion must be approximately $0.1M$. It requires two CN^- ions for each Ag^+ to form the complex; hence the residual CN^- concentration must be $1.0 - 0.2 = 0.8M$. Then, substituting in the expression, we have

$$[Ag^+] = \frac{2 \times 10^{-19} \times 0.1}{(0.8)^2}$$
$$= 3 \times 10^{-20}M$$

Dissociation constants may be combined with solubility products, as shown by the following exercise.

PROBLEM: Would it be possible to precipitate AgCl by adding Cl^- ions to the solution (above) which contains $3 \times 10^{-20}M$ Ag^+?

SOLUTION: The solubility product of AgCl is

$$[Ag^+] \times [Cl^-] = 1.7 \times 10^{-10}$$

To obtain a precipitate, the Cl^- concentration would have to be such that $[Ag^+] \times [Cl^-]$ would be in excess of 1.7×10^{-10}. As $[Ag^+] = 3 \times 10^{-20}M$, this would require $[Cl^-]$ to be *greater* than

$$\frac{1.7 \times 10^{-10}}{3 \times 10^{-20}} = 5 \times 10^{9}M$$

This is an impossibly large concentration; no precipitate of AgCl could be obtained.

The use of dissociation constants as given above can at best produce only approximate results. The reason for this is that loss or exchange of ligands actually takes place step by step. The dissociation

$$Cu(NH_3)_4^{2+} \rightleftharpoons Cu^{2+} + 4NH_3$$

actually involves the loss of one NH_3 at a time, with each step having its own equilibrium constant. As might be expected, this leads to considerable complication in the calculations. We shall leave these complications to more advanced texts.

29.5 *Valence Problems in Coordination Complexes*

The difficulties encountered in connection with valence forces in metal carbonyls reappear in aggravated form in coordination complexes, of which most authors consider the carbonyls to be a class. In this section some of the properties most closely related to valence will be presented, and some current theories of valence in complexes will be touched upon briefly.

The tendency for transition elements to form coordination complexes suggests that unfilled orbitals are important, if not essential, for this kind of chemical reactivity. Equally important is the observation that in the lanthanides (and to a degree in the actinides), with their shielded $4f$ and $5f$ electrons, complex formation is much diminished. Coordination complexes are formed primarily by elements with unfilled, or just filled, d orbitals. Virtual proof of the involvement of d orbitals and d electrons is to be found in the magnetic properties of complexes. It will be recalled (Sec. 24.2) that, in the free ion, d electrons tend to remain unpaired in accordance with Hund's rule until they are forced to pair. The ion Fe^{3+} has a d orbital capable of holding ten electrons, but only five are present. These remain unpaired and the ion, in its compounds, is paramagnetic, with a high magnetic moment corresponding to five unpaired electrons. This is found to be the case in many iron compounds and even in such coordination complexes as $Fe(H_2O)_6^{3+}$, FeF_6^{3-}, and $Fe(NH_3)_6^{3+}$. But, the complex $Fe(CN)_6^{3-}$ has a magnetic moment corresponding to only one unpaired electron; $Co(NH_3)_6^{3+}$ is actually diamagnetic, as is $Fe(CN)_6^{4-}$. There are innumerable examples in which the number of unpaired electrons in the complex is far less than in the free ion.

Other evidence concerning valence in complexes is found in the manner in which oxidation states that are rare or unknown in simple compounds become common in complexes. An example is cobalt, which normally in the 3+ oxidation state is a powerful and unstable oxidizing agent. But the complex $Co(NH_3)_6^{3+}$ is quite stable and is not a good oxidizing agent in any sense. This tendency of unusual oxidation states to be stabilized in complexes is, of course, related to the oxidation potentials. Thus, for the oxidation,

$$Mn^{2+} \rightleftharpoons Mn^{3+} + e^- \qquad E_0 = -1.51 \text{ volts}$$

This means that Mn^{3+} is a strong enough oxidizing agent to oxidize water, liberating O_2. But for the cyanide complex of Mn^{3+}, the situation is quite different:

$$Mn(CN)_6^{4-} \rightleftharpoons Mn(CN)_6^{3-} + e^- \qquad E_0 = +0.22 \text{ volt}$$

The complex will certainly not oxidize water. Any complete theory of valence in coordination complexes must be able to explain the stabilization of unusual oxidation states.

The final property to be described is the lability of complexes, mentioned in the preceding section. Two examples will be sufficient to show the general nature of this property. The hexa-ammine cobalt(III) ion reacts with acidified water in the following manner:

$$Co(NH_3)_6^{3+} + 6H_3O^+ \rightleftharpoons Co(H_2O)_6^{3+} + 6NH_4^+$$

For this reaction, the equilibrium constant is about 10^{25} so that the ammine is thermodynamically unstable, the equilibrium lying very far to the right. But this reaction must have a high activation energy because the ammine will remain unchanged in dilute acid for a long time. Its lability is low. By contrast the stability of $Ni(CN)_4^{2-}$ is high, but if radioactive carbon is added in the form of $^*CN^-$ to a solution containing $Ni(CN)_4^{2-}$, it will be found that the exchange reaction

$$Ni(CN)_4^{2-} + 4(^*CN^-) \rightleftharpoons Ni(^*CN)_4^{2-} + 4CN^-$$

proceeds with almost immeasurably high velocity. This reaction of $Ni(CN)_4^{2-}$ is highly *labile*; it has a high lability.

Many studies have been made of the lability of complexes, both from the point of view of changing the central atom and of changing the

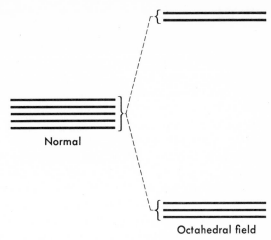

Fig. 29.2 *Splitting of d orbitals of normally equal energy into a group of two and a group of three by an octahedral electric field produced by six ligands.*

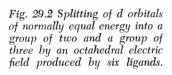

Normal

Octahedral field

ligands, and a great variety of different labilities has been found. It must suffice here to say that these phenomena also deserve explanation in any comprehensive theory of valence.

At one time it was thought that the diminution of magnetic moment in, say, $Fe(CN)_6^{3-}$ as compared with FeF_6^{3-} showed that the CN^- ion forms a covalent bond with the iron and that the F^- ion forms an ionic bond. But this idea was not able to explain the lability of the CN^-. A more realistic approach is based on the fact that the energy levels, as described in Chapter 6, may be split into sublevels in the presence of an electric field. This effect, called the *Stark effect*, may take place on an atomic scale because an atom surrounded by other atoms or especially by ions is, of course, in the electric field created by those ligands. From this it follows that the distribution of electrons in various orbitals in a coordination complex is not necessarily the same as in a free atom or ion. The theoretical treatment of this effect has been successful in solving some, but not all, problems involving valence and structure. It is known as the *crystal field theory*. How the crystal field theory accounts for the magnetic properties of complexes will be illustrated for one simple example, namely, an octahedral complex in which the central atom is surrounded by six negative ions.

In a free metal atom of the first transition series the five $3d$ orbitals all have the same energy, and occupancy of any of or all these by electrons is equally probable. But in the octahedral field created by the six ligands, the five orbitals are split into two groups of differing energy. One group contains three orbitals, the other two. This is shown diagrammetrically in Fig. 29.2. Now electrons tend to concentrate in the group of lower energy, and if there are more than three electrons present, some pairing will result, with accompanying diminution of the magnetic moment. Fig.

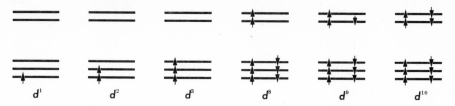

Fig. 29.3 *Distribution of 1, 2, 3, 8, 9, and 10 electrons respectively in the split d orbitals formed in octahedral complexes. The arrows show relative direction of electron spin.*

29.3 shows how a set of d orbitals containing 1, 2, 3, 8, 9, or 10 electrons could have magnetic moments corresponding to 1, 2, 3, 2, 1, and 0 unpaired electrons, respectively. The case for 4, 5, 6, and 7 electrons (referred to as the d^4, d^5, d^6, and d^7 configurations) is more complicated, and two possibilities present themselves, depending in part on the difference in energy produced by the crystal field effect. We need not elaborate this idea further and will merely point out that the theory has been able to predict magnetic moments in numerous cases.

The crystal field theory uses a purely electrostatic approach, and as such it cannot account for many of the complexities encountered. An approach that is an attempt to combine the crystal field approach with some of the features of molecular orbital theory (outlined very briefly in Sec. 27.7), has proved successful to a degree in correlating both physical and chemical properties of coordination complexes. This is known as the *ligand field theory*. The ligand field theory is still merely an approximation, but instead of calculating orbital splitting directly from the strength and symmetry of the field produced by the ligands regarded as point charges in space, the splitting produced is modified to take into consideration the effect of overlap between the orbitals of the central atom and those of the ligands. This modification may be arbitrary (it is always a decrease) or it may be based on experimental data. It has had a considerable degree of success in the prediction of physical properties and even of chemical properties, including reaction rates in ligand lability.

EXERCISES

1. List at least a dozen compounds of the metals that are volatile at or near room temperature.
2. What circumstances may, in general, be said to lead to volatile compounds of the metals?

3. Compute the "effective atomic number" for chromium hexa-carbonyl, and for the hexa-amminecobalt (III) ion.

4. Give examples of a coordination complex in the form of a positive ion, a neutral molecule, and a negative ion.

5. Would it be possible to conceive of a coordination complex becoming part of an infinite lattice compound? If so, give examples.

6. Name the following: $[Co(NO_2)_3(NH_3)_3]$, $[CrClen(H_2O)_2]$ $(NO_3)_2$, $K[PtCl_3(NH_3)]$.

7. Write formulas for the following: carbonatotetra-amminecobalt (III) chloride; potassium tetranitrodiamminecobaltate(III); potassium trioxalatoferrate (III).

8. Four ligands may be arranged around a central atom either as at the corners of a tetrahedron or as at the corners of a square. How many isomers are possible for the complex $[MX_2Y_2]$ in each of the two configurations?

9. Consider the compounds having the composition (a) $K_2:Co:Cl_5:NH_3$; (b) $Co:Cl_4:(NH_3)_5$; and (c) $Co:Cl_3:(NH_3)_3$. If these in turn are dissolved in water and subjected to electrolysis, will the cobalt (in its complex) be found to migrate toward the anode or the cathode?

10. Take 1 gram of each of the compounds given in the preceding question, dissolve it in water, and add dilute silver nitrate solution in slight excess. What weight of AgCl will precipitate in each case?

11. Write a structural formula for *trans*-$[CoCl_2en_2]^+$. How many isomers are possible?

12. Write a structural formula for two isomers of *cis*-$[CoCl_2en_2]^+$. (The kind of isomerism illustrated here is known as optical isomerism because of the opposite effect of the two compounds in rotating the plane of polarized light. Optical isomers differ as the right hand does from the left.)

13. Could $[Coen_3]^{3+}$ form optical isomers?

14. A solution contains $0.1M$ $AgNO_3$, and sufficient NaCl is added to make $[Cl^-] = 0.5M$. What concentration of NH_4OH must be present to prevent precipitation of AgCl?

15. What is the concentration of Ag^+ in a solution in which $[S_2O_3^{2-}] = 1M$, and to which excess of AgBr has been added?

16. A high concentration of Cl^- tends to dissolve AgCl, owing to formation of $AgCl_2^-$. What concentration of Ag^+ is present in equilibrium with $0.005M$ $NaAgCl_2$?

17. With the exception of vanadium hexacarbonyl, all metal carbonyls appear to be diamagnetic. Why should $V(CO)_6$ be an exception?

18. A solution containing Fe^{2+} is mixed with one containing Fe^{3+}. Write directions for an experiment to determine if the "electron-transfer" reaction

$$Fe^{2+} + Fe^{3+} \rightleftharpoons Fe^{3+} + Fe^{2+}$$

can occur.

19. Write expressions for the rate law for each of the following two substitution reactions:

(a)   *cis*-$[PtCl_2en] + OH^- \rightarrow [PtOHClen] + Cl^-$

which is found to be first order in the complex but independent of the OH^- concentration.

(b)   *trans*-$[PtCl(NH_3)_3]^+ + NO_2^- \rightarrow PtNO_2(NH_3)_3]^+ + Cl^-$

which is first order in both complex and entering ligand.

20. Show how the crystal field theory can predict the observed magnetic moment of zero for the ion hexacyanoferrate (II).

21. A certain vitamin contains 0.712 percent by weight of coordinated cobalt. What is the minimum possible molecular weight for this compound?

22. Is it possible for any element of Group Zero in the Periodic Table to form a coordination complex?

23. Explain the difference between a chelate and a clathrate.

24. The ion FeF_6^{3-} bears some superficial resemblance to the compound UF_6, but there are important differences. What are these differences?

30

Organic Compounds
of Carbon

30.1 Introduction to Organic Chemistry

In earlier chapters there have been presented many compounds of which carbon is a component. With few exceptions these compounds have contained in their formulas one, and only one, carbon atom. Most such compounds are considered to belong to the realm of inorganic chemistry.

But carbon forms myriads of other compounds, and no introduction to general chemistry may be considered complete without reference to some of them. These compounds fall into the broad area called *organic chemistry*. The name "organic" is derived from the early belief (long since abandoned) that all such compounds are necessarily related to, and derived from, living matter.

All organic compounds contain carbon; nearly all contain two or more carbon atoms in the formula, and nearly all contain hydrogen. Organic compounds have certain unique properties that make it convenient to treat them as a special branch of chemistry, but it must be emphasized that the general principles described in this book apply to all substances, inorganic or organic. The division into two branches is one of convenience for presentation, for study, and for specialization.

The properties that make organic compounds unique are (in addition to their vast numbers) as follows:

1. Nearly all organic compounds contain chains of carbon atoms connected directly to each other; for instance: —C—C—C—C—. This property, which is called *catenation*, is not restricted to carbon; it is shown by silicon (Sec. 25.4), by phosphorus (Sec. 25.3), and by boron. But in these cases the atoms are generally connected through oxygen as in —Si—O—Si—O. It is true that sulfur forms chains, as of —S—S—S—S— (Sec. 19.6), as does phosphorus (Sec. 19.6) to a limited degree, but carbon possesses this property to a degree not approached by any other element.

2. The chemical properties of organic compounds are determined to a large extent by certain combinations of atoms. These combinations (which determine, for example, whether a compound is an alcohol, an ether, or an organic acid) are called *functional groups*. Organic compounds consist of carbon chains (or rings) to which are attached one or more functional groups. This situation is, of course, quite different from that which normally occurs in inorganic chemistry, although it is not unknown in the oxy-acids of phosphorus.

3. Valence bonding in organic chemistry is almost exclusively covalent, although many complications are known. Ionic bonding is comparatively rare, and there is nothing comparable to metallic bonding or to nonstoichiometry. In all but a handful of organic compounds the carbon atom exhibits four valence bonds.

30.2   *Hydrocarbons*

Any binary compound containing carbon and hydrogen is called a *hydrocarbon*. The simplest of these, namely, methane, CH_4, was described in Secs. 22.4, 22.5, and 22.6. It will be recalled that this compound is a gas consisting of CH_4 molecules in which the four hydrogens are covalently bonded to the carbon as at the corners of a tetrahedron (Sec. 22.5), the angle between any two valence bonds being about 109 degrees.

Methane is the chief constituent in natural gas, and it is formed as a by-product in the petroleum industry, but methane is by no means the only important hydrocarbon. The compound ethane, C_2H_6, is also found abundantly as a constituent of petroleum gases, or as a by-product of the petroleum industry. It is also a colorless gas, the structural formula of which is

$$
\begin{array}{c}
\text{H}\text{H} \\
| | \\
\text{H}-\text{C}-\text{C}-\text{H} \\
| | \\
\text{H}\text{H}
\end{array}
$$

ethane

Other compounds related to methane and ethane include propane, C_3H_8; butane, C_4H_{10}; pentane, C_5H_{12}; and hexane, C_6H_{14}.

The structural formula for propane offers no special difficulty; there is obviously only one possibility:

$$
\begin{array}{ccc}
\text{H} & \text{H} & \text{H} \\
| & | & | \\
\text{H}-\text{C}-\text{C}-\text{C}-\text{H} \\
| & | & | \\
\text{H} & \text{H} & \text{H}
\end{array}
$$

propane

But when we come to butane, there are clearly two possible structures:

$$
\begin{array}{cccc}
\text{H} & \text{H} & \text{H} & \text{H} \\
| & | & | & | \\
\text{H}-\text{C}-\text{C}-\text{C}-\text{C}-\text{H} \\
| & | & | & | \\
\text{H} & \text{H} & \text{H} & \text{H}
\end{array}
\qquad
\begin{array}{ccc}
\text{H} & \text{H} & \text{H} \\
| & | & | \\
\text{H}-\text{C}-\text{C}-\text{C}-\text{H} \\
| & | & | \\
\text{H} & & \text{H} \\
& \text{H}-\text{C}-\text{H} \\
& | \\
& \text{H}
\end{array}
$$

n-butane   isobutane

There are actually two known butanes of formula C_4H_{10} and of molecular weight 58. The boiling point of one is $-0.5°$ C; that of the other, $-12°$ C. They differ also somewhat in density and in other properties. One butane cannot, without considerable difficulty, be converted into the other. There is not the slightest doubt that these are different chemical substances. They are referred to as *structural isomers,* which are substances of the same empirical formula and the same molecular weight but in which the geometric arrangement of the atoms is different. The two butanes are called normal (*n*) butane and isobutane. For pentane there are three possible structural isomers; for hexane, there are five; and the number then increases very rapidly.

It will be noted that all these compounds may be represented by a general formula: C_nH_{2n+2}. Compounds for which such a general formula is possible constitute a *homologous series.* The particular homologous series representable by C_nH_{2n+2} is called the *paraffin* series. This series of hydrocarbons is said to be *saturated* because these compounds are less active chemically than certain other hydrocarbons.

A very large number of saturated hydrocarbons, or paraffins, is known. An even greater number is theoretically possible. Table 30.1 gives the name, formula, boiling point, melting point, and number of structural isomers for some members of the series up to C_{40}.

It will be noted that the lower (few carbon atoms) paraffins are gases; those from C_5 to C_{20} are liquids at room temperature; the higher

TABLE 30.1 SOME SATURATED HYDROCARBONS

Name	bp,* °C	mp,* °C	Number of structural isomers
Methane, CH_4	−161.7	−182.6	1
Ethane, C_2H_6	−88.6	−172.0	1
Propane, C_3H_8	−42.1	−187.1	1
Butane, C_4H_{10}	−0.5	−135.0	2
Pentane, C_5H_{12}	36.1	−129.7	3
Hexane, C_6H_{14}	68.7	−94.0	5
Heptane, C_7H_{16}	98.4	−90.5	9
Octane, C_8H_{18}	125.6	−56.8	18
Nonane, C_9H_{20}	150.7	−53.7	35
Decane, $C_{10}H_{22}$	174.0	−29.7	75
Undecane, $C_{11}H_{24}$	195.8	−25.6	159
Dodecane, $C_{12}H_{26}$	216.3	−9.6	355
Tridecane, $C_{13}H_{28}$	234	−6	802
Tetradecane, $C_{14}H_{30}$	251	5.5	1858
Eicosane, $C_{20}H_{42}$	345	36	366, 319
Tetracontane, $C_{40}H_{82}$		81	62, 491, 178, 805, 831

* Normal isomer.

members are solids. These hydrocarbons constitute the mixtures known as "bottled gas," gasoline, kerosene, diesel fuel, lubricating oils, and certain waxes.

There is a type of saturated hydrocarbon that does not fall into the C_nH_{2n+2} class. Examples of this other class include C_3H_6 and C_6H_{12}. It will be noted that these contain two less hydrogen atoms than do the paraffins. These compounds have closed ring structures, as follows:

cyclopropane   cyclohexane

These are known respectively as cyclopropane and cyclohexane. They are considered to be members of the series of *cycloparaffins*.

If ethanol is passed over heated aluminum oxide, the ethanol decomposes, yielding ethylene, C_2H_4, and water. In this reaction, the alumina acts as a catalyst:

$$C_2H_5OH \rightleftharpoons C_2H_4 + H_2O$$

ethanol   ethylene

Industrially, the reverse process is important, ethanol being made from ethylene and water. Ethylene is available on a large scale as a by-product of the petroleum industry.

Ethylene, C_2H_4, has fewer hydrogen atoms than does the corresponding saturated hydrocarbon ethane C_2H_6. The structural formula, which seems to be necessary for ethylene, and which is supported by the reactions of this compound, is one containing two valence bonds between the carbon atoms:

$$
\begin{array}{cc}
H & H \\
| & | \\
C & = C \\
| & | \\
H & H
\end{array}
$$

ethylene

The molecule is said to contain a double bond and to be *unsaturated*.

In modern valence theory, methane and other saturated hydrocarbons do not give much difficulty. The carbon atom has the configuration $1s^2\, 2s^2\, 2p^2$, and it is thought that in forming methane (the two $2s$ orbitals and the three $2p$ orbitals) *hybridize* to yield four strong, equal bonds directed as at the corners of a tetrahedron. Four electrons from the carbon and four from the four hydrogen atoms occupy these hybrid orbitals. The ability of atoms to rotate freely about such bonds leads to the possibility of long flexible chains of carbon atoms. But in ethylene the situation is more complicated. After formation of σ bonds between the two carbon atoms and between each carbon and two hydrogens, there are two p orbitals (one on each carbon) left over. These project at right angles, as shown in Fig. 30.1, and they are available to form a π bond between the carbon atoms and also to participate in reactions with other atoms, as described below.

The most characteristic reactions of ethylene, and those that distinguish it sharply from the saturated hydrocarbons, are those in which the double bond is removed. For instance, ethylene reacts with hydrogen in the presence of platinum as a catalyst. The product is ethane:

$$
\begin{array}{ccc}
H\ \ H & & H\ \ H \\
|\ \ \ | & & |\ \ \ | \\
C = C & + H_2 \rightarrow & H-C-C-H \\
|\ \ \ | & & |\ \ \ | \\
H\ \ H & & H\ \ H
\end{array}
$$

Even more characteristic is the speed and manner with which bromine or chlorine react with ethylene:

$$\underset{\overset{|}{H}}{\overset{\overset{|}{H}}{C}}=\underset{\overset{|}{H}}{\overset{\overset{|}{H}}{C}} + Br_2 \rightarrow H-\underset{\overset{|}{Br}}{\overset{\overset{|}{H}}{C}}-\underset{\overset{|}{Br}}{\overset{\overset{|}{H}}{C}}-H$$

ethylene dibromide[1]

A drop or two of bromine water shaken with a test tube full of ethylene is almost instantly decolorized, owing to formation of ethylene dibromide. Rapid reactions such as these are used for the identification of unsaturated hydrocarbons.

Like methane, ethylene is the first member of a homologous series. There is no compound (for example, CH_2) containing only one carbon atom in this series. The general formula of the series is C_nH_{2n}. Examples other than ethylene are propylene and butylene:

propylene   butylene

These substances all show the characteristic reactions of unsaturation. The homologous series C_nH_{2n} is known as the *olefin series* (sometimes as the ethylenic series) of unsaturated hydrocarbons.

If calcium carbide, CaC_2, is treated with water, there is evolved a gas with the formula C_2H_2. This is acetylene:

$$CaC_2 + 2H_2O \rightarrow Ca(OH)_2 + C_2H_2$$

As does ethylene, acetylene reacts vigorously with bromine, but 2 moles of halogen are required for every mole of acetylene, instead of 1 as for ethylene:

$$C_2H_2 + 2Br_2 \rightarrow C_2H_2Br_4$$

[1] A more nearly complete formula for ethylene dibromide would be

$$H-\underset{\overset{\cdot\cdot}{:Br:}}{\overset{\overset{|}{H}}{C}}---\underset{\overset{\cdot\cdot}{:Br:}}{\overset{\overset{|}{H}}{C}}-H$$

but we shall omit those electrons present in the valence shell, and which are not used in bonding, unless there is some particular reason for drawing attention to them.

The structural formula assigned to acetylene involves a triple bond, as follows:

$$H—C{\equiv}C—H$$
acetylene

Acetylene is the first member of a homologous series of unsaturated hydrocarbons having the general formula C_nH_{2n-2}. The second member is methylacetylene:

$$\begin{array}{c} H \\ | \\ H—C—C{\equiv}C—H \\ | \\ H \end{array}$$
methylacetylene

These compounds are often called *acetylenic hydrocarbons*.

It is possible for a molecule to contain two or more double or triple bonds. One example of such a compound is butadiene:

$$\begin{array}{c} H\ \ H\ \ H\ \ H \\ |\ \ \ |\ \ \ |\ \ \ | \\ C{=}C—C{=}C \\ |\ \ \ \ \ \ \ \ \ \ \ | \\ H\ \ \ \ \ \ \ \ \ \ H \end{array}$$
butadiene

If soft coal is heated in the absence of air, there is obtained a variety of useful substances of which benzene, C_6H_6, is one. The formula of this compound suggests an unsaturated structure related to that of acetylene, but benzene does not exhibit the properties characteristic of olefins or of acetylenic hydrocarbons. The structural formula proposed by A. Kekulé in 1865, and still regarded as being near the truth, was that the benzene molecule is a ring having alternate single and double bonds, but that it exists in two inseparable forms; thus,

In modern terminology we say that *resonance* exists between the two hypothetical forms of benzene. In still more modern valence bond theory, it appears that benzene gains its stability from the π bonds overlapping as they protrude from each of the six carbons. For simplicity we shall frequently use the single hexagon

to indicate the benzene ring, but we shall always mean the resonance forms as given above.

The series of hydrocarbons of which benzene is a member is called the *aromatic* series, to distinguish it from the *aliphatic* or chainlike series previously described. But cyclohexane belongs to the aliphatic series; it is the ring plus the resonance that gives the aromatic series its characteristic properties. A few examples of other aromatic hydrocarbons are given as follows:

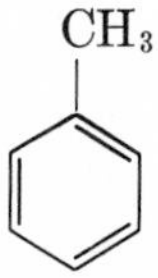

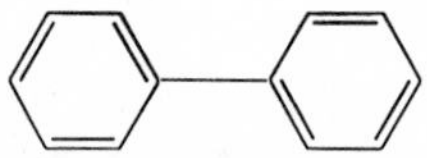

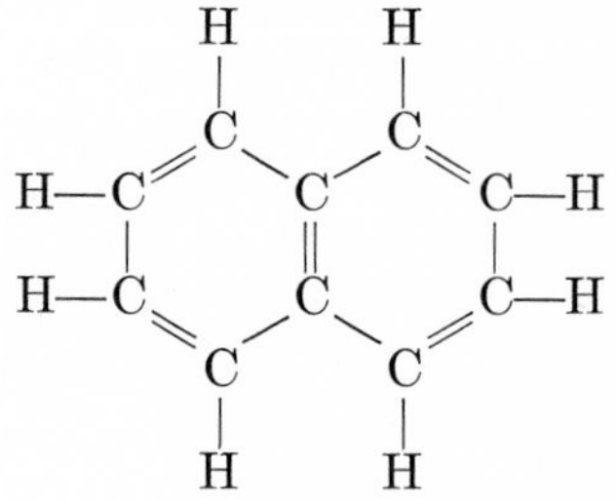

toluene   diphenyl   naphthalene

Furthermore, it is not necessary that carbon be the only element present as part of a ring structure. Examples of aromatic heterocyclic molecules containing atoms other than carbon are shown below. (Aliphatic heterocyclics are also known.)

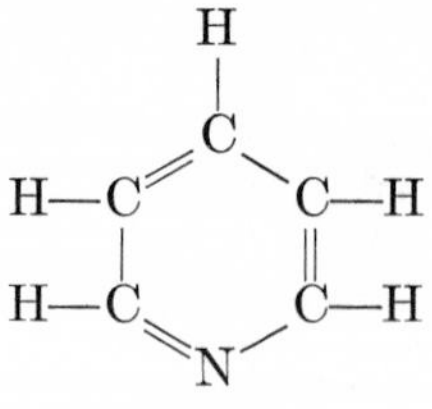

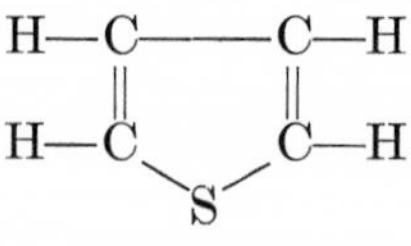

pyridine   thiophene

All these and many others are derived from petroleum or from other carbonaceous materials.

30.3   Functional Groups

If methane is treated with chlorine in the presence of light or a catalyst, one or more hydrogen atoms in the methane may be replaced by a chlorine atom:

$$CH_4 + Cl_2 \rightarrow CH_3Cl + HCl$$

This is called a reaction of *substitution*. The product CH_3Cl is methyl chloride; further substitution yields methylene chloride, CH_2Cl_2; chloroform, $CHCl_3$; and finally carbon tetrachloride, CCl_4.

Halogens other than chlorine may be used in substitution reactions, and all hydrocarbons exhibit such reactions, although unsaturated hydrocarbons show other reactions as well. If we write R—X as a general formula for any such compound, where X is any halogen, then the symbol R obviously stands for any hydrocarbon molecule less one hydrogen atom. Such a group is called an *alkyl group*. A few important alkyl groups are as follows: methyl, CH_3—; ethyl, C_2H_5—; propyl, C_3H_7—; butyl, C_4H_9—; amyl (or pentyl), C_5H_{11}—; and hexyl, C_6H_{13}—.

Any compound formed by the union of a halogen atom with an alkyl group is called an *alkyl halide*. A series of compounds of this nature, differing only in the alkyl group present, is also called a *homologous series*. The members of a homologous series show considerable resemblance in chemical properties. This resemblance in the alkyl halides is, of course, due primarily to the halogen atom, which is therefore referred to as a *functional group*.

If an alkyl halide is treated with moist silver oxide (which simulates the action of silver hydroxide), the following reaction takes place:

$$R—X + AgOH \rightarrow R—OH + AgX$$

The formula R—OH is a general formula for a class of compounds called *alcohols*. The functional group here is —OH. Two common alcohols are methanol (methyl alcohol) and ethanol (ethyl alcohol), the structural formulas of which are

$$
\begin{array}{cc}
\begin{array}{c}
\text{H} \\
| \\
\text{H—C—OH} \\
| \\
\text{H} \\
\text{methanol}
\end{array}
&
\begin{array}{c}
\text{H \ H} \\
| \ \ | \\
\text{H—C—C—OH} \\
| \ \ | \\
\text{H \ H} \\
\text{ethanol}
\end{array}
\end{array}
$$

But for propanol (propyl alcohol), two structural isomers are possible, and many isomers occur for alcohols of higher molecular weight:

$$
\begin{array}{ccc}
& \text{H} \quad \text{H} \quad \text{H} & \\
& | \quad\;\; | \quad\;\; | & \\
\text{H} & -\text{C}-\text{C}-\text{C}- & \text{OH} \\
& | \quad\;\; | \quad\;\; | & \\
& \text{H} \quad \text{H} \quad \text{H} &
\end{array}
\qquad
\begin{array}{ccc}
& \text{H} \quad \text{OH} \quad \text{H} & \\
& | \quad\;\; | \quad\;\; | & \\
\text{H} & -\text{C}-\text{C}-\text{C}- & \text{H} \\
& | \quad\;\; | \quad\;\; | & \\
& \text{H} \quad \text{H} \quad \text{H} &
\end{array}
$$

normal propanol   isopropanol

(a primary alcohol)   (a secondary alcohol)

If an alcohol is dehydrated (as with concentrated sulfuric acid), two molecules of the alcohol may combine, with elimination of a molecule of water:

$$2ROH \rightarrow R{-}O{-}R + H_2O$$

The product R—O—R is called an *ether*, and the functional group is —O—. An example is dimethyl ether, $CH_3{-}O{-}CH_3$, but the two R groups in an ether need not be the same. It may be noted that ethanol and dimethyl ether are structural isomers.

An alcohol, instead of being dehydrated, may be oxidized, as with oxygen in the presence of hot copper. In this case the product obtained depends not only on the alkyl group present but also on the particular isomer, if two or more are possible. Oxidation of methanol yields formaldehyde, CH_2O:

$$
2\,\text{H}-\!\!\underset{\underset{\textstyle \text{H}}{|}}{\overset{\overset{\textstyle \text{H}}{|}}{\text{C}}}\!\!-\text{OH} + O_2 \rightarrow 2\,\text{H}-\overset{\overset{\textstyle O}{\|}}{\text{C}}-\text{H} + 2H_2O
$$

Oxidation in this way of normal propanol yields an *aldehyde:*

$$
2\,\text{H}-\!\!\underset{\underset{\textstyle \text{H}}{|}}{\overset{\overset{\textstyle \text{H}}{|}}{\text{C}}}\!\!-\underset{\underset{\textstyle \text{H}}{|}}{\overset{\overset{\textstyle \text{H}}{|}}{\text{C}}}\!\!-\underset{\underset{\textstyle \text{H}}{|}}{\overset{\overset{\textstyle \text{H}}{|}}{\text{C}}}\!\!-\text{OH} + O_2 \longrightarrow 2\,\text{H}-\underset{\underset{\textstyle \text{H}}{|}}{\overset{\overset{\textstyle \text{H}}{|}}{\text{C}}}\!\!-\underset{\underset{\textstyle \text{H}}{|}}{\overset{\overset{\textstyle \text{H}}{|}}{\text{C}}}\!\!-\overset{\overset{\textstyle O}{\|}}{\text{C}}-\text{H} + 2H_2O
$$

normal propanol   yields   propionaldehyde

(a primary alcohol)   (an aldehyde)

but oxidation of isopropanol yields a *ketone:*

$$
2\,\text{H}-\!\!\underset{\underset{\textstyle \text{H}}{|}}{\overset{\overset{\textstyle \text{H}}{|}}{\text{C}}}\!\!-\underset{\underset{\textstyle \text{H}}{|}}{\overset{\overset{\textstyle \text{OH}}{|}}{\text{C}}}\!\!-\underset{\underset{\textstyle \text{H}}{|}}{\overset{\overset{\textstyle \text{H}}{|}}{\text{C}}}\!\!-\text{H} + O_2 \longrightarrow 2\,\text{H}-\underset{\underset{\textstyle \text{H}}{|}}{\overset{\overset{\textstyle \text{H}}{|}}{\text{C}}}\!\!-\overset{\overset{\textstyle O}{\|}}{\text{C}}-\underset{\underset{\textstyle \text{H}}{|}}{\overset{\overset{\textstyle \text{H}}{|}}{\text{C}}}\!\!-\text{H} + 2H_2O
$$

isopropanol   yields   acetone

(a secondary alcohol)   (a ketone)

The general formula for an aldehyde is

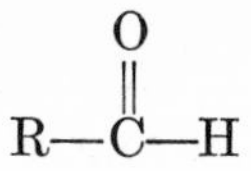

$$\begin{array}{c} \text{O} \\ \| \\ \text{R} \!-\! \text{C} \!-\! \text{H} \end{array}$$

the functional group being

$$\begin{array}{c} \text{O} \\ \| \\ -\text{C} \!-\! \text{H} \end{array}$$

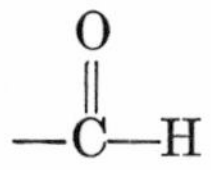

The general formula for a ketone is

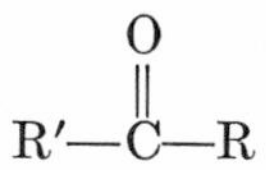

$$\begin{array}{c} \text{O} \\ \| \\ \text{R}' \!-\! \text{C} \!-\! \text{R} \end{array}$$

the functional group being

$$\begin{array}{c} \text{O} \\ \| \\ -\text{C} \!-\! \text{R} \end{array}$$

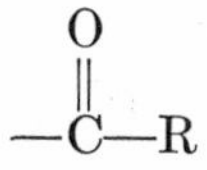

The two R groups need not be the same.

If a primary alcohol is oxidized past the stage of the aldehyde, the product is an *organic acid:*

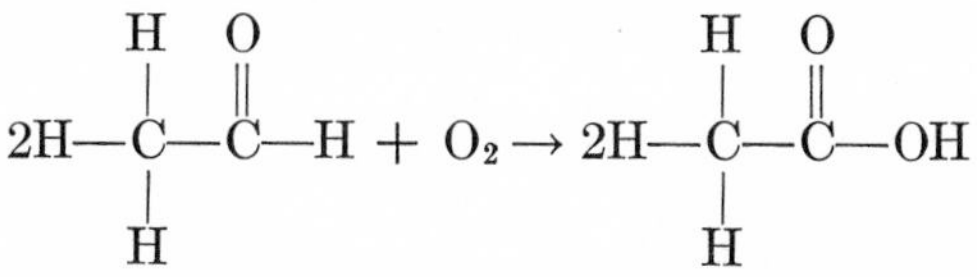

$$\begin{array}{cccc} \text{H} & \text{O} & & \text{H} & \text{O} \\ | & \| & & | & \| \\ 2\text{H} \!-\! \text{C} \!-\! \text{C} \!-\! \text{H} + \text{O}_2 \rightarrow 2\text{H} \!-\! \text{C} \!-\! \text{C} \!-\! \text{OH} \\ | & & & | \\ \text{H} & & & \text{H} \end{array}$$

acetic acid

A general formula for organic acids is

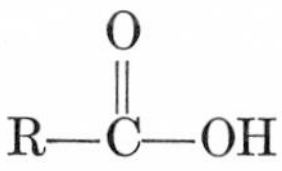

$$\begin{array}{c} \text{O} \\ \| \\ \text{R} \!-\! \text{C} \!-\! \text{OH} \end{array}$$

the functional group being

$$\begin{array}{c} \text{O} \\ \| \\ -\text{C} \!-\! \text{OH} \end{array}$$

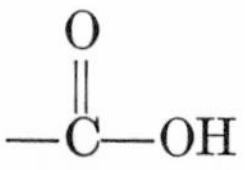

Organic acids will react directly with alcohols to form compounds know as *esters.*

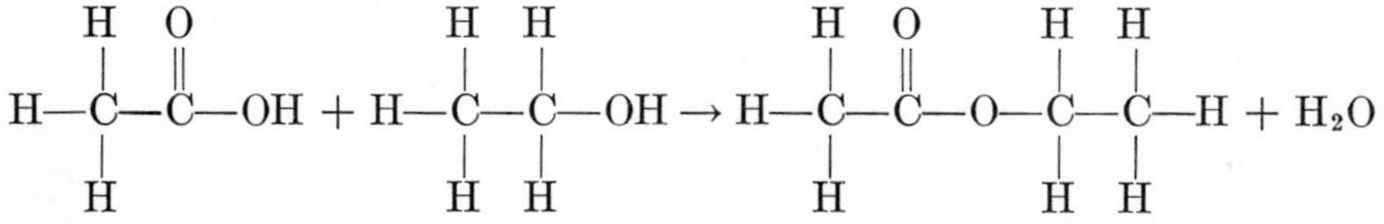

$$\begin{array}{ccccccc} \text{H} & \text{O} & & \text{H} & \text{H} & & \text{H} & \text{O} & & \text{H} & \text{H} \\ | & \| & & | & | & & | & \| & & | & | \\ \text{H} \!-\! \text{C} \!-\! \text{C} \!-\! \text{OH} + \text{H} \!-\! \text{C} \!-\! \text{C} \!-\! \text{OH} \rightarrow \text{H} \!-\! \text{C} \!-\! \text{C} \!-\! \text{O} \!-\! \text{C} \!-\! \text{C} \!-\! \text{H} + \text{H}_2\text{O} \\ | & & & | & | & & | & & & | & | \\ \text{H} & & & \text{H} & \text{H} & & \text{H} & & & \text{H} & \text{H} \end{array}$$

ethylacetate

TABLE 30.2

Type	General formula	Functional group	Example	Name
Paraffin	R—H	—H	CH_4	methane
Alkyl halide	R—X	—X	C_2H_5Cl	ethyl chloride
Alcohol	R—OH	—OH	CH_3OH	methyl alcohol
Ether	R'—O—R	—O—R	CH_3—O—C_2H_5	methylethyl ether
Aldehyde	$R-\overset{O}{\overset{\|}{C}}-H$	$-\overset{O}{\overset{\|}{C}}-H$	$CH_3-\overset{O}{\overset{\|}{C}}-H$	acetaldehyde
Ketone	$R'-\overset{O}{\overset{\|}{C}}-R$	$-\overset{O}{\overset{\|}{C}}-R$	$CH_3-\overset{O}{\overset{\|}{C}}-CH_3$	acetone
Organic acid	$R-\overset{O}{\overset{\|}{C}}-OH$	$-\overset{O}{\overset{\|}{C}}-OH$	$CH_3\overset{O}{\overset{\|}{C}}-OH$	acetic acid
Ester	$R'-\overset{O}{\overset{\|}{C}}-OR$	$-\overset{O}{\overset{\|}{C}}-OR$	$CH_3\overset{O}{\overset{\|}{C}}-OC_2H_5$	ethyl acetate
Amine	R—NH_2	—NH_2	$C_2H_5NH_2$	ethylamine
Amide	$R-\overset{O}{\overset{\|}{C}}-NH_2$	$-\overset{O}{\overset{\|}{C}}-NH_2$	$CH_3\overset{O}{\overset{\|}{C}}-NH_2$	acetamide

The general formula for an ester is

$$R-\overset{O}{\overset{\|}{C}}-O-R'$$

the functional group being

$$-\overset{O}{\overset{\|}{C}}-O-R'$$

If, in a hydrocarbon, a hydrogen atom is replaced by an —NH_2 group, the product is called an *amine*. The general formula for an amine is the R—NH_2. But if, in an organic acid, the —OH group is replaced by —NH_2, the product is called an *amide*. The general formula for an amide is

$$-\overset{O}{\overset{\|}{C}}-NH_2$$

As we shall see later, amines and amides are important in the chemistry of living matter. Both amine and amides are able to act as Brönsted bases, adding a proton to the nitrogen just as does ammonia:

$$-NH_2 + H^+ \rightarrow -NH_3^+$$

Pyridine (Sec. 30.2) is a substituted amine, capable of acting as a Brönsted base.

Table 30.2 summarizes the information given above concerning classes of compounds and functional groups.

30.4 Selected Organic Compounds

This section will be devoted to describing briefly the preparation and properties of some representative organic compounds. Some of these compounds have a relatively simple molecular structure, and some are very complex. But almost all organic compounds have in common that they form particulate molecules. It is an unusual organic substance for which we cannot write a molecular weight, although sometimes the molecular weight is very large. All this is, of course, a contrast to inorganic chemistry in which infinite ionic or covalent lattice structures are commonplace.

Methanol is made commercially by the catalytic reaction of carbon monoxide with hydrogen:

$$CO + 2H_2 \rightarrow CH_3OH$$

This compound is a colorless liquid used as an antifreeze in automobiles and as a solvent for shellac and varnish. It is poisonous; sublethal doses lead to blindness. Ethanol is made by fermentation of sugar or starch in the presence of yeast. The fermentation of glucose, $C_6H_{12}O_6$, is an example of this reaction:

$$C_6H_{12}O_6 \rightarrow 2C_2H_5OH + 2CO_2$$

The water-alcohol solution obtained may be purified by fractional distillation, but ethanol may also be made through the action of ethylene on sulfuric acid, followed by hydrolysis. The pure alcohol is a colorless liquid of very faint odor. Most ethanol is used as an antifreeze and as a solvent. It is also the essential ingredient in alcoholic beverages.

It is quite possible for an organic compound to have more than one functional group in the molecule, and these need not be the same. An example of an alcohol with more than one functional group is glycerol, which has three:

```
          H                              OH
          |                              |
     H—C—OH                             C
          |                       H—C       C—H
     H—C—OH                            ‖
          |                       H—C       C—H
     H—C—OH                             C
          |                              |
          H                              H
      glycerol                        phenol
```

It is also possible for benzene derivatives to form alcohols. One example is phenol which, however, also has some acid properties and is therefore sometimes called carbolic acid.

One example of the ethers will suffice. Diethylether is a liquid, but it boils at 34.6° C and therefore evaporates very quickly at room temperature. This compound is used as a solvent in chemical processes, but it is also used in surgical anesthesia. Breathing the vapor produces unconsciousness and muscular relaxation. The patient may suffer some nausea, but otherwise awakens unharmed.

The simplest aldehyde is formaldehyde, formed through oxidation of methanol:

```
          H                        O
          |                        ‖
    2H—C—OH + O₂ → 2H—C—H + 2H₂O
          |
          H
```

This is a colorless gas with a disagreeable odor. Its chief use is in manufacturing plastics. Other aldehydes are acetaldehyde and benzaldehyde:

```
                                       O
                                        ＼
                                          C—H
                                          
                                          C
                                   H—C       C—H
          H   O                         ‖
          |   ‖                    H—C       C—H
     H—C—C—H                            C
          |                              |
          H                              H
    acetaldehyde                    benzaldehyde
```

Benzaldehyde is oil of bitter almonds. All aldehydes are good reducing agents: that is, they are easily oxidized. If an ammoniacal solution of silver is treated with an aldehyde, the silver is reduced, forming a silver mirror. This reaction serves both as a test for aldehydes and in making mirrors:

$$R{-}\overset{\displaystyle O}{\overset{\|}{C}}{-}H + 2Ag(NH_3)_2^+ + OH^- \rightarrow \left[R{-}\overset{\displaystyle O}{\overset{\|}{C}}{-}O\right]^- + 2NH_4^+ + 2Ag + 2NH_3$$

Ketones, in contrast to aldehydes, are not readily oxidized and hence do not act as reducing agents. Acetone (dimethyl ketone), which is made either by the oxidation of secondary propyl alcohol or by fermentation of starch, is a colorless liquid with a pronounced and not unpleasant odor. It is widely used in paint and varnish removers and as a solvent.

Organic acids constitute one of the most important classes of organic compounds. The simplest such acid is formic, H_2CO_2, which is prepared by treating sodium hydroxide with carbon monoxide to yield sodium formate:

$$CO + NaOH \rightarrow H{-}\overset{\displaystyle O}{\overset{\|}{C}}{-}ONa$$

This, if treated with dilute sulfuric acid, yields formic acid by displacement (Sec. 22.4). The acid may be concentrated by distillation.

Acetic acid is made by air oxidation of ethanol, or by hydration of acetylene to acetaldehyde followed by oxidation. But acetic acid is also a product of oxidative fermentation of ethanol. This is the ancient method for preparing vinegar, of which acetic acid is the sour ingredient.

It may be wondered why these compounds are acids. The reason is that the

$$\overset{\displaystyle O}{\overset{\|}{-C}}{-}OH$$

functional group is capable of losing a proton and is thus a Brönsted acid:

$$\overset{\displaystyle O}{\overset{\|}{-C}}{-}OH \rightleftharpoons \left[\overset{\displaystyle O}{\overset{\|}{-C}}{-}O\right]^- + \quad H^+$$

organic acid   acid ion   hydrogen ion

Most organic acids are weak acids, although a few such as

$$CCl_3\overset{\displaystyle O}{\overset{\|}{C}}{-}OH$$

are strong. It will be noted that the acetic acid molecule has four hydrogen atoms, but that only one of these may be removed as an ion. The three hydrogens attached directly to a carbon atom have no acid properties. Organic acids, as do all oxy-acids, form oxy-salts, of which sodium acetate,

$$CH_3\overset{\displaystyle O}{\overset{\|}{C}}-ONa$$

is one. These are, for the most part, true ionic structures like the sodium phosphates. Most such compounds, being salts of weak acids, are subject to extensive hydrolysis in water.

Organic acids may contain two or more functional groups. One such acid is oxalic:

oxalic acid   lactic acid

Acid functional groups may also be present with other functional groups. An example is lactic acid, which contains both acid and alcohol functional groups. Citric acid contains an alcohol group plus three acid groups:

citric acid   benzoic acid

An example of an organic acid derived from an aromatic hydrocarbon is benzoic acid.

Esters, as previously shown, may be made by the reaction of an alcohol with an organic acid, but many esters occur naturally in animal and vegetable matter. Ethyl formate and amylacetate are examples of sweet-smelling esters which occur in flowers and which are used in making perfumes:

$$\underset{\text{ethyl formate}}{\text{H}-\overset{\overset{\displaystyle\text{O}}{\|}}{\text{C}}-\text{O}-\text{C}_2\text{H}_5} \qquad \underset{\text{amyl acetate}}{\text{H}-\overset{\overset{\displaystyle\text{H}}{|}}{\underset{\underset{\displaystyle\text{H}}{|}}{\text{C}}}-\overset{\overset{\displaystyle\text{O}}{\|}}{\text{C}}-\text{O}-\text{C}_5\text{H}_{11}}$$

More complicated esters such as those derived from glycerol (as the alcohol) are found in animal and vegetable fats. Glyceryl tributyrate occurs in butter and glyceryl tristearate is one of several glyceryl esters present in beef fat:

$$\underset{\text{glyceryl tributyrate}}{\begin{array}{c}\text{H}-\overset{\overset{\displaystyle\text{H}}{|}}{\text{C}}-\text{O}-\overset{\overset{\displaystyle\text{O}}{\|}}{\text{C}}-\text{C}_3\text{H}_7\\[1em]\text{H}-\overset{|}{\text{C}}-\text{O}-\overset{\overset{\displaystyle\text{O}}{\|}}{\text{C}}-\text{C}_3\text{H}_7\\[1em]\text{H}-\overset{|}{\underset{\underset{\displaystyle\text{H}}{|}}{\text{C}}}-\text{O}-\overset{\overset{\displaystyle\text{O}}{\|}}{\text{C}}-\text{C}_3\text{H}_7\end{array}} \qquad \underset{\text{glyceryl tristearate}}{\begin{array}{c}\text{H}-\overset{\overset{\displaystyle\text{H}}{|}}{\text{C}}-\text{O}-\overset{\overset{\displaystyle\text{O}}{\|}}{\text{C}}-\text{C}_{17}\text{H}_{35}\\[1em]\text{H}-\overset{|}{\text{C}}-\text{O}-\overset{\overset{\displaystyle\text{O}}{\|}}{\text{C}}-\text{C}_{17}\text{H}_{35}\\[1em]\text{H}-\overset{|}{\underset{\underset{\displaystyle\text{H}}{|}}{\text{C}}}-\text{O}-\overset{\overset{\displaystyle\text{O}}{\|}}{\text{C}}-\text{C}_{17}\text{H}_{35}\end{array}}$$

Esters, if treated with a base such as sodium hydroxide, undergo hydrolysis to yield the original alcohol plus a salt of the acid. If, for instance, glyceryl tristearate is heated with sodium hydroxide solution, it is converted into glycerol plus sodium stearate:

$$\underset{\substack{\text{glyceryl tristearate}\\\text{(a fat)}}}{\begin{array}{c}\text{H}-\overset{\overset{\displaystyle\text{H}}{|}}{\text{C}}-\text{O}-\overset{\overset{\displaystyle\text{O}}{\|}}{\text{C}}-\text{C}_{17}\text{H}_{35}\\[1em]\text{H}-\overset{|}{\text{C}}-\text{O}-\overset{\overset{\displaystyle\text{O}}{\|}}{\text{C}}-\text{C}_{17}\text{H}_{35}\\[1em]\text{H}-\overset{|}{\underset{\underset{\displaystyle\text{H}}{|}}{\text{C}}}-\text{O}-\overset{\overset{\displaystyle\text{O}}{\|}}{\text{C}}-\text{C}_{17}\text{H}_{35}\end{array}} + 3\text{NaOH} \rightarrow \underset{\text{glycerol}}{\begin{array}{c}\text{H}-\overset{\overset{\displaystyle\text{H}}{|}}{\text{C}}-\text{OH}\\[1em]\text{H}-\overset{|}{\text{C}}-\text{OH}\\[1em]\text{H}-\overset{|}{\underset{\underset{\displaystyle\text{H}}{|}}{\text{C}}}-\text{OH}\end{array}} + \underset{\text{sodium stearate}\atop\text{(a soap)}}{3\text{C}_{17}\text{H}_{35}\overset{\overset{\displaystyle\text{O}}{\|}}{\text{C}}-\text{ONa}}$$

Sodium stearate is an example of a soap, and it is a principal constituent of ordinary soap. The process shown is therefore called *saponification,* which is approximately the reverse of the process of esterification by which the ester can be made from the alcohol plus the acid.

Aromatic groups also participate in ester formation. One example is methyl salicylate or oil of wintergreen:

| salicylic acid | methanol | methyl salicylate | water |

Many amines may be prepared by the reaction of alkyl (or aryl) halides with ammonia. The overall reaction (which occurs in two steps) is as follows:

$$RX + 2NH_3 \rightarrow RNH_2 + NH_4X$$

Amines may thus be considered as ammonia in which one (or more) hydrogens have been replaced by organic groups. Our chief interest in these compounds will be in relation to living matter, as described in Sec. 30.6. The same is true of the amides, which may be considered as ammonia in which one (or more) hydrogens have been replaced by an acid group. An important diamide is urea, which is an end product of animal metabolism:

carbonic acid   urea

Urea is the diamide of carbonic acid. Do not confuse an amide with an aminoacid. The latter is a compound containing both an acid and an amine functional group. We shall have much to say about amino acids later.

acetamide   aminoacetic acid

Vegetable matter always contains large amounts of organic compounds called carbohydrates. These consist of carbon, hydrogen, and oxygen, and in most cases, the proportion of hydrogen to oxygen is the same as in water, namely, two atoms to one. There are various kinds of carbohydrates, which range in molecular weight from the sugars, such as glucose, $C_6H_{12}O_6$, through starches to celluloses, $C_m(H_2O)_n$, in which the

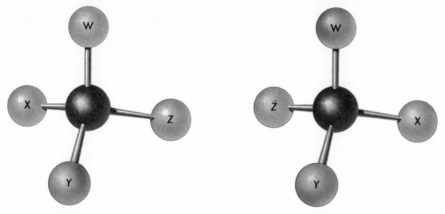

Fig. 30.1 Mirror images (optical) isomers. The four atoms, or groups of atoms, labeled W, X, Y, and Z around the central carbon atom may be arranged as shown in either of two ways. This possibility gives rise to optical isomerism.

molecular weight is very large. Cotton, linen, and paper are almost pure cellulose.

All carbohydrates possess many alcohol functional groups. Glucose, a common constituent in plants, is a relatively simple carbohydrate, although it has several possible configurations, of which two are shown:

aldehyde (chain) form of glucose   hemiacetal (ring) form of glucose

It will be noted that glucose has an aldehyde group. This makes it a good reducing agent, and this is the basis for a chemical test for the disease diabetes. While glucose and several other carbohydrates possess six carbon atoms, other carbohydrates have more or less. An important five-carbon carbohydrate, to which we shall have reference later, is ribose.

It was mentioned in Chapter 29 that certain compounds have the ability to rotate the plane of polarized light. Such substances, of which glucose is one, have this ability and are said to be *optically active*. Optical activity may arise whenever a carbon atom is surrounded by four different groups, as shown in Fig. 30.1. The straight-chain structural formula for glucose shows that there are four such carbon atoms (the four central atoms) in the molecule. Molecules that differ only in the direction in which they rotate the plane of polarized light are said to be *optical isomers.* Many natural compounds exhibit this effect.

Carbohydrates are synthesized in nature by the reaction of carbon dioxide with water under the influence of light and in the presence of chlorophyll as a catalyst. The overall reaction may be written as

$$2nCO_2 + 2nH_2O \rightarrow (CH_2O)_{2n} + nO_2$$

The structural formula for chlorophyll is

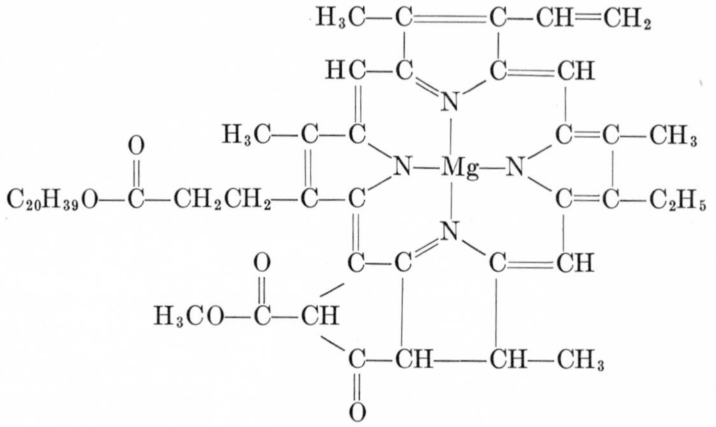

chlorophyll

This section will be concluded by reference to some organic compounds, of major interest because of their physiological activity. The first of these is cocaine, which relieves pain but produces drug addiction. There is also shown the formula for procaine (novocaine), which is a synthetic compound prepared in the (successful) hope of retaining the useful properties of cocaine but of eliminating the dangerous properties. Procaine is widely used in minor surgical operations, as in tooth extraction.

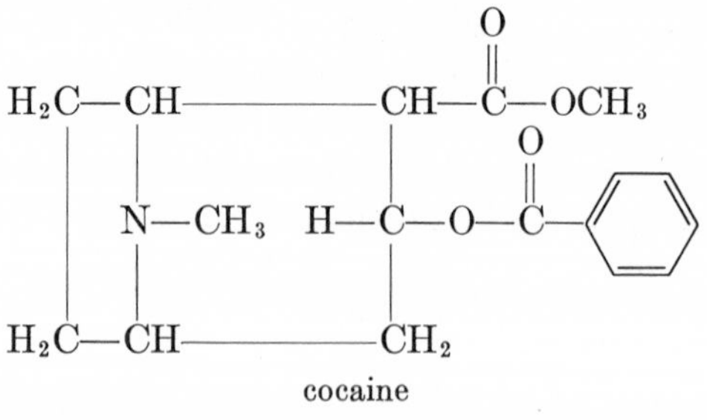

cocaine

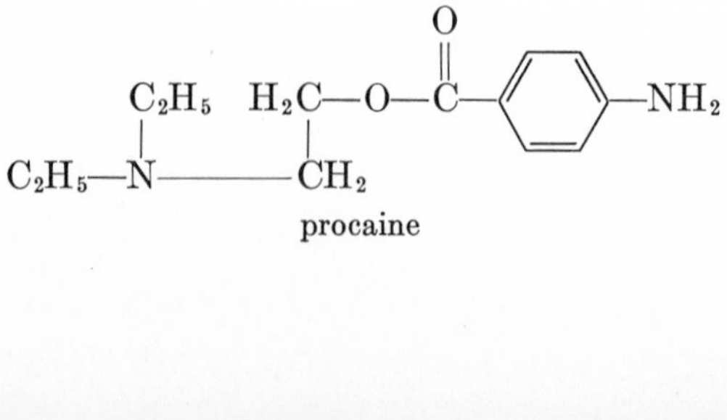

procaine

Another compound of extraordinary value is penicillin, which was the first of the antibiotics to be discovered. These compounds have revolutionized the treatment of many infectious diseases. The structure of one form of the molecule is

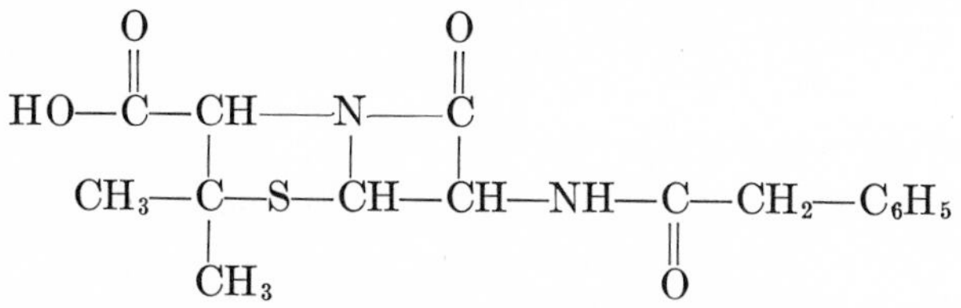

one form of penicillin (benzylpenicillin G)

There are many substances used in small quantities, but which are essential parts of the diet of humans and animals, if health is to be maintained. Such substances are called *vitamins*, one example being thiamine. This is also known as vitamin B_1. Lack of this substance in the diet causes the Asiatic disease called beriberi.

The vitamins may be considered as organic catalysts. Another kind of organic catalyst that is generated in the healthy animal body is called a *hormone*. One of these is thyroxin, lack of which causes hypothyroidism. The formula is shown below, as is that for adrenaline, which has an effect on the cardiovascular system leading to constriction of blood vessels and increase of blood pressure.

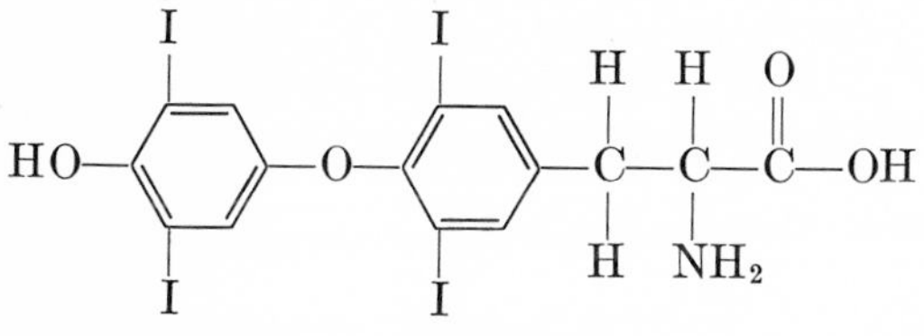

thyroxin

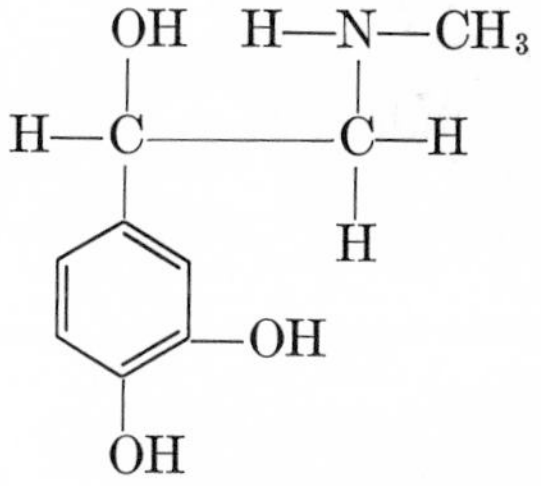

adrenaline

Two final examples of hormones are the steriods estradiol and testosterone. These control sexual processes and secondary sexual characteristics in the female and the male, respectively. They are therefore known as sex hormones.

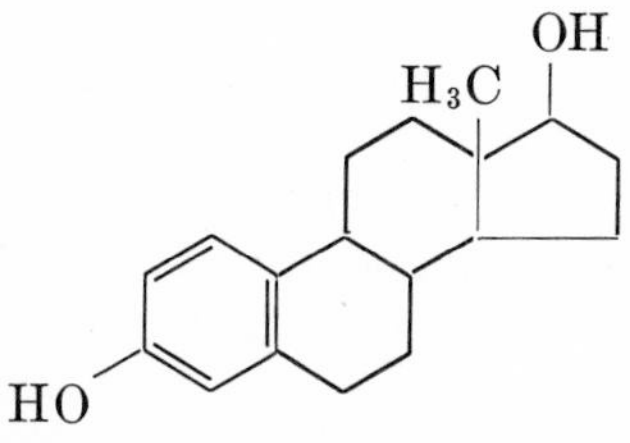

estradiol

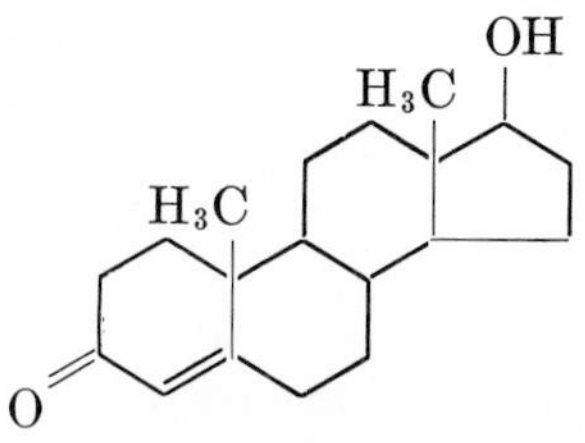

testosterone

30.5   *High Polymers*

In Sec. 25.6 reference was made to the way in which some oxides such as SiO_2 form continuous structural lattices, and in Sec. 28.6, it was shown that many oxy-salts are formed of chain, thread, or honeycomb anion structures, which may extend indefinitely in space. Similarly, polymerized structures are found among the compounds of carbon. If the molecular weight is very large, or infinite, these compounds are called *high polymers.*

The polymeric anions of silicon previously referred to were based on a tetrahedral grouping of four oxygens around each silicon atom. Another possible arrangement involves replacement of some of the oxygens by hydrogen to form a siloxane, of which one example is

$$\underset{\displaystyle \text{trisiloxane}}{H-\overset{\displaystyle H}{\underset{\displaystyle H}{Si}}-O-\overset{\displaystyle H}{\underset{\displaystyle H}{Si}}-O-\overset{\displaystyle H}{\underset{\displaystyle H}{Si}}-H}$$

Siloxanes may form very long molecules, by addition of more H_2SiO groups, to form polysiloxanes:

$$\underset{\displaystyle \text{polysiloxane}}{H-\overset{\displaystyle H}{\underset{\displaystyle H}{Si}}-O-\left[-\overset{\displaystyle H}{\underset{\displaystyle H}{Si}}-O\right]_n-\overset{\displaystyle H}{\underset{\displaystyle H}{Si}}-H}$$

Now the hydrogen atoms may be replaced by alkyl (or aryl) groups, in which case the recurring unit is

$$\left[-\overset{\displaystyle R}{\underset{\displaystyle R}{Si}}-O-\right]$$

Polymers formed in this way are called *silicones,* from the mistaken belief that they were similar in structure to ketones. Silicones have a **number** of uses in lubrication and for electrical insulation.

Carbon also forms polymers in which the links between recurring **units** involve oxygen. One example of these compounds is an ester formed from terephthalic acid and ethylene glycol. These compounds may unite, eliminating water, as follows:

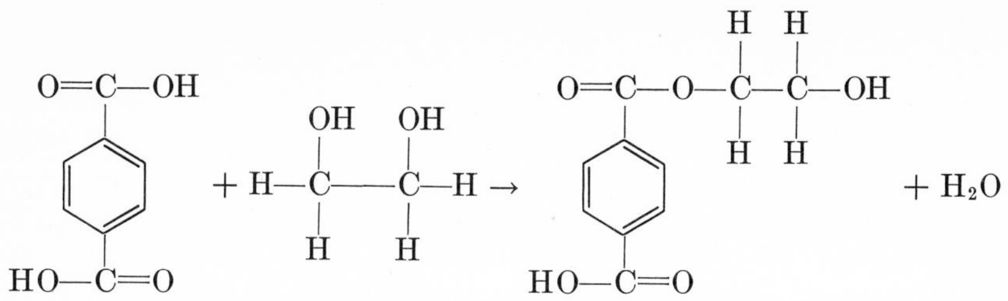

$$O=C-OH \quad + \quad H-\overset{OH}{\underset{H}{C}}----\overset{OH}{\underset{H}{C}}-H \rightarrow \quad O=C-O-\overset{H}{\underset{H}{C}}-\overset{H}{\underset{H}{C}}-OH \quad + H_2O$$

HO—C=O   HO—C=O

terephthalic   ethylene   ester
acid   glycol

Terephthalic acid has two functional groups, as does ethylene glycol. These groups may continue to react, eliminating water, to form very long polymer molecules, as shown:

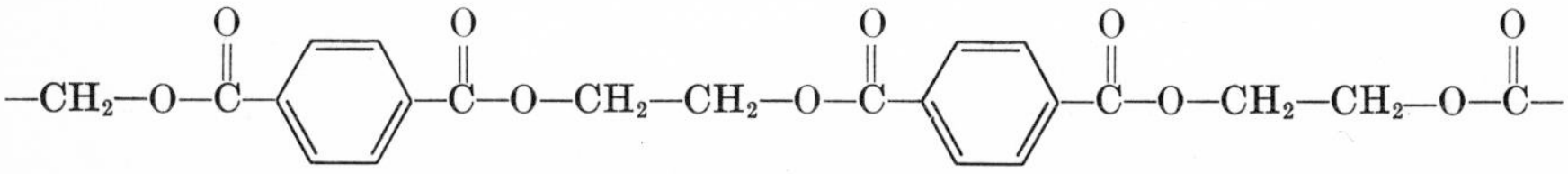

$$-CH_2-O-\overset{O}{\overset{\|}{C}}-\bigcirc-\overset{O}{\overset{\|}{C}}-O-CH_2-CH_2-O-\overset{O}{\overset{\|}{C}}-\bigcirc-\overset{O}{\overset{\|}{C}}-O-CH_2-CH_2-O-\overset{O}{\overset{\|}{C}}-$$

Dacron

The product is a polyester called polyethylene terephthalate, but more familiarly known under its trade name Dacron.

   Other important and familiar kinds of high polymers include the polyamides. If an organic acid reacts with an amine, the product is a substituted amide (substituted because R groups take the place of one or both hydrogens in the $-NH_2$ group).

$$CH_3\overset{O}{\overset{\|}{C}}-OH + CH_3NH_2 \rightarrow CH_3\overset{O}{\overset{\|}{C}}-\underset{\underset{H}{|}}{N}CH_3 + H_2O$$

acid   amine   amide

If now both acid and amine possess two functional groups, then continuous condensation to form a high polymer is possible. One of the several kinds of nylon is formed from adipic acid and hexamethylenediamine.

$$H_2N-CH_2-CH_2-CH_2-CH_2-CH_2-CH_2-NH_2$$

hexamethylenediamine

$$HO-\overset{O}{\overset{\|}{C}}-CH_2-CH_2-CH_2-CH_2-\overset{O}{\overset{\|}{C}}-OH$$

adipic acid

Abbreviating these somewhat, we have

$$nH_2N—(CH_2)_6—NH_2 + nHO—\overset{\overset{\displaystyle O}{\|}}{C}—(CH_2)_4—\overset{\overset{\displaystyle O}{\|}}{C}—OH \xrightarrow{\text{(eliminate } H_2O)}$$

$$\cdots—\overset{\overset{\displaystyle O}{\|}}{C}—(CH_2)_4—\overset{\overset{\displaystyle O}{\|}}{C}—\underset{\underset{\displaystyle H}{|}}{N}—(CH_2)_6—\underset{\underset{\displaystyle H}{|}}{N}—\overset{\overset{\displaystyle O}{\|}}{C}—(CH_2)_4—\overset{\overset{\displaystyle O}{\|}}{C}—\underset{\underset{\displaystyle H}{|}}{N}—(CH_2)_6—\underset{\underset{\displaystyle H}{|}}{N}—\cdots$$

nylon

The formal name of this compound is polyhexamethylene adipamide. Nylon is related chemically to silk and other proteins.

All the high polymers described above form particulate molecules, although the molecular weights may exceed 100,000. It is also possible for high polymers to exist as ions, and these are often prepared with recurrent functional groups. If, for instance, the polymer contains sulfonic groups or trimethylammonium hydroxide groups, then the polymer (or resin, as it is more frequently called) becomes an ion exchanger, as described in Sec. 21.7.

All the high polymers described above involve the elimination of water and are said to be formed by *condensation polymerization.* If an olefin is subjected to high pressure in the presence of a catalyst, the following reaction takes place:

$$n\underset{\underset{\displaystyle H}{|}}{\overset{\overset{\displaystyle H}{|}}{C}}=\underset{\underset{\displaystyle H}{|}}{\overset{\overset{\displaystyle H}{|}}{C} \rightarrow —\underset{\underset{\displaystyle H}{|}}{\overset{\overset{\displaystyle H}{|}}{C}}—\underset{\underset{\displaystyle H}{|}}{\overset{\overset{\displaystyle H}{|}}{C}}—\underset{\underset{\displaystyle H}{|}}{\overset{\overset{\displaystyle H}{|}}{C}}—\underset{\underset{\displaystyle H}{|}}{\overset{\overset{\displaystyle H}{|}}{C}}—\underset{\underset{\displaystyle H}{|}}{\overset{\overset{\displaystyle H}{|}}{C}}— \quad \text{or} \quad n\underset{\underset{\displaystyle H}{|}}{\overset{\overset{\displaystyle H}{|}}{C}}=\underset{\underset{\displaystyle H}{|}}{\overset{\overset{\displaystyle H}{|}}{C} \rightarrow \left[—\underset{\underset{\displaystyle H}{|}}{\overset{\overset{\displaystyle H}{|}}{C}}— \right]_{2n}}$$

ethylene   polyethylene

The reaction generally continues until all the monomer is used. The product is the familiar article of commerce called "polyethylene." Polypropylene and many other high polymers derived from ethylene derivatives are also known. The preparation of these involves no elimination of water. The products are said to be formed by *vinyl* (or *addition*) *polymerization.* A few examples of polymer chains formed in this way are (in addition to polypropylene), polyvinyl chloride, and polymethylmethacrylate (sold under the trade names of Lucite and Plexiglas):

$$—\underset{\underset{\displaystyle H}{|}}{\overset{\overset{\displaystyle H}{|}}{C}}—\underset{\underset{\displaystyle H}{|}}{\overset{\overset{\displaystyle CH_3}{|}}{C}}—\underset{\underset{\displaystyle H}{|}}{\overset{\overset{\displaystyle H}{|}}{C}}—\underset{\underset{\displaystyle H}{|}}{\overset{\overset{\displaystyle CH_3}{|}}{C}}—\underset{\underset{\displaystyle H}{|}}{\overset{\overset{\displaystyle H}{|}}{C}}—\underset{\underset{\displaystyle H}{|}}{\overset{\overset{\displaystyle CH_3}{|}}{C}}—\underset{\underset{\displaystyle H}{|}}{\overset{\overset{\displaystyle H}{|}}{C}}—$$

polypropylene

```
      H   Cl  H   Cl  H   Cl  H
      |   |   |   |   |   |   |
   —C—C—C—C—C—C—C—
      |   |   |   |   |   |   |
      H   H   H   H   H   H   H
```

polyvinyl chloride

```
        OCH₃          OCH₃          OCH₃
        |             |             |
   H  O=C        H  O=C        H  O=C         H
   |    |        |    |        |    |         |
  —C————C————C————C————C————C————C—
   |    |        |    |        |    |         |
   H   CH₃  H   CH₃  H   CH₃  H
```

polymethylmethacrylate

30.6   *Proteins*

The chemical substances present in greatest abundance in living matter are carbohydrate, fat, and protein. Most members of the animal kingdom contain also a bony skeleton made chiefly of complicated calcium phosphates. Reference has already been made to carbohydrates, fats, and phosphates. This concluding section will be devoted to proteins. No problem in all science exceeds in complexity the structural chemistry of protein, and few have been the subject of more brilliant advances in recent years.

Proteins are characterized by extremely high molecular weight, by always containing nitrogen, and by a marked instability to heat and to chemical treatment. They have no definite melting point, only occasionally may they be crystallized, and in general their study is tedious and complex. Examples of various proteins are egg albumin, myosinogen (from muscle), glutenin (from wheat), zein (from corn), elastin (from ligament), and globin (from hemoglobin). Proteins are often found combined with other compounds. Examples of such *conjugated proteins* are found in glandular tissue, bone, milk, and egg yolk. The chemical elements always present in proteins are carbon, hydrogen, oxygen, and nitrogen. Many proteins also contain sulfur; phosphorus and other elements are not infrequently present. Molecular weights run from 20,000 to 20,000,000.

Proteins have several characteristic chemical reactions, one of which is *denaturation*. Heat, the action of strong acids or bases, and a considerable variety of chemical reagents have the ability to bring about this change. The coagulation of an egg during cooking is an example of denaturation. During this process, proteins always lose such physiological activity as they may possess. By physiological activity is meant such properties as the hormone action of the conjugated protein, of which

thyroxine is an essential part, and the oxygen-carrying capacity of hemoglobin, the red coloring matter in the blood.

Another property of proteins is the reaction of hydrolysis. A relatively
simple protein treated with dilute acid or base, or with certain organic
catalysts called enzymes, undergoes hydrolysis to yield a mixture of amino
acids. This reaction has led, more than any other, to the understanding
we possess concerning the chemical structure of proteins. It will be
recalled that an amino acid contains the functional groups of both an
organic acid and an amine and that aminoacetic is a simple example.
Aminoacetic acid, previously mentioned in Sec. 30.4 and often called
glycine, is frequently found among the hydrolysis products obtained from
protein. A surprising feature is that in spite of the great number and
complexity of proteins only about 24 different aminoacids have been derived
from them. All proteins yield a mixture of amino acids, but the relative
abundance varies widely. For instance, gelatin is rich in glycine and contains
minor proportions of other amino acids. Egg albumin yields no glycine,
but is rich in other amino acids.

We shall not take space to describe all the amino-acid groups that
occur in proteins, but shall show the structure of a few, in addition to
glycine. Those selected are as follows:

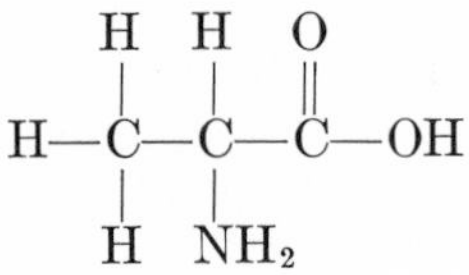

alanine (Ala)

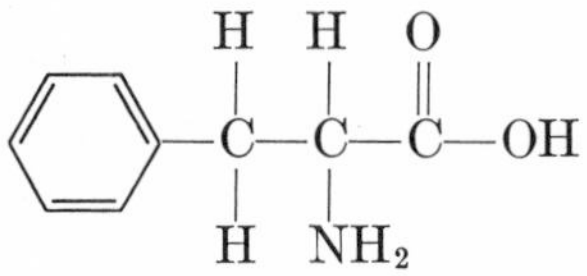

phenylalanine (Phe)

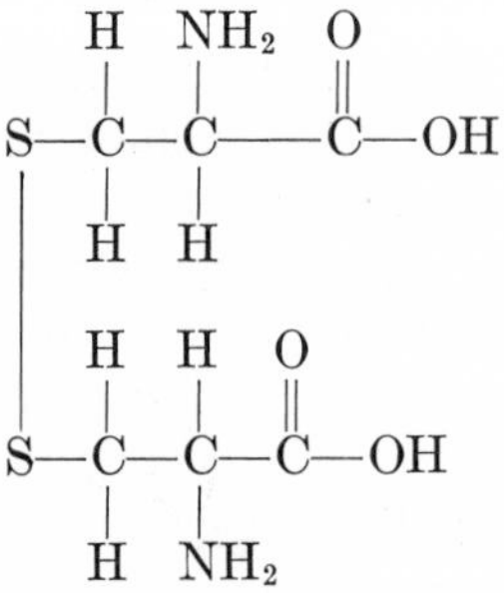

cystine (Cy-S)

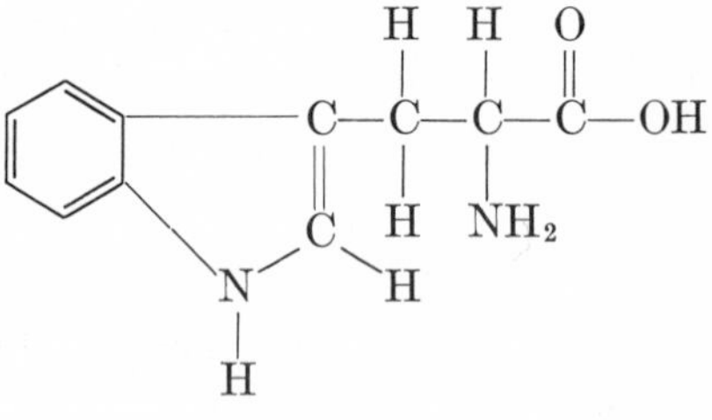

tryptophan (Try)

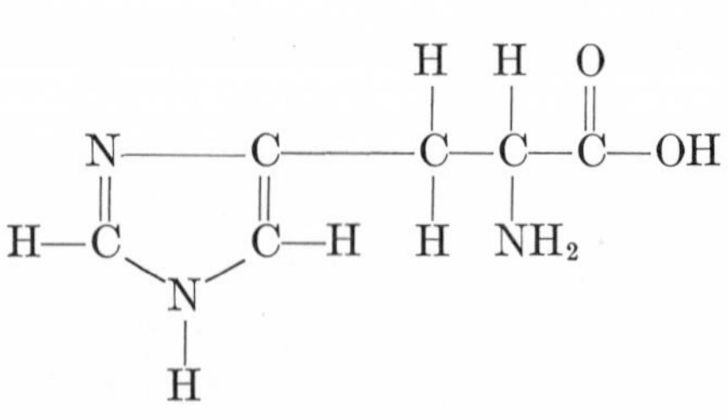

histidine (His)

The remaining 20 or so amino acids derived from proteins are of complexity comparable to those given above. Their names and abbreviations, to which we shall refer below, are as follows: arginine (Arg), asparagine (Asp-NH_2), aspartic acid (Asp), cysteine (Cy), glutamic acid (Glu), glutamine (Glu-NH_2), glycine (Gly), hydroxylysine (Lys-OH), hydroxyproline (Pro-OH), isoleucine (Ileu), leucine (Leu), lysine (Lys), methionine (Met), proline (Pro), serine (Ser), threonine (Thr), thyroxine (Thy), tyrosine (Tyr), and valine (Val).

The fact that amino acids are found in the hydrolysate from proteins gives a clue to the structure of the proteins. We have already shown that amines are capable of reacting with organic acids, as was described in connection with the polyamide nylon in the preceding section. The union of two glycine units is similarly possible (with elimination of water) as follows:

$$\text{H--}\overset{\overset{\displaystyle H}{|}}{\underset{\underset{\displaystyle H\text{--N--H}}{|}}{C}}\text{--}\overset{\overset{\displaystyle O}{\|}}{C}\text{--}\boxed{OH} + \text{H--}\overset{\overset{\displaystyle H}{|}}{\underset{\underset{\displaystyle \boxed{H}\text{--N--H}}{|}}{C}}\text{--}\overset{\overset{\displaystyle O}{\|}}{C}\text{--OH} \rightarrow \text{H}_2\overset{\overset{\displaystyle}{}}{\underset{\underset{\displaystyle NH_2}{|}}{C}}\text{--}\overset{\overset{\displaystyle O}{\|}}{C}\text{--}\overset{\overset{\displaystyle}{}}{\underset{\underset{\displaystyle H}{|}}{N}}\text{--}\overset{\overset{\displaystyle H}{|}}{\underset{\underset{\displaystyle H}{|}}{C}}\text{--}\overset{\overset{\displaystyle O}{\|}}{C}\text{--OH} + \text{H}_2\text{O}$$

glycine $+$ glycine $\rightarrow$ glycylglycine (a dipeptide)

The product (glycylglycine) so formed is called a *dipeptide,* and if the polymerization process goes further (with glycine or other amino acid), the product is called a *polypeptide.* Proteins appear to be polypeptides of unusual complexity and very large molecular weight.

In view of success in making high polymers, it might be thought that the synthesis of proteins would not be too difficult; and it is true that polypeptides may be synthesized fairly readily. But the precise order in which the amino acid groups are arranged is altogether a different problem.

The order in which the amino acid groups are arranged was not known for any protein until in 1952, when F. Sanger proved the structure of the protein insulin. This was done by hydrolyzing insulin into di- and tripeptides and then separating and identifying the fragments by an adaptation of chromatography called paper chromatography. Sanger's structure for insulin is shown on page 554. It will be understood that each amino acid unit is shown merely by the abbreviated symbols given above.

The structure of insulin (and of those for a few other proteins thus far studied) is seen to be comparable to the heteropolyacids mentioned in Sec. 28.5) but of very substantially greater complexity. Our next question is, therefore: How is nature able to *transmit* orders for the appropriate sequence of amino acid groups in the multitude of different proteins being synthesized in any living and growing organism?

The way in which this formation is transmitted is through the *genetic code.* The ultimate carrier of this code in most living organisms is a linear

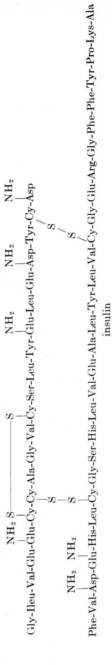

Fig. 30.2 The structure of insulin. Each symbol, such as Gly, represents an amino acid group as identified on pages 552–553.

polymer called deoxyribonucleic acid (DNA). This long-chain polymer bears some slight resemblance to polyethylene terephthalate (Dacron) in that it is a polyester. Information concerning DNA comes in part from studies on a simpler polyester high polymer, namely, ribonucleic acid (RNA), which also plays a part in directing protein synthesis on a molecular scale.

DNA and RNA consist of long chains of ribose (the 5-carbon sugar mentioned in Sec. 30.4) condensed with *ortho*-phosphoric acid. But each ribose molecule is itself attached to one of four possible nitrogen-containing organic bases distantly related to pyridine (Sec. 30.2). The four organic bases are as follows: *

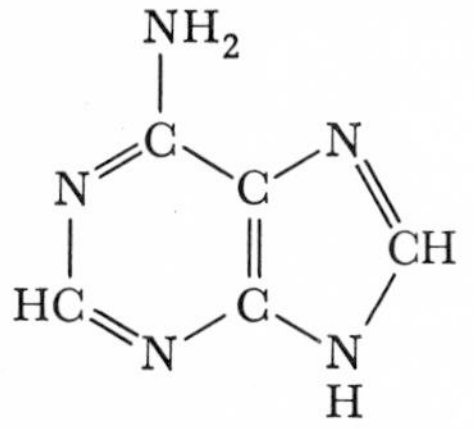

adenine (A)

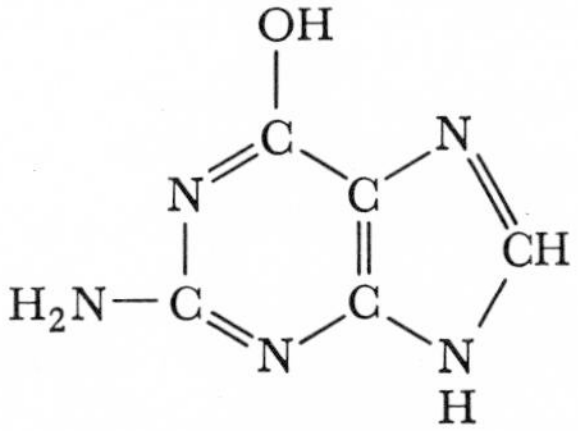

guanine (G)

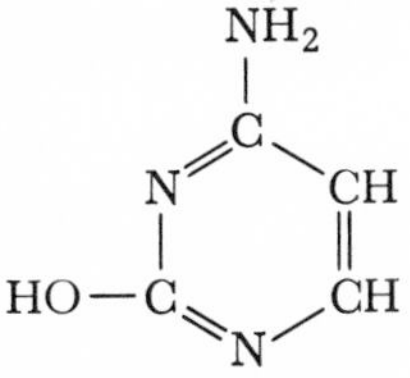

cytosine (C)

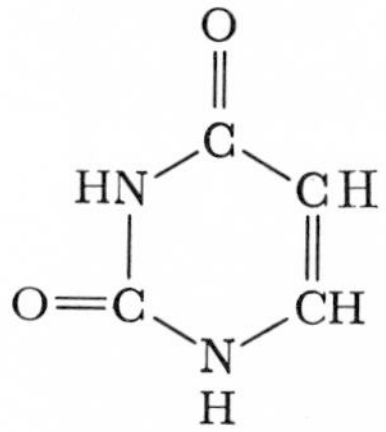

uracil (U)

The manner in which these bases are attached to the ribose is shown below for the case of adenine:

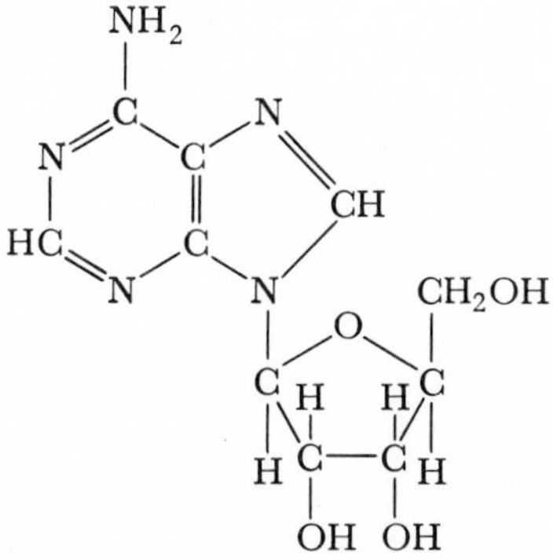

adenosine

* In DNA a different base, thymine, is substituted for uracil, and the ribose is also modified to deoxyribose.

Now the ribose, which is attached to one of the four bases, is condensed with *ortho*-phosphoric acid as shown:

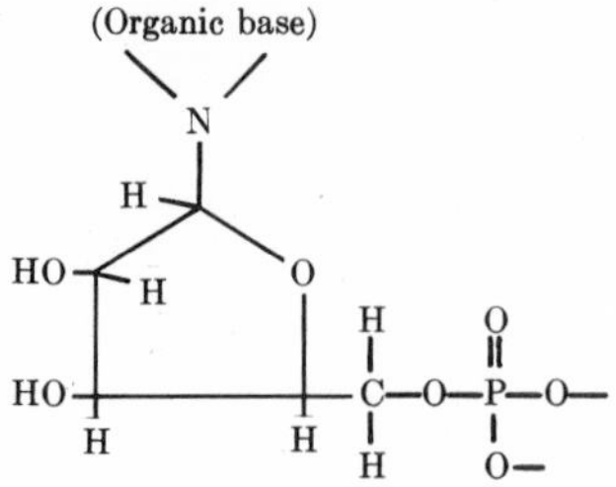

This structure is then condensed to another PO_4 group through the HO at the left, and to another ribose through the P—O— group at the right, until a very high molecular weight polymer is achieved.

In the formula given above, the organic base present has been merely indicated. A fragment of formula for the complete RNA might be as follows:

where r stands for the ribose fragment and p for the phosphate PO_4, group. In this formula the four possible bases are abbreviated to A, G, C, and U (for adenine, guanine, cytosine, and uracil). It is these four base groups that carry the genetic code. By means not yet completely known, the specific order in which these four groups are arranged is able to direct the combination of amino acids into proteins of all the vastly varied kinds that occur in nature. This is the code system by which inherited characteristics are passed in one molecule from parent to child. If one man's hair is red and another's black, it is because somewhere in a DNA molecule there is a sequence of the groups A, G, C, and U which so directs.

It may be wondered how so much information may be carried by only four separate "signals," but it must be remembered that the Morse code consists of even fewer (a dash, a dot, and a space between them). Yet the Morse code is capable of conveying all the written knowledge of mankind.

This brings us to the question of how life originated, and of what it is. Some authorities think that life is a set of properties related to increasing molecular complexity. When molecules become big enough and complex enough they may begin to exhibit the properties of self-reproduction, mutation, and of antibody formation characteristic of living matter. Certainly some molecules, such as those constituting viruses, seem to be at the very border of living and nonliving matter, possessing properties of both. It has been proved that simple molecules, such as H_2O, CO_2, CH_4, H_2, and NH_3, which might be expected to be present in the primitive atmosphere of the young earth, are able to react, forming organic acids including amino acids. It is also well known that some reactions are autocatalytic in that the products themselves serve to accelerate the re- action by which they are formed. It seems not impossible that—given appropriate conditions of temperature, partial pressure, and raw materials— nature may have prepared over the ages all the amino acids necessary for protein synthesis, and that these proteins in due course were formed. From that stage to the further elaboration leading to manifestations of life does not seem too difficult a step for a nature capable of such exquisite variety and complexities, a very few of which have been described in this book.

EXERCISES

1. A substance has the following percentage composition by weight: C, 39.7; H, 1.65; Cl, 58.7. It is also found that 6.75 grams of the substance dissolved in 50 grams of benzene lowers the freezing point 3.80 degrees. The molal freezing point constant for benzene is 5.12 degrees. Find the correct molecular weight and write the structural formula for the compound.

2. A certain hydrocarbon sample weighing 1.411 grams was burned in oxygen. The water produced was collected in a calcium chloride tube and found to weigh 0.799 gram. The carbon dioxide was collected in a sodium hydroxide tube and found to weigh 4.884 grams. By the freezing point depression method, the molecular weight was found to be 128. Find the correct molecular formula.

3. Reference has been made to the following types of reactions shown by organic compounds: oxidation, reduction, hydrogenation, substitution, dehydration, esterification, and saponification. Illus- trate each with an example.

4. Write structural formulas for each of the following: ethylamyl ether, methylbutyl ketone, all possible isomers of butylene C_4H_8, propyl acetate, propylene glycol, cyclopropane.

5. The term *respiratory quotient* is used by physiologists. It is defined as the ratio by volume of exhaled carbon dioxide to oxygen absorbed during the oxidation of any particular type of food. Compare the respiratory quotient of glucose with that of ethanol.

6. In the formation of an ester, it has been shown that if the alcohol

contains some enrichment in ^{18}O, the by-product water contains only normal oxygen. With the aid of structural formulas interpret this result in terms of the mechanism of esterification.

7. Given that

$$C_2H_4 + 3O_2 \rightarrow 2CO_2 + 2H_2O + 332 \text{ kcal}$$
$$2C_2H_6 + 7O_2 \rightarrow 4CO_2 + 6H_2O + 737 \text{ kcal}$$
$$2H_2 + O_2 \rightarrow 2H_2O(g) + 137 \text{ kcal}$$

find the heat of hydrogenation of ethylene to ethane.

8. An amino acid has the unique ability to react with itself, so to speak, because the acid proton is able to migrate and attach itself to the amine group, thus in effect neutralizing it. For aminoacetic acid the equilibrium set up is

The product is called a *zwitterion*. Write the zwitterion formula for the amino acid tryptophan.

9. Of the five amino acids—glycine, alanine, phynylalanine, tryptophan, and histidine—which may be expected to exhibit optical activity?

10. Indicate the formation of a polypeptide by phenylalanine.

11. Write a possible structural formula for polystyrene, which is made from styrene:

12. The high polymer polyvinylpyrrolidine has sometimes been used in solution as a substitute for blood plasma in treating shock and loss of blood. This substance is made from vinylpyrrolidine, the formula for which is

Show the structural formula for a section of the polymer.

13. It would seem that the photosynthesis reaction, under the in-

fluence of chlorophyll as a catalyst, is the reverse of the metabolism reaction whereby carbohydrate is converted to carbon dioxide and water. But catalysts are not supposed to be able to shift a chemical equilibrium. Explain this apparent contradiction.

14. A solution consisting of 0.0910 gram of acetic acid dissolved in 60.0 grams of benzene lowers the freezing point of the benzene by 0.0602 degrees. The molal freezing-point constant for benzene is 5.12 degrees. What explanation may be offered?

15. (a) Predict the approximate hardness and electrical conductivity of methane. (b) Of the five substances CH_4, CH_3Cl, CH_2Cl_2, $CHCl_3$, and CCl_4, which might be expected to exhibit a permanent dipole moment?

16. Dinitrobenzene may exist in three different isomeric forms. These three and their identifying prefixes are shown below:

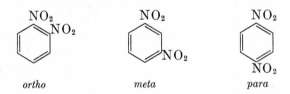

| ortho | meta | para |

How many trinitrobenzenes may be formed from each of the dinitrobenzenes?

17. The calcium salts of the higher (longer chain) fatty acids are insoluble in water. Write an equation showing the action of hard water, containing calcium ions, on soap.

18. Give the structural formula for a hydrocarbon which is optically active.

19. The clinical test for diabetes is based on the reducing action of sugars containing aldehyde functional groups (and therefore called aldoses). The test is made by taking a sample of the body fluid and heating it with an alkaline solution containing cupric, Cu^{2+} ions, and to which citrate ion (in the form of sodium citrate) has been added to complex the cupric ion and thereby prevent the precipitation of cupric hydroxide.

Assuming that the Cu^{2+} ion shows its normal coordination number of four, and that the citrate ion acts as a bidentate chelating agent, show with the use of structural formulas how glucose reduces the copper to the red cuprous oxide, which is the diagnostic indication for the presence of sugar and hence of a possible diabetic condition.

20. The kinetics of ester hydrolysis has been much studied. Saponification of ethyl butyrate to yield the butyrate ion, plus ethanol

is an example. In an experiment the initial concentration of the ester, $[Bu]_o$, and the initial concentration of the base, $[OH^-]_o$, were the same, namely, $0.010M$. The following data were obtained: (The base concentration is given in millimoles liter^{-1}:

Time (min)	0	3	5	7	10	15	21	25
$[OH^-]$		10.0	7.40	6.34	5.50	4.64	3.63	2.88	2.54

Determine the order of the reaction and write the rate law.

21. The amyl ester of dichloracetic acid, if heated, undergoes dissociation to form dichloracetic acid and amylene as follows:

$$Cl-\overset{\overset{\displaystyle H}{|}}{\underset{\underset{\displaystyle Cl}{|}}{C}}-\overset{\overset{\displaystyle O}{\|}}{C}-OC_5H_{11} \rightleftharpoons Cl-\overset{\overset{\displaystyle H}{|}}{\underset{\underset{\displaystyle Cl}{|}}{C}}-\overset{\overset{\displaystyle O}{\|}}{C}-OH + C_5H_{10}$$

A study of the equilibrium for the liquid phase reaction was made by treating, in each run, 1.00 mole of the acid with the quantities of the olefin given below. (The volumes were, of course, different at the start of each reaction, and are shown.) After equilibrium had been reached, the number of moles of ester present was determined.

Run	Moles acid at start	Moles olefin at start	Volume at start	Moles ester at equilibrium
1	1.00	1.05	0.215	0.455
2	1.00	5.91	0.794	0.658
3	1.00	15.36	1.83	0.703

Find the equilibrium constant

22. Pyridine, as does any Brönsted base, reacts with water. For pyridine, pK at room temperature is 8.8. Find the pH of a $0.10M$ solution of pyridine in water.

References

The serious student will find it useful to own a source of numerical data related to chemistry and physics. At this level, a recent edition of Handbook of Chemistry and Physics, Chemical Rubber Publishing Co., Cleveland, Ohio, is acceptable.

Various books give more advanced information concerning certain topics treated in this text. The areas covered and the books suggested are as follows:

1. The general laws and concepts of chemistry:
   W. J. MOORE, *Physical Chemistry,* 3d ed. Englewood Cliffs, N.J.: Prentice-Hall, 1962.

2. General advanced inorganic chemistry including theories of structure and reaction:
   GOULD, E. S., *Inorganic Reactions and Structure,* rev. ed. New York: Holt, Rinehart and Winston, 1962.
   COTTON, F. A., and G. WILKINSON, *Advanced Inorganic Chemistry.* New York: Interscience (Wiley), 1962.

3. The geometrical structure of inorganic compounds:
   WELLS, A. F., *Structural Inorganic Chemistry,* 3d ed. New York: Oxford, 1962.

4. Chemical reactions and equations. A useful source, given below, is somewhat outdated as to theoretical interpretation, but it contains (in two volumes) a vast number of facts.
SIDGWICK, N. V., *The Chemical Elements and Their Compounds.* New York: Oxford, 1950.

5. Radioactivity:
SEMAT, H., *Introduction to Atomic and Nuclear Physics,* 4th ed. New York: Holt, Rinehart and Winston, 1962.

6. Organic molecules and reactions:
MORRISON, R. T., and R. N. BOYD, *Organic Chemistry.* Boston: Allyn and Bacon, 1959.

7. For surveys of industrial products and reactions there is no better source than the 17 volumes of:
KIRK-OTHMER, *Encyclopedia of Chemical Technology.* New York: Interscience (Wiley), 1960.

8. For a comprehensive though elementary presentation of physics:
SEARS, F. W., and M. W. ZEMANSKY, *College Physics,* 3d ed. Reading, Mass.: Addison-Wesley, 1960.

World-wide current chemical research is abstracted in the form of notes, giving authors, author's affiliations, and a brief summary of the work and its results. The English language source of this information is AMERICAN CHEMICAL SOCIETY, *Chemical Abstracts.*

Many review articles on timely subjects will be found in the *Journal of Chemical Education.*

Appendix

Common Prefixes

Prefix	Meaning
mega-	million
kilo-	thousand
centi-	one-hundredth
milli-	one-thousandth
micro-	one-millionth

Units of Measurement

MASS AND WEIGHT: Mass is a fundamental property of matter for which no simple definition is available. The mass of a body of matter is the same under all conditions except at speeds approaching that of light. The mass of one body may be compared with that of another by comparison of their inertias. Inertia is the tendency of a moving body to resist change in its speed.

The weight of a body of matter is the force with which the mass of the body is attracted by the mass of the earth. The weight of a body depends on the location of the body. In outer space, far from any planet or star, a body has mass but no weight. A beam balance compares the weight of one body with that of another (standard) body. On a beam balance, a given body appears to weigh the same at any location. But a spring balance will show that a body weighing 1000 grams in Panama will weigh 4 grams more in Iceland.

In the United States the legal unit of mass is a cylinder of platinum-iridium alloy kept at the National Bureau of Standards in Washington. One kilogram is the mass of a similar cylinder kept in Paris. The unit of mass in the system commonly used in scientific work is the gram.

> 1 kilogram (kg) = 1000 grams (g) = 10^6 milligrams (mg)
> 1 kg = 2.205 pounds (lb) avoirdupois
> 1 lb = 453.6 grams
> 1000 kg = 1 metric ton

LENGTH AND VOLUME: The international standard of length is based on a spectroscopic wave length emitted by the isotope krypton-86; 1,650,763.73 times this wave length is called a meter.

> 1 kilometer (km) = 1000 meters (m) = 0.6214 mile
> 1 m = 100 centimeters (cm) = 1000 millimeters (mm)
> 1 cm = 0.3937 inches (in.)
> 1 in. = 2.54 cm
> 1 angstrom unit (Å) = 10^{-8} cm

Volume may be measured in cubic centimeters. One cubic centimeter is the volume of a cube that is 1 cm on a side.

Another commonly used measure of volume is the liter. One liter is the volume of 1 kg of water at its temperature of maximum density (3.98° C). One liter is equal to 1000.028 cm³. The difference between a cubic centimeter and a milliliter is so small that, for our present purposes, it will be ignored. We shall say that 1 ml equals 1 cm. (A movement is on foot to redefine the liter so that 1 cm³ will equal 1 ml.)

> 1 liter = 1000 milliliters (ml)
> 1 cubic centimeter (cc or cm³) = 1 ml (see discussion above)
> 1 liter = 1.057 quarts (U.S.)

WORK AND ENERGY: If a force acts on a body in such a way as to change its speed, then work is done. Suppose that a body of mass 1 gram is subjected to a force such that the speed of the body changes at the rate of 1 cm/sec in every second. The force is then said to be 1 dyne. If a force of 1 dyne acts on a body through a distance of 1 cm, the work done is called 1 erg. The erg, in cgs units, has the dimensions gram-cm²-sec⁻².

Energy is the ability to do work. The same units may be used for both energy and work. The following units and conversion factors may be useful in connection with topics treated in this text.

$$1 \text{ erg} = 2.39 \times 10^{-8} \text{ calories (cal)}$$
$$1 \text{ kilocalorie (kcal)} = 1000 \text{ cal}$$
$$1 \text{ joule} = 10^7 \text{ ergs}$$
$$1 \text{ British thermal unit (BTU)} = 252 \text{ cal}$$
$$1 \text{ electron-volt (ev)} = 1.602 \times 10^{-12} \text{ erg}$$

ELECTRICITY: The volt is the common unit of electric potential. Quantity of electricity is measured in coulombs. An ampere is a current (flow) of electricity of 1 coulomb/sec. Hence

$$\text{Coulombs} = \text{amperes} \times \text{seconds}$$

The unit of electric power is the watt:

$$\text{Watts} = \text{volts} \times \text{amperes}$$

A kilowatt (kw or kva) = 1000 watts. Energy and work may be measured in kilowatt-hours. One kilowatt-hour is 1 kw for 1 hr. This is the unit in which electric energy is generally sold.

$$1 \text{ kilowatt-hour (kwh)} = 8.60 \times 10^5 \text{ cal}$$

Some Fundamental Quantities

$$1 \text{ atomic mass unit (amu)} = 1.6603 \times 10^{-24} \text{ gram}$$
Avogadro's number $6.023 \times 10^{23} \text{ mole}^{-1}$
Rest mass* of an electron = 9108×10^{-31} gram
Charge of an electron = 1.592×10^{-19} coulomb
1 faraday = 96,520 coulombs gram-equivalent
Velocity of light, $c = 3.00 \times 10^{10}$ cm sec^{-1}
Planck's constant, $h = 6625 \times 10^{-30}$ erg sec
Gas constant, $R = 0.08208$ liter atm mole^{-1} deg^{-1}

* The mass of a body depends on its speed and approaches infinity at the speed of light. Rest mass is the mass at zero speed.

THE CHEMICAL ELEMENTS

Element	Symbol	Atomic no.	Atomic weight
Actinium	Ac	89	
Aluminum	Al	13	26.9815
Americium	Am	95	
Antimony	Sb	51	121.75
Argon	Ar	18	39.948
Arsenic	As	33	74.9216
Astatine	At	85	
Barium	Ba	56	137.34
Berkelium	Bk	97	
Beryllium	Be	4	9.0122
Bismuth	Bi	83	208.980
Boron	B	5	10.811
Bromine	Br	35	79.909
Cadmium	Cd	48	112.40
Calcium	Ca	20	40.08
Californium	Cf	98	
Carbon	C	6	12.01115
Cerium	Ce	58	140.12
Cesium	Cs	55	132.905
Chlorine	Cl	17	35.453
Chromium	Cr	24	51.996
Cobalt	Co	27	58.9332
Copper	Cu	29	63.54
Curium	Cm	96	
Dysprosium	Dy	66	162.50
Einsteinium	Es	99	
Erbium	Er	68	167.26
Europium	Eu	63	151.96
Fermium	Fm	100	
Fluorine	F	9	18.9984
Francium	Fr	87	
Gadolinium	Gd	64	157.25
Gallium	Ga	31	69.72
Germanium	Ge	32	72.59
Gold	Au	79	196.967
Hafnium	Hf	72	178.49
Helium	He	2	4.0026
Holmium	Ho	67	164.930
Hydrogen	H	1	1.00797
Indium	In	49	114.82
Iodine	I	53	126.9044
Iridium	Ir	77	192.2
Iron	Fe	26	55.847

THE CHEMICAL ELEMENTS (*Continued*)

Element	Symbol	Atomic no.	Atomic weight
Krypton	Kr	36	83.80
Lanthanum	La	57	138.91
Lead	Pb	82	207.19
Lithium	Li	3	6.939
Lutetium	Lu	71	174.97
Magnesium	Mg	12	24.312
Manganese	Mn	25	54.9380
Mendelevium	Md	101	
Mercury	Hg	80	200.59
Molybdenum	Mo	42	95.94
Neodymium	Nd	60	144.24
Neon	Ne	10	20.183
Neptunium	Np	93	
Nickel	Ni	28	58.71
Niobium	Nb	41	92.906
Nitrogen	N	7	14.0067
Nobelium	No	102	
Osmium	Os	76	190.2
Oxygen	O	8	15.9994
Palladium	Pd	46	106.4
Phosphorus	P	15	30.9738
Platinum	Pt	78	195.09
Plutonium	Pu	94	
Polonium	Po	84	
Potassium	K	19	39.102
Praseodymium	Pr	59	140.907
Promethium	Pm	61	
Protactinium	Pa	91	
Radium	Ra	88	
Radon	Rn	86	
Rhenium	Re	75	186.2
Rhodium	Rh	45	102.905
Rubidium	Rb	37	85.47
Ruthenium	Ru	44	101.07
Samarium	Sm	62	150.35
Scandium	Sc	21	44.956
Selenium	Se	34	78.96
Silicon	Si	14	28.086
Silver	Ag	47	107.870
Sodium	Na	11	22.9898
Strontium	Sr	38	87.62
Sulfur	S	16	32.064
Tantalum	Ta	73	180.948

THE CHEMICAL ELEMENTS (*Continued*)

Element	Symbol	Atomic no.	Atomic weight
Technetium	Tc	43	
Tellurium	Te	52	127.60
Terbium	Tb	65	158.924
Thallium	Tl	81	204.37
Thorium	Th	90	232.038
Thulium	Tm	69	168.934
Tin	Sn	50	118.69
Titanium	Ti	22	47.90
Tungsten	W	74	183.85
Uranium	U	92	238.03
Vanadium	V	23	50.942
Xenon	Xe	54	131.30
Ytterbium	Yb	70	173.04
Yttrium	Y	39	88.905
Zinc	Zn	30	65.37
Zirconium	Zr	40	91.22

Elements that do not occur in nature have no atomic weight in the usually accepted meaning of the term. The same is true of some radioactive elements.

EQUILIBRIUM VAPOR PRESSURE OF WATER

Temperature, °C	Pressure, mm	Temperature, °C	Pressure, mm
0	4.6	50	92.0
5	6.5	60	148.9
10	9.1	70	233.3
15	12.7	80	354.9
16	13.5	90	525.5
17	14.4	95	633.7
18	15.3	96	657.4
19	16.3	97	681.9
20	17.4	98	707.1
21	18.5	99	733.1
22	19.6	99.2	738.5
23	20.9	99.4	743.8
24	22.1	99.6	749.2
25	23.5	99.8	754.6
26	25.0	100	760.0
27	26.5	100.2	765.5
28	28.1	100.4	771.0
29	29.7	100.6	776.5
30	31.5	101	787.6
35	41.8	106	906.4
40	54.9	110	1075.4

Solubilities of Some Salts

The following table gives information concerning the solubilities of a number of frequently encountered ionic solids. Positive ions are listed at the top; negative, at the left. Thus the solubility of silver arsenate, Ag_3AsO_4, is given as "ins."

Solubilities are divided into four categories: "sol" means a solubility of over 1 gram solute/100 grams water at room temperature; "sls" means a solubility of between 1 gram and 0.1 gram/100 grams H_2O; "ins" means less than 0.1 gram/100 grams H_2O; and "hyd" means that the compound is hydrolyzed in water to such a degree as to be essentially a new compound or compounds. It will be understood that hydrolysis may often be decreased by changing the pH of a solution. Thus, $Fe(NO_3)_3$ is hydrolyzed in water, but in the presence of a moderate excess of HNO_3, it forms a clear colorless solution.

	Ag$^+$	Al^{3+}	Ba^{2+}	Ca^{2+}	Co^{2+}	Cr^{3+}	Cu$^+$	Cu^{2+}	Fe^{2+}	Fe^{3+}	Hg$_2^{2+}$	Hg^{2+}	K$^+$	La^{3+}
AsO$_4^{3-}$	ins	ins	ins	ins	ins			ins	ins	ins	ins	ins	sol	sol
Br$^-$	ins	hyd	sol	sol	sol	sol	ins	sol	sol	hyd	ins	sls	sol	sol
Cl$^-$	ins	hyd	sol	sol	sol	sol	ins	sol	sol	hyd	ins	sol	sol	sol
ClO$_3^-$	sol	hyd	sol	sol	sol			sol	sol	hyd	sol	sol	sol	
ClO$_4^-$	sol		sol	sol	sol				sol	hyd			sls	
CO$_3^{2-}$	ins	hyd	ins	ins	ins		ins		ins		ins	ins	sol	ins
CrO$_4^{2-}$	ins		ins	sol	ins						ins	hyd	sol	
F$^-$	sol	hyd	sls	ins	sol	sls	ins	sls	sls	sls	hyd	hyd	sol	ins
I$^-$	ins	hyd	sol	sol	sol		ins		sol		ins	ins	sol	sol
IO$_3^-$	ins		ins	ins	sls			sls			ins	ins	sol	sol
MnO$_4^-$	sls		sol	sol							hyd		sol	
NO$_2^-$	sls	hyd	sol	sol	sol	sol	ins	sol	sol	hyd	sol	sol	sol	sol
NO$_3^-$	sol	ins	sol	sol	ins	ins	ins	ins	ins	ins	sol	sol	sol	sol
O^{2-}	ins	ins	hyd	hyd	ins	ins	ins	ins	ins	ins		ins	hyd	ins
OH$^-$		ins	sol	sls	ins	hyd		ins	ins	ins			sol	ins
PO$_4^{3-}$	ins	ins	ins	ins	ins	sol		ins	ins	hyd	ins	ins	sol	ins
S^{2-}	ins	hyd	hyd	hyd	ins	hyd	ins	ins	ins	hyd	ins	ins	hyd	hyd
SO$_3^{2-}$			ins	ins	ins	sls			sls				sol	
SO$_4^{2-}$	sls	hyd	ins	sls	sol	sol	hyd	sol	sol	hyd	sol	hyd	sol	sls
SeO$_4^{2-}$			ins	sol	sol			sol					sol	
SiO$_4^{4-}$		ins	ins	ins	ins								hyd	ins
S$_2$O$_3^{2-}$	sls		sls						sol				sol	

	Li⁺	Mg²⁺	Mn²⁺	Na⁺	NH₄⁺	Ni²⁺	Pb²⁺	Pt²⁺	Sn²⁺	Sn⁴⁺	Tl⁺	U⁴⁺	Zn²⁺
AsO_4^{3-}	ins	ins		sol		ins	ins						ins
Br^-	sol	sol	sol	sol	sol	sol	sls	ins	sol	hyd	ins	hyd	sol
Cl^-	sol	sol	sol	sol	sol	sol	sls	ins	sol	hyd	sls	hyd	sol
ClO_3^-	sol	sol		sol	sol	sls	sol				sol		sol
ClO_4^-	sol	sol		sol	sol	sol	sol				sol		sol
CO_3^{2-}	sol	ins	ins	sol	hyd	ins	ins				sol		ins
CrO_4^{2-}	sol	sol		sol	sol		ins				ins		ins
F^-	sls	ins	ins	sol	sol	sls	ins	ins	sol	sol	sol	ins	sls
I^-	sol	sol	sol	sol	sol	sol	ins	ins	sol		ins	hyd	sol
IO_3^-	sol	sol		sol	sol	sol	ins						sls
MnO_4^-	sol			sol	sol								sol
NO_2^-	sol			sol	sol		sol						
NO_3^-	sol	sol	sol	sol	sol	sol	sol	ins	hyd	hyd	sol	ins	sol
O^{-2}	hyd	ins	ins	hyd		ins	ins		hyd	hyd	hyd	ins	ins
OH^-	sol	ins	ins	sol	sol	ins			ins	ins	sol		ins
PO_4^{3-}	ins	ins	ins	sol	hyd	ins	ins	ins	ins		sls		ins
S^{2-}	hyd	hyd	ins	hyd	hyd	ins	ins	ins	ins		ins		ins
SO_3^{2-}	sol	sol	sol	sol	sol	ins	ins		sol		sol		sls
SO_4^{2-}	sol	sol	sol	sol	sol	sol	ins	sol	sol	sol	sol	hyd	sol
SeO_4^{2-}		sol	sol	sol	sol	sol	ins		sol	sol	sol	hyd	
SiO_4^{4-}	ins	ins		sol									ins
$S_2O_3^{2-}$		sol		sol	sol		ins						

COMMON LOGARITHMS OF NUMBERS

n	0	1	2	3	4	5	6	7	8	9
10	0000	0043	0086	0128	0170	0212	0253	0294	0334	0374
11	0414	0453	0492	0531	0569	0607	0645	0682	0719	0755
12	0792	0828	0864	0899	0934	0969	1004	1038	1072	1106
13	1139	1173	1206	1239	1271	1303	1335	1367	1399	1430
14	1461	1492	1523	1553	1584	1614	1644	1673	1703	1732
15	1761	1790	1818	1847	1875	1903	1931	1959	1987	2014
16	2041	2068	2095	2122	2148	2175	2201	2227	2253	2279
17	2304	2330	2355	2380	2405	2430	2455	2480	2504	2529
18	2553	2577	2601	2625	2648	2672	2695	2718	2742	2765
19	2788	2810	2833	2856	2878	2900	2923	2945	2967	2989
20	3010	3032	3054	3075	3096	3118	3139	3160	3181	3201
21	3222	3243	3263	3284	3304	3324	3345	3365	3385	3404
22	3424	3444	3464	3483	3502	3522	3541	3560	3579	3598
23	3617	3636	3655	3674	3692	3711	3729	3747	3766	3784
24	3802	3820	3838	3856	3874	3892	3909	3927	3945	3962
25	3979	3997	4014	4031	4048	4065	4082	4099	4116	4133
26	4150	4166	4183	4200	4216	4232	4249	4265	4281	4298
27	4314	4330	4346	4362	4378	4393	4409	4425	4440	4456
28	4472	4487	4502	4518	4533	4548	4564	4579	4594	4609
29	4624	4639	4654	4669	4683	4698	4713	4728	4742	4757
30	4771	4786	4800	4814	4829	4843	4857	4871	4886	4900
31	4914	4928	4942	4955	4969	4983	4997	5011	5024	5038
32	5051	5065	5079	5092	5105	5119	5132	5145	5159	5172
33	5185	5198	5211	5224	5237	5250	5263	5276	5289	5302
34	5315	5328	5340	5353	5366	5378	5391	5403	5416	5428
35	5441	5453	5465	5478	5490	5502	5514	5527	5539	5551
36	5563	5575	5587	5599	5611	5623	5635	5647	5658	5670
37	5682	5694	5705	5717	5729	5740	5752	5763	5775	5786
38	5798	5809	5821	5832	5843	5855	5866	5877	5888	5899
39	5911	5922	5933	5944	5955	5966	5977	5988	5999	6010
40	6021	6031	6042	6053	6064	6075	6085	6096	6107	6117
41	6128	6138	6149	6160	6170	6180	6191	6201	6212	6222
42	6232	6243	6253	6263	6274	6284	6294	6304	6314	6325
43	6335	6345	6355	6365	6375	6385	6395	6405	6415	6425
44	6435	6444	6454	6464	6474	6484	6493	6503	6513	6522
45	6532	6542	6551	6561	6571	6580	6590	6599	6609	6618
46	6628	6637	6646	6656	6665	6675	6684	6693	6702	6712
47	6721	6730	6739	6749	6758	6767	6776	6785	6794	6803
48	6812	6821	6830	6839	6848	6857	6866	6875	6884	6893
49	6902	6911	6920	6928	6937	6946	6955	6964	6972	6981
50	6990	6998	7007	7016	7024	7033	7042	7050	7059	7067
51	7076	7084	7093	7101	7110	7118	7126	7135	7143	7152
52	7160	7168	7177	7185	7193	7202	7210	7218	7226	7235
53	7243	7251	7259	7267	7275	7284	7292	7300	7308	7316
54	7324	7332	7340	7348	7356	7364	7372	7380	7388	7396

COMMON LOGARITHMS OF NUMBERS

n	0	1	2	3	4	5	6	7	8	9
55	7404	7412	7419	7427	7435	7443	7451	7459	7466	7474
56	7482	7490	7497	7505	7513	7520	7528	7536	7543	7551
57	7559	7566	7574	7582	7589	7597	7604	7612	7619	7627
58	7634	7642	7649	7657	7664	7672	7679	7686	7694	7701
59	7709	7716	7723	7731	7738	7745	7752	7760	7767	7774
60	7782	7789	7796	7803	7810	7818	7825	7832	7839	7846
61	7853	7860	7868	7875	7882	7889	7896	7903	7910	7917
62	7924	7931	7938	7945	7952	7959	7966	7973	7980	7987
63	7993	8000	8007	8014	8021	8028	8035	8041	8048	8055
64	8062	8069	8075	8082	8089	8096	8102	8109	8116	8122
65	8129	8136	8142	8149	8156	8162	8169	8176	8182	8189
66	8195	8202	8209	8215	8222	8228	8235	8241	8248	8254
67	8261	8267	8274	8280	8287	8293	8299	8306	8312	8319
68	8325	8331	8338	8344	8351	8357	8363	8370	8376	8382
69	8388	8395	8401	8407	8414	8420	8426	8432	8439	8445
70	8451	8457	8463	8470	8476	8482	8488	8494	8500	8506
71	8513	8519	8525	8531	8537	8543	8549	8555	8561	8567
72	8573	8579	8585	8591	8597	8603	8609	8615	8621	8627
73	8633	8639	8645	8651	8657	8663	8669	8675	8681	8686
74	8692	8698	8704	8710	8716	8722	8727	8733	8739	8745
75	8751	8756	8762	8768	8774	8779	8785	8791	8797	8802
76	8808	8814	8820	8825	8831	8837	8842	8848	8854	8859
77	8865	8871	8876	8882	8887	8893	8899	8904	8910	8915
78	8921	8927	8932	8938	8943	8949	8954	8960	8965	8971
79	8976	8982	8987	8993	8998	9004	9009	9015	9020	9025
80	9031	9036	9042	9047	9053	9058	9063	9069	9074	9079
81	9085	9090	9096	9101	9106	9112	9117	9122	9128	9133
82	9138	9143	9149	9154	9159	9165	9170	9175	9180	9186
83	9191	9196	9201	9206	9212	9217	9222	9227	9232	9238
84	9243	9248	9253	9258	9263	9269	9274	9279	9284	9289
85	9294	9299	9304	9309	9315	9320	9325	9330	9335	9340
86	9345	9350	9355	9360	9365	9370	9375	9380	9385	9390
87	9395	9400	9405	9410	9415	9420	9425	9430	9435	9440
88	9445	9450	9455	9460	9465	9469	9474	9479	9484	9489
89	9494	9499	9504	9509	9513	9518	9523	9528	9533	9538
90	9542	9547	9552	9557	9562	9566	9571	9576	9581	9586
91	9590	9595	9600	9605	9609	9614	9619	9624	9628	9633
92	9638	9643	9647	9652	9657	9661	9666	9671	9675	9680
93	9685	9689	9694	9699	9703	9708	9713	9717	9722	9727
94	9731	9736	9741	9745	9750	9754	9759	9763	9768	9773
95	9777	9782	9786	9791	9795	9800	9805	9809	9814	9818
96	9823	9827	9832	9836	9841	9845	9850	9854	9859	9863
97	9868	9872	9877	9881	9886	9890	9894	9899	9903	9908
98	9912	9917	9921	9926	9930	9934	9939	9943	9948	9952
99	9956	9961	9965	9969	9974	9978	9983	9987	9991	9996

Index

P E R I O D I C

(an alphabetical list of the elements

Key

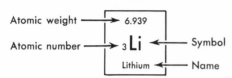

Atomic weight ⟶ 6.939

Atomic number ⟶ ₃Li ⟵ Symbol

Lithium ⟵ Name

I A	II A							
6.939 ₃Li Lithium	9.012 ₄Be Beryllium							
22.99 ₁₁Na Sodium	24.31 ₁₂Mg Magnesium	III A	IV A	V A	VI A	VII A		VIII
39.10 ₁₉K Potassium	40.08 ₂₀Ca Calcium	44.96 ₂₁Sc Scandium	47.90 ₂₂Ti Titanium	50.94 ₂₃V Vanadium	52.00 ₂₄Cr Chromium	54.94 ₂₅Mn Manganese	55.85 ₂₆Fe Iron	58.93 ₂₇Co Cobalt
85.47 ₃₇Rb Rubidium	87.62 ₃₈Sr Strontium	88.91 ₃₉Y Yttrium	91.22 ₄₀Zr Zirconium	92.91 ₄₁Nb Niobium	95.94 ₄₂Mo Molybdenum	₄₃Tc Technetium	101.1 ₄₄Ru Ruthenium	102.9 ₄₅Rh Rhodium
132.9 ₅₅Cs Cesium	137.3 ₅₆Ba Barium	(see below) 57-71	178.5 ₇₂Hf Hafnium	180.9 ₇₃Ta Tantalum	183.8 ₇₄W Tungsten	186.2 ₇₅Re Rhenium	190.2 ₇₆Os Osmium	192.2 ₇₇Ir Iridium
₈₇Fr Francium	₈₈Ra Radium	(see below) 89-103						

Lanthanides ⟶	138.9 ₅₇La Lanthanum	140.1 ₅₈Ce Cerium	140.9 ₅₉Pr Praseodymium	144.2 ₆₀Nd Neodymium	₆₁Pm Promethium	150.4 ₆₂Sm Samarium	151.9 ₆₃Eu Europium
Actinides ⟶	₈₉Ac Actinium	232.0 ₉₀Th Thorium	₉₁Pa Protactinium	238.0 ₉₂U Uranium	₉₃Np Neptunium	₉₄Pu Plutonium	₉₅Am Americium